W9-BMQ-988

# Macmillan Mathematics

**TINA THOBURN**
Senior Author

**MACMILLAN PUBLISHING COMPANY**
New York

**COLLIER MACMILLAN PUBLISHERS**
London

**Cover Photography:** Jeff Smith

**Technical Art:** Dave Hannum, Denise Mickalson, Gary Tong

**Illustrations:** Michael Adams 368-369; Vara Allot 164, 181; David Febland 130, 258-259; Angela Fernan 300, 364; Meryl Henderson 367; Hima Pamoedjo 62-63; Tom Powers 14, 15, 98, 102, 248, 272-273; Herb Reed 354; Jonathan Rosenbaum 152, 164, 282; Chris Spollen 16, 28; Deb Troyer 57, 109, 150, 198, 290, 304, 305, 345; Gary Undercuffler 253; Eva Burg Vagreti 23, 56, 69, 131, 164, 181, 188, 189, 190, 191, 201, 252, 261, 277, 296, 412, 413, 414, 439, 442, 444, 448; Victor Valla 214; Glenn Wolff 32, 138, 234, 274, 309.

**Photography:** Clara Aich Photography 12, 20, 24, 26, 48, 66, 132, 136, 162, 168, 174, 177, 242, 252, 284, 358, 373; Jim Balog / Photo Researchers 116; Eric Carle / Shostal Assoc. 84; Michel Craig Photo 149; Tim Eagan / Woodfin Camp & Associates 115; Nicholas Foster / The Image Bank 193; Brett Froomer / The Image Bank 389; Cliff Fuelner / The Image Bank 77; Si Chi Ko / The Image Bank 269; Don Landwehrle / The Image Bank 47; Tom McHugh / Photo Researchers 241; Magnum Photos, Inc. 356; Ray Manly / Shostal Assoc. 35; Larry Mulvehill / Photo Researchers 254; Thomas Nebbia / Woodfin Camp & Associates 11; Bruce Roberts / Photo Researchers 64; Frank Siteman 233; Jeff Smith 1; Norman Snyder 105, 122, 276, 279, 376-377; Harold Sund / The Image Bank 353; Wasyl Szodzinsky / Photo Researchers 280; Simon Trevor, D.B. / Bruce Coleman, Inc. 371; Edmund Warner 307.



Parts of this work were published in earlier editions of SERIES M: Macmillan Mathematics.

Macmillan Publishing Company
866 Third Avenue
New York, N.Y. 10022
Collier Macmillan Canada, Inc.

Printed in the United States of America

ISBN 0-02-105990-X
9 8 7 6 5 4 3 2 1

# Contents


## REVIEW OF WHOLE NUMBER ARITHMETIC 1–10

Place Value, Comparison, and Rounding ... 2
Adding Whole Numbers ... 3
Mental Math: Addition ... 4
Subtracting Whole Numbers ... 5
Mental Math: Subtraction ... 6
Multiplying Whole Numbers ... 7
Mental Math: Multiplication ... 8
Dividing Whole Numbers ... 9
Mental Math: Division ... 10

## 1 WHOLE NUMBERS: PROBLEM SOLVING 11–46

1-1 PROBLEM SOLVING: A 5-Step Plan ... 12
1-2 PROBLEM SOLVING: Using Subtraction ... 14
1-3 PROBLEM SOLVING: Using Multiplication ... 16
1-4 PROBLEM SOLVING: Using Division ... 18
1-5 PROBLEM SOLVING: Answering the Question ... 20
1-6 PROBLEM SOLVING: Working with Rates ... 22
1-7 PROBLEM SOLVING: Two-Step Problems ... 24
1-8 PROBLEM SOLVING: Three-Step Problems ... 26
1-9 PROBLEM SOLVING: More Three-Step Problems ... 28
1-10 PROBLEM SOLVING: More Than Three Steps ... 30
1-11 PROBLEM SOLVING: Finding Needed Data ... 32
1-12 PROBLEM SOLVING: Selecting Needed Data ... 34
1-13 PROBLEM SOLVING: Completing Forms ... 36
*Technology: Using a Calculator to Perform Operations in Problems* ... 38
PROBLEM SOLVING STRATEGY: Use Logical Reasoning ... 39
PROBLEM SOLVING PROJECT: Reconciling a Bank Statement ... 40
*Unit Review* ... 42
*Enrichment: Other Numeration Systems* ... 44
*Cumulative Review* ... 46

## 2 WHOLE NUMBERS: ALGEBRA 47–76

2-1 Arithmetic Expressions and Sentences ... 48
2-2 Algebraic Expressions ... 50
2-3 Algebraic Sentences ... 52
2-4 Relationships between Operations ... 54
2-5 Solving Equations with Addition and Subtraction ... 56
2-6 Solving Equations with Multiplication and Division ... 58
2-7 Solving Other Equations ... 60
2-8 PROBLEM SOLVING: Using Equations ... 62
2-9 PROBLEM SOLVING: Using Formulas ... 64
2-10 PROBLEM SOLVING: Using Flowcharts ... 66
*Technology: The Computer System* ... 68
PROBLEM SOLVING STRATEGY: Draw a Diagram ... 69
PROBLEM SOLVING PROJECT: Drawing and Using Graphs ... 70
*Unit Review* ... 72
*Enrichment: Other Expanded Forms* ... 74
*Cumulative Review* ... 76

## 3 DECIMALS 77–114

3-1 Decimals to Millionths ... 78
3-2 Comparing with Decimals ... 80
3-3 Rounding with Decimals ... 82
3-4 Adding and Subtracting with Decimals ... 84
3-5 Multiplying with Decimals ... 86
3-6 PROBLEM SOLVING: Comparison Shopping ... 88
3-7 Dividing with Decimals ... 90
3-8 Rounding Decimals for Quotients ... 92
3-9 Powers of Ten and Decimals ... 94
3-10 Decimals for Divisors ... 96
3-11 More Decimals for Divisors ... 98
3-12 Estimation ... 100

3-13 PROBLEM SOLVING: Unit Pricing .......................... 102
3-14 PROBLEM SOLVING: Installment Plans .......................... 104
*Technology: Using a Calculator in Division* .......................... 106
PROBLEM SOLVING STRATEGY: Logical Reasoning with Clues ....... 107
PROBLEM SOLVING PROJECT: Finding Total Earnings ............... 108
*Unit Review* .......................... 110
*Enrichment: Truth Tables* ............... 112
*Cumulative Review* .................... 114

## 4 NUMBER THEORY AND FRACTIONS 115–148

4-1 Exponents .......................... 116
4-2 Greatest Common Factor (GCF) ....... 118
4-3 Divisibility Tests .......................... 120
4-4 Least Common Multiple (LCM) ......... 122
4-5 Prime and Composite Numbers ........ 124
4-6 Prime Factorization .................... 126
4-7 Using Prime Factorization to Find GCF and LCM .................. 128
4-8 Fractions and Equivalent Fractions .......................... 130
4-9 Fractions, Mixed Numerals, and Standard Numerals ............. 132
4-10 Least Common Denominator .......... 134
4-11 Comparing with Fractions ............. 136
4-12 PROBLEM SOLVING: Using Equivalent Fractions ................. 138
*Technology: Instructions to a Computer* ....................... 140
PROBLEM SOLVING STRATEGY: Mixed Strategies .................... 141
PROBLEM SOLVING PROJECT: Computing the Electric Bill .......... 142
*Unit Review* .......................... 144
*Enrichment: Numeration Systems* .......................... 146
*Cumulative Review* .................... 148

## 5 FRACTIONS AND MIXED NUMERALS 149–186

5-1 Addition and Subtraction: Common Denominators ............. 150
5-2 Addition: Unlike Denominators ....................... 152
5-3 Subtraction: Unlike Denominators ....................... 154
5-4 Comparing with Mixed Numerals .......................... 156
5-5 Addition with Mixed Numerals ......... 158
5-6 Subtraction with Mixed Numerals .......................... 160
5-7 PROBLEM SOLVING: Related Problems ................... 162
5-8 Multiplication with Fractions ........... 164
5-9 Division with Fractions ................. 166
5-10 Multiplication and Division with Mixed Numerals ................ 168
5-11 Decimals and Fractions ................ 170
5-12 PROBLEM SOLVING: Using Easier Numbers ..................... 172
5-13 PROBLEM SOLVING: Choosing the Easier Method ................... 174
5-14 Algebra: Solving Equations ............ 176
*Technology: Using a Calculator to Find Prime Factorizations* ................ 178
PROBLEM SOLVING STRATEGY: Work a Simpler Problem ............ 179
PROBLEM SOLVING PROJECT: Latitude and Longitude .............. 180
*Unit Review* .......................... 182
*Enrichment: Methods for Squaring Numbers* .................. 184
*Cumulative Review* .................... 186

## PROBLEM SOLVING SITUATIONS 187–192

Black and White or Color Film? .................. 187
Train or Plane? .......................... 188
Renting a Fishing Boat .......................... 189
Taking a Taxi .......................... 190
Competing in a Triathlon ........................ 191
Choice of Carpenters .......................... 192

## 6 INTEGERS AND RATIONAL NUMBERS 193–232

6-1 Integers .......................... 194
6-2 Rational Numbers ...................... 196
6-3 Addition .......................... 198
6-4 More Addition ......................... 200
6-5 Subtraction .......................... 202
6-6 Multiplication .......................... 204
6-7 Division .......................... 206
6-8 PROBLEM SOLVING: Using Number Scales ...................... 208
6-9 Integers as Exponents ................. 210
6-10 Scientific Notation ..................... 212
6-11 PROBLEM SOLVING: Using Scientific Notation .................. 214
6-12 Real Numbers .......................... 216
6-13 Using a Square-Root Table .......................... 218
6-14 Estimating Square Roots .............. 220
6-15 Graphs of Sentences:

One Variable ........................ 222
*Technology: Computers: A Spreadsheet Tool* ........................ 224
PROBLEM SOLVING STRATEGY: Make a Table ........................ 225
PROBLEM SOLVING PROJECT: Drawing and Using Graphs ........................ 226
*Unit Review* ........................ 228
*Enrichment: Modular Arithmetic* ........................ 230
*Cumulative Review* ........................ 232

## 7 MEASUREMENT SYSTEMS 223–268

7-1 Metric Units ........................ 234
7-2 The Metric System ........................ 236
7-3 Changing Units ........................ 238
7-4 Changing Units— Multiples ........................ 240
7-5 PROBLEM SOLVING: Using Metric Measures ........................ 242
7-6 PROBLEM SOLVING: Special Metric Relations ........................ 244
7-7 Units of Time ........................ 246
7-8 Clock Time ........................ 248
7-9 Elapsed Time ........................ 250
7-10 Customary Units ........................ 252
7-11 Changing Customary Units ........................ 254
7-12 PROBLEM SOLVING: Using Customary Units ........................ 256
7-13 PROBLEM SOLVING: Special Customary Relations ........................ 258
*Technology: Using a Calculator to Find Volume, Mass, and Time* ........................ 260
PROBLEM SOLVING STRATEGY: Guess and Check ........................ 261
PROBLEM SOLVING PROJECT: Time Zones ........................ 262
*Unit Review* ........................ 264
*Enrichment: Topology* ........................ 266
*Cumulative Review* ........................ 268

## 8 RATIO, PROPORTION, AND PERCENT 269–306

8-1 Ratio and Proportion ........................ 270
8-2 PROBLEM SOLVING: Using Proportions ........................ 272
8-3 PROBLEM SOLVING: Scale Drawings ........................ 274
8-4 Percent ........................ 276
8-5 More About Percent ........................ 278
8-6 The Basic Percent Formula: Finding the Part ........................ 280
8-7 The Basic Percent Formula: Finding the Rate ........................ 282
8-8 The Basic Percent Formula: Finding the Base ........................ 284
8-9 More About Fractions and Percents ........................ 286
8-10 PROBLEM SOLVING: Percent Increase or Decrease ........................ 288
8-11 PROBLEM SOLVING: Buying and Selling ........................ 290
8-12 PROBLEM SOLVING: Income Tax ........................ 292
8-13 PROBLEM SOLVING: The Simple Interest Formula ........................ 294
8-14 PROBLEM SOLVING: Compound Interest ........................ 296
*Technology: Kinds of Computer Languages* ........................ 298
PROBLEM SOLVING STRATEGY: Mixed Strategies ........................ 299
PROBLEM SOLVING PROJECT: Precision and Relative Error ........................ 300
*Unit Review* ........................ 302
*Enrichment: Working with Money* ........................ 304
*Cumulative Review* ........................ 306

## 9 GEOMETRY 307–352

9-1 Figures, Terms, and Symbols ........................ 308
9-2 Angles and Angle Measures ........................ 310
9-3 Lines and Angles ........................ 312
9-4 Constructions ........................ 314
9-5 Triangles ........................ 316
9-6 Polygons and Circles ........................ 318
9-7 Special Quadrilaterals ........................ 320
9-8 Similar Triangles ........................ 322
9-9 Congruent Triangles ........................ 324
9-10 PROBLEM SOLVING: Using Perimeter Formulas ........................ 326
9-11 PROBLEM SOLVING: Using Area Formulas ........................ 328
9-12 The Rule of Pythagoras ........................ 330
9-13 Circles ........................ 332
9-14 PROBLEM SOLVING: Circle Graphs ........................ 334
9-15 Prisms and Pyramids ........................ 336
9-16 Cylinders, Cones, and Spheres ........................ 338
9-17 PROBLEM SOLVING: Using Formulas (Metric) ........................ 340
9-18 PROBLEM SOLVING: Using Formulas (Customary) ........................ 342
*Technology: Using a Calculator with Geometric Formulas* ........................ 344
PROBLEM SOLVING STRATEGY: Make a Model ........................ 345
PROBLEM SOLVING PROJECT: Trigonometry ........................ 346
*Unit Review* ........................ 348
*Enrichment: Symmetry and Transformations* ........................ 350
*Cumulative Review* ........................ 352

## 10 PROBABILITY AND STATISTICS 353–388


10-1 Probability .... **354**
10-2 PROBLEM SOLVING: Empirical Probability .... **356**
10-3 Using "Or" in Compound Statements .... **358**
10-4 Multiple Selections: Independent Statements .... **360**
10-5 Multiple Selections: Dependent Statements .... **362**
10-6 Listing Outcomes .... **364**
10-7 Permutations .... **366**
10-8 Combinations .... **368**
10-9 Mean, Median, Mode, and Range .... **370**
10-10 Grouped Data and Histograms .... **372**
10-11 PROBLEM SOLVING: Using Probability and Statistics .... **374**
10-12 PROBLEM SOLVING: Using Sampling .... **376**
10-13 PROBLEM SOLVING: Interpreting Information .... **378**
*Technology: Computers: Data Base* .... **380**
PROBLEM SOLVING STRATEGY: Make an Organized List .... **381**
PROBLEM SOLVING PROJECT: Using Probability to Approximate Pi .... **382**
*Unit Review* .... **384**
*Enrichment: Standard Deviation* .... **386**
*Cumulative Review* .... **388**


## 11 COORDINATE GRAPHING 389–410


11-1 The Real Number Plane .... **390**
11-2 Algebra: Graphing Equations in Two Variables .... **392**
11-3 Algebra: More Graphing Equations in Two Variables .... **394**
11-4 PROBLEM SOLVING: Using Graphs .... **396**
11-5 Algebra: Solving Systems of Equations by Graphing .... **398**
11-6 PROBLEM SOLVING: Using Systems of Equations .... **400**
*Technology: Computer Graphics and Communications* .... **402**
PROBLEM SOLVING STRATEGY: Mixed Strategies .... **403**
PROBLEM SOLVING PROJECT: Trigonometry .... **404**
*Unit Review* .... **406**
*Enrichment: Variation* .... **408**
*Cumulative Review* .... **410**


## PROBLEM SOLVING SITUATIONS 411–416


Fair Pricing .... 411
Carpeting a Room .... 412
Maximize Profit .... 413
Buying a Car .... 414
Buy or Rent a Computer? .... 415
Choosing Land .... 416


## WHOLE NUMBER REVIEW 418–432


Place Value .... 418
Comparing Whole Numbers .... 419
Adding Whole Numbers .... 420
Subtracting Whole Numbers .... 422
Multiplying by Ones, Tens, Hundreds, Thousands 424
More Multiplying .... 426
Dividing by Ones, Tens, Hundreds, and Thousands .... 428
More Dividing .... 432


## COMPUTER PROGRAMMING 433–448


BASIC—A Computer System .... 433
Programming with BASIC .... 435
Decision Steps in BASIC Programs .... 437
FOR—NEXT Statements .... 439
Redefining a Variable in BASIC Programs .... 441
Structured BASIC Programs .... 443
Using Arrays in BASIC .... 445
Types of Errors and Debugging a Program .... 447


## HOMEWORK 449–516

## CHALLENGE PROBLEMS 517–522


Tables of Measure .... 523
Estimation Strategies .... 524
Mental Math Strategies .... 525
Glossary .... 526
Index .... 532

# Review of Whole Number Arithmetic


Place Value, Comparison, and Rounding . . . 2
Adding Whole Numbers . . . 3
Mental Math: Addition . . . 4
Subtracting Whole Numbers . . . 5
Mental Math: Subtraction . . . 6
Multiplying Whole Numbers . . . 7
Mental Math: Multiplication . . . 8
Dividing Whole Numbers . . . 9
Mental Math: Division . . . 10

# Place Value, Comparison, and Rounding

## Inventory

*What does the digit 8 mean in each numeral?*

**1.** 548,019 **2.** 98,917,563 **3.** 180,914,766,321

*Write the standard numeral.*

**4.** sixty-three million, forty-two thousand, nine

**5.** five billion, four million, three thousand, two

*Write $<$, $>$, or $=$ for ●.*

**6.** 6,314,982 ● 6,319,482 **7.** 1,456,718 ● 994,870

*Round to the nearest billion; to the nearest million.*

**8.** 4,569,816,247 **9.** 23,999,728,516 **10.** 993,479,839

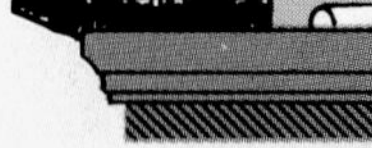

## Estimation

Most methods of estimating answers are based on rounding. Often rounding to the leftmost place will give you numbers that you can add, subtract, multiply, or divide to get reasonable estimates.

To round to the leftmost place, look at the second digit in the numeral. If that digit is 5 or more, round up. If the digit is less than 5, round down.

| Round 54,376 to the leftmost place. | Round 5,687 to the leftmost place. |
|---|---|
| 54,376 | 5,687 |
| ↑ | ↑ |
| $4 < 5$ | $6 > 5$ |
| 54,376 rounds down to 50,000. | 5,687 rounds up to 6,000. |

### CLASS EXERCISES

*Round each number to the leftmost place.*

**1.** 469,836 **2.** 743 **3.** 5,999 **4.** 63,678 **5.** 250,000

**6.** 42,999 **7.** 949 **8.** 76,421 **9.** 123,809 **10.** 98,674



Whole Number Review pages 418–419

# Adding Whole Numbers

## Inventory

*Add.*

**1.** 52,697 + 81,309

**2.** 309,861 + 29,973

**3.** 2,916,458 + 5,793,884

**4.** $458.73 + 639.28

**5.** 703,565 + 896,448

**6.** 28,806 + 71,949

**7.** 33,383 + 72,811

**8.** $788.42 + 221.05

**9.** 96,875 + 8,989 + 776 = ■

**10.** 58 + 496,917 + 8,797 = ■

## Estimation

To estimate the sum in an addition exercise, round each addend to the leftmost place of the largest addend. Then add the rounded addends.

Estimate the sum of 54,567 and 65,446.

| | |
|---|---|
| 54,567 | 50,000 |
| + 65,446 | + 70,000 |
| | 120,000 |

The sum is about 120,000.

Estimate the sum of 65,908 and 7,204.

| | |
|---|---|
| 65,908 | 70,000 |
| + 7,204 | + 10,000 |
| | 80,000 |

The sum is about 80,000.

## CLASS EXERCISES

*Estimate the sum. Then use your calculator to find the exact sum.*

**1.** 135,896 + 468,398

**2.** 45,078 + 8,900

**3.** $356.84 + 447.98

**4.** 34,907 + 34,004

**5.** 5,499 + 5,499

## Mental Math: Addition

Even when calculators and computers are available, the ability to compute mentally is useful. Few people would reach for a calculator to add 6 and 3. With some practice, and by using a few simple strategies, you can extend your mental computational skills to larger numbers. Try adding from left to right.

$$\begin{array}{r} 2{,}517 \\ +\,9{,}383 \\ \hline \end{array}$$

*Think:* 11,000 + 800 + 90 + 10

11,000...11,800...11,890...11,900

The sum is 11,900.

Another strategy is to start with the first number and add the second number from left to right.

$$\begin{array}{r} 2{,}517 \\ +\,9{,}383 \\ \hline \end{array}$$

*Think:* 2,517 + 9,000 + 300 + 80 + 3 = 11,900

2,517...11,517...11,817...11,897...11,900

The sum is 11,900.

Still another strategy uses compensation.

$$\begin{array}{r} 2{,}517 \\ +\,9{,}383 \\ \hline \end{array}$$

*Think:* 17 + 83 = 100

$$\begin{array}{rr} 2{,}517 + 83 = & 2{,}600 \\ 9{,}383 - 83 = & 9{,}300 \\ \hline & 11{,}900 \end{array}$$

The sum is 11,900.

### CLASS EXERCISES

*Add mentally. Write the answer only.*

**1.** $\begin{array}{r} 4{,}763 \\ +3{,}235 \\ \hline \end{array}$ **2.** $\begin{array}{r} 3{,}658 \\ +\,4{,}241 \\ \hline \end{array}$ **3.** $\begin{array}{r} 2{,}753 \\ +\,3{,}346 \\ \hline \end{array}$ **4.** $\begin{array}{r} 6{,}998 \\ +\,3{,}002 \\ \hline \end{array}$ **5.** $\begin{array}{r} 3{,}454 \\ +\,4{,}538 \\ \hline \end{array}$

**6.** $\begin{array}{r} 8{,}491 \\ +\,2{,}309 \\ \hline \end{array}$ **7.** $\begin{array}{r} 4{,}274 \\ +\,2{,}825 \\ \hline \end{array}$ **8.** $\begin{array}{r} 8{,}336 \\ +\,3{,}233 \\ \hline \end{array}$ **9.** $\begin{array}{r} 4{,}228 \\ +\,5{,}452 \\ \hline \end{array}$ **10.** $\begin{array}{r} 6{,}664 \\ +\,3{,}436 \\ \hline \end{array}$

**11.** $\begin{array}{r} 4{,}573 \\ +\,3{,}427 \\ \hline \end{array}$ **12.** $\begin{array}{r} 3{,}487 \\ +\,2{,}313 \\ \hline \end{array}$ **13.** $\begin{array}{r} 4{,}772 \\ +\,5{,}235 \\ \hline \end{array}$ **14.** $\begin{array}{r} 4{,}298 \\ +\,4{,}302 \\ \hline \end{array}$ **15.** $\begin{array}{r} 2{,}356 \\ +\,5{,}344 \\ \hline \end{array}$

# Subtracting Whole Numbers

## Inventory

*Subtract.*

1. $\begin{array}{r} 6{,}000 \\ -\ 5{,}478 \\ \hline \end{array}$

2. $\begin{array}{r} \$560.04 \\ -\ 80.17 \\ \hline \end{array}$

3. $\begin{array}{r} 3{,}000{,}402 \\ -\ 951{,}516 \\ \hline \end{array}$

4. $\begin{array}{r} \$7{,}006.81 \\ -\ 482.70 \\ \hline \end{array}$

5. $\begin{array}{r} 30{,}003 \\ -\ 20{,}004 \\ \hline \end{array}$

6. $\begin{array}{r} 23{,}383 \\ -\ 18{,}287 \\ \hline \end{array}$

7. $\begin{array}{r} 18{,}816 \\ -\ 7{,}393 \\ \hline \end{array}$

8. $\begin{array}{r} 100{,}192 \\ -\ 99{,}991 \\ \hline \end{array}$

9. $12{,}456 - 2{,}310 = \blacksquare$

10. $22{,}681 - 7{,}562 = \blacksquare$

### Estimation

To estimate the difference in a subtraction exercise, round each number to the leftmost place of the larger number. Then subtract the rounded numbers. Sometimes to get a better estimate you may wish to round to some other place. This is especially helpful when the number of digits in the numbers being subtracted differs.

Estimate the difference of 62,153 and 42,501.

$\begin{array}{r} 62{,}153 \\ -\ 42{,}501 \\ \hline \end{array}$ $\qquad$ $\begin{array}{r} 60{,}000 \\ -\ 40{,}000 \\ \hline 20{,}000 \end{array}$

The difference is about 20,000.

Estimate the difference of 85,703 and 7,415.

$\begin{array}{r} 85{,}703 \\ -\ 7{,}415 \\ \hline \end{array}$

Round to thousands.

$\begin{array}{r} 86{,}000 \\ -\ 7{,}000 \\ \hline 79{,}000 \end{array}$

The difference is about 79,000.

### CLASS EXERCISES

*Estimate the difference. Then use your calculator to find the exact difference.*

1. $\begin{array}{r} 324{,}983 \\ -\ 178{,}594 \\ \hline \end{array}$

2. $\begin{array}{r} 47{,}128 \\ -\ 22{,}697 \\ \hline \end{array}$

3. $\begin{array}{r} \$355.76 \\ -\ 16.87 \\ \hline \end{array}$

4. $\begin{array}{r} 64{,}981 \\ -\ 28{,}192 \\ \hline \end{array}$

5. $\begin{array}{r} 42{,}843 \\ -\ 4{,}561 \\ \hline \end{array}$

Whole Number Review pages 422-423

# Mental Math: Subtraction

One method used to compute sums mentally can be modified to compute differences. Start with the first number and subtract the second number from left to right.

$$\begin{array}{r} 5{,}873 \\ -\ 4{,}286 \\ \hline \end{array}$$

*Think:* 5,873 − 4,000 − 200 − 80 − 6

5,873 . . . 1,873 . . . 1,673 . . . 1,593 . . . 1,587

The difference is 1,587.



Another strategy uses compensation. In subtraction exercises try to make the bottom number the easy number.

$$\begin{array}{r} 5{,}873 \\ -\ 4{,}286 \\ \hline \end{array}$$

*Think:* 86 + 14 = 100

5,873 + 14 = 5,887
4,286 + 14 = 4,300
1,587

The difference is 1,587.

## CLASS EXERCISES

*Subtract mentally. Write the answer only.*

1. 7,856 − 5,445
2. 7,685 − 3,566
3. 4,884 − 3,693
4. 5,678 − 4,764
5. 8,076 − 3,676
6. 6,384 − 4,562
7. 6,448 − 5,999
8. 8,357 − 6,163
9. 8,642 − 4,581
10. 4,448 − 3,647
11. 3,766 − 1,997
12. 4,821 − 3,798
13. 9,736 − 7,647
14. 7,445 − 6,998
15. 8,654 − 3,435
16. 8,445 − 7,545
17. 7,567 − 4,448
18. 4,630 − 3,999
19. 4,606 − 2,997
20. 4,578 − 3,678

# Multiplying Whole Numbers

## Inventory

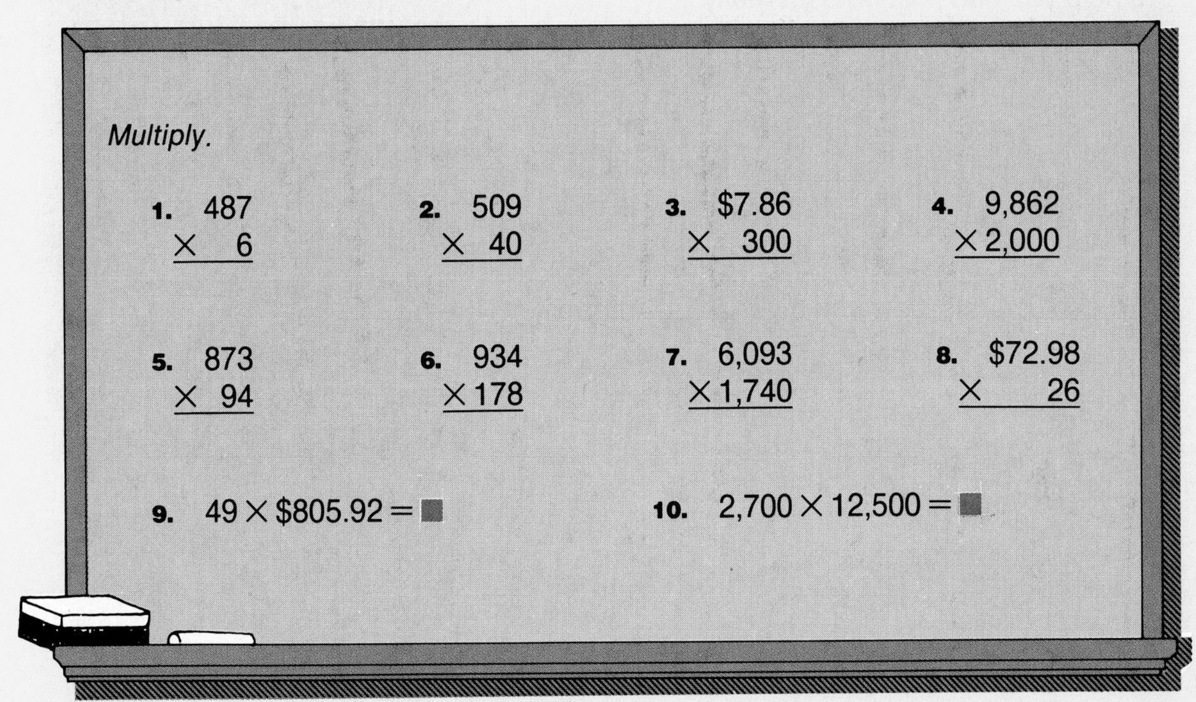


### Estimation

To estimate a product, round each factor to the leftmost place. Then multiply the rounded factors. When multiplying a large number by a 1-digit or 2-digit number, you may wish to round the larger factor to a place further to the right to get a better estimate.

Estimate the product of 74,784 and 547.

```
   74,784           Note:
×     547        70,000 ←— 4 zeros
               ×    500 ←— 2 zeros
             35,000,000 ←— 6 zeros
```

The product is about 35,000,000.

Estimate the product of 76,895 and 48.

```
   76,895      Round to thousands.
×      48        77,000 ←— 3 zeros
               ×     50 ←— 1 zero
              3,850,000 ←— 4 zeros
```

The product is about 3,850,000.

### CLASS EXERCISES

*Estimate the product. Then use your calculator to find the exact product.*

1. 2,376 × 24
2. 7,205 ×× 367
3. 5,621 × 3,183
4. 5,213 × 8,691
5. 4,320 × 755

Whole Number Review pages 424–427

## Mental Math: Multiplication

You can use the distributive property to help you find products mentally.

$5 \times 24 = ■$ *Think:* 24 is 20 + 4.

$5 \times 20 \quad + \quad 5 \times 4$

$100 \quad + \quad 20 \quad 120$

The product is 120.

You can use this idea with even larger numbers.

$15 \times 36 = ■$ *Think:* 36 is 40 − 4.

$15 \times 40 \quad - \quad 15 \times 4$

$600 \quad - \quad 60 \quad 540$

The product is 540.

$7 \times 342 = ■$ *Think:* 342 is 300 + 40 + 2.

$7 \times 300 \quad + \quad 7 \times 40 \quad + \quad 7 \times 2$

$2{,}100 \quad + \quad 280 \quad + \quad 14 \quad 2{,}394$

The product is 2,394.

### CLASS EXERCISES

*Multiply mentally. Write the answer only.*

**1.** $6 \times 32 = ■$ **2.** $8 \times 48 = ■$ **3.** $5 \times 65 = ■$ **4.** $3 \times 55 = ■$

**5.** $4 \times 71 = ■$ **6.** $5 \times 47 = ■$ **7.** $8 \times 92 = ■$ **8.** $7 \times 53 = ■$

**9.** $2 \times 86 = ■$ **10.** $3 \times 97 = ■$ **11.** $7 \times 65 = ■$ **12.** $9 \times 43 = ■$

**13.** $15 \times 17 = ■$ **14.** $18 \times 99 = ■$ **15.** $12 \times 53 = ■$ **16.** $11 \times 77 = ■$

**17.** $46 \times 19 = ■$ **18.** $23 \times 28 = ■$ **19.** $22 \times 43 = ■$ **20.** $12 \times 46 = ■$

**21.** $21 \times 49 = ■$ **22.** $15 \times 48 = ■$ **23.** $13 \times 27 = ■$ **24.** $10 \times 47 = ■$

**25.** $5 \times 123 = ■$ **26.** $7 \times 425 = ■$ **27.** $2 \times 512 = ■$ **28.** $3 \times 363 = ■$

**29.** $3 \times 421 = ■$ **30.** $9 \times 311 = ■$ **31.** $6 \times 123 = ■$ **32.** $4 \times 425 = ■$

# Dividing Whole Numbers

## Inventory

*Divide. Give a mixed numeral for the quotient when the remainder is not 0.*

**1.** $9\overline{)214}$  **2.** $7\overline{)563}$  **3.** $40\overline{)1,267}$  **4.** $80\overline{)4,047}$

*Divide. Give a whole number quotient and remainder when the remainder is not 0.*

**5.** $6\overline{)\$120.54}$  **6.** $700\overline{)25,291}$  **7.** $9,000\overline{)604,500}$

**8.** $76\overline{)15,890}$  **9.** $42\overline{)\$402.78}$  **10.** $87\overline{)70,907}$

**11.** $329\overline{)19,297}$  **12.** $452\overline{)\$2,264.52}$  **13.** $7,128\overline{)406,300}$

## Estimation

Estimates in division can be done in several ways. Two methods are shown below for estimating the quotient when dividing 4,652 by 31.

**Method 1:** Find the first digit of the real quotient. Then affix zeros to set the decimal point.

$$\begin{array}{r} 100 \\ 31\overline{)4,652} \\ 3\,1\phantom{,652} \\ \hline 1\,5\phantom{,652} \end{array}$$

15 < 31

The quotient is about 100.

**Method 2:** Round the divisor and the dividend to the leftmost digit. Then cancel zeros and do a simpler division exercise.

$$30\overline{)5,000} \rightarrow \begin{array}{r} 166 \text{ R2} \\ 3\overline{)500} \end{array}$$

The quotient is about 167.

better estimate

### CLASS EXERCISES

*Estimate the quotient. Then use your calculator to find the exact quotient.*

**1.** $27\overline{)5,830}$  **2.** $624\overline{)742,683}$  **3.** $56\overline{)98,732}$  **4.** $423\overline{)847,025}$

Whole Number Review pages 428–432

## Mental Math: Division

When you use short division to find a quotient, you use mental math to do the multiplications and subtractions.

**Long Division**

```
    245 R2
6)1,472
  1 2
    27
    24
     32
     30
      2
```

**Short Division**

```
   2 4 5 R2
6)1,4²7³2
```

2 × 6 = 12
14 − 12 = 2

4 × 6 = 24
27 − 24 = 3

5 × 6 = 30
32 − 30 = 2

You can also use the distributive property to find quotients mentally. In division you must be careful to write the quotient as a sum in which the first addend is divisible by the divisor.

6)252 *Think:* 252 = 240 + 12

240 ÷ 6 + 12 ÷ 6

40 + 2

42 The quotient is 42.

9)8,209 *Think:* 8,209 = 8,100 + 109

9)8,100 + 9)109

900 + 12 R1

912 R1 The answer is 912 R1.

CLASS EXERCISES

*Use short division.*

1. 8)6,367
2. 5)3,146
3. 6)12,783
4. 7)93.452
5. 3)53,107
6. 2)10,539
7. 4)79,102
8. 9)31,646

*Use the distributive property.*

9. 4)1,623
10. 5)2,125
11. 7)4,929
12. 6)3,120
13. 8)4,866
14. 9)8,198
15. 3)3,013
16. 7)3,546

# Whole Numbers: Problem Solving

**POPULATIONS AND AREAS OF AFRICAN NATIONS**

| Nation | Population | Area □ = 100,000 square miles |
|---|---|---|
| Botswana | 1,063,000 | □ □ |
| Chad | 4,941,000 | □ □ □ □ □ |
| Egypt | 47,395,000 | □ □ □ □ |
| Ethiopia | 35,295,000 | □ □ □ □ ◺ |
| Sudan | 21,191,000 | □ □ □ □ □ □ □ □ □ ◺ |
| Zaire | 30,430,000 | □ □ □ □ □ □ □ □ □ |

# Problem Solving READ • PLAN • DO • ANSWER • CHECK

## 1-1 A 5-Step Plan

The table gives the number of cars produced by major American companies in one year. How many cars in all did these companies produce during the year?

| Company | Cars Produced |
|---|---|
| American Motors | 156,984 |
| Chrysler | 1,236,359 |
| Ford | 2,555,867 |
| General Motors | 5,259,623 |

Use a 5-step plan to solve the problem.

1. **Read the problem.**

*Must find:* Number of cars in all
*Know:* American Motors produced 156,984 cars.
Chrysler produced 1,236,359 cars.
Ford produced 2,555,867 cars.
General Motors produced 5,259,623 cars.

2. **Plan what to do.** Decide what operation to use. Add to find how many in all.

Number of cars in all = American Motors cars + Chrysler cars + Ford cars + General Motors cars
= 156,984 + 1,236,359 + 2,555,867 + 5,259,623

3. **Do the arithmetic.**

Estimate.
200,000
1,200,000
2,600,000
+5,300,000
9,300,000

```
 1 2 2 2 2 2
     156,984
   1,236,359
   2,555,867
 + 5,259,623
   9,208,833
```

4. **Give the answer.**

The companies produced 9,208,833 cars that year.

5. **Check your answer.** Add from bottom to top.

```
   5,259,623
   2,555,867
   1,236,359
 +   156,984
   9,208,833
```

## CLASS EXERCISES

*Estimate. Then find the answer.*

**1.** The high school library has 45,993 books. The junior high library has 31,850 books. How many books in all are in the two school libraries?

**2.** There are 3,476 students in the community college, and 11,549 students in the university. How many students in all attend the two schools?

## PROBLEMS

**1.** One year the USA produced 244 million boxes of grapefruit, 75 million boxes of oranges, 26 million boxes of lemons, and 1 million boxes of limes. How many boxes in all were produced?

**2.** Mr. Janis spent $8,300 to have aluminum siding put on his house. Then he spent $2,700 for a new garage and $1,575 for a driveway. How much in all did Mr. Janis spend on home improvements?

**3.** In four years, the Cross family drove their car 115,200 kilometers (km), and drove their van 67,200 km. Find the total number of kilometers driven.

**4.** Sidney wrote 1,963 words for a composition on Monday. On Tuesday, he wrote 1,738 words. How many words in all were in the composition?

**5.** One year Japan produced 5,424,000 passenger cars and 3,072,000 trucks and buses. How many motor vehicles did Japan produce that year?

**6.** One year the USA imported 1,128,936 cars from Japan, 825,590 cars from Canada, and 582,223 cars from other countries. How many cars in all were imported?

★ **7.** The table gives the populations of the four largest cities in California. Is the population of Los Angeles greater or less than the total population of the others?

| City | Population |
|---|---|
| San Francisco | 674,063 |
| San Jose | 625,763 |
| Los Angeles | 2,950,010 |
| San Diego | 697,471 |

## ON YOUR OWN

Find the population of the four largest cities in your state. Is the population of the largest city greater than the total population of the other three?

1. 346 million

Homework page 449

# Problem Solving

**READ • PLAN • DO • ANSWER • CHECK**

## 1-2 Using Subtraction

**A.** One year a newspaper's delivery trucks drove 120,225 kilometers (km). The following year the trucks drove 94,975 km. How many more kilometers did the trucks drive during the first year?

**READ** *Must find:* How many more km during the first year
*Know:* 120,225 km during the first year
94,975 km during the following year

**PLAN** Decide what operation to use. Subtract to find how many more.

Number more = Number of km for first year − Number of km for following year
= 120,225 − 94,975

**DO**

Estimate.
120,000
− 90,000
30,000

$$\begin{array}{r} 120{,}225 \\ -\ 94{,}975 \\ \hline 25{,}250 \end{array}$$

**ANSWER** The trucks drove 25,250 km more during the first year.

**CHECK** Use addition.

$$\begin{array}{r} 25{,}250 \\ +\ 94{,}975 \\ \hline 120{,}225 \end{array}$$

**B.** A newspaper gives an award to any carrier who takes in \$50 or more in one week. So far, Kelly has taken in \$39.85 this week. How much more does she have to take in to win an award?

Subtract to find how much more is needed.

Estimate.
\$50
− 40
\$10

$$\begin{array}{r} \$50.00 \\ -\ 39.85 \\ \hline \$10.15 \end{array}$$

Kelly has to take in \$10.15 more.

## CLASS EXERCISES

*Estimate. Then solve the problem.*

1. Miss Jackson's vacation trip will cost $587.45. She made a down payment of $175.45. How much does she still owe?

2. Mr. Sven's payments for his new car will total $9,735.42. He still owes $3,964.83. How much has he paid so far?

## PROBLEMS

1. In 1970 the population of Chicago was 3,369,357. In 1980, it was 2,969,570. How many fewer people lived in Chicago in 1980?

2. A recording star sold 986,571 copies of an album. How many more copies must he sell in order to have sold 1 million copies?

3. A taxi driver drove 2,318 km in the first week of February, 3,117 km in the second week, 1,989 km in the third week, and 2,714 km in the fourth week. How many km did he drive in February?

4. A newspaper has 2,309,874 subscribers. 527,313 of these subscribers do not take the Sunday paper. How many subscribers do take the Sunday paper?

5. The attendance at the Saturday night basketball game was 18,537. The attendance at the Monday night basketball game was only 9,749. How many more people attended the Saturday night game?

6. The table gives the seating capacity of six National Football League stadiums. How many more people can be seated in the stadium with the most seats than in the stadium with the fewest seats?

| Stadium | Capacity |
|---|---|
| Rich Stadium | 80,020 |
| Cleveland Stadium | 79,891 |
| Arrowhead Stadium | 78,198 |
| Orange Bowl | 75,449 |
| Pontiac Silverdome | 80,638 |
| Giants Stadium | 76,500 |

## THINK!

### Visual Perception

Which of the following patterns could be folded into a cube?

A. 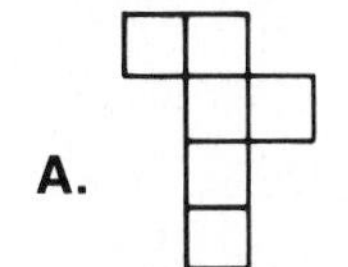

B. 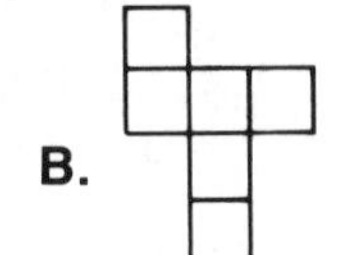

C. 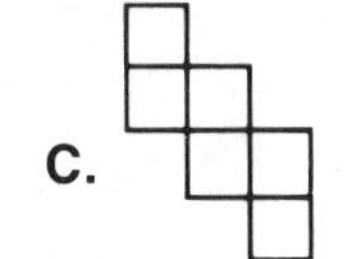

D. 

E. 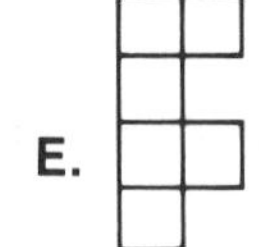

1. 399,787 people



Homework page 449

# Problem Solving READ • PLAN • DO • ANSWER • CHECK

## 1-3 Using Multiplication

**A.** A transport truck can hold 256 Geiger counters. How many Geiger counters in all can be transported by 24 trucks of the same size?

**READ** *Must find:* Geiger counters in all
*Know:* 256 Geiger counters in each truck
24 trucks

**PLAN** Decide what operation to use.
Multiply to find how many in all when you have sets with the same number in each.

In all = Number of trucks × Number in each truck
= 24 × 256

**DO**

Estimate.
300
× 20
6,000

$$\begin{array}{r} 256 \\ \times \quad 24 \\ \hline 1024 \\ 5120 \\ \hline 6{,}144 \end{array}$$

**ANSWER** 6,144 Geiger counters can be transported.

**CHECK** The answer is near the estimate. ✓

**B.** The diameter of the sun is about 109 times the diameter of the earth. If the diameter of the earth is 12,755 km, what is the diameter of the sun?

Diameter of sun = 109 × Diameter of earth
= 109 × 12,755

100 × 13,000 = ■
about 1,300,000

$$\begin{array}{r} 12{,}755 \\ \times \quad 109 \\ \hline 114795 \\ 1275500 \\ \hline 1{,}390{,}295 \end{array}$$

The diameter of the sun is about 1,390,295 km.

## CLASS EXERCISES

*Estimate. Then solve the problem.*

1. A train has completed 352 km of a 920-km journey. How much farther must the train travel to complete the journey?

2. A truck holds 256 TV sets. Each set has a mass of 29 kilograms (kg). What is the total mass of the TV sets on the truck?

## PROBLEMS

1. It costs the Brite Lite Company $21.86 each to manufacture a certain type of lamp. How much does it cost the company to manufacture 520 of these lamps?

2. In a mayoral election 6,395 persons from the East District voted, and 6,087 persons from the West District voted. How many persons in all voted?

3. In 1974 the U.S. Government spent $300,000,000 on energy. In 1979 it spent about 6 times that amount. How much was spent in 1979?

4. Northern Appliances sold 96 Kool Room air conditioners for $149.97 each. How much did the store take in from the sale?

5. The volume of Earth is about 1 trillion $km^3$ (cubic km). The volume of Saturn is 815 times the volume of Earth. What is the volume of Saturn?

6. A lab shipped 144 lead boxes of radioactive substances in each truck. If 27 trucks were used, how many boxes were shipped?

7. In Claremont City there are 33,275 people who are eligible to vote. During an election 21,639 people cast their votes. How many eligible voters did not go out to vote?

★ 8. The mass of the sun is about 333,000 times the mass of the earth. If the mass of the earth is 5,340,000,000,000,000,000,000 metric tons, what is the mass of the sun?

## THINK!

**Visual Reasoning**

Examine these three views of the same cube. What color is the bottom face in Figure 1?

1

2

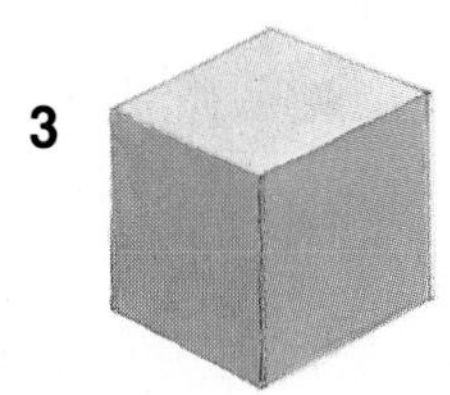

3

1. $11,367.20

Homework page 450

# Problem Solving READ • PLAN • DO • ANSWER • CHECK

## 1-4 Using Division

**A.** Kullur Appliances shipped 2,420 TVs in 11 trucks. What was the average number of TVs in a truck?

READ *Must find:* Average number of TVs in a truck
*Know:* 2,420 TVs
11 trucks

PLAN Decide what operation to use.
Divide to find how many in each set.

Average number of TVs = Total number of TVs ÷ Number of trucks
= 2,420 ÷ 11

DO

Estimate.
$11\overline{)2,420}$ = 200
Quotient is at least 200.

$$\begin{array}{r} 220 \\ 11\overline{)2,420} \\ \underline{2\,2}\phantom{00} \\ 22\phantom{0} \\ \underline{22}\phantom{0} \\ 00 \\ \underline{0} \\ 0 \end{array}$$

ANSWER There was an average of 220 TVs in a truck.

CHECK

$$\begin{array}{r} 220 \\ \times\ 11 \\ \hline 220 \\ 2,200 \\ \hline 2,420 \end{array}$$

**B.** Sunny Appliances spends $825 to ship a truckload of TVs. The trucking bill for January was $23,925. How many truckloads of TVs were shipped?

Divide to find how many sets.

24,000 ÷ 800 = 30

$$\begin{array}{r} 29 \\ \$825\overline{)\$23,925} \\ \underline{1650}\phantom{0} \\ 7425 \\ \underline{7425} \\ 0 \end{array}$$

29 truckloads of TVs were shipped.

**C.** Sometimes there is a remainder when you divide. The remainder tells how many or how much is left over. Here are two ways to show the remainder.

1.
$$\begin{array}{r} 83\text{ R4} \\ 7\overline{)585} \\ \underline{56}\phantom{0} \\ 25 \\ \underline{21} \\ 4 \end{array}$$
quotient and remainder

2.
$$\begin{array}{r} 83\tfrac{4}{7} \\ 7\overline{)585} \\ \underline{56}\phantom{0} \\ 25 \\ \underline{21} \\ 4 \end{array}$$
mixed numeral

## CLASS EXERCISES

*Estimate. Then solve the problem.*

1. In 1970, 623,988 people lived in Memphis. In 1980, 644,838 people lived in Memphis. How many more people lived in Memphis in 1980?

2. A cosmetics company packaged 9,480 bottles of shampoo in cartons that hold 24 bottles each. How many cartons were needed?

## PROBLEMS

1. In one day, Jennifer's Sweaters Inc. took in $645. If the sweaters sold for $15 each, how many sweaters did the store sell?

2. Jeremy has 390 meters (m) of rope. If he cuts the rope into 13 pieces of equal length, how long is each piece?

3. Ms. Wong is a commercial artist. In 15 weeks, she earned $12,825. What was her average weekly pay?

4. If Ms. Wong worked 675 hours to earn $12,825, what were her average hourly earnings?

5. John spent $13.69 for records. If he gave the clerk $20, how much change should he get?

6. Flosswood High's basketball team scored 1,848 points in 28 games. What was its average score?

7. Ms. Scott bought 72 boxes of raisins for her classes. If there were 6 boxes of raisins in each package, how many packages did she buy?

8. An appliance retailer took in $59,322.50 from a sale on TVs. If the store sold 305 sets, what was the average selling price for a set?

9. A grocer had 405 ears of corn. He made 67 packages with the same number of ears of corn in each package. How many were in each package? How many were left over?

★ 10. A manufacturing plant produces 453 television sets during each work shift. If each shift is 8 hours, how many television sets does the plant produce each 24 hours?

## THINK!

### A Counting Problem

Robert numbered the pages of his report from 1 to 100. How many times did he write the digit 1?

1. 43 sweaters

Homework page 450

# Problem Solving READ • PLAN • DO • ANSWER • CHECK

## 1-5 Answering the Question

If there is a remainder when you use division to solve a problem, you must interpret it when you give the answer.

**A.** A farmer sells eggs in trays of 36. If 1,052 eggs are collected, how many trays can be filled?

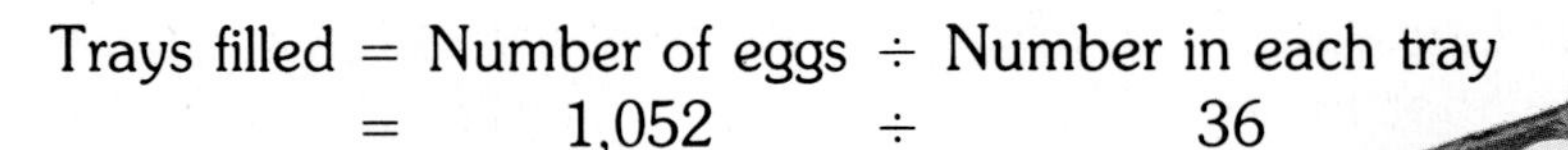

Trays filled = Number of eggs ÷ Number in each tray
= 1,052 ÷ 36

If there is a remainder, ignore it. The leftover eggs will not fill a tray.

$$36\overline{)1{,}052} = 29\text{ R}8$$

*Answer:* 29 trays can be filled.

**B.** A farmer wants to ship 11,189 eggplants. A crate holds 144 eggplants. How many crates are needed?

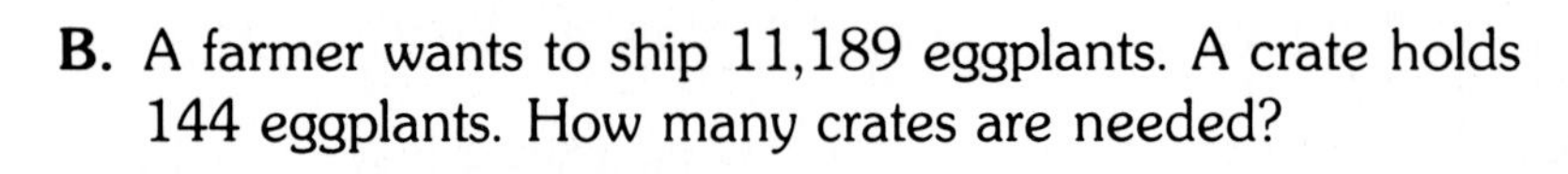

Crates needed = Number of eggplants ÷ Number in each crate
= 11,189 ÷ 144

If there is a remainder, an extra crate will be needed for the leftover eggplants.

$$144\overline{)11{,}189} = 77\text{ R}101$$

*Answer:* 78 crates are needed to ship all the eggplants.

**C.** A farmer planted 719 acres of land using the same amount of land for a potato crop, a corn crop, and a cabbage crop. How much land was used for each crop?

Land for each crop = Total land ÷ Number of crops
= 719 ÷ 3

If there is a remainder, part of the leftover land is used for each crop. Write a mixed numeral.

$$3\overline{)719} = 239\tfrac{2}{3}$$

*Answer:* $239\frac{2}{3}$ acres were used for each crop.

## CLASS EXERCISES

1. Large rolls of binder twine cost $65 each. If a farmer budgeted $850 for binder twine, how many rolls can he buy?

2. A farmer put 3,017 eggs in trays that hold 36 eggs each. How many trays were needed to hold all of the eggs?

## PROBLEMS

1. If 46 students fit on a bus, how many buses are needed to take 151 students to an amusement park?

2. A farmer has 4,701 turnips. How many crates of 72 turnips each can he fill?

3. If 453 sets take 906 meters (m) of electric cord, how much cord does each TV have?

4. If Dale scored a total of 540 points in 3 TV games, what was her average score?

5. When Gary did his homework, he spent the same amount of time on each subject. If he spent 7 hours on 4 subjects, how much time did he spend on each subject?

6. A rancher owned 2,590 acres of land. She bought an adjoining 5,180 acres and another 1,295 acres in a different state. How much land did she own then?

7. A publisher shipped 9,864 books in 411 boxes of the same size. How many books were in each box?

8. A store sells packages of 12 pencils for $3.46. How much would 1 pencil cost?

9. If a junior high school paid $2,074.38 for 231 eighth-year textbooks, what was the average cost of each book?

★10. If 16 scouts can fit in a large tent, what is the smallest number of scouts for which 19 tents would be needed?

## MIXED REVIEW

**Add, subtract, multiply, or divide.**

1. $8,596 \times 307$

2. $90,054 - 44,898$

3. $73,895 + 37,546$

4. $47\overline{)329,846}$

5. 62 × $8.99 =

6. $361.05 − $3.87 =

7. $160.92 ÷ 6 =

1. 4 buses

Homework page 451

# Problem Solving READ • PLAN • DO • ANSWER • CHECK

## 1-6 Working with Rates

A rate compares quantities of different kinds of things or measures. A rate is often written with a slash (/). The slash is read 'per'.

**A.** A road worker is paid at the rate of \$9.17/h (\$9.17 per hour). How much does she earn in 36 hours?

Total \$ = Number of hours × Rate in \$/h
= 36 × \$9.17
= \$330.12

40 × \$9 = \$360

The worker earns \$330.12 in 36 hours.

**B.** A job foreman lives 137 km from a construction site. He drives at an average rate of 60 kilometers per hour (km/h). How long does it take him to drive from home to the site?

Number of hours = Total kilometers ÷ Rate in kilometers per hour
= 137 ÷ 60
= $2\frac{17}{60}$

Estimate.
140 ÷ 60
about 2

It takes the foreman $2\frac{17}{60}$ hours to get from home to the construction site.

**C.** Mr. Kelvin laid 805 bricks in 7 hours. What is the rate at which he laid the bricks?

Rate in bricks per hour = Total bricks ÷ Number of hours
= 805 ÷ 7
= 115

Estimate.
800 ÷ 7
about 100

Mr. Kelvin laid the bricks at a rate of 115 bricks per hour.

### CLASS EXERCISES

1. A construction firm pays 13¢/km to workers who drive to and from a site. How much was Ken paid to drive 108 km to and from a site?

2. An automobile mechanic was paid \$305.37 for 39 hours of work. What is the mechanic's rate of pay in \$/h?

## PROBLEMS

1. Mr. Jakowski is driving at a rate of 85 km/h. How far will he travel in 5 hours driving at the same rate?

2. A secretary can type at a rate of 50 words per minute. How long will it take him to type a 2,500-word report?

3. Ms. Turner drives her car at an average speed of 80 km/h. At this rate, how long will it take her to drive 960 km?

4. A gasoline pump can pump at a rate of 28 liters per minute (L/min). How much gasoline can it pump in 35 minutes?

5. A city with a population of 143,629 annexed a community with a population of 12,396. What is the total population of the city?

6. Alexander's car goes 8 kilometers per liter (km/L) of fuel. The fuel tank holds 64 L. How far can he travel on a full tank of fuel?

7. A freelance editor was paid $378 for 42 hours of work. What was his rate of pay in $/h?

8. How long will it take Ms. Cumins to drive 504 km if she drives at an average rate of 72 km/h?

9. Ms. Harris can drive 395 km in the city or 560 km on the highways with a full tank of fuel. How much farther can she travel on the highways with a full tank of fuel?

10. Ace Gardening Center sold all 45 of its snowblowers at a preseason sale. If the snowblowers sold for $259.90 each, how much was taken in from their sale?

11. On a clear day and with strong tail winds, a pilot flew a jet plane 4,950 km in 5 hours. What was the average speed in km/h?

★12. The star Proxima Centauri is about 4 light-years, or 36 trillion km, from Earth. How many kilometers are in a light-year?

THINK!

**Logical Reasoning**

3 people are seated as shown at the right. 3 hats are selected from a box containing 2 red hats and 3 blue hats. No person can see the color of her or his hat, but Joe and Karl can see the hat(s) of the person(s) in front of them. When asked, in turn, "What is the color of your hat?", the answers were:
Joe: "I don't know." Karl: "I don't know."
Gail: "I know, and my hat is ■."

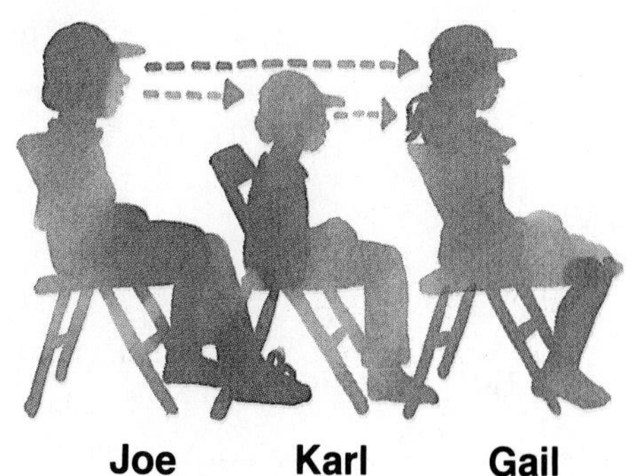


1. 425 km

Homework page 451

# Problem Solving

READ • PLAN • DO • ANSWER • CHECK

## 1-7 Two-Step Problems

Sometimes you must use two steps to solve a problem.

A large record store had 46,294 records in stock at the beginning of June. During the month it sold 8,706 records and received shipments of 15,750 records. How many records in all were in stock at the end of June?

**READ** *Must find:* Records in stock
*Know:* Had 46,294 records
Sold 8,706 records
Received 15,750 records

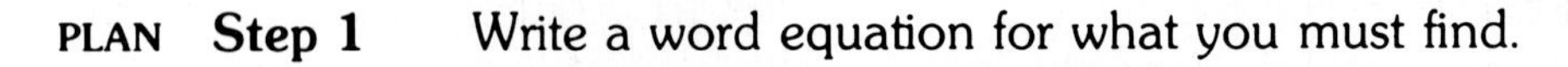

**PLAN** **Step 1** Write a word equation for what you must find.

Records in stock = Had in all − Sold
= Had in all − 8,706

**Step 2** Write a word equation to find what you do not know.

Had in all = Number at start + Number received
= 46,294 + 15,750

46,000 + 16,000 = 62,000

**DO** Do Step 2 first. Had in all = 46,294 + 15,750
= 62,044

Now you can do Step 1. Records in stock = 62,044 − 8,706
= 53,338

62,000 − 9,000 = 53,000

**ANSWER** The store had 53,338 records in stock at the end of June.

**CHECK** The answer is close to the estimate.

## CLASS EXERCISES

*Use word equations to solve.*

**1.** Ronnie bought 7 records at $4.99 each, and a tape for $7.98. How much did he spend in all?

**2.** Bobbie bought 5 records. She paid $35.59. The tax was $2.64. What was the average price (without tax) per record?

## PROBLEMS

**1.** Mr. Giles bought a scarf for $10.99 and a tie for $7.56. He gave the clerk $50. How much change did he get?

**2.** A store bought 72 white shirts and 36 blue shirts for $1,426.68. What was the average cost of a shirt?

**3.** There are 37,740 seats in a baseball stadium. The stadium charges $5 for each seat. If 9,216 seats are empty at a game, how much did the stadium take in?

**4.** At another stadium, 8,650 seats have been sold. The stadium could take in another $149,340 if the unsold seats were sold at $6 each. How many seats are in the stadium?

**5.** The range of an auto is the distance it can travel using a full tank of gasoline. What is the range of an auto with a tank that holds 64 liters (L) if it travels at 14 km/L of gasoline?

**6.** On Saturday 936,500 newspapers were printed and 919,816 were sold. On Sunday 26,192 of the printed papers were left unsold. How many fewer papers were unsold on Saturday than on Sunday?

**7.** A bookstore had 648 copies of a new book. At inventory, 465 copies remained unsold. If the store sold each copy of the book for $13.95, how much did it take in on the book?

**8.** If a truck is 596 km from the end of its trip when it starts out, and 374 km from the end of its trip 3 hours later, what was the average speed of the truck for the 3 hours it travelled?

**9.** A record store marked down the price of 3,094 records for a sale. On the first day, 1,216 records were sold. On the second day, 1,029 records were sold. How many records were left after the 2 days?

**★10.** Ms. Bayes plans to spend $92.50 per month for clothing. She spends 4 times this amount on rent and 3 times this amount on food. What are her monthly expenses for rent, food, and clothing?

### Escape Plan

A snail is at the bottom of a well that is 40 feet deep. The snail tries to escape by climbing up the well wall. Each day it climbs up 3 feet, but each night it slips back 2 feet. At this rate how long will it take the snail to reach the top?

1. $31.45

Homework page 452

## 1-8 Three-Step Problems

Sometimes you must use three steps to solve a problem.

An audio shop paid $10,867.30 for a shipment of clock radios. It sold 342 of the radios one week and the remaining 279 radios the next week. The shop received $15,493.75 for the radios. What was the shop's gross profit (profit before expenses and taxes) on each radio?

**READ** *Must find:* Gross profit per radio

*Know:* $10,867.30 paid
342 radios sold first week
279 radios sold second week
$15,493.75 taken in

**PLAN** **Step 1** Write a word equation for what you must find.

Gross profit per radio = Gross profit ÷ Number of radios

**Steps 2** and **3** Write two more word equations for what you do not know.

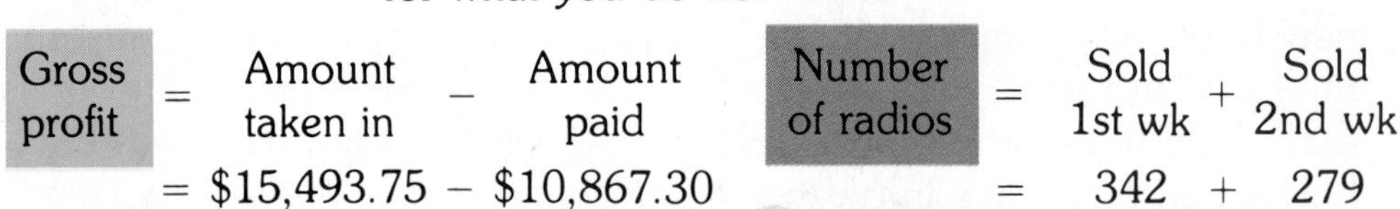

Gross profit = Amount taken in − Amount paid
= $15,493.75 − $10,867.30

Number of radios = Sold 1st wk + Sold 2nd wk
= 342 + 279

**DO** Do Steps 2 and 3 first. 15,000 − 11,000 = 4,000 300 + 300 = 600

Gross profit = $15,493.75 − $10,867.30
= $4,626.45

Number of radios = 342 + 279
= 621

Now you can do Step 1.

Gross profit per radio = $4,626.45 ÷ 621
= $7.45

Estimate.
$5,000 ÷ 600
about $8

**ANSWER** The shop's gross profit per radio was $7.45.

**CHECK** The answer is close to the estimate.

## CLASS EXERCISES

*Use word equations to solve.*

Lesley bought a sound system on an installment plan. She must pay $83.99 each month for 36 months. If $12.78 of each payment is interest, what was the cost of the sound system without interest?

**2.** The audio shop puts 3 cassettes in a package. Each package costs the shop 82¢. How much would the shop receive from the sale of 216 cassettes if it adds a profit of 25¢ to the cost of each package?

## PROBLEMS

**1.** A plane flew 2,720 km in 4 hours and 3,310 km in 5 hours. What was its average speed for the two flights?

**2.** A store bought 4 sofas for $689 each, and 8 chairs for $347 each. What was the total cost?

**3.** Diane sold two paintings through a gallery. The first painting sold for $525 and the gallery kept $210 for selling it. The second painting sold for $375 and the gallery kept $150. How much did Diane receive for the paintings?

**4.** On the first day of a two-game series a stadium sold 13,496 adults' tickets and 6,918 children's tickets. The next day it sold all but 2,107 of its 37,502 tickets. How many tickets in all were sold for the two games?

**5.** An airline company has 12 planes that can carry 246 people each, and 14 planes that can carry 128 people each. How many people in all can be carried on these planes?

**6.** Joanna had $11.36 left after buying a scarf that cost $14.95 and matching gloves that cost $17.49. How much did Joanna have before she shopped?

**7.** A truck driver earns $10.80/h. If he drove 648 km in 9 hours, what was his average pay for each kilometer?

**8.** An art dealer mailed 2 statues for $2.13 each and 8 prints for 89¢ each. What was the total postage?

**9.** The star Sirius A is 81 trillion km from Earth. The star LP 425-140 is 216 trillion km from Earth. How much farther is LP 425-140?

★**10.** Tim spent the same amount on 4 shirts as on 2 sweaters. If he spent $104 and the shirts were all the same price, how much was each shirt?

**Guess and Check**

The sum of the digits of a two-digit number is 9. If the order of the digits is reversed, the new number is 27 more than the original number. Find the original number.

1. 670 km/h



Homework page 452

## Problem Solving READ • PLAN • DO • ANSWER • CHECK

### 1-9 More Three-Step Problems

Leeds Greenhouses needed 1,800 trays for starting seed. It received 312 trays from its warehouse on Monday, and received a shipment of 36 boxes with 26 trays in each on Tuesday. How many trays were still needed?

**READ** *Must find:* Number of trays still needed
*Know:* 1,800 needed in all
Received 312 on Monday
Received 36 boxes on Tuesday
26 trays in each box

**PLAN** **Step 1** Number still needed = Needed in all − Number received
= 1,800 − ?

**Step 2** Number received = Received on Monday + Received on Tuesday
= 312 + ?

**Step 3** Received on Tuesday = Number of boxes × Number in each box
= 36 × 26

one up 30
one down × 30
900

**DO** Do Step 3 first. Received on Tuesday = 36 × 26
= 936

Do Step 2 next. Number received = 312 + 936
= 1,248

300 + 900 = 1,200

Now you can do Step 1. Number still needed = 1,800 − 1,248
= 552

1,800 − 1,200 = 600

**ANSWER** Leeds still needed 552 trays.

**CHECK** The answer is close to the estimate.

## CLASS EXERCISES

*Use word equations to solve.*

1. A tray of 8 pepper plants costs $2.59. A tray of 6 tomato plants costs $1.98. How much did Larry spend for 8 pepper plants and 18 tomato plants?

2. Zlata spent $7.98 for a spider plant, $5.98 each for 3 begonias, and $27.59 for a large Southern yew. How much change should she get from $60?

## PROBLEMS

1. A theatre sold 216 tickets for a Thursday night performance. It sold twice that many for the Friday night performance. If tickets cost $9.50 each, how much did the theatre take in for the two nights?

2. Vivian made two phone calls to Canada. The first call cost 61¢. The second cost 26¢ for the first minute and 19¢ for each of the extra 23 minutes. What was the total cost of the two calls?

3. A can of fuel will fill the tank of a heater 3 times and burn for a total of 54 h. If the tank holds 6 L of fuel, and 1 L of fuel costs 45¢, what is the cost per hour of running the heater?

4. To be on schedule, a plane must fly at an average speed of 696 km/h. If it completes all but 860 km of its 2,972-km flight in 3 h, how much faster than the required 696 km/h is it travelling?

5. Ron spent $8.54 for 3 bags of soil and a package of plant food. If the tax was 28¢ and the plant food cost $2.59, what was the price (without tax) of each bag of soil?

6. Ernst spent $143.75 each for 2 Siamese kittens, and $78.02 for pet supplies. If the sales tax was $29.24, and Ernst gave the clerk $400.76, how much change did he get back?

7. Mort is 12 years old. His brother Alex is 3 years older. Mort's father is 3 times as old as Alex, and Mort's mother is 2 years younger than his father. How old is Mort's mother?

★8. Water boils at 100°C (degrees Celsius). The boiling point of gold is 29 times that of water. Silver boils at 690°C less than gold, and platinum boils at 1615°C greater than silver. What is the boiling point of platinum?

### Seating Arrangements

Mrs. Kane is having a party for 50 people next week. She is going to use small tables that seat one person on each side. The tables will be arranged end to end in a long row. How many tables will Mrs. Kane need?

1. $6,156

Homework page 453

# Problem Solving READ • PLAN • DO • ANSWER • CHECK

## 1-10 More Than Three Steps

Joan's car travels 15 kilometers per liter (km/L) on the highway and 12 km/L of gasoline in the city. If she pays 42 cents per liter (42¢/L) for gasoline, how much did it cost her for gasoline if she drove 105 km on the highway and 96 km in the city?

**READ** *Must find:* Cost of gasoline
*Know:* Car goes 15 km/L on the highway
Car goes 12 km/L in the city
Gasoline costs 42¢/L
Drove 105 km on the highway
Drove 96 km in the city

**PLAN** **Step 1** Cost of gasoline = Number of L × Cost/L
= ? × \$.42

**Step 2** Number of L = L on highway + L in city
= ? + ?

**Step 3** L on highway = Km on highway ÷ Km/L on highway
= 105 ÷ 15

**Step 4** L in city = Km in city ÷ Km/L in city
= 96 ÷ 12

**DO** Do Steps 3 and 4 first.

L on highway = 105 ÷ 15
= 7

L in city = 96 ÷ 12
= 8

Do Step 2 next.

Number of L = 7 + 8
= 15

Now you can do Step 1.

Cost of gasoline = 15 × \$.42
= \$6.30

**ANSWER** It cost Joan \$6.30 for gasoline.

**CHECK** Work the problem again. See if you get the same answer.

## CLASS EXERCISES

*Use word equations to solve.*

1. A company allows its salespersons $65.50 each night for a hotel room. Miss Torres paid $63.50 each night for the 4 nights she spent in Houston, and $66.75 each night for the 5 nights she spent in Dallas. How much less did she spend for the 9 nights than her company allowed?

2. One week Prof. Draper bought gasoline 3 times. She paid 37¢/L for 13 L, 41¢/L for 15 L, and 42¢/L for 12 L. What was the average cost/L of the gasoline she bought?

## PROBLEMS

1. At a sale, a store reduced sofas from $743.99 each to $596.85 each, and reduced chairs from $345.50 each to $237.95 each. How much did Ralph save by buying a sofa and 2 chairs on sale?

2. In 1981 Dr. Hennigan subscribed to 3 journals at $45 per year each, bought 63 books at an average of $14.59 each, and took 3 professional trips at an average of $702.11 each. How much did he spend in all?

3. A market bought 50 boxes of lemons with 5 sacks of 25 lemons each. It paid $2.95 for each sack. The market sold the lemons in bags of 5 each and charged $1.19 for each bag. What was the market's gross profit?

4. An auto dealer paid $63,760 for 10 new cars. She needs to make a gross profit of $26,240 on their sale. If she sells 6 of the cars for $8,750 each, what should be the average selling price of the other 4 cars?

5. A gym has 12 rows of seats with 56 seats in each. If 665 students and 19 teachers come to a pep rally, how many will not get seats?

6. Jan bought 3 bandanas for $2.65 each and 4 pieces of rawhide for $1.95 each. How much change should she get from $20?

7. Mr. May worked 8 hours per day for 4 days. $45.76 was deducted from his pay. He received $183.04. What was his pay per hour before deductions?

★8. Mike had $55.41 and spent it all on a basketball and a gym suit. If the suit cost twice as much as the ball, what did each cost?

### THINK!

**Find a Pattern**

How many different squares are there in this figure?

1. $362.24

Homework page 453

# Problem Solving

READ • PLAN • DO • ANSWER • CHECK

## 1-11 Finding Needed Data

**A.** Sometimes there is not enough numerical information, or data, in a problem to enable you to solve it.

If the life expectancy of a giraffe is 34 years, how old is a giraffe that has lived beyond its life-expectancy?

There is not enough data to find what you do not know. You can't answer this question.

**READ** *Must find:* Age of giraffe
*Know:* Life expectancy is 34 years

**PLAN** Age of giraffe = Life expectancy + Years beyond life expectancy
= 34 + ?

**B.** Sometimes you can find what you do not know by remembering, investigating, or making a good estimate of the missing data.

1. Use the magazine clipping. How much more energy per person did the people of the United States use last year compared with the Canadians?

Professor Morgan noted that the country with the highest energy consumption per capita is the United States. Last year each person used an energy equivalent of 10,999 kilograms of coal. He added that Canada had the second highest energy consumption per capita.

Mark found in the almanac that Canadians used an energy equivalent of 9,880 kilograms of coal per person last year.

10,999 − 9,880 = 1,119

11,000 − 10,000 = 1,000

People in the United States used 1,119 kilograms of coal per person more than the Canadians did.

2. Use the advertisement. How much would the car cost if the cost of air conditioning were added to the basic price?

| Base price | $8,540 |
|---|---|
| Standard equipment | |
| Fuel injection | yes |
| 5-speed overdrive trans. | yes |
| Rack and pinion steering | yes |
| 4-wheel disc brakes | yes |
| Tinted glass | yes |

Olga phoned a car dealer and was told it would cost $785 to air condition the car.

$8,540 + $785 = $9,325

$8,500 + 800 = $9,300

The car would cost $9,325.

## CLASS EXERCISES

*Tell what data is missing and how you would look for it. Consider items a–i as possibilities.*

**a.** Use a reference book.
**b.** Make an estimate.
**c.** Make a measurement.
**d.** Use a calculator.
**e.** Use the library.
**f.** Count the objects.
**g.** Make a guess.
**h.** Remember a fact.
**i.** Make a phone call.

**1.** The life expectancy of an owl is 24 years. How much greater is the life expectancy of a dolphin?

**2.** Each section of a fence is 2 m long. What is the total length of the fence?

## PROBLEMS

*Find or estimate the missing data and solve.*

**1.** The distance from New Orleans to Atlanta is 789 km. How long would it take to drive from New Orleans to Atlanta?

**2.** A company replaced all of the windshield wipers on the 136 cars it owns. How many windshield wipers did it use?

**3.** In 1898, the record speed attained by a car was 63 km/h. How much greater was the record speed attained in 1970?

**4.** Jamie bought 2 packages of zinnia seeds and 3 packages of marigold seeds. How much did he spend in all for the seeds?

**5.** An airplane flew an average of 4,562 km/day during the month of December. How many kilometers in all did the plane fly in December?

**6.** If you were to be given a travel voucher worth $5 for every full month you have lived, what would be the value of the voucher?

**7.** A toy company packages toy cars in boxes of 1 dozen each. How many boxes can be filled with the toy cars it makes in 8 hours if it makes 125 toys per hour?

★**8.** Tanya has 6 nickels, 9 dimes, 12 quarters, 2 dollar bills, and 1 five-dollar bill. Does she have enough money for a shirt that costs $11 if the sales tax is 77¢?

## THINK!

### Making Logical Choices

The statement on the box containing:
**i)** $100 is true **ii)** 10¢ is false
**iii)** nothing is either true or false
Which box contains $100? 10¢?

| A | B | C |
|---|---|---|
| Box C is empty. | Box A contains 10¢ | This box is empty. |

1. About 10 h at an average speed of 78 km/h


Homework page 454

# Problem Solving

READ • PLAN • DO • ANSWER • CHECK

## 1-12 Selecting Needed Data

To solve some problems, you must select the needed data from a source that also contains some data you do not need.

**1.** Use the graph. How many more factory shipments of home appliances were made in 1979 than in 1980?

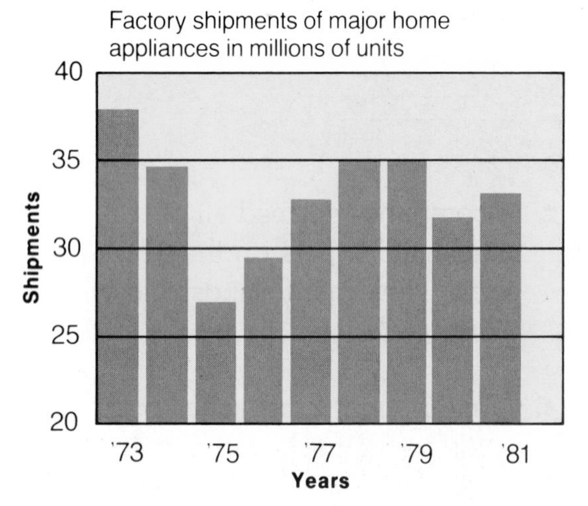


35 million − 32 million = 3 million

3 million more appliances were shipped in 1979.

**2.** Use the train schedule. Mr. Allen lives in Ronkonkoma and takes the train to work in New York. What is the latest train he can take to get to New York before 9 A.M. on Thursday?

| MONDAY TO FRIDAY, EXCEPT HOLIDAYS | | | | | |
|---|---|---|---|---|---|
| Leave | | | Arrive | | |
| Ronkonkoma | Central Islip | Brentwood | Jamaica | Brooklyn | New York |
| AM | AM | AM | AM | AM | AM |
| 4:40 | 4:47 | 4:52 | 5:55 | 6:15 | 6:15 |
| 5:28 | 5:35 | 5:40 | 6:39 | 7:01 | 6:57 |
| 6:00 | 6:07 | 6:12 | 7:07 | 7:28 | 7:29 |
| 6:22 | 6:30 | 6:35 | 7:36 | 7:56 | 7:59 |
| 6:37 | 6:45 | 6:50 | 7:45 | 8:07 | 8:07 |
| 6:49 | 6:57 | 7:02 | 8:01 | 8:22 | 8:26 |
| 7:25 | 7:32 | 7:37 | 8:40 | 9:01 | 9:01 |
| 8:22 | 8:31 | 8:36 | 9:31 | 9:50 | 9:49 |
| 9:33 | 9:41 | 9:46 | 10:52 | 11:12 | 11:12 |
| 10:23 | 10:32 | 10:37 | 11:34 | **12:02** | **12:02** |
| **12:23** | **12:32** | **12:37** | **1:43** | **2:03** | **2:03** |
| **2:23** | **2:32** | **2:37** | **3:38** | **3:58** | **3:58** |
| **4:29** | **4:37** | **4:42** | **5:52** | **6:19** | **6:16** |
| **8:00** | **8:08** | **8:13** | **9:24** | **9:43** | **9:45** |
| **9:00** | **9:08** | **9:13** | **10:21** | **10:50** | **10:49** |
| **9:50** | **10:04** | **10:14** | **11:24** | **11:44** | **11:47** |
| **10:46** | **10:55** | **11:00** | 12:00 | 12:19 | 12:20 |
| **11:30** | **11:39** | **11:44** | 12:58 | 1:33 | 1:27 |
| PM | PM | PM | AM | AM | AM |

From the schedule: Last train to arrive in New York before 9 A.M. arrives at 8:26. This train leaves Ronkonkoma at 6:49. Mr. Allen must take the 6:49 train.

**3.** Use the classified ad. If Ms. Lewin makes a down payment of $44,250, how much must she borrow from the bank on a mortgage?

$180,000 − $44,000 = $136,000

$177,000 − $44,250 = $132,750

Ms. Lewin must borrow $132.750

**4.** People have been known to live to the age of 114, blue and fin whales have been known to live to the age of 100, and Asiatic elephants have been known to live to the age of 70. One 70-year-old Asiatic elephant died in 1965. In what year was it born?

1965 − 70 = 1895

The elephant was born in 1895.

## CLASS EXERCISES

1. Use the graph on page 34. What was the average number of units shipped per year in the five years from 1976 to 1980?

2. Use the classified ad on page 34. What is the area of the patio? (Area = Length × Width)

## PROBLEMS

1. Mrs. Perkins worked 39 h and was paid $6.95/h. Mr. Trebel worked 41 h and was paid $6.70/h. Who was paid more per h?

2. One day is 24 h or 1,440 minutes (min). One h is 60 min or 3,600 seconds. One minute is 60 seconds. How many seconds are in a day?

3. An airplane from St. Louis to Kansas City is traveling at a speed of 11 km/min. What is its speed in km/h?

4. A temperature range for a city is the difference between the average minimum temperature and the average maximum temperature. The range for Dawson City is 49°C. The range for Singapore is 3°C. What is the temperature range for London if temperatures usually vary from 6°C to 23°C?

★5. It takes Mercury 59 days to rotate about its axis and 88 days to orbit around the sun. It takes Neptune 16 hours to rotate about its axis and 164 years 300 days to orbit around the sun. How much longer does it take Neptune than Mercury to orbit around the sun?

## THINK!

**Make 20**

Use each of the numbers from 1 to 9 exactly once. Fill in the blank hexagons so that the sum of the numbers in each row of four is 20.

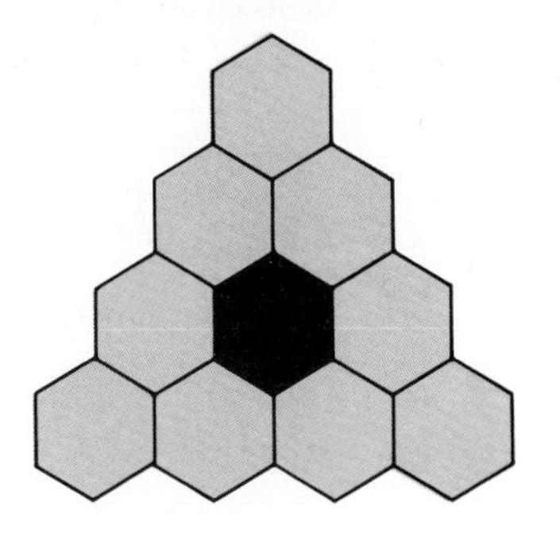

1. Mrs. Perkins

Homework page 454

# Problem Solving READ • PLAN • DO • ANSWER • CHECK

## 1-13 Completing Forms

**A.** This form is a checkbook record:

| Date | Check Number | Item | Amount of Check | Amount of Deposit | Balance |
|---|---|---|---|---|---|
| | | | | | $109.95 |
| 9/20 | 604 | Ken's Housewares | $27.50 | | $ 82.45 |
| 9/21 | | Deposit | | $276.40 | |
| 9/23 | 605 | Citywide Electric | $43.95 | | |
| | | | | | |

The **balance** is the amount of money in the checking account. What is the balance for September 23?

**Step 1** 9/23 balance = 9/21 balance − Check 605
= ? − $43.95

money taken out: subtract

**Step 2** 9/21 balance = 9/20 balance + Deposit
= $82.45 + $276.40
= $358.85

money put in: add

$80 + $280 = $360

Now do Step 1. 9/23 balance = $358.85 − $43.95
= $314.90

$360 − $40 = $320

The balance for September 23 is $314.90.

**B.** These are listings from a mail order catalog:

**Tent.** 2-person tent is full 5x7′ with 42″ height. 100% urethane-treated nylon, including floor. Water repellant and fire retardant. Zippered screen door and storm flap. Lightweight—easy to pack.
885-004 .......................... $34.95

**Lantern** lights 100-ft. circle. 2-pint tank. Easy-lite. 13½″ high.
867-051 .......................... $27.95

**Sleeping Bag.** 33x75.″ 100″ nylon zipper (2 bags can zip together). 3 lbs., drawstring carry bag.
867-259 ..........................

Here is a completed catalog order form for 3 sleeping bags and 1 lantern. In what amount should the check be written?

| Quantity | Item | Number | Price Each | Total |
|---|---|---|---|---|
| 3 | Sleeping bag | 867-259 | $36.95 | $110.85 |
| 1 | Lantern | 867-051 | $27.95 | $ 27.95 |
| | | | Total Order: | $138.80 |
| | | | Handling Charge: | +$2.00 |
| | | | Total Payment: | $140.80 |

Quantity × Price Each

Cost of 3 sleeping bags and 1 lantern

Send a check for $140.80

## CLASS EXERCISES

1. Use the checkbook record on Page 26. What would the balance be on 9/24 if check 606 were written in the amount of $140.80?

2. Use the catalog listings on page 36. Complete an order form showing a purchase of 1 tent, 2 sleeping bags, and 1 lantern.

3. Use the catalog listings at the right. Complete an order form showing a purchase of 3 pairs of knee socks, 3 fishnet T-shirts, and 2 pairs of athletic sox. The handling charge is $1.50.

4171H **Women's Knee Socks,** three pairs for $9.00

1973H **White Fishnet T-Shirts,** $6.50 each
Two for $12.25

1931H **Men's Athletic Sox,** 3 pairs for $8.00

## PROBLEMS

*Complete a checkbook record for the following transactions. The starting balance is $98.23.*

1. October 3: Check Number 478 to Towne Fashions for $84.72
2. October 6: Deposit of $450
3. October 6: Check Number 479 to Unionville Telephone Company for $33.17
4. October 10: Check Number 480 to Cash for $50
5. October 10: Check Number 481 to State Insurance for $104.30
6. October 11: Check Number 482 to Bruno's Supermarket for $71.67
7. October 15: Deposit of $160.50

*Complete a catalog order form for each purchase. Use the catalog listings at the right. The handling charge is 89¢.*

8. Jack purchased 3 white trillium, 3 purple trillium, and 6 Jack-in-the-pulpit.
9. Tina purchased 1 trumpet vine, 1 purple wisteria, and 9 purple trillium.
10. Bob purchased 2 white trillium, 2 purple wisteria, 1 Jack-in-the-pulpit, and 4 trumpet vines.

**1529-7 Jack-in-the-Pulpit** *(Arisaema triphyllum)* Unusual flowers with green "hoods". Needs damp shade. Ht. 1-2 ft. **3 for $9.95**

**1531-3 Purple Trillium** *(T. erectum)* Good companion to white variety. Similar habit. **3 for $8.25**

**1530-5 White Trillium** *(T. grandiflorum)* One of first flowers in spring. Delightful spreading plants with three-petalled pure white flowers that glow in shady areas. Ht. 12-18 in. **3 for $11.95**

**1160-1 Purple Wisteria** *(Wisteria sinensis)* Grape-like clusters of lilac-mauve flowers in May-June. Rapid-growing vine for porches, trellises, fences. Grows 20 to 30 ft. **Each $5.95; 3 or more, $5.25 each**

**1169-2 Trumpet Vine** *(Bignonia radicans)* Clings to any rough surface, growing 30 ft. Long, trumpet-shaped, orange-red blooms in July-August. Prefers an open location, fertile soil. Yellow Trumpet Vine, see page 166. **2 for $9.90; 3 or more, $4.25 each**

1. $13.51

Homework page 455

# TECHNOLOGY

## Solving Problems with a Calculator

**A.** Winnie's Sports World sold 147 sweatshirts at \$5.79 each and 93 warmup jackets at \$14.25 each. How much money did the store receive for these items?

**Plan the solution.**

(147 × \$5.79) + (93 × \$14.25) = ■

Estimate. About (150 x \$6) + (100 × \$14) = ■
\$900 + \$1,400 = \$2,300

**Use the calculator.**

Press:

[1] [4] [7] [×] [5] [.] [7] [9] [=] [M+]

[9] [3] [×] [1] [4] [.] [2] [5] [=] [M+]

[RM] 2176.38

Add each product to the memory.

The display shows \$2,176.38. This answer is close to \$2,300. Winnie's Sports World received \$2,176.38.

**B.** If your calculator has keys for parentheses, you may be able to work multiple-step problems without using the memory. To solve the problem above, press:

[(] [1] [4] [7] [×] [5] [.] [7] [9] [)] [+] [(] [9] [3] [×] [1] [4] [.] [2] [5] [)] [=]

The display shows the same answer, \$2,176.38.

**C.** A customer spent \$7.98 each for 3 baseball bats, \$13.80 each for 2 gloves, and paid sales tax of \$2.05. If she gave the clerk \$60, how much change did she receive?

3 × \$8 = \$24
2 × \$14 = \$28
+ \$ 2
\$54
\$60 − \$54 = \$ 6

**With the memory key**

[3] [×] [7] [.] [9] [8] [=] [M+]

[2] [×] [1] [3] [.] [8] [=] [M+]

[2] [.] [0] [5] [M+]

[6] [0] [−] [RM] [=] 6.41

**With parentheses keys**

[(] [3] [×] [7] [.] [9] [8] [)] [+]

[(] [2] [×] [1] [3] [.] [8] [)] [+]

[2] [.] [0] [5] [=] [M+]

[6] [0] [−] [RM] [=] 6.41

The customer received \$6.41 change.

*Use a calculator to solve.*

1. If you used a \$20 bill to pay for 4 T-shirts at \$3.56 each, how much change should you receive?

2. Find the total cost of 5 caps at \$2.23 each, 3 sweaters at \$11.50 each, and a jogging suit at \$28.98.

# Problem Solving Strategy

READ · PLAN · DO · ANSWER · CHECK

## Use Logical Reasoning

Some problems can be solved without computation. Use a logical, systematic approach to solve the problems below. These problems are known as **imitation-coin problems.**

**Example 1**
Suppose you have 2 coins that look exactly alike. One is a good coin, and the other is a heavier imitation coin. You can tell which is the imitation coin in 1 use of a balance.

$C_1$ is the imitation coin.

*If you have 3 coins and 1 is a heavy imitation coin, you can find the imitation in 1 use of a balance. There are 3 possibilities. Tell which is the imitation in each.*

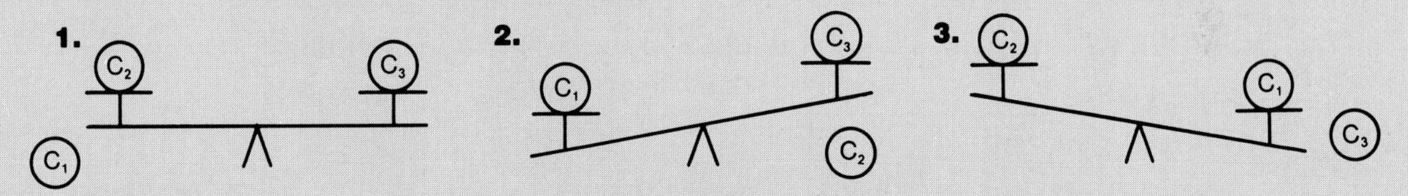


**Example 2**

If you have 4 coins and 1 is a heavy imitation coin, it takes 2 uses of the balance to find the imitation coin.

**Step 1**

or

**Step 2** If $C_1$ and $C_2$ are heavier, use them in a 2-coin test.

If $C_3$ and $C_4$ are heavier, use them in a 2-coin test.

*Find the number of uses of the balance in which you can find the 1 heavy imitation in a set with each number of coins.*

**4.** 5 **5.** 6 **6.** 7 **7.** 8 **8.** 9 **9.** 10

*Solve.*

**10.** Find the greatest number of coins for which the 1 heavy imitation can be found using the balance no more than 3 times.

**11.** What is the least number of times you must use the balance if you have 5 coins and do not know whether the 1 imitation is heavy or light?

Challenge Problems: page 517

# Problem Solving Project

READ • PLAN **DO** ANSWER • CHECK

## Reconciling a Bank Statement

**A.** Mr. Potter has a personal checking account. Once a month he gets a **bank statement.** It shows the **transactions,** deposits, and withdrawals for the month. Here is his statement for September.

| Date of last statement → 08-31 | | Balance on last statement → 361.41 | | |
|---|---|---|---|---|
| **Item** | **Checks** | **Deposits** | **Date** | **Balance** |
| CHECK 307 | 275.00 | | 09-03 | 86.41 |
| DEPOSIT | | 352.50 | 09-05 | 438.91 |
| CHECK 308 | 49.16 | | 09-07 | 389.75 |
| CHECK 309 | 84.32 | | 09-09 | 305.43 |
| CHECK 312 | 50.00 | | 09-12 | 255.43 |
| DEPOSIT | | 352.50 | 09-19 | 607.93 |
| CHECK 310 | 129.85 | | 09-25 | 478.08 |
| SERVICE CHARGE | 1.70 | | 09-30 | 476.38 |

1. What was the **balance** in Mr. Potter's account at the end of August? at the end of September?

2. What are the numbers of the checks that **cleared** (were paid by the bank)?

3. On what dates did Mr. Potter make deposits?

4. How much did the bank charge Mr. Potter for its services during September?

**B.** Mr. Potter compared the bank statement with his **checkbook record,** shown on page 33.

First, Mr. Potter checked off (✓) all of the checks that had cleared and the deposits he had made.

Next, Mr. Potter recorded the service charge. He subtracted to find the new checkbook balance:

$343.03 $1.70 = $341.33

often not the same amount as the balance on the bank statement

| RECORD ALL CHARGES OR CREDITS THAT AFFECT YOUR ACCOUNT | | | | | | | | | | |
|---|---|---|---|---|---|---|---|---|---|---|
| NUMBER | DATE | DESCRIPTION OF TRANSACTION | PAYMENT/DEBIT (−) | | ✓ | FEE (IF ANY) (−) | DEPOSIT/CREDIT (+) | | BALANCE | |
| | | | | | | | | | $ 361 | 41 |
| 306 | 09/01 | American Florists | 25 | 00 | | | | | 336 | 41 |
| 307 | 09/01 | City Apartments, Inc. | 275 | 00 | ✓ | | | | 61 | 41 |
| | 09/05 | deposit | | | ✓ | | 352 | 50 | 413 | 91 |
| 308 | 09/05 | County Telephone Co. | 49 | 16 | ✓ | | | | 364 | 75 |
| 309 | 09/06 | Midwest Oil Company | 84 | 32 | ✓ | | | | 280 | 43 |
| 310 | 09/10 | Allied Credit Industries | 129 | 85 | ✓ | | | | 150 | 58 |
| 311 | 09/10 | Smart Shops, Inc. | 62 | 40 | | | | | 88 | 18 |
| 312 | 09/12 | Cash | 50 | 00 | ✓ | | | | 38 | 18 |
| | 09/19 | deposit | | | ✓ | | 352 | 50 | 380 | 68 |
| 313 | 09/25 | Northern Insurance Co. | 37 | 65 | | | | | 343 | 03 |
| | 09/30 | service charge | 1 | 70 | | | | | 341 | 33 |
| | | | | | | | | | | |
| REMEMBER TO RECORD AUTOMATIC PAYMENTS/DEPOSITS ON DATE AUTHORIZED | | | | | | | | | | |

5. Mr. Potter wrote some checks that have not yet cleared. What are the numbers of those checks?

6. When was check 310 written? When was it cleared?

C. Mr. Potter could not tell just by looking if the bank statement agreed with his checkbook record. The back of the bank statement has a method for **reconciling** the statement with the checkbook record. Mr. Potter used the method to check his balance.

DIFFERENCE should be $0.00

| | |
|---|---|
| Balance on this statement | $476.38 |
| *Add deposits* not shown on this statement. | + ______ |
| SUBTOTAL **1** | ______ |
| Find *total value* of checks not shown on this statement. | ______ |
| | ______ |
| | + ______ |
| SUBTOTAL **2** | ______ |
| Subtract **2** from **1**. | ______ |
| Your checkbook balance. | $341.33 |
| DIFFERENCE | ______ |

7. Copy this form and follow the steps to check Mr. Potter's checkbook balance. Did he make any mistakes?

ON YOUR OWN

## Data Search

Obtain copies of as many different sample bank statements as you can. Bring the samples to class and discuss the features of each. For example, see if the method of listing checks, deposits, and service charges is the same. Do the samples describe a reconciliation method? Are the methods all the same?

# Unit Review

*Solve the problems.* *(pages 12–23)*

1. The Millers took a plane flight that cost $169 per person. How much did it cost in all for the 5 members of the Miller family to take their flight?

2. Nicholas wrote a 1,873-word essay for science, and a 1,640-word essay for social studies. How many words in all did Nicholas write?

3. A grocer packs 6 tomatoes in each package. He has a total of 271 tomatoes. How many packages can he fill? How many will be left over?

4. The bleachers in the gym each hold approximately 136 people. There are 6 bleachers in the gym. About how many people can they hold in all?

*Solve the problems.* *(pages 12–23)*

5. There are 24 ties in each box. How many ties are there in all in 18 boxes?

6. Ms. Hayes drove 675 km in 9 h. What was her average speed?

7. The coach has $219.78 left of the $3,046.45 expense fund for the entire season. How much has the coach spent?

8. Each box will hold 36 cans. How many boxes must be used if 1,025 cans must be put into boxes?

9. Mr. Bueno earned $14,796.50 in one year and $16,429.30 the next year. How much did he earn in all for the two years?

10. A buyer has $2,075 to spend for jackets. How many jackets can she buy if the jackets cost $52 each?

*Use word equations to solve.* *(pages 24–25)*

11. Quincy spent $7.96 for a book and $15.45 for records. He gave the clerk $50. How much change did he receive?

12. Each carton contains 288 boxes, with 12 pencils in each box. How many pencils are there in 56 cartons?

13. An airplane flew 13,400 km one day and 11,400 km the next day. Its total flight time was 31 h. What was its average speed for these 31 h of flying?

14. Of 26,419 registered voters, 4,892 did not vote in an election. The winner received 15,716 votes. How many of those who voted did not vote for the winner?

*Solve the problems. (pages 26–31)*

**15.** Each large box contains 24 cameras. Each small box contains 12 cameras. How many cameras are in a shipment of 15 large boxes and 20 small boxes?

**16.** Helen wants to sell 100 packages of seeds. After she had sold 17 packages, she sold 4 boxes of 8 packages each. How many more packages does she have to sell to reach her goal?

**17.** In 9 h one truck completed all but 247 km of its 860 km trip. In 8 h a second truck traveled 584 km. How much greater was the average speed of the second truck?

**18.** Don bought 3 shirts for $16.50 each, 2 ties for $6.75 each, and a jacket for $32.50. He gave the clerk $100. How much change did Don receive?

*Solve the problems. (pages 32–35)*

**19.** José earned $5.60/h for each of the 38 h he worked. Ella earned $5.95/h for each of the 36 h she worked. Who earned more per hour? How much more?

**20.** Ms. Helms worked an average of 156 h/month for 3 years. How many hours did she work in all in these 3 years?

*Complete the forms. (pages 36–37)*

*Complete a checkbook record for these transactions. The starting balance is $306.14.*

**21.** March 12: Check number 291 to Home Dairy for $24.75

**22.** March 16: Deposit of $225.90

**23.** March 20: Check number 292 to United Airlines for $139.00

**24.** Use the catalog listings at the right. Complete an order form for a purchase of 2 men's shirts, 3 women's shirts, and 2 winter jackets. The handling charge is $2.50.

| Catalog number | Item | Price |
|---|---|---|
| 5192A | Men's Shirts | $13.75 |
| 6043T | Women's Shirts | $14.60 |
| 0210M | Winter Jackets | $37.98 |

## Other Numeration Systems

**A.** One of the earliest systems of numeration is the *Egyptian system,* which dates back as far as 3000 B.C. The Egyptians, who lived along the Nile River, used hieroglyphic (picture) symbols of familiar objects to represent numbers. The following table shows some of the symbols used and the equivalent *Hindu-Arabic* numerals we use today.

| Hindu-Arabic Numeral | Egyptian Numeral | Description of Symbol |
|---|---|---|
| 1 | \| | Vertical Staff |
| 10 | ∩ | Heel bone |
| 100 | 𓍢 | Scroll |
| 1,000 | 𓆼 | Lotus flower |
| 10,000 | 𓂭 | Bent finger |
| 100,000 | 𓆐 | Tadpole |
| 1,000,000 | 𓁨 | Astonished man |

In the Egyptian system, numerals were formed by repeating symbols and using the additive principle. The arrangement of the symbols for the same number could vary; for example, 15 could be written ∩||||| or |||||∩ or ||∩||| and so on. Since the value of a symbol did not change according to location, the Egyptian system did not use the concept of *place value.* (In our system, 34 ≠ 43 even though the same symbols are used in both numerals.)

A few more examples of Egyptian numerals are shown.

| | | | | | |
|---|---|---|---|---|---|
| 122 | 𓍢∩∩\|\|\| | 2,134 | 𓆼𓆼𓍢∩∩∩\|\|\|\| | 10,540 | 𓂭𓍢𓍢𓍢𓍢𓍢∩∩∩∩ |

*Write each of the following as a Hindu-Arabic numeral.*

**1.** ∩∩∩|||　　**2.** 𓍢𓍢𓍢𓍢∩∩||　　**3.** 𓆼𓆼𓆼∩∩∩∩|||||||

*Write each of the following as an Egyptian numeral.*

**4.** 59　　**5.** 231　　**6.** 1,408　　**7.** 35,162　　**8.** 120,515

**9.** Add ∩∩|||||| + ∩∩∩∩|||| . Remember to regroup if necessary.

**B.** The Mayan Indians of Central America developed a very interesting numeration system. We do not know exactly how old the system is, but 16th-century Spanish explorers found evidence of its use. The twenty basic symbols are shown below.

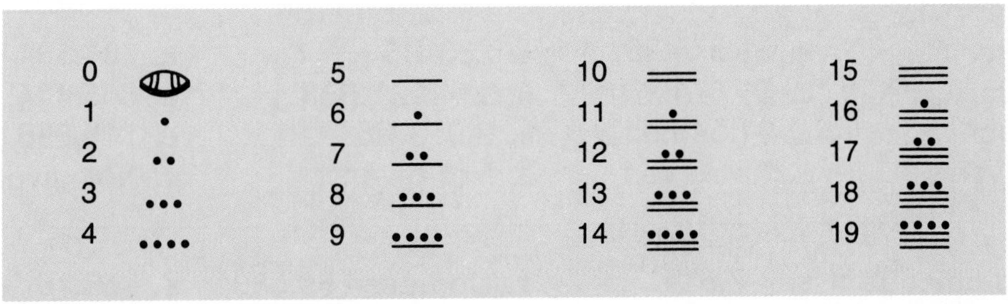

| | | | |
|---|---|---|---|
| 0 | 5 | 10 | 15 |
| 1 | 6 | 11 | 16 |
| 2 | 7 | 12 | 17 |
| 3 | 8 | 13 | 18 |
| 4 | 9 | 14 | 19 |

Mayan numerals were written vertically, and the positions from bottom to top represented place values of 1, 20, (18) (20), 18 (20) (20), 18 (20) (20) (20), and so on. Therefore, the Mayans had a type of base twenty system except that beginning at the third place from the bottom, one factor of 18 was used. Historians believe this was due to the fact that the Mayan year had 360 days.

Look at the following examples.

Start at the bottom. ↑

| | | |
|---|---|---|
| 2 (18) (20) (20) | | 14,400 |
| 0 (18) (20) | ⟶ | 0 |
| 11 (20) | | 220 |
| 7 | | + 7 |
| | | 14,627 |

The Mayan numeral represents 14,627.

*Write each of the following as a Hindu-Arabic numeral.*

**10.**

**11.**

**12.**

*Write each of the following as a Mayan numeral. Think carefully. Remember what each position from bottom to top represents.*

**13.** 56 **14.** 400 **15.** 768 **16.** 1,809 **17.** 3,672

# Cumulative Review

**1.** $452{,}698 + 293{,}407$

a. 645,095
b. 756,105
c. 746,105
d. Not given

**2.** $\$62.97 \times 25$

a. $1,574.25
b. $1,674.25
c. $1,548.95
d. Not given

**3.** $27\overline{)55{,}436}$

a. 253 R5
b. 114,121 R5
c. 2,053 R5
d. Not given

**4.** $800{,}302 - 5{,}716$

a. 784,584
b. 805,414
c. 715,596
d. Not given

**5.** Round 569,603 to the nearest thousand.

a. 570,000
b. 569,000
c. 560,000
d. Not given

**6.** $7{,}614 \times 907$

a. 738,558
b. 121,824
c. 6,905,898
d. Not given

**7.** Compare 69,583 and 69,518.

a. $69{,}518 > 69{,}583$
b. $69{,}518 < 69{,}583$
c. $69{,}518 = 69{,}583$
d. Not given

**8.** $\$65.10 \div 7 = \blacksquare$

a. $930
b. $9.30
c. $93
d. Not given

**9.** $5{,}497 + 83{,}786 + 998 = \blacksquare$

a. 90,281
b. 238,556
c. 89,171
d. Not given

**10.** $\$12{,}000 - \$97.76 = \blacksquare$

a. $10,224
b. $11,903.76
c. $11,123.34
d. Not given

**11.** Mona bought 3 books for $7.95 each and 4 records for $8.69 each. How much did she spend in all for these seven items?

a. $16.64
b. $56.61
c. $30.54
d. Not given

**12.** There are 6,819 TV sets in a warehouse. 516 must be shipped to one store and 293 must be shipped to another store. How many TV sets will be left in the warehouse after these shipments?

a. 6,010
b. 6,306
c. 809
d. Not given

**13.** Each box will hold 48 cans. How many boxes must be used if 820 cans must be put into boxes?

a. 17
b. 17 R4
c. 18
d. Not given

**14.** The Smiths drove a total of 39 h. Their average speed was 78 km/h. How far did they drive in all?

a. 117 km
b. 3,042 km
c. 881 km
d. Not given

# 2 Whole Numbers: Algebra

**NATIONAL PARKS WITH CANYONS**

| National Park | Area | Deepest Canyon |
|---|---|---|
| Bryce Canyon | 35,835 acres | 1,000 feet |
| Canyonland | 337,570 acres | 3,000 feet |
| Grand Canyon | 1,218,375 acres | 5,280 feet |
| Yellowstone | 2,219,832 acres | 300 feet |
| Zion | 146,551 acres | 3,500 feet |

## 2-1 Arithmetic Expressions and Sentences

**A.** Numerals and operation signs are used to write **arithmetic expressions.** These are arithmetic expressions:

$9 + 7$ $\quad 32 \div 2$ $\quad 29 + 3 \times (12 \div 2)$ $\quad 15 - [22 - (7 + 3)]$

**B.** To **simplify** an arithmetic expression, write a standard numeral for its value. Work from left to right doing multiplications and divisions first and then additions and subtractions.

**Example 1**

$64 - 8 \times 5$
$64 - 40$
$24$

**Example 2**

$23 + 4 \times 3 + 8 \div 2$
$23 + 12 + 4$
$39$

**C.** If **parentheses** occur in an expression, work inside the parentheses first.

**Example 1**

$40 - (6 + 5)$
$40 - 11$
$29$

**Example 2**

$40 + 5 \times [30 - (9 + 3)] \div 10$
$40 + 5 \times [30 - 12] \div 10$
$40 + 5 \times 18 \div 10$
$40 + 90 \div 10$
$40 + 9$
$49$

**Example 3**

$(40 - 6) + 5$
$34 + 5$
$39$

**D.** Arithmetic expressions, standard numerals, and relation signs are used to write **arithmetic sentences.**

These are arithmetic sentences:

$3 + 4 = 7$ $\quad 11 > 9 - 6$ $\quad 32 \div 8 < 12 \times 2$

$6 + 2 \neq 23$ $\quad 5 \times 9 \geq 3 \times 9$ $\quad 18 - 3 \leq 3 \times 5$

is not equal to

is greater than or equal to

is less than or equal to

**E.** Arithmetic sentences make statements that are true or false.

$8 \times 9 \neq 63$ true $\quad 5 \times 3 > 2 \times 9$ false $\quad 3 \div 3 \leq 1$ true

## CLASS EXERCISES

*Simplify.*

**1.** $12 \times 2 - 23 + 7 \times 3$ **2.** $32 - (8 + 7) + 22 \div 11$ **3.** $1 - (3 \div 3)$

**4.** $11 + 13 - [12 \div (1 + 2) + 16]$ **5.** $[38 - (12 + 7)] \times (20 + 9)$

*Tell whether the statement is true or false.*

**6.** $32 \times 3 = 69$ **7.** $7 + 9 < 16$ **8.** $15 - 8 \geq 7$ **9.** $6 \times 9 \neq 54$

**10.** $(42 + 4) \div 2 \leq 23$ **11.** $6 \times 5 > 5 \times 6$ **12.** $45 \div 9 + 8 = 13$

## EXERCISES

*Simplify.*

**1.** $36 \div 6 + 3$ **2.** $35 - 11 \times 3$ **3.** $16 + 3 \times 9$ **4.** $40 - 7 \times 3$

**5.** $18 \div (15 - 6)$ **6.** $(16 + 3) \times 9$ **7.** $81 \div (19 - 16)$ **8.** $(40 - 7) \times 3$

**9.** $39 - 9 \times 4$ **10.** $(39 - 9) \times 4$ **11.** $56 + 4 \div 2$ **12.** $(56 + 4) \div 12$

**13.** $63 \div (3 + 4)$ **14.** $(63 \div 3) + 4$ **15.** $64 \div (8 - 4)$ **16.** $64 \div 8 - 4$

**17.** $30 + 27 \div 3$ **18.** $27 \div 3 + 30$ **19.** $(27 + 3) \div 3$ **20.** $60 \div (14 + 6)$

**21.** $13 \times (9 + 4)$ **22.** $9 + 4 \times 13$ **23.** $9 \times (8 - 7)$ **24.** $12 \times (7 + 5)$

**25.** $9 \times [13 - (12 \div 6)]$ **26.** $(9 \times 8) - (9 \times 7)$ **27.** $15 + (6 \div 3) + 4$

**28.** $12 - [7 \div (7 + 0) + 5] - 2$ **29.** $6 \times (4 + 5) - 14 \div (15 - 8)$

**30.** $17 + 3 \times [40 - (8 \times 3)] \div 3$ **31.** $23 - 6 \div [30 - (6 \times 4)] \times 2$

★**32.** $(9 + 6) \div [5 \div (3 - 2)] \times (8 + 3)$ ★**33.** $(7 + 2) \times [6 + (6 \div 2)] \div 9$

*Tell whether the statement is true or false.*

**34.** $9 \times 6 \geq 56$ **35.** $17 - 9 \leq 8$

**36.** $63 \div 9 > 7 - 1$ **37.** $7 \times 9 = 54 + 9$

**38.** $19 - 7 \neq 12$ **39.** $49 \div 7 = 6$

**40.** $18 + 7 \geq 25 \div 5$ **41.** $144 \div 24 > 5$

**42.** $8 + 7 < 20$ **43.** $21 - 13 \leq 7$

★**44.** $(9 + 9) - 2 \neq 72 \div 8 - (2 - 1)$

★**45.** $15 + 9 \times 12 = 246 \div 2 + 0 + 17$

### THINK!

**What Do You See?**

How many cubes do you see?

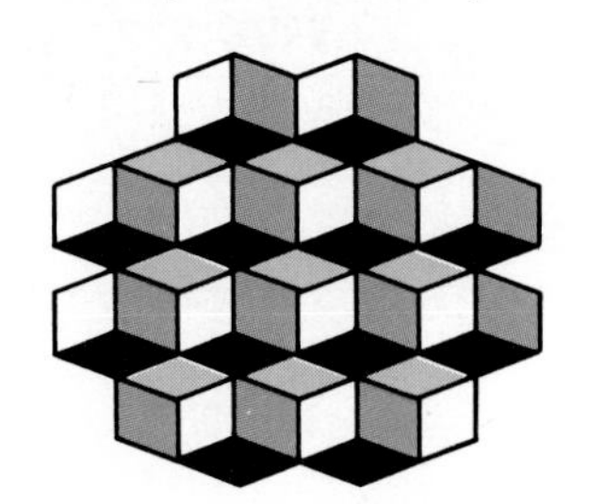

1. 9  5. 2  25. 99  34. false

Homework page 456

## 2-2 Algebraic Expressions

**A.** A **variable** is a letter that represents any number in a set. Variables, numerals, and operation signs are used to write **algebraic expressions.** These are algebraic expressions:

$x + 3$ $\quad$ $4 \cdot w$ $\quad$ $y - (z + 9)$ $\quad$ $2m + 8$ $\quad$ $\frac{3r}{2}$

$4 \times w$ $\quad$ $2 \times m$ $\quad$ $3 \times r \div 2$

**B.** Algebraic expressions can replace word expressions.

Twice the distance (d) of your walk $\longleftrightarrow$ $2d$ or $2 \cdot d$

17 years less than your father's age (a) $\longleftrightarrow$ $a - 17$

4 cm more than 3 times your height (h) $\longleftrightarrow$ $3h + 4$ or $3 \cdot h + 4$

A number (n) divided by 5 $\longleftrightarrow$ $\frac{n}{5}$ or $n \div 5$

The product of two numbers (x and y) divided by 8 $\longleftrightarrow$ $\frac{xy}{8}$ or $xy \div 8$

**C.** Each number a variable represents is a **value** of the variable. An algebraic expression has values for values of its variables.

**Example 1**

Find the value of $\frac{3r}{2}$ when the value of $r$ is 12.

value of r

$$\frac{3 \times 12}{2} = \frac{36}{2} = 18$$

**Example 2**

Find the value of $y - (z + 9)$ when the value of $y$ is 11 and the value of $z$ is 2.

value of y $\quad$ value of z

$$11 - (2 + 9) = 11 - 11 = 0$$

**D.** A table can be used to show values of an expression for several values of its variables.

| Value of $x$ | 0 | 1 | 2 | 5 | 7 | 11 |
|---|---|---|---|---|---|---|
| Value of $y$ | 8 | 3 | 1 | 1 | 5 | 7 |
| Value of $5x + 9 - y$ | 1 | 11 | 18 | 33 | 39 | 57 |

$5 \times 0 + 9 - 8$

## CLASS EXERCISES

*Write an algebraic expression for each word expression.*

**1.** 4 km more than 10 times the distance ($d$) **2.** A number ($n$) divided by 5

*Complete the table.*

| Value of $y$ | 1 | 3 | 5 | 7 | 9 |
|---|---|---|---|---|---|
| Value of $z$ | 0 | 1 | 2 | 3 | 4 |
| Value of $3y + 4z$ | **3.** | **4.** | **5.** | **6.** | **7.** |

## EXERCISES

*Find the value of each algebraic expression when the value of $x$ is 3.*

**1.** $x + 5$ **2.** $4x$ **3.** $2x - 5$ **4.** $\frac{11x}{3}$ **5.** $\frac{4x}{3}$

*Find the value of each algebraic expression when the value of $r$ is 5.*

**6.** $r + 7$ **7.** $r - 4$ **8.** $7r - 20$ **9.** $\frac{2r}{5}$ **10.** $12r$

*Complete the table.*

| Value of $x$ | 0 | 1 | 1 | 2 |
|---|---|---|---|---|
| Value of $y$ | 2 | 4 | 7 | 16 |
| Value of $z$ | 0 | 3 | 6 | 12 |
| Value of $2x + 3y$ | **11.** | **12.** | **13.** | **14.** |
| Value of $\frac{4z}{3}$ | **15.** | **16.** | **17.** | **18.** |
| Value of $y \cdot (5 - x) + 2z$ | ★ **19.** | ★ **20.** | ★ **21.** | ★ **22.** |

## PROBLEMS

*Write the algebraic expression and find its value when $s$ is 10.*

**23.** 6 points less than your team's score ($s$)

**24.** 4 times the number of shirts ($s$) on each shelf

### Picture This

A group of students are lined up so that there are 2 students in front of a student, 1 student behind a student, and 1 student in the middle. How many students are there?

9 ·ll 8 ·l



Homework page 456

# Algebraic Sentences

**A.** Algebraic expressions, numerals, and relation signs are used to write **algebraic sentences.** These are algebraic sentences:

$x + 3 = 8$ $\qquad 5x - (3 + w) \geq 0$ $\qquad \frac{n+2}{7} \neq 0$ $\qquad 6u < 19 - v$

**B.** Algebraic sentences can replace word sentences.

The sum of two numbers (q and r) is less than 13. $\quad q + r < 13$

5 less than 3 times a number (n) is 22. $\quad 3n - 5 = 22$

The height of the willow tree (w) is greater than 15 m. $\quad w > 15$

**C.** Some algebraic sentences give true statements for some values of the variables and false statements for other values of the variables.

**Example 1**

Is $2x - z = 1$ true or false when x is 3 and z is 5?

$$2\quad - z = 1$$
$$\downarrow \quad \downarrow$$
$$2 \times \quad - 5 = 1$$
$$6 - 5 = 1$$
$$1 = 1 \quad \text{true}$$

**Example 2**

Is $2x - z = 1$ true or false when x is 4 and z is 6?

$$2\quad - z = 1$$
$$\downarrow \quad \downarrow$$
$$2 \times \quad - 6 = 1$$
$$8 - 6 = 1$$
$$2 = 1 \quad \text{false}$$

**Example 3**

Is $4t - 3 > 9$ true or false when t is 3?

$$4\quad - 3 > 9$$
$$\downarrow$$
$$4 \times \quad - 3 > 9$$
$$12 - 3 > 9$$
$$9 > 9 \quad \text{false}$$

**Example 4**

Is $4t - 3 > 9$ true or false when t is 6?

$$4\quad - 3 > 9$$
$$\downarrow$$
$$4 \times \quad - 3 > 9$$
$$24 - 3 > 9$$
$$21 > 9 \quad \text{true}$$

**D.** Some algebraic sentences give true statements for all values of the variables.

For all whole number values of x, $x + 4 = 4 + x$.
Example: $11 + 4 = 4 + 11$

## CLASS EXERCISES

*Write an algebraic sentence for each word sentence.*

**1.** The number of tomato plants (t) is twice the number of pepper plants (p).

**2.** The number of cucumbers picked (c) is less than the number of tomatoes picked (t).

*Tell whether the sentence is true or false for the given values of u and v.*

**3.** $3u - 7 = 23$ when u is 10

**4.** $4u - v \leq 16$ when u is 3 and v is 11

**5.** $3u = 4v + 6$ when u is 2 and v is 6

**6.** $\frac{5u}{4v} \geq 15$ when u is 8 and v is 2

## EXERCISES

*Tell whether the sentence is true or false for the given values of the variables.*

**1.** $42 - x = 30$ when x is 12

**2.** $4t + 3 \leq 15$ when t is 4

**3.** $r + 7 = 10$ when r is 6

**4.** $x > 10$ when x is 15

**5.** $y + z = 8$ when y is 7 and z is 3

**6.** $4z - 2 \leq 10$ when z is 3

**7.** $6r \neq 0$ when r is 0

**8.** $6x + 2y \geq 11$ when x is 2 and y is 0

**9.** $\frac{7s}{2} = 4t$ when s is 4 and t is 6

**10.** $\frac{n - 3}{10} < 3m$ when n is 33 and m is 1

**11.** $26 = 3x - 6y$ when x is 9 and y is 3

**12.** $44x - 22y = 44$ when x is 2 and y is 2

**13.** $9 + y = 2x - 7$ when y is 4 and x is 10

**14.** $5m \geq 17n$ when m is 10 and n is 3

★**15.** $y \geq 0$ for all whole number values of y

★**16.** $u > u + 1$ for all whole number values of u

## PROBLEMS

*Write the algebraic sentence and tell whether it is true or false when x is 34 and y is 10.*

**17.** The number of bicycles in the shop (x) is 4 more than 3 times the number of snowmobiles (y).

**18.** The number of desks (x) is greater than or equal to 1 more than the number of students (y).

1. true 5. false

Homework page 457

## 2-4 Relationships between Operations

Algebraic sentences that give true statements for all values of the variables can be used to state relationships between operations.

**A.** Addition and subtraction are related.

For all whole number values of x and y,
$x + y - y = x$ and when $x \geq y$, $x - y + y = x$.

Subtraction "undoes" addition.

Addition "undoes" subtraction.

**Example 1**

When y is 3, $x + 3 - 3 = x$

**Example 2**

When y is 5, $x - 5 + 5 = x$

**B.** Multiplication and division are related.

For all whole number values of x and y, when $y \neq 0$,
$x \cdot y \div y = x$ and $(x \div y) \cdot y = x$.

Division "undoes" multiplication.

Multiplication "undoes" division.

**Example 1**

When y is 7, $x \cdot 7 \div 7 = x$

**Example 2**

When y is 4, $(x \div 4) \cdot 4 = x$

**C.** You can distribute multiplication over addition.

For all whole number values of x, y, and z,
$x \cdot (y + z) = xy + xz$ and $(y + z) \cdot x = yx + zx$.

To distribute multiplication over addition, multiply each addend.

**Example 1**

When x is 3 and z is 5,
$3 \cdot (y + 5) = 3y + 15$

**Example 2**

When x is 7 and y is 8,
$(8 + z) \cdot 7 = 56 + 7z$

**D.** The distributive properties with subtraction are like those with addition.

For all whole number values of x, y, and z, when $y \geq z$,
$x \cdot (y - z) = xy - xz$ and $(y - z) \cdot x = yx - zx$.

## CLASS EXERCISES

*Use the relationships between addition and subtraction to complete.*

**1.** $x - 2 + \blacksquare = x$ **2.** $q + \blacksquare - 9 = q$ **3.** $t = t + 5 - \blacksquare$

*Use the relationships between multiplication and division to complete.*

**4.** $w \cdot \blacksquare \div 11 = w$ **5.** $(z \div 4) \cdot \blacksquare = z$ **6.** $(x \div 2) \cdot 2 = \blacksquare$

*Use the distributive properties to complete.*

**7.** $3 \cdot (v + 5) = 3v + \blacksquare$ **8.** $7 \cdot (t - 5) = \blacksquare - 35$ **9.** $(r + 1) \cdot 5 = \blacksquare + 5$

*Use operation signs and/or numerals to complete.*

**10.** $3 \cdot (2 - w) = 6 \bullet 3w$ **11.** $7 \cdot x \bullet 7 = x$ **12.** $y + 6 \bullet \blacksquare = y$

## EXERCISES

*Use the relationships between operations to complete.*

**1.** $x = 2 + x - \blacksquare$ **2.** $x - 10 + \blacksquare = x$ **3.** $q - 8 + 8 = \blacksquare$

**4.** $z = z + \blacksquare - 13$ **5.** $21 + v - 21 = \blacksquare$ **6.** $y + 5 - \blacksquare = y$

**7.** $x \cdot 6 \div \blacksquare = x$ **8.** $x = 3 \cdot x \div \blacksquare$ **9.** $\frac{y}{5} \cdot \blacksquare = y$

**10.** $n \cdot 15 \div 15 = \blacksquare$ **11.** $\blacksquare = 17 \cdot t \div 17$ **12.** $\blacksquare = 23 + m - 23$

**13.** $4 \cdot (q + 3) = \blacksquare + 12$ **14.** $(p - 6) \cdot 10 = 10p - \blacksquare$

**15.** $20 \cdot (4y + 11) = \blacksquare + \blacktriangle$ ★ **16.** $6r \div 6 + 19 - 19 = \blacksquare$

*Use operation signs and/or numerals to complete.*

**17.** $4 \cdot (t + 1) = 4t \bullet 4$ **18.** $x = x - 29 \bullet 29$ **19.** $7 \cdot (9 - v) = 63 \bullet 7v$

**20.** $\frac{z}{5} \bullet \blacksquare = z$ **21.** $4 \cdot w \bullet \blacksquare = w$ **22.** $t = 12t \bullet \blacksquare$

**23.** $z = (z \div 8) \bullet \blacksquare$ **24.** $31 \cdot w \bullet \blacksquare = w$ **25.** $t = t - 17 \bullet \blacksquare$

**26.** $t = 3t \bullet \blacksquare$ **27.** $\frac{y}{2} \bullet \blacksquare = y$ ★ **28.** $3q \div \blacksquare + 5 \bullet \blacktriangle = q$

## THINK!

### Making a Logical Choice

Of the first two items on a true-false test, *exactly one* has the correct answer "true." *At least one* of these following statements about the answer is false:

The answer for question 1 is "true." The answer for question 2 is "false." What are the correct answers for these questions?

1. 2 7. 6 10. n 17. +



Homework page 457

# Solving Equations with Addition and Subtraction

**A.** **Equations** are sentences that contain an equality sign (=). **Solutions** of algebraic equations are values of their variables that give true statements.

| | | | |
|---|---|---|---|
| *Equation:* | $x = 9$ | $2 + w = 6$ | $x - 7 = 2$ |
| *Solution:* | 9 | 4 | 9 |
| *Check:* | $9 = 9$ | $2 + 4 = 6$ | $9 - 7 = 2$ |
| | | $6 = 6$ | $2 = 2$ |

**B.** Equations with the same solutions are **equivalent equations.** $x = 9$ and $x - 7 = 2$ are equivalent equations. They both have the solution 9.

**C.** To **solve** an equation is to find all its solutions. You can solve an "easy" equation like $x = 9$ by inspection.

| | | | |
|---|---|---|---|
| *Equation:* | $t = 10$ | $y = 4$ | $17 = g$ |
| *Solution:* | 10 | 4 | 17 |
| *Check:* | $10 = 10$ | $4 = 4$ | $17 = 17$ |

**D.** To solve an equation like $x - 7 = 2$, solve an "easy" equivalent equation. You can add the same number to both sides, or subtract the same number from both sides of the equation, to find the "easy" equation.

**Example 1**

Solve. $x + 2 = 7$

*Equation:* $x + 2 = 7$

Subtract 2 from both sides.

$x + 2 \quad = 7$

$x = 5$

*Solution:* 5

*Check:* $+ 2 = 7$

↓

$+ 2 = 7$

$7 = 7$

**Example 2**

Solve. $z - 6 = 3$

*Equation:* $z - 6 = 3$

Add 6 to both sides.

$z - 6 \quad = 3$

$z = 9$

*Solution:* 9

*Check:* $- 6 = 3$

↓

$- 6 = 3$

$3 = 3$

## CLASS EXERCISES

*Solve the equations. Check.*

| | | | |
|---|---|---|---|
| **1.** $y - 8 = 12$ | **2.** $z + 17 = 29$ | **3.** $x - 45 = 0$ | **4.** $x = 41$ |
| **5.** $14 + y = 26$ | **6.** $48 = x - 65$ | **7.** $63 = 21 + t$ | **8.** $0 = w$ |

## EXERCISES

*Solve the equations. Check.*

| | | | |
|---|---|---|---|
| **1.** $x + 19 = 57$ | **2.** $y - 23 = 36$ | **3.** $w + 25 = 49$ | **4.** $z - 27 = 50$ |
| **5.** $w + 39 = 39$ | **6.** $14 + x = 41$ | **7.** $69 + z = 106$ | **8.** $75 = m + 19$ |
| **9.** $x - 100 = 34$ | **10.** $34 = w - 11$ | **11.** $y + 49 = 51$ | **12.** $87 = 73 +$ |
| **13.** $z - 273 = 27$ | **14.** $79 = x + 16$ | **15.** $19 + y = 21$ | **16.** $70 = 13 +$ |
| **17.** $m - 896 = 0$ | **18.** $56 = x - 47$ | **19.** $x + 43 = 50$ | **20.** $84 + u = 84$ |
| **21.** $17 = w + 7$ | **22.** $t - 38 = 49$ | **23.** $0 = x - 916$ | **24.** $18 = x + 2$ |
| **25.** $45 = 17 + t$ | **26.** $x = 867$ | **27.** $24 = 16 + x$ | **28.** $v + 7 = 19$ |
| **29.** $q - 21 = 42$ | **30.** $72 = 12 + x$ | **31.** $y + 32 = 32$ | **32.** $56 = z$ |

★ **33.** $x + 29 - 17 + 11 = 23$

★ **34.** $79 + n - 23 = 45 + 28$

★ **35.** $410 - 20 = r + 45 + 74$

★ **36.** $210 + 101 = 87 + w - 87$

## PROBLEMS

*Write the equation. Solve.*

**37.** 5 less than a number (n) is 11. What is the number?

**38.** 3 increased by a number (n) is 8. What is the number?

**39.** A number (n) decreased by 19 is 4. What is the number?

**40.** 23 is equal to 14 plus a number (n). What is the number?

**41.** 45 more than a number (n) is 57. What is the number?

★ **42.** A number (n) decreased by 7 is 5 less than 12. What is the number?

1. 38 9. 134

Homework page 458

## THINK!

### Building Fences

A rancher wants to use exactly four straight fences to separate these horses into 11 areas. The fences may cross. How can this be done?

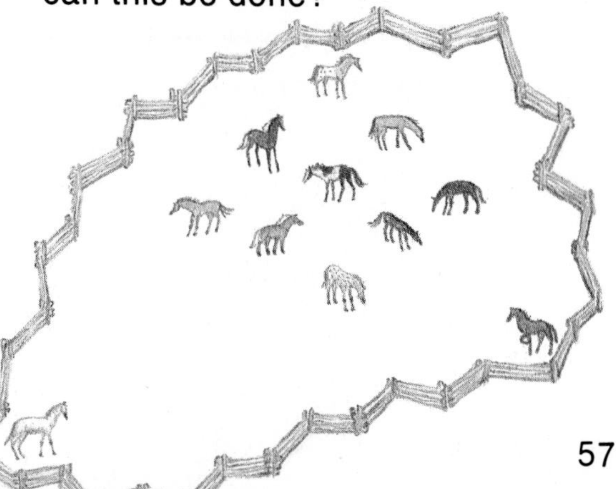

## 2-6 Solving Equations with Multiplication and Division

**A.** Multiplication and division can occur in algebraic equations.

| | | | |
|---|---|---|---|
| *Equation:* | $\frac{y}{4} = 10$ | $5w = 35$ | $z \div 8 = 2$ |
| *Solution:* | 40 | 7 | 16 |
| *Check:* | $\frac{40}{4} = 10$ | $5 \times 7 = 35$ | $16 \div 8 = 2$ |
| | $10 = 10$ true | $35 = 35$ true | $2 = 2$ true |

**B.** To solve an equation like $5w = 35$ or $z \div 8 = 2$, solve an equivalent "easy" equation. You can multiply or divide both sides of an equation by the same number (except 0) to find the "easy" equation.

**Example 1**

Solve. $\frac{t}{9} = 14$

*Equation:* $t \div 9 = 14$

Multiply both sides by 9.

$$(t \div 9) \cdot 9 = 14 \cdot 9$$
$$t = 126$$

*Solution:* 126

*Check:* $\frac{t}{9} = 14$

$126 \div 9 = 14$

$14 = 14$ true

**Example 2**

Solve. $16s = 80$

*Equation:* $16 \cdot s = 80$

Divide both sides by 16.

$$16 \cdot s \div 16 = 80 \div 16$$
$$s = 5$$

*Solution:* 5

*Check:* $16s = 80$

$16 \cdot 5 = 80$

$80 = 80$ true

**C.** Sometimes you must multiply *and* divide to get an "easy" equation.

| | | | |
|---|---|---|---|
| Solve. | $\frac{3x}{4} = 6$ | *Check:* | $\frac{3x}{4} = 6$ |
| Multiply both sides by 4. | $3x = 24$ | | $3 \times 8 \div 4 = 6$ |
| Divide both sides by 3. | $x = 8$ | | $24 \div 4 = 6$ |
| *Solution:* | 8 | | $6 = 6$ true |

## CLASS EXERCISES

*Solve the equations. Check.*

**1.** $\frac{x}{10} = 7$ **2.** $9y = 45$ **3.** $t - 16 = 34$ **4.** $\frac{z}{20} = 40$

**5.** $180 = 12u$ **6.** $59 = 14 + w$ **7.** $\frac{5x}{8} = 10$ **8.** $28 = \frac{7y}{3}$

**9.** $115 = q$ **10.** $3r \div 3 = 7$ **11.** $9z = 72$ **12.** $w \div 9 = 9$

## EXERCISES

*Solve the equations. Check.*

**1.** $4x = 48$ **2.** $\frac{x}{8} = 12$ **3.** $2y = 38$ **4.** $\frac{u}{7} = 11$

**5.** $\frac{m}{12} = 4$ **6.** $z + 35 = 40$ **7.** $3z = 42$ **8.** $\frac{x}{11} = 8$

**9.** $6p = 96$ **10.** $120 = 10y$ **11.** $z \div 6 = 13$ **12.** $3x = 51$

**13.** $30 = \frac{t}{2}$ **14.** $u - 92 = 4$ **15.** $12w = 12$ **16.** $27 = \frac{v}{3}$

**17.** $\frac{2x}{5} = 8$ **18.** $\frac{3y}{4} = 9$ **19.** $16x = 64$ **20.** $89 = 45 + w$

**21.** $0 = 89s$ **22.** $7m \div 4 = 21$ **23.** $27 = n - 43$ **24.** $36 = 9t \div 2$

**25.** $\frac{11w}{4} = 22$ **26.** $18 = \frac{x}{6}$ **27.** $16 = \frac{8y}{3}$ **28.** $144 = 8p$

**29.** $18 = \frac{9x}{7}$ **30.** $38 + y = 38$ **31.** $\frac{w}{20} = 9$ **32.** $58 = x + 2$

**33.** $11m = 484$ **34.** $25 = \frac{5t}{6}$ **35.** $q - 146 = 4$ **36.** $\frac{x}{1} = 409$

**37.** $110 = 76 + v$ **38.** $\frac{2w}{3} = 108$ **39.** $130 = 26n$ ★ **40.** $\frac{7q}{10} = 42 \div 3 \times 7$

## PROBLEMS

*Write the equation. Solve.*

**41.** 3 times a number (n) divided by 9 is 2. What is the number?

**42.** 52 is twice a number (n). What is the number?

## MIXED REVIEW

*Round to the nearest ten-thousand; to the nearest million.*

**1.** 7,695,316 **2.** 65,164,914 **3.** 92,744,653 **4.** 199,503,377

*Write >, <, or = for ●.*

**5.** 843,741 ● 84,741 **6.** 10,213,981 ● 10,213,918 **7.** 101,101,010 ● 101,110,101

*Estimate.*

**8.** $422 \times 943{,}736$ **9.** $76{,}899 + 481{,}510$ **10.** $79{,}673 \div 83$

1. 12 5. 48 17. 20



Homework page 458

## 2-9 Using Formulas

A **formula** states a relation among numbers. Formulas can be useful plans for solving problems.

**A.** Woodland High School's basketball team made 24 field goals and 11 free throws during a game. What was the team's total score?

Use this formula:

$$S = 2g + f$$

total score — field goals — free throws

$$\begin{aligned} S &= 2 \times 24 + 11 \\ &= 48 + 11 \\ &= 59 \end{aligned}$$

The team's total score was 59.

**B.** Bayard High School's basketball team got a total score of 66 points. If the team made 14 free throws, how many field goals did it make?

Use this formula again:

$$\begin{aligned} S &= 2g + f \\ 66 &= 2g + 14 \\ 66 - 14 &= 2g + 14 - 14 \\ 52 &= 2g \\ 52 \div 2 &= 2g \div 2 \\ 26 &= g \end{aligned}$$

The team made 26 field goals.

## CLASS EXERCISES

*Use the formula* $S = 2g + f$ *to complete the table.*

| Game | Team | S | g | f |
|---|---|---|---|---|
| 1st | Woodland | **1.** | 29 | 10 |
| | Bayard | **2.** | 28 | 9 |
| 2nd | Woodland | 77 | 32 | **3.** |
| | Bayard | 80 | **4.** | 16 |

## PROBLEMS

*Use the formulas in the table to solve the problems.*

| Formula | Meaning |
|---|---|
| $d = r \cdot t$ | The distance (d) travelled is equal to the rate (r) of speed times the time (t) it takes to travel that distance. |
| $M = m \cdot v$ | The momentum (M) of a moving body is equal to its mass (m) times its velocity (v). |
| $g = \frac{f + s + t}{3}$ | The average of 3 grades (g) is the sum of the first (f), second (s), and third (t) grades divided by 3. |

**1.** Eric got grades of 85, 82, and 91 on his history tests. What was Eric's average grade on his history tests?

**2.** Charlie drove for 4 h at an average speed of 85 km/h. How far did Charlie drive?

**3.** Ms. Bently drove 344 km in 4 h. What was the average speed at which she drove?

**4.** Ingrid got two 100's and a 97 on her math tests. What was Ingrid's average grade on her math tests?

**5.** Arlana got two 99's and a 54 on her science tests. What was her average grade on her science tests?

**6.** If Kevin drove 576 km at an average speed of 72 km/h, how long did he drive?

★ **7.** If Paul got the same grade in each of his 3 English tests and his average grade for the 3 tests was 87, what was his grade on the second test?

★ **8.** Joan hit a golf ball with a mass of 60 g and gave the ball a velocity of 70 m/second. What was the ball's momentum?

Homework page 460

## 2-10 Using Flowcharts

If Jan runs once around her block she runs 627 m. How many times (n) must Jan run around her block to run a total distance (D) of 5,000 m or more and end up where she started?

The **flowchart** below gives a plan for solving the problem. You can follow the arrows in the flowchart to get the answer.

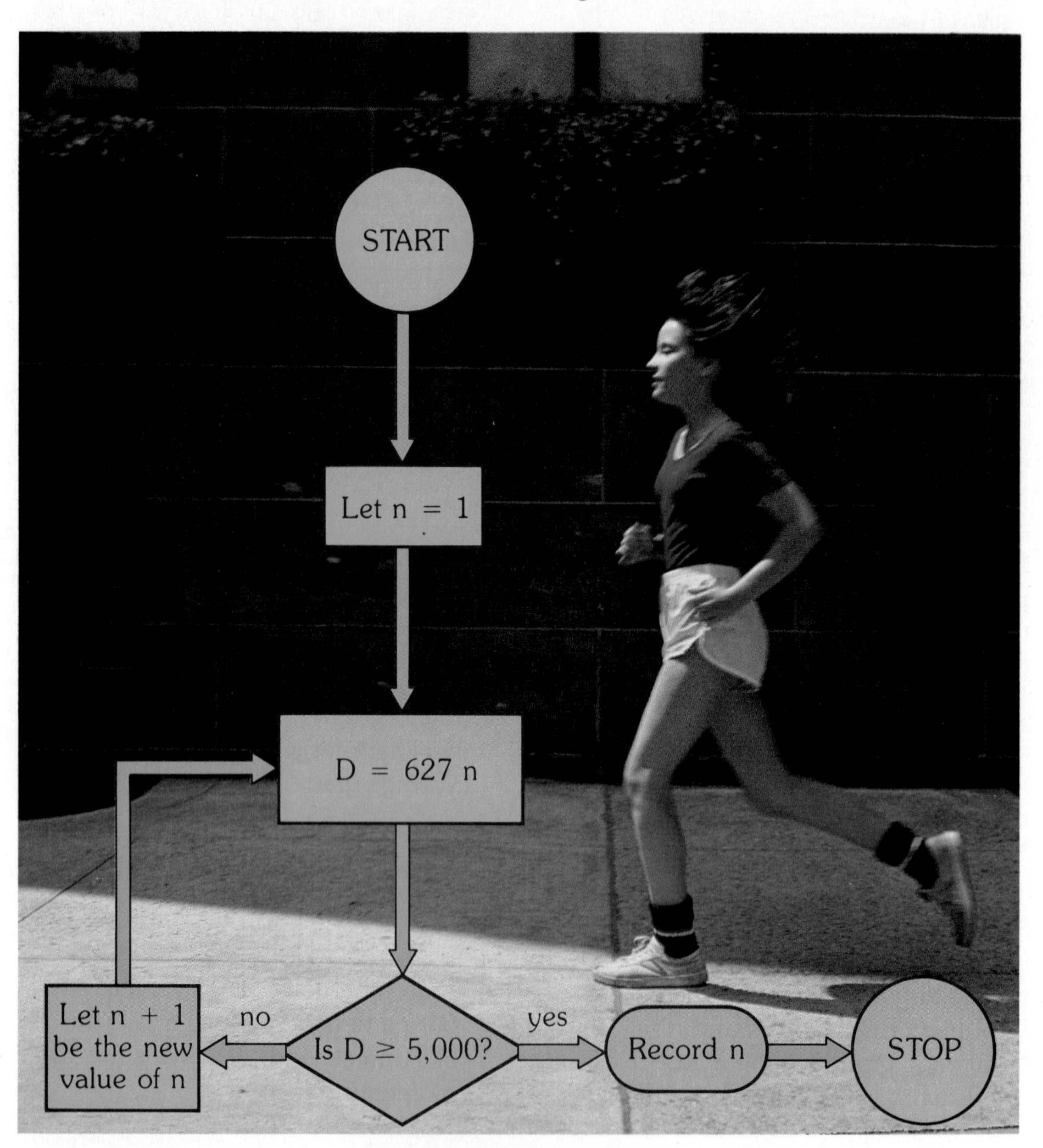

## CLASS EXERCISES

*Use the flowchart on page 66.*

1. The circles in the flowchart are **alert boxes.** What do the alert boxes tell you?

2. The first oval in the flowchart is an **input box.** What is the value of n given in the input box?

3. A rectangle in a flowchart is an **instruction box.** The first instruction box tells you how to find the value of D. What is the value of D when n is 1?

4. The arrow from the second instruction box is a **loop.** You must now find the value of D when the value of n has been increased by 1. What is the new value of D?

5. The "no" arrow after the diamond leads you to an instruction box that tells you to change the value of n. What is the value of n after n is 1?

6. The diamond is a **decision box.** Answer the question and follow the appropriate arrow. Is D greater than or equal to 5,000 when n is 1?

7. You must continue to go through the loop until the answer to the decision box leads you to "stop." How many times must you go through the loop?

8. The second oval in the flowchart is an **output box.** It tells you to write the answer to the problem. How many times must Jan run around her block?

## PROBLEMS

*Write a flowchart to plan for solving each problem. Then solve the problem.*

1. If Ray runs around his block once he runs 513 m. How many times must Ray run around his block to run 4,000 m or more and end up where he started?

2. If Charlotte swims the perimeter of the pool once, she swims 150 m. How many times must Charlotte swim around the pool to swim a total of 1,800 m?

★ 3. Mary deposited \$50. If the money earns 2¢ per dollar interest every 3 months, how much was in the account after 18 months?

## ON YOUR OWN

How many copies of the smaller triangle are in the large triangle?

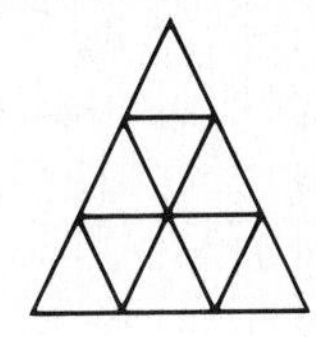

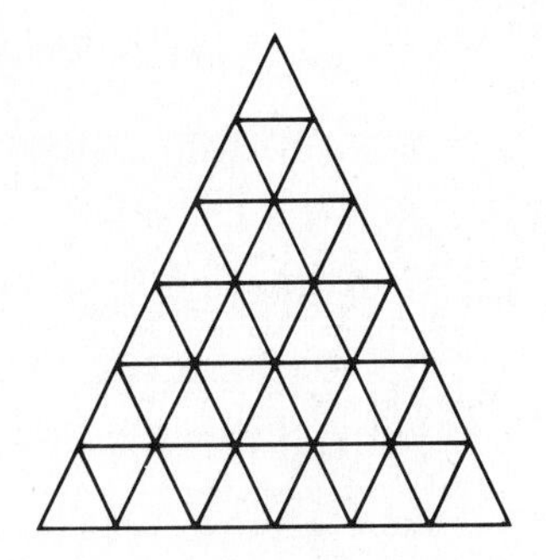

Homework page 460

## The Computer System

**A.** A **computer system** processes information, or **data.** It has three major parts: input device, central processing unit, and output device.

An **input device** is used to give data—the **input**—to the computer. Most school computers have a keyboard for input.

The **central processing unit (CPU)** is the computer's "brain." It has two parts: processor and memory. The **processor** controls the system, makes decisions, and calculates. Data is stored in the **memory.**

An **output device** is used to get data—the **output**—from the computer. Most school computers have a TV monitor for output.

Input and output devices and the computer itself are called **hardware.**

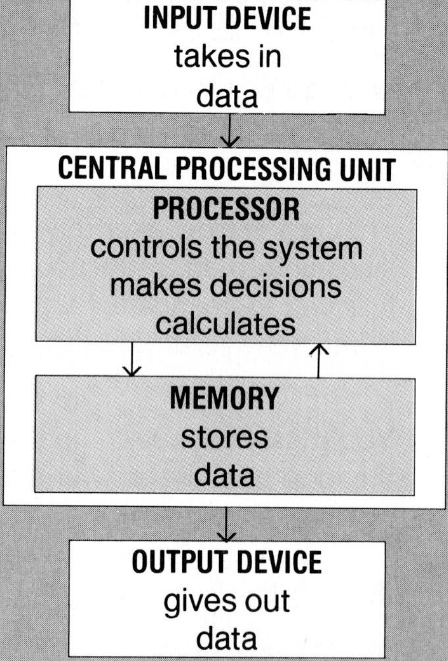


**B.** Computer memory has two parts. **Read-only memory (ROM)** is permanent; it contains the information the computer needs to operate. **Random-access memory (RAM)** may be changed or erased; it contains information that is used temporarily.

The amount of data a computer can store in its memory is measured in bytes. A **byte** is a single character, such as a digit or a space. A **kilobyte,** or **1 KB,** is 1,024 bytes; a **megabyte,** or **1 MB,** is 1,024 KB. Small computers, called **microcomputers,** often have 4-KB ROMs and RAMs of 64 KB to 256 KB.

Because a computer's inside memory may not be large enough, **storage media** that are outside the computer are used to extend its memory. Floppy disks and cassette tapes are storage media used with school microcomputers.

1. What part of a computer system performs each task?
   a. stores data
   b. gives out data
   c. makes decisions
2. In which part of a computer's memory would you find:
   a. input just received?
   b. rules for running its system?
3. A book page may contain about 2,500 characters. About how many pages that size could be stored in a 64-KB memory? About how many kilobytes of memory would be needed to store a 300-page book?

# Problem Solving Strategy

READ | PLAN | DO • ANSWER • CHECK

## Draw a Diagram

A forest ranger leaves the station house and travels 6 km north, 7 km east, 9 km south, 5 km west, and 3 km north. How far and in what direction must the ranger now travel to get back to the station house?

A good strategy to use to solve this type of problem is to **draw a diagram.** Use the data given in the problem and work step by step to construct your diagram.

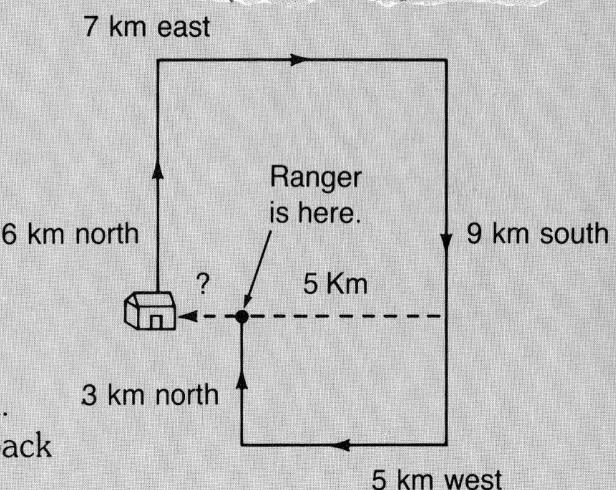


Now it is easy to see the solution from the diagram. The ranger only needs to travel 2 km west to get back to the ranger station.

*Solve.*

1. The Lim family leave their cabin to tour the forest. They drive 30 km west, 45 km south, 10 km west, 25 km north, and 40 km east. How far and in what direction must the Lim family travel to get back to their cabin?

2. The oak tree is 115 cm taller than the maple. The birch tree is 165 cm taller than the maple. The willow, at 559 cm, is 20 cm shorter than the oak. List the trees from shortest to tallest, and give their heights.

3. Ranger Joe leaves the station house and rides 13 km east, 9 km south, 7 km west, and 5 km south. Ranger Jane leaves the station house and rides 8 km north, 11 km west, 17 km south, 6 km east, and 5 km south. How far and in what direction must Ranger Joe travel to meet Ranger Jane?

4. The Woodland Tour Train consists of a motorman's car, a passenger coach, and a snack car. The coach is 3 times as long as the snack car. The snack car is twice as long as the motorman's car. The snack car is 4 meters long. How long are the passenger coach and motorman's car?

Challenge Problems page 517

## Drawing and Using Graphs

**A.** You have used a broken-line graph to show values measured at specific time intervals such as each year. A **curved-line graph** shows values measured continuously. The green curved-line graph shows changes in temperature over a 6-hour period as they might be measured in a weather station. The red broken-line graph shows the temperature readings measured at 1-hour intervals.

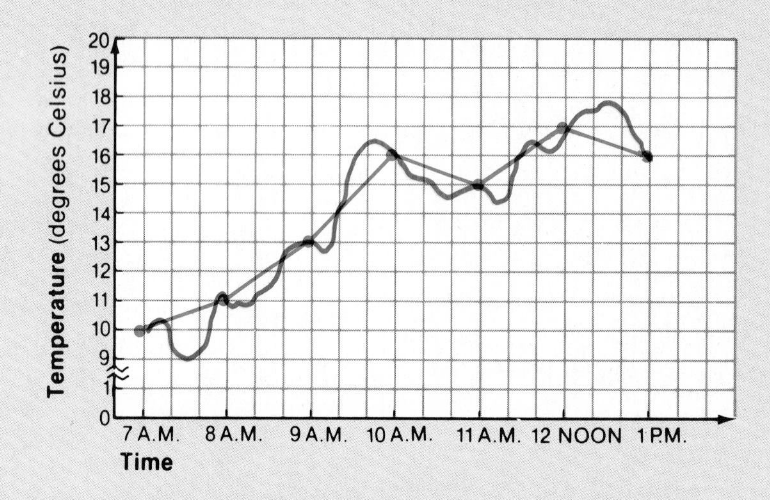


1. What is the highest temperature shown by the curved-line graph? by the broken-line graph?
2. What is the lowest temperature shown by the curved-line graph? by the broken-line graph?
3. The broken-line graph shows a decrease in temperature from 10:00 A.M. to 11:00 A.M. According to the curved-line graph, did this decrease begin before or after 10:00 A.M.?

**B.** Other curved-line graphs have "smooth" curves, like the one shown at the top of page 71. This graph is used by archaeologists to determine the ages of very old objects that were made from parts of plants or animals.

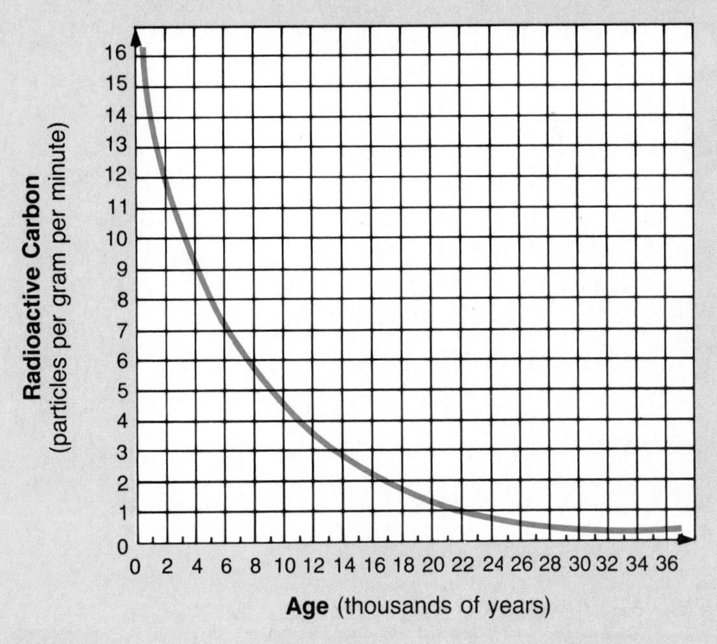


*How old is each object?*

4. wooden bowl: gives off 7.3 particles per gram per minute

5. ivory tube: gives off 1.3 particles per gram per minute

*How many particles would be given off by each object?*

6. reed basket: 3,000 years old

7. animal bone: 11,000 years old

*The double-curve graph shows the results of speed tests for a race car and a motorcycle.*

8. What was the speed of each after 5 s? after 10 s?

9. Which increased speed more quickly?

10. How long did it take for each to reach 50 km/h? 100 km/h?

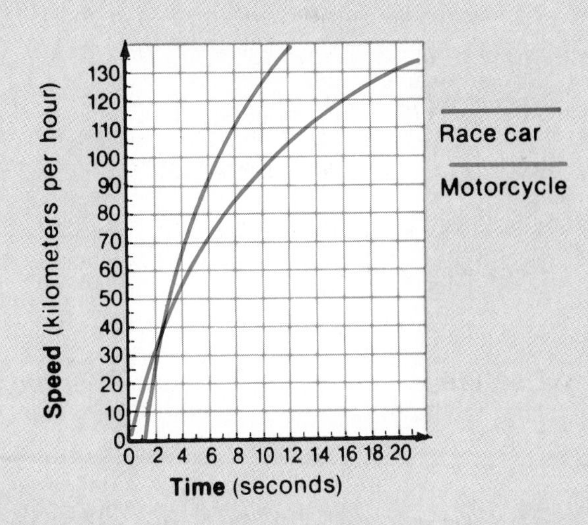


## ON YOUR OWN

Look in old magazines or newspapers for examples of graphs. For each example, discuss what the graph measures and tell whether it is a broken-line or curved-line graph. Are the curved-line graphs smooth?

# Unit Review

*Simplify. (pages 48–49)*

**1.** $37 - 5 \times 2$ **2.** $(12 + 6) \div 3$ **3.** $8 \times 4 \div 2$

**4.** $8 \times (4 \div 2)$ **5.** $16 \times 8 - 6$ **6.** $16 \times (8 - 6)$

**7.** $9 + 3 \times 10$ **8.** $(2 + 7) \times (15 - 4)$ **9.** $9 \times 3 + 10$

**10.** $[50 - (12 + 7)] \times 3$ **11.** $16 + 11 - [15 \div (3 + 2) + 4]$

*Tell whether each statement is true or false. (pages 48–49)*

**12.** $8 \times 7 \leq 56$ **13.** $19 + 6 \neq 25$ **14.** $63 \div 9 < 9$ **15.** $18 > 6 \times 3$

*Complete the table. (pages 50–51)*

| Value of $x$ | 1 | 2 | 3 | 4 |
|---|---|---|---|---|
| Value of $y$ | 0 | 1 | 2 | 4 |
| Value of $3x + 2y$ | **16.** | **17.** | **18.** | **19.** |
| Value of $2 \cdot (5x - y)$ | **20.** | **21.** | **22.** | **23.** |
| Value of $x \cdot (x + y)$ | **24.** | **25.** | **26.** | **27.** |

*Tell whether each sentence is true of false for the given values of the variables. (pages 52–53)*

**28.** $5x + 1 > 10$ when $x$ is 2. **29.** $3y - 7 = 15$ when $y$ is 6.

**30.** $13 - 2z = 7$ when $z$ is 3. **31.** $2m + 3n = 11$ when $m$ is 4 $n$ is 1.

**32.** $18 - 3t \leq 10$ when $t$ is 4. **33.** $5x - 2y = 8$ when $x$ is 6 and $y$ is 4.

*Use the relationships between operations to complete. (pages 54-55)*

**34.** $w = w + 8 - ■$ **35.** $5 \cdot (s + 2) = 5s + ■$ **36.** $\frac{m}{10} \cdot ■ = m$

**37.** $12 \cdot z \div ■ = z$ **38.** $2p - 6 = 2 \cdot (p - ■)$ **39.** $k - 7 + ■ = k$

*Solve. (pages 56–59)*

**40.** $x - 9 = 11$ **41.** $16 = 8y$ **42.** $9 + m = 17$ **43.** $\frac{z}{6} = 5$

**44.** $w + 12 = 12$ **45.** $u - 5 = 13$ **46.** $12 = \frac{3y}{5}$ **47.** $10n = 80$

*Solve. (pages 60–61)*

**48.** $2x - 3 = 17$ **49.** $\frac{t}{8} + 2 = 10$ **50.** $20 = 3y + 5$ **51.** $\frac{3z}{4} - 7 = 5$

**52.** $4m + 9 = 53$ **53.** $6 + \frac{w}{7} = 8$ **54.** $9k - 10 = 26$ **55.** $8 + x = 17$

**56.** $15 + 8z = 79$ **57.** $12 = \frac{n}{7}$ **58.** $15 = \frac{4s}{5} + 11$ **59.** $6 = z - 19$

*Write an equation. Solve. (pages 62–63)*

**60.** A number (n) divided by 12 is 9. What is the number?

**61.** The sum of 7 times a number (n) and 13 is 48. What is the number?

**62.** $12 more than 3 times Lynn's allowance is $33. How much is Lynn's allowance?

**63.** Bertha picked 19 boxes of berries. This was 5 boxes more than twice the amount James picked. How many boxes of berries did James pick?

**64.** The losing team scored 43 points. This was 11 more than the result of dividing the winning team's score by 2. What was the winning team's score?

**65.** Karen said that if she had $12 more than 5 times the amount of money she has she would have $87. How much money does Karen have?

*Solve. Use the formulas on page 64. (pages 64–65)*

**66.** How many field goals did a team make if 13 free throws were made and the team's total score was 55 points?

**67.** A plane flew 3,280 km at an average speed of 820 km/h. For how many hours did the plane fly?

*Write a flowchart. Solve. (pages 66–67)*

**68.** How many times must a runner go around a 425 m track to run at least 7,000 m and end up at the starting line?

**69.** How many times must the runner in Exercise **68** go around the track to run at least 10,000 m?

**70.** Ms. Carson's starting salary was $10,000 per year. Each year after the first she received 6¢ per dollar more than the preceding year. How much was Ms. Carson earning 5 years after she started?

**71.** Mr. Peters' starting salary was $9,500 per year. Each year after the first he received 8¢ per dollar more than the preceding year. How much was Mr. Peters earning 7 years after he started?

# Enrichment

**A.** A **function** is a rule that pairs each number of its **domain** with exactly one number of its **range.**

**Example** The function f pairs each number of its domain A with exactly one number of its range B.

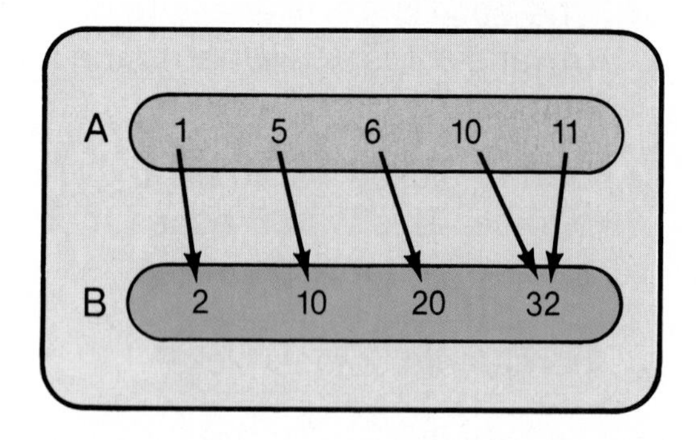


f: $A \rightarrow B$

| | | |
|---|---|---|
| $1 \rightarrow 2$ | or | $f(1) = 2$ |
| $5 \rightarrow 10$ | or | $f(5) = 10$ |
| $6 \rightarrow 20$ | or | $f(6) = 20$ |
| $10 \rightarrow 32$ | or | $f(10) = 32$ |
| $11 \rightarrow 32$ | or | $f(11) = 32$ |

**1.** Write a function g using domain X and range Y.

**B.** Some rules that pair numbers are not functions.

**Example**

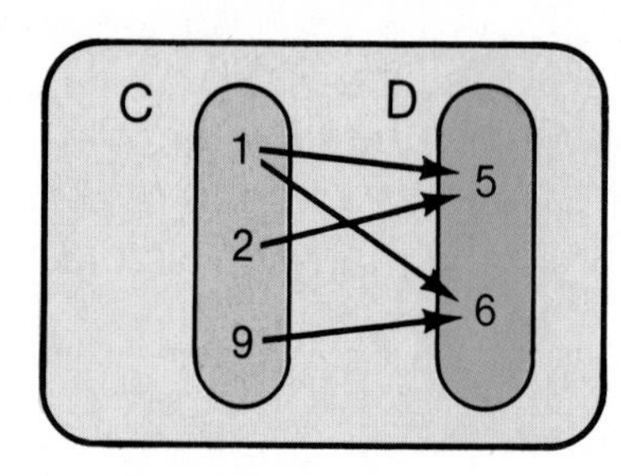


h: $C \rightarrow D$

$1 \rightarrow 5$

$1 \rightarrow 6$

$2 \rightarrow 5$

$9 \rightarrow 6$

A function pairs each number of its domain with exactly one number of its range. h is not a function.

*Tell which rules are functions.*

Domain: $A = \{0, 1, 2\}$
Range: $B = \{4, 5, 6\}$

Domain: $C = \{0, 1, 2, 3\}$
Range: $D = \{5, 10, 15\}$

**2.** f: $A \rightarrow B$
$0 \rightarrow 4$
$1 \rightarrow 5$
$2 \rightarrow 5$
$2 \rightarrow 6$

**3.** g: $A \rightarrow B$
$0 \rightarrow 6$
$1 \rightarrow 4$
$2 \rightarrow 5$

**4.** F: $C \rightarrow D$
$0 \rightarrow 5$
$1 \rightarrow 5$
$2 \rightarrow 10$
$3 \rightarrow 15$

**5.** h: $C \rightarrow D$
$3 \rightarrow 5$
$2 \rightarrow 10$
$1 \rightarrow 15$
$0 \rightarrow 5$

**6.** Write the pairings in Exercises 3 and 4 in the form f(■) = ▲.

**C.** When the domain of a function is an endless or **infinite set** of numbers, use a variable to show the numbers that are paired.

**Example** Domain: $W = \{0, 1, 2, 3, \ldots\}$

Function: f: $x \to 2x + 3$ or $f(x) \to 2x + 3$

| | | |
|---|---|---|
| $0 \to 3$ | or | $f(0) = 3$ |
| $1 \to 5$ | or | $f(1) = 5$ |
| $2 \to 7$ | or | $f(2) = 7$ |
| $3 \to 9$ | or | $f(3) = 9$ |
| ... | | ... |
| $15 \to 33$ | or | $f(15) = 33$ |
| ... | | ... |

$2 \times 0 + 3$

$2 \times 3 + 3$

The domain of each function is the set of all whole numbers.

*Copy and complete.*

**7.** $f(x) = 3x + 1$
$f(0) = $ ■
$f(2) = $ ■
$f(7) = $ ■

**8.** $g(x) = 4x + 2$
$g(0) = $ ■
$g(1) = $ ■
$g(2) = $ ■

**9.** $h(y) = 2y + 3$
$h(0) = $ ■
$h(3) = $ ■
$h(9) = $ ■

**10.** $g(x) = (x)(x)$
$g(0) = $ ■
$g(1) = $ ■
$g(5) = $ ■

**11.** $h(x) = \frac{x}{2} + 1$
$h(0) = $ ■
$h(2) = $ ■
$h(8) = $ ■

**12.** $f(z) = z(z + 4)$
$f(1) = $ ■
$f(3) = $ ■
$f(7) = $ ■

**13.** $g(z) = (z + 1)(z + 2)$
$g(0) = $ ■
$g(2) = $ ■
$g(17) = $ ■

**14.** $h(w) = (w + 3)(w + 3)$
$h(0) = $ ■
$h(5) = $ ■
$h(6) = $ ■

**15.** $f(x) = 5x - 4$
$f(1) = $ ■
$f(11) = $ ■
$f(13) = $ ■

*Use* $f(x) = 2x + 1$ *and* $g(x) = 5x + 2$.
*Find the values.*

**16.** $f(2) + g(2)$

**17.** $f(3) \times g(3)$

**18.** $g(4) - f(4)$

**19.** $f(0) + f(5)$

**20.** $g(4) \times g(0)$

**21.** $f(3) - f(1)$

**22.** $f(1) + g(6)$

**23.** $f(6) + g(1)$

**24.** $g(4) - f(5)$

**25.** $g(0) + g(10)$

**26.** $g(0) \times g(11)$

**27.** $f(5) + g(20)$

# Cumulative Review

**1.** Simplify.
$120 \div (10 - 4)$

**a.** 8
**b.** 3
**c.** 20
**d.** Not above

**2.** Round 76,943 to the nearest hundred.

**a.** 77,000
**b.** 76,900
**c.** 80,000
**d.** Not above

**3.** Solve:
$x + 16 = 40$

**a.** 24
**b.** 26
**c.** 56
**d.** Not above

**4.** $9{,}067 \times 540$

**a.** 489,618
**b.** 4,896,180
**c.** 816,030
**d.** Not above

**5.** Solve.
$2y - 9 = 25$

**a.** 34
**b.** 8
**c.** 16
**d.** Not above

**6.** Estimate.
$2{,}645 + 487 = \blacksquare$

**a.** 3,500
**b.** 2,500
**c.** 3,100
**d.** Not above

**7.** Find the value of $6t - 9$ when the value of $t$ is 15.

**a.** 81
**b.** 90
**c.** 12
**d.** Not above

**8.** $56\overline{)13{,}440}$

**a.** 24
**b.** 240
**c.** 231
**d.** Not above

**9.** Show how to read 6,004,000.

**a.** six thousand four
**b.** six million four thousand
**c.** six billion four thousand
**d.** Not above

**10.** $10{,}005 - 2{,}043 = \blacksquare$

**a.** 7,062
**b.** 8,042
**c.** 7,162
**d.** Not above

**11.** Eight more than 3 times a number is 41. Find the number.

**a.** 33
**b.** 38
**c.** 11
**d.** Not above

**12.** An airplane flew 4,704 km in 6 h. What was the plane's average speed for the flight?

**a.** 28,224 km/h
**b.** 4,710 km/h
**c.** 784 km/h
**d.** Not above

**13.** Mr. Kane spent $50 for a jacket and bought 4 shirts for $16 each. He gave the salesperson $150. How much change did he receive?

**a.** $116
**b.** $84
**c.** $66
**d.** Not above

**14.** A truck traveled 648 km one day and 593 km the next day. The total distance the truck had to travel was 1,509 km. How far did it still have to go after the two days travel?

**a.** 1,241 km
**b.** 268 km
**c.** 2,157 km
**d.** Not above

# 3 Decimals

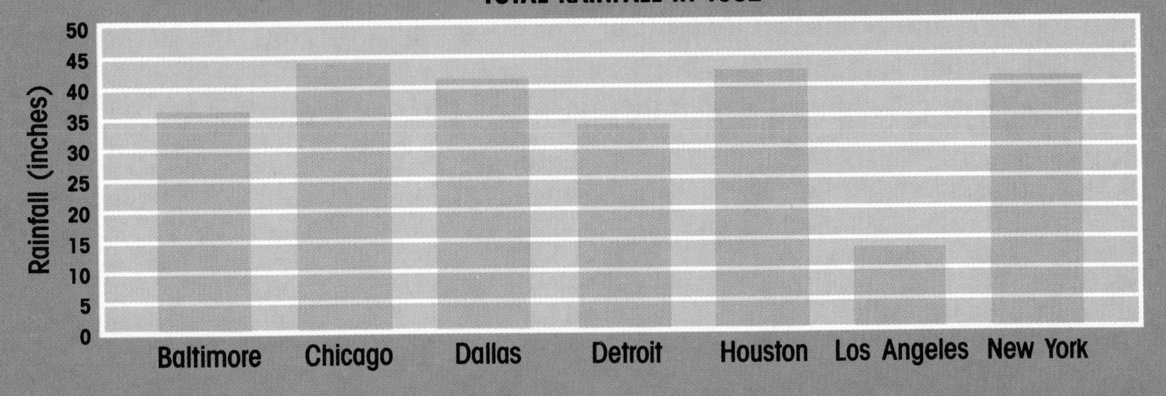

TOTAL RAINFALL IN 1982
Rainfall (inches)
50
45
40
35
30
25
20
15
10
5
0
Baltimore
Chicago
Dallas
Detroit
Houston
Los Angeles
New York

# 3-1 Decimals to Millionths

You can extend the place value pattern for standard numerals to write **decimals** for numbers that are not whole numbers. Use a **decimal point** to the right of the ones place.

**A.** How much is shaded?

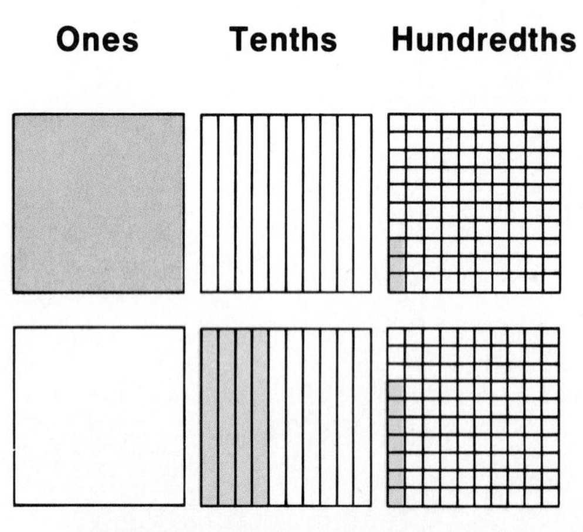


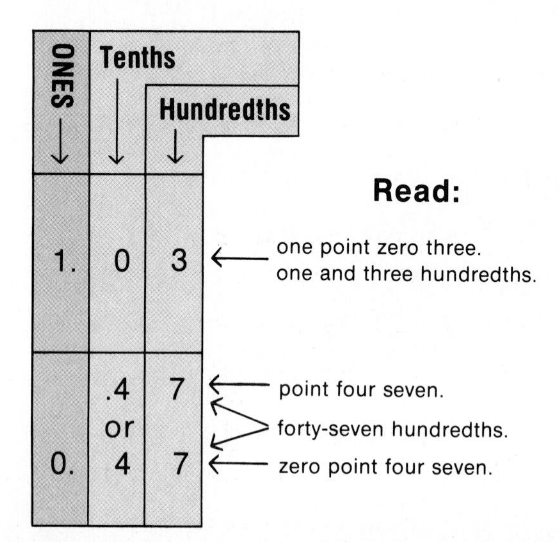


**B.**

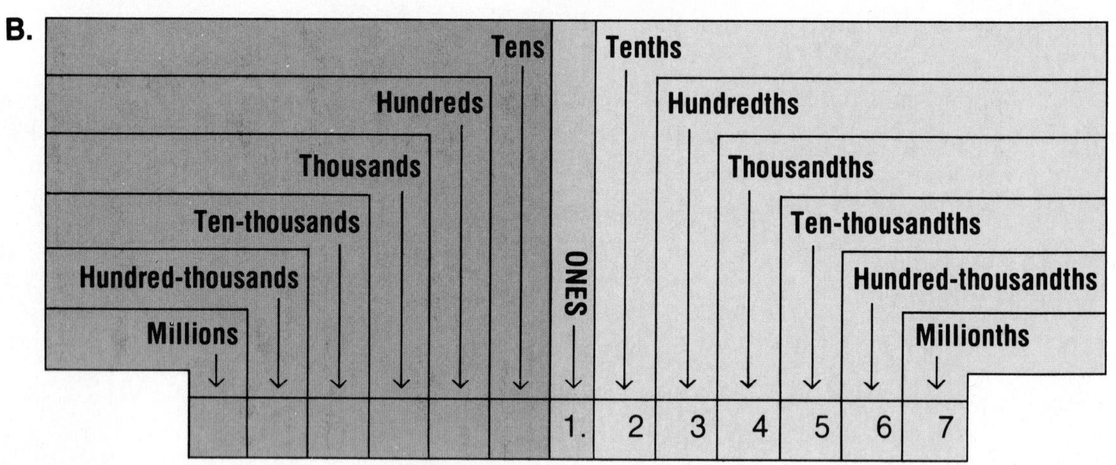


1.234567 means 1 one, 2 tenths, 3 hundredths, 4 thousandths, 5 ten-thousandths, 6 hundred-thousandths, 7 millionths.

**Read:** one and two hundred thirty-four thousand, five hundred sixty-seven **millionths** ← Place name of the **last** digit
or one point two three four five six seven.

**C.** You can write different decimals that name the same number.

**Example 1**
.24 = .240 = .2400 = · · ·

**Example 2**
73 = 73.0 = 73.00 = · · ·

## CLASS EXERCISES

*Show two ways to read each decimal.*

**1.** 2.325 **2.** .5027 **3.** .000615 **4.** 8.00305

*Name the place of the digit 7 in each decimal.*

**5.** .037061 **6.** 8.009387 **7.** 1.0709 **8.** .000076

*Tell what the digit 4 means in each decimal.*

**9.** 873.426839 **10.** 807.042936 **11.** 517.336492 **12.** 537.962143

*Write a decimal for each.*

**13.** eighty-four and seven thousand, five hundred sixty-two ten-thousandths
**14.** two and five hundred sixty-four hundred-thousandths
**15.** forty-two and eighty-seven thousandths **16.** four thousand millionths

## EXERCISES

*Show two ways to read each decimal.*

**1.** 7.82 **2.** 5.4068 **3.** .709000 **4.** 0.004627

*Name the place of the digit 3 in each decimal.*

**5.** .736521 **6.** 4.586831 **7.** .04435 **8.** 8.512003

*Tell what the digit 6 means in each decimal.*

**9.** 57.643924 **10.** 462.098321 **11.** 3.706429 **12.** 29.300586

*Write a decimal for each.*

**13.** fifty-three thousandths **14.** fifty-one and eight hundred forty-six millionths
**15.** one thousand, three hundred eighty-six ten-thousandths
**16.** seventy-five hundred-thousandths **17.** five hundred hundred-thousandths

*Which name the same number?*

| **18.** | **19.** | **20.** | **21.** |
|---|---|---|---|
| .046 | 82.00 | .007100 | .300 |
| .0046 | 82.000 | .0071 | 0.3 |
| .0460 | 8.200 | .007010 | .030 |
| .0406 | 82.0 | .071000 | .30 |

THINK!

### Logical Reasoning

Seven students, A, B, C, D, E, F, and G, discover that their birthdays are on seven consecutive days. A's birthday is on Tuesday. D's is the day after B's. A's is halfway between G's & B's. F's is 3 days after G's. C's is 2 days after E's. On which day does each have a birthday.

**5.** hundredths **9.** 6 tenths **13.** .053



Homework page 461

## 3-3 Rounding with Decimals

**A.** Rounding with decimals is similar to rounding whole numbers.

Round .20803 and 4.996959 to the **nearest ten-thousandth.**

**Step 1** Circle the digit in the place to which you are rounding.

.2 0 8 (0) 3 4.9 9 6 (9) 5 9

**Step 2** Look at the digit to its right.

If the digit is less than 5, keep the circled digit. Drop all digits to the right.

.2 0 8 (0) | 3

.2 0 8 0 |

If the digit is 5 or more, add 1 to the circled digit. Drop all digits to the right.

4.9 9 6 (9) | 5 9
\+ 1
4.9 9 7 0 |

**B.** Round $64.972 to the nearest cent.

$ 6 4.9 (7) | 2 ← 2 < 5, so keep the circled digit.

$ 6 4.9 7 |

$64.972 rounded to the nearest cent is $64.97.

**C.** The number line shows what it means to round with decimals.

Round 4.992 and 5.038 to the nearest hundredth.

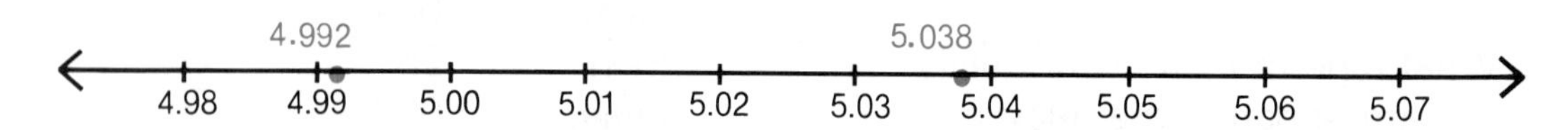


4.992 is between 4.99 and 5.00.
4.992 is closer to 4.99, so
4.992 rounds to 4.99.

5.038 is between 5.03 and 5.04.
5.038 is closer to 5.04, so
5.038 rounds to 5.04.

**D.** If a 0 appears in the place to which you are rounding, it must be written.

| *Nearest hundredth* | *Nearest tenth* | *Nearest one* |
|---|---|---|
| 4.9(8)7 → 4.99 | 4.(9)87 → 5.0 | (4).987 → 5 |
| 5.0(0)3 → 5.00 | 5.(0)03 → 5.0 | (5).003 → 5 |
| 5.0(5)0 → 5.05 | 5.(0)50 → 5.1 | (5).050 → 5 |
| 0.2(9)5 → 0.30 | 0.(2)95 → 0.3 | (0).295 → 0 |

## CLASS EXERCISES

*Complete the table.*

| Round to the nearest | 7.541935 | 2.699473 | .439997 | 2.300706 |
|---|---|---|---|---|
| hundred-thousandth | 1. | 2. | 3. | 4. |
| ten-thousandth | 5. | 6. | 7. | 8. |
| thousandth | 9. | 10. | 11. | 12. |
| hundredth | 13. | 14. | 15. | 16. |
| tenth | 17. | 18. | 19. | 20. |
| one | 21. | 22. | 23. | 24. |

## EXERCISES

*Complete the table.*

| Round to the nearest | 15.635924 | 64.935286 | .477899 | 7.364928 |
|---|---|---|---|---|
| one | 1. | 2. | 3. | 4. |
| thousandth | 5. | 6. | 7. | 8. |
| hundredth | 9. | 10. | 11. | 12. |
| hundred-thousandth | 13. | 14. | 15. | 16. |
| ten-thousandth | 17. | 18. | 19. | 20. |
| tenth | 21. | 22. | 23. | 24. |
| ten | 25. | 26. | 27. | 28. |

*Round to the nearest cent.*

**29.** \$7.2727 **30.** \$.6275 **31.** \$9.999 **32.** \$3.2985

## PROBLEMS

★ **33.** The table shows what parts of a sample of air consisted of these gases. Round each number to the nearest ten-thousandth.

| | | | |
|---|---|---|---|
| nitrogen | .78084 | helium | .00000524 |
| oxygen | .20946 | krypton | .00000114 |
| argon | .00934 | hydrogen | .0000005 |
| carbon dioxide | .00032 | nitrous oxide | .0000005 |

## THINK!

**Logical Reasoning**

If four people eat 4 loaves of bread in 4 days, how many loaves of bread will 20 people eat in 20 days?

**1.** 16 **9.** 15.64 **17.** 15.6359 **29.** \$7.27



Homework page 462

# 3-4 Adding and Subtracting with Decimals

**A.** Adding and subtracting with decimals is like adding and subtracting whole numbers.

| Estimate. | **Example 1** | *Check:* Use the commutative property. |
|---|---|---|
| 2.48675 → 2 | 2.48675 | .92715 |
| + .92715 → 1 | + .92715 | +2.48675 |
| 3 | 3.41390 | 3.41390 ✓ |

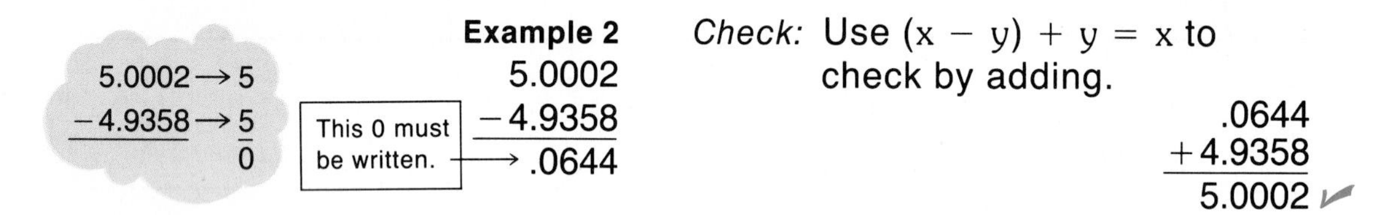

| | **Example 2** | *Check:* Use $(x - y) + y = x$ to check by adding. |
|---|---|---|
| 5.0002 → 5 | 5.0002 | .0644 |
| − 4.9358 → 5 | − 4.9358 | + 4.9358 |
| 0 | .0644 | 5.0002 ✓ |

This 0 must be written. → .0644

**B.** Of the total value of principal crops produced in the United States, .324 is earned from corn, .26 from soybeans, .14 from hay, .117 from wheat, and .068 from cotton. In all, what part of the total value is earned from these five crops?

Add to find the part.

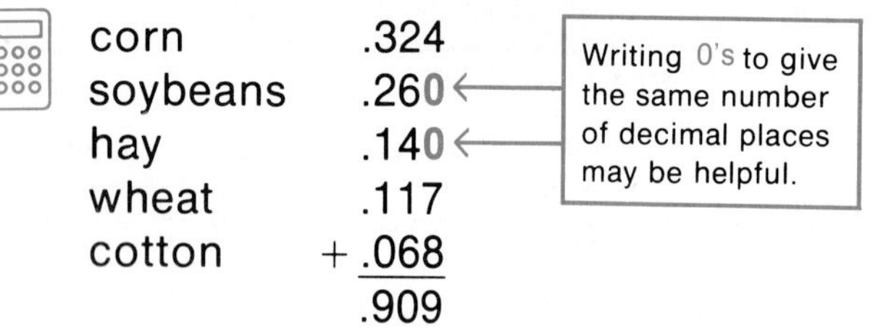

| | |
|---|---|
| corn | .324 |
| soybeans | .260 |
| hay | .140 |
| wheat | .117 |
| cotton | + .068 |
| | .909 |

Writing 0's to give the same number of decimal places may be helpful.

.909 of the total value is earned from the five crops.

**C.** Solve: $x + 3.452 = 6$

$$x + 3.452 = 6$$
$$(x + 3.452) - 3.452 = 6 - 3.452$$
$$x = 2.548$$

| |
|---|
| 6.000 |
| −3.452 |
| 2.548 |

The solution is 2.548.

*Check:*
$$x + 3.452 = 6$$
$$2.548 + 3.452 = 6$$
$$6.000 = 6 \checkmark$$

## CLASS EXERCISES

*Estimate. Find the sum or difference.*

**1.** 3.23046 + .13975

**2.** 17.6351 − 6.7286

**3.** \$700 − 9.95

**4.** .777 + 28.3

**5.** .0058 − .004946

**6.** .3142 + .8432 + .5176 = ■

**7.** 23,000.9 − .89736 = ■

*Solve each equation.*

**8.** $n - .36 = .53$

**9.** $.065 + w = .7$

**10.** $p - 3.905 = 4$

## EXERCISES

*Estimate. Add or subtract.*

**1.** .5312 + .7439

**2.** 3.024 − 1.573

**3.** 2.0332 − .9542

**4.** 96.39 + .4658

**5.** 52.395 − 41.62

**6.** 3.24136 + .54802 + 3.56192

**7.** .467 − .00938

**8.** .0384 + 21.969

**9.** .0965 + .00823 + .488

**10.** 66.5 − 3.9284

**11.** 20.00721 − .39215 = ■

**12.** .0586 − .009349 = ■

**13.** .0175 + 21 + .073659 + 7.58 = ■

**14.** .95863 + .754 = ■

*Solve, then check in the original equation.*

**15.** $x + 3.5 = 4.9$

**16.** $m - 4.7 = 3.6$

**17.** $a + 8.13 = 10.9$

**18.** $z - 6.002 = 4.8$

**19.** $d - .036 = 4.598$

**20.** $k + .231 = .467$

**21.** $.00726 = c - .00054$

**22.** $.219 = y - .137$

**23.** $.000392 + g = 1.5$

## PROBLEMS

**24.** The U.S. produced 1.288 million bushels of soybeans in 1976, and 1.716 million bushels in 1977. How many more bushels were produced in 1977? How much was produced all together?

**★ 25.** In 1977 Canada produced 0.722 billion bushels of wheat. The U.S. produced 2.026 billion bushels. How much less than 3 billion bushels was produced by the two countries?

## THINK!

### Decimal Digit Arrangements

Use 1, 2, 3, 4, and a decimal point. List all the numbers you can make between 30 and 40.

1. 1.2751 11. 19.61506 15. 1.4

Homework page 462

# 3-5 Multiplying with Decimals

Multiplying with decimals is like multiplying whole numbers.

**A.** Find: $2.8 \times 3.67 = \blacksquare$

**Step 1** Do $28 \times 367$. **Step 2** Place the decimal point.

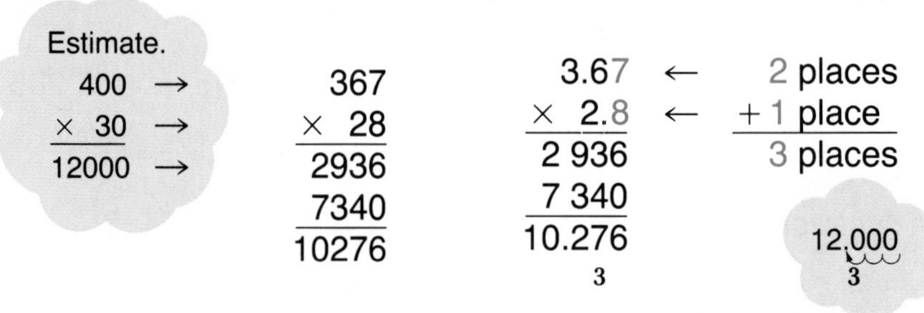


**B.** You may have to write one or more zeros at the **left** of a product *before* you can place the decimal point.

Multiply .084 by .09.

**Step 1** Do $9 \times 84$.

$$\begin{array}{r} 80 \\ \times 10 \\ \hline 800 \end{array} \qquad \begin{array}{r} 84 \\ \times\ 9 \\ \hline 756 \end{array}$$

**Step 2** Place the decimal point.

$$\begin{array}{rcr} .084 & \leftarrow & 3 \text{ places} \\ \times\ .09 & \leftarrow & +2 \text{ places} \\ \hline .00756 & \leftarrow & 5 \text{ places} \end{array}$$

.00800

**C.** A furniture salesperson is paid a **salary** of $225 per week, plus a **commission** of .13 of the value of her sales for the week. What should be her pay for a week in which she sells furniture with a total value of $5,386.50?

**Step 1** Pay = Salary + Commission

**Step 2** Commission = Part × Total sales

.13
$5,400 × (.10 + .03)
$540 + $162 = $702

= .13 × $5,386.50
= $700.25

To the nearest cent

$$\begin{array}{rcr} \$5{,}386.50 & \leftarrow & 2 \\ \times\ .13 & \leftarrow & +2 \\ \hline 161\ 5950 & & 4 \\ 538\ 6500 & & \\ \hline \$700.2450 & \leftarrow & \end{array}$$

Now you can use the result of Step 2 to do Step 1.

Pay = Salary + Commission
= $225 + $700.25
= $925.25

Her pay should be $925.25.

## CLASS EXERCISES

*Estimate. Find the product.*

1. $43 \times .7$
2. $.43 \times .7$
3. $.043 \times .07$
4. $\$8{,}000 \times .075$
5. $.32 \times 452.6$
6. $.07 \times .0008 =$ ■
7. $.053 \times .067 =$ ■
8. $24.3 \times \$7.80 =$ ■

## EXERCISES

*Estimate. Multiply.* **Estimates may vary.**

1. $8.6 \times .06$
2. $63.4 \times .8$
3. $\$2.06 \times 24$
4. $8.43 \times .7$
5. $.019 \times .3$
6. $.13 \times .09$
7. $18.3 \times 5.7$
8. $1{,}836 \times .072$
9. $.027 \times .004$
10. $\$60.03 \times 700$
11. $\$.98 \times 48$
12. $120 \times .003$
13. $\$87.74 \times 2.5$
14. $\$27.09 \times 18$
15. $\$.63 \times 582$
16. $9.214 \times 3.7$
17. $.007 \times 7.65$
18. $4.56 \times .0037$
19. $5.92 \times 30.7$
20. $.061 \times 2.351$
21. $1.3 \times \$47.50 =$ ■
22. $.002 \times .04 =$ ■
23. $.034 \times 2.776 =$ ■
24. $9.403 \times .061 =$ ■
25. $.0024 \times 8.36 =$ ■
26. $\$10{,}000 \times .06 =$ ■

★27. $2.8 \times (.0513 \times 96.42) =$ ■

★28. $(.0513 \times 2.8) \times 96.42 =$ ■

## PROBLEMS

29. A clothing salesperson is paid a salary of $800 per month, plus a commission of .18. What is her total pay for a month in which her sales were $7,264.25?

30. Mr. Cosmo spends .34 of his earnings for rent and .2 of his earnings for food. How much more does he spend for rent than for food, if he earns $1,362.50 per month?

### Visual Reasoning

Copy the figure below. Draw an x on five intersections so that no two are on the same line.

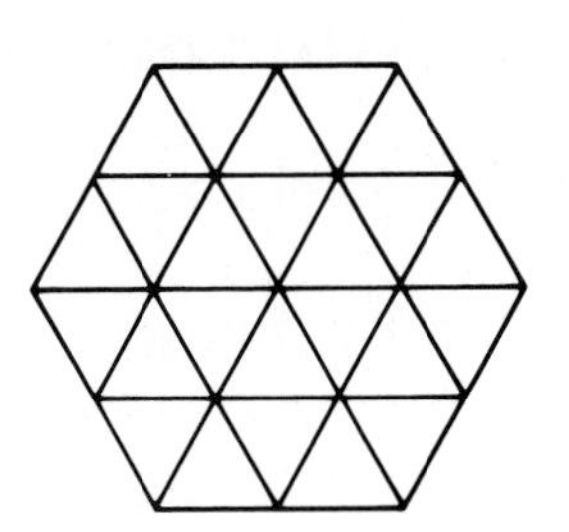

1. .516   6. .0117   21. $61.75

Homework page 463

## 3-6 Comparison Shopping

This table shows the price **per kilogram** of three items at each of three stores.

| Item | Price per Kilogram | | |
|---|---|---|---|
| | Store I | Store II | Store III |
| Apples | $ .74 | $ .79 | $ .86 |
| Potatoes | .31 | .35 | .29 |
| Hamburger | 4.59 | 4.39 | 4.44 |

**A.** At which store does it cost the least to buy 1 kg of each of the three items?

**Total Cost** = Cost of 1 kg of apples + Cost of 1 kg of potatoes + Cost of 1 kg of hamburger

*At Store I:* **Total cost** = $.74 + $.31 + $4.59 = **$5.64**
*At Store II:* **Total cost** = $.79 + $.35 + $4.39 = **$5.53** ← Least
*At Store III:* **Total cost** = $.86 + $.29 + $4.44 = **$5.59**

It costs the least at Store II.

**B.** Find the cost of 1 kg of each of the three items purchased at the store where each item costs the least.

**Total Cost** = Least cost of 1 kg of apples + Least cost of 1 kg of potatoes + Least cost of 1 kg of hamburger

= $.74 (Store I) + $.29 (Store III) + $4.39 (Store II) = **$5.42**

The total cost is $5.42. ← $.11 less than at Store II

**C.** At which store would you pay the least for 2.5 kg of potatoes and 1.75 kg of hamburger? (Round each cost to the nearest cent.)

**Total cost** = Cost of 2.5 kg of potatoes + Cost of 1.75 kg of hamburger

= (2.5 × Cost of 1 kg of potatoes) + (1.75 × Cost of 1 kg of hamburger)

*At Store I:* **Total cost** = (2.5 × $.31) + (1.75 × $4.59)
= $.78 + $8.03 = $8.81
*At Store II:* **Total cost** = (2.5 × $.35) + (1.75 × $4.39)
= $.88 + $7.68 = $8.56
*At Store III:* **Total cost** = (2.5 × $.29) + (1.75 × $4.44)
= $.73 + $7.77 = $8.50 ← Least

## CLASS EXERCISES

*Use the table on the previous page.*

1. At which store does it cost the least to buy 3 kg of apples and 4.5 kg of potatoes?
2. At which store does it cost the least to buy 4.25 kg of apples and 1 kg of hamburger?
3. For what reasons might you buy at a store other than the one where your purchases cost least? Why might you shop at one store, even though buying at two or three different stores would reduce the total cost of your purchases?

## PROBLEMS

*Use this list of prices. Complete the table below.*

| Item | Price per Kilogram | | |
|---|---|---|---|
| | Store A | Store B | Store C |
| Oranges | $ .90 | $ .94 | $ .88 |
| Peppers | $ .87 | $ .85 | $ .90 |
| Cheese | $4.78 | $5.09 | $5.05 |
| Pork Chops | $5.69 | $5.63 | $5.49 |

| Purchase | | | | Least Cost | |
|---|---|---|---|---|---|
| Oranges | Peppers | Cheese | Pork Chops | Bought at one store | Bought where each costs least |
| 1 kg | 1 kg | 1 kg | 1 kg | 1. ? | 2. ? |
| 1 kg | 1 kg | | 1 kg | 3. ? | 4. ? |
| | | 1 kg | 2 kg | 5. ? | 6. ? |
| 1.5 kg | 0.5 kg | | | 7. ? | 8. ? |
| 2 kg | | 0.25 kg | 2.4 kg | 9. ? | 10. ? |

## MIXED REVIEW

*Simplify.*

1. $15 \times 7 - 12$
2. $60 - 2 \times 11$
3. $[80 - (13 + 5)] \times 4$

*Solve.*

4. $2x - 5 = 19$
5. $\frac{m}{7} + 4 = 11$
6. $9 = n - 33$

*Find the value of each expression when $x = 3$ and $y = 5$.*

7. $4 \cdot (3x - y)$
8. $5x + 3y - 2$
9. $(6y \div 2x) + 8$

Homework page 463

## 3-7 Dividing with Decimals

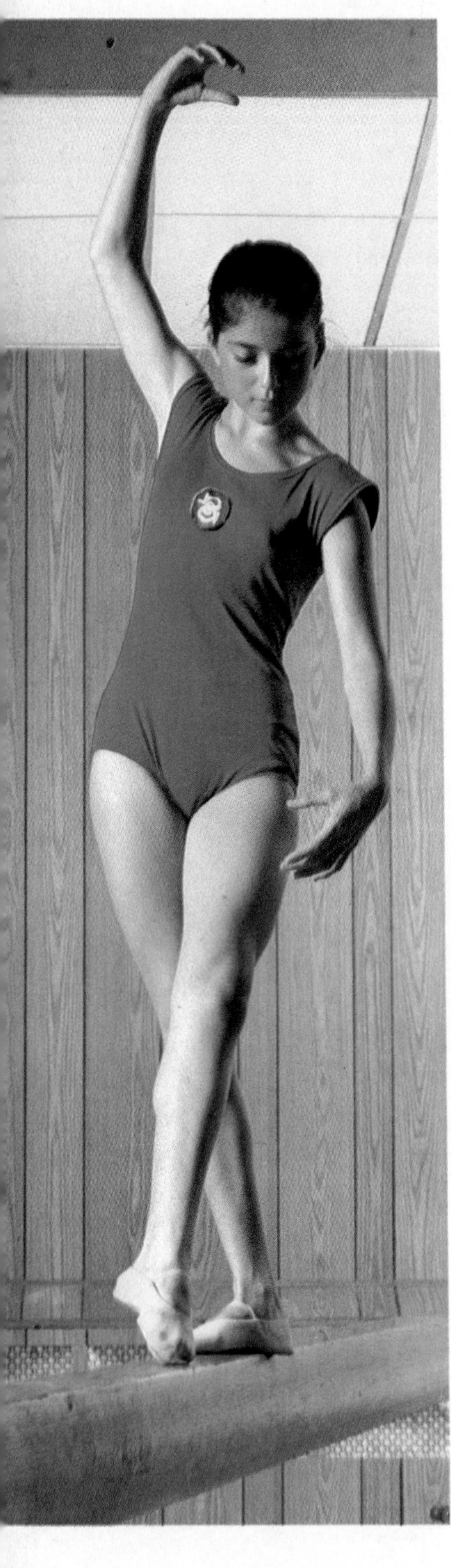

**A.** In a gymnastics meet Sue earned a total of 41.50 points in 5 events. What was her average score?

Divide as with whole numbers. Be sure to place the decimal point in the quotient.

40 ÷ 5 = 8

```
    8.30
5)41.50
  40
   1 5
   1 5
     00
      0
      0
```

*Check:*

```
  8.30
×    5
 41.50 ✓
```

Sue's average score was 8.30 points.

**B.** After you have placed the decimal point, you may need to record zeros in the quotient.

```
    7          .7         .07        .007
45)315     45)31.5    45)3.15    45).315
   315        31 5        0          0
     0           0      3 15        31
                        3 15         0
                           0       315
                                   315
                                     0
```

**C.** When finding decimals for quotients, do not report a remainder. Instead, **round** your answer.

Find 216)182.965. Round to the nearest hundredth.

```
        .847 → .85, to the nearest
216)182.965     hundredth
    172 8
     10 16
      8 64
      1 525
      1 512
         13
```

182 ÷ 216 = a little less than 1

182.965 ÷ 216 ≐ .85

The symbol ≐ means "is about equal to."

## CLASS EXERCISES

*Estimate. Find the quotients.*

**1.** 4)$15.72 **2.** 8).64 **3.** 61)3.233 **4.** 498)2.988 **5.** 1,575)$456.75

*Divide. Round to the nearest hundredth.*

**6.** 7)1.284 **7.** 6).296 **8.** 39)6.825 **9.** 650)3.641 **10.** 119)36.808

## EXERCISES

*Find the quotients.*

**1.** 3).417 **2.** 9)40.77 **3.** 70)35.140 **4.** 25)$221.50 **5.** 18)45.054

**6.** 52).4316 **7.** 67)18.76 **8.** 300)28.200 **9.** 150)$952.50 **10.** 97).291

**11.** 14)60.004 **12.** 472)633.424 **13.** 835)2.0875 **14.** 200)1,460.0 **15.** 520)24.960

*Divide. Round to the nearest hundredth.*

**16.** 3)58.639 **17.** 7)3.019 **18.** 40)6.925 **19.** 52)2.460 **20.** 38)24.326

*Divide. Round to the nearest thousandth.*

**21.** 5).0187 **22.** 7).3816 **23.** 9)1.3452 **24.** 20)16.4586 **25.** 74)91.4130

**26.** 82)1.3779 **27.** 243)15.175 **28.** 998).6145 **29.** 321)7.0894 **30.** 39)7.995

*Simplify.*

**31.** $1868.1 \div 13$ **32.** $201.69 \div 27$ ★**33.** $(1.8154 + .5038) \div 26$

## PROBLEMS

**34.** The gymnastics coach spent $528.50 on uniforms, $273.20 on mats, and $470 on transportation. The team has 15 members. What was the average spent per team member?

★**35.** The odometer on the bus read 48,632 km before a trip and 49,159 km after the trip. The driver spent $47.43 for expenses. What was the cost per kilometer driven?

## THINK!

### Guess and Check

At the market you can buy 3 potatoes and 1 ear of corn for the same price as 2 tomatoes. A purchase of 1 potato, 2 ears of corn, and 3 tomatoes cost $2.50. How much does each vegetable cost?

**1.** .139 **6.** .0083 **16.** 19.55 **21.** .004

Homework page 464

# 3-8 Rounding Decimals for Quotients

When finding a decimal for a quotient, plan your rounding before you divide. You may have to write one or more 0's to give the dividend one more place than your rounded answer will have.

**A.** Find 36)83.4. Then round.

*To the nearest tenth:*
Use 83.4 = 83.40

```
     2.31 → 2.3, to the
36)83.40     nearest tenth
   72
   11 4
   10 8
      60
      36
      24
```

*To the nearest hundredth:*
Use 83.4 = 83.400

```
     2.316 → 2.32, to the
36)83.400     nearest hundredth
   72
   11 4
   10 8
      60
      36
      240
      216
       24
```

**B.** If you are not told what place to round to, you must decide for yourself. A good rule is:

*Plan to round* to the nearest thousandth *but* give the exact quotient if you find it while dividing to ten-thousandths.

**Example 1**

Find 34)26.8.

```
     .7882 → .788
34)26.8000
   23 8
    3 00
    2 72
      280
      272
       80
       68
       12
```

26.8 ÷ 34 ≐ .788

**Example 2**

Find 80)19.

```
      .2375
80)19.0000
   16 0
    3 00
    2 40
      600
      560
       400
       400
         0
```

.2375 is exact.

19 ÷ 80 = .2375

**Example 3**

Find 27)16.74.

```
     .62
27)16.7400
   16 2
      54
      54
       0
```

Stop! .62 is exact.

16.74 ÷ 27 = .62

## CLASS EXERCISES

*Divide. Round to the nearest tenth.*

**1.** $4\overline{)2.7}$ **2.** $53\overline{)6.2}$ **3.** $5\overline{)3}$ **4.** $23\overline{)59}$ **5.** $68\overline{)8}$

*Divide.*

**6.** $7\overline{)6.4}$ **7.** $40\overline{)95}$ **8.** $9\overline{)7.4}$ **9.** $87\overline{)15}$ **10.** $800\overline{)94}$

## EXERCISES

*Divide. Round to the nearest hundredth.*

**1.** $30\overline{)10.4}$ **2.** $9\overline{)62}$ **3.** $40\overline{)\$.94}$ **4.** $13\overline{)8.3}$ **5.** $8\overline{)4.7}$

**6.** $7\overline{)1.2}$ **7.** $3\overline{)4.6}$ **8.** $63\overline{)19.5}$ **9.** $40\overline{)87}$ **10.** $35\overline{)60.9}$

**11.** $90\overline{)6.52}$ **12.** $25\overline{)4.7}$ **13.** $16\overline{)100}$ **14.** $45\overline{)32.4}$ **15.** $703\overline{)5.2}$

*Divide.*

**16.** $2\overline{)37}$ **17.** $6\overline{)95}$ **18.** $50\overline{)\$487}$ **19.** $30\overline{).266}$ **20.** $64\overline{).872}$

**21.** $16\overline{)5}$ **22.** $700\overline{).46}$ **23.** $28\overline{)47}$ **24.** $66\overline{)8.76}$ **25.** $500\overline{)49}$

**26.** $80\overline{).92}$ **27.** $29\overline{)3}$ **28.** $32\overline{)2.48}$ **29.** $7\overline{)1.27}$ **30.** $210\overline{)987}$

*Simplify.*

**31.** $(7.38 - 4.646) \div 8$ **32.** $(13.98 + 4.7) \div 24$ ★**33.** $(21.5 \div 6) \div 6$

## PROBLEMS

**34.** In 1972 the Chicago Cubs played 155 games and won 85. The Houston Astros played 153 games and won 84. What part of their games did each team win?

★ **35.** In 1976 the Montreal Expos won 55 baseball games and lost 107. What part of their games did they win?

### Visual Reasoning

Make seven squares by moving two of the matches.

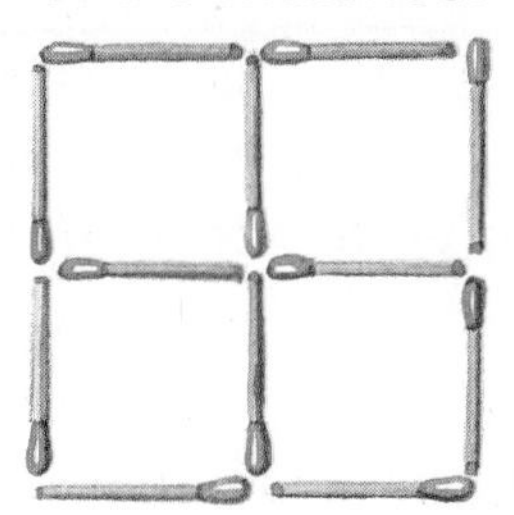

**1.** .35 **6.** .17 **16.** 18.5 **21.** .3125

**Homework** page 464

# 3-9 Powers of Ten and Decimals

**A.** These examples show a shortcut for multiplying a decimal by a power of ten.

**By multiplying:**

```
  4.082          4.082          4.082
×    10        ×   100        ×1,000
 40.820        408.200     4,082.000
```

$10 \times 4.082 = 40.82$ (decimal point moved 1 place)

$100 \times 4.082 = 408.2$ (decimal point moved 2 places)

$1,000 \times 4.082 = 4082.$ (decimal point moved 3 places)

**Shortcut:**

You may have to write zeros on the right.

$10 \times 53.6 = 536.$ (1)  $100 \times 53.6 = 5360.$ (2)  $1,000 \times 53.6 = 53600.$ (3)

$10 \times 192 = 1920.$ (1)  $100 \times 192 = 19200.$ (2)  $1,000 \times 192 = 192000.$ (3)

**B.** These examples show a shortcut for dividing a decimal by a power of ten.

**By dividing:**

```
       64.19            6.419                .6419
 10)641.90       100)641.900       1,000)641.9000
    60               600                600.0
     41               419                 41 90
     40               400                 41 90
      19               190                  1900
      10               100                  1000
       90               900                  9000
       90               900                  9000
        0                 0                     0
```

**Shortcut:**

$641.9 \div 10 = 64.19$ (1)

$641.9 \div 100 = 6.419$ (2)

$641.9 \div 1,000 = .6419$ (3)

You may have to write zeros on the left.

$.82 \div 10 = .082$ (1)  $.82 \div 100 = .0082$ (2)  $.82 \div 1,000 = .00082$ (3)

$3 \div 10 = .3$ (1)  $3 \div 100 = .03$ (2)  $3 \div 1,000 = .003$ (3)

## CLASS EXERCISES

*Use the shortcut to find the product.*

**1.** 10 × 5.24 = ■ **2.** 100 × 5.821 = ■ **3.** 100 × .2356 = ■

**4.** 1,000 × 2.43 = ■ **5.** 1,000 × .793 = ■ **6.** 10,000 × 63.25 = ■

*Use the shortcut to find the quotient.*

**7.** 38.62 ÷ 10 = ■ **8.** 53.47 ÷ 100 = ■ **9.** 3.926 ÷ 100 = ■

**10.** 784.5 ÷ 1,000 = ■ **11.** 8.27 ÷ 1,000 = ■ **12.** 57.92 ÷ 10,000 = ■

## EXERCISES

*Multiply or divide.*

**1.** 100 × 53.692 = ■ **2.** 763.4 ÷ 10 = ■ **3.** 1,000 × .03759 = ■

**4.** 2.357 ÷ 1,000 = ■ **5.** 10 × 62.5 = ■ **6.** 37.48 ÷ 100 = ■

**7.** 100 × 79.2341 = ■ **8.** 896.4 ÷ 100 = ■ **9.** 10,000 × 3.412 = ■

**10.** 381.5 ÷ 1,000 = ■ **11.** 1,000 × 37.4 = ■ **12.** 4,921 ÷ 1,000 = ■

**13.** 1,000 × .00056 = ■ **14.** 52.83 ÷ 10,000 = ■ **15.** 100 × 238.4 = ■

**16.** 382 ÷ 1,000 = ■ **17.** 10 × 4.872 = ■ **18.** .005 ÷ 100 = ■

**19.** 1,000 × .00679 = ■ **20.** .0063 ÷ 10 = ■ **21.** 10,000 × .0205 = ■

**22.** 46 ÷ 1,000 = ■ **23.** 100 × .000038 = ■ **24.** 46.91 ÷ 10,000 = ■

★**25.** 100 × (2.37 + 1.42) ÷ 1,000 = ■ ★**26.** 10 × (57 − 6.5) ÷ 10,000 = ■

## PROBLEMS

**27.** A factory shipped 35 cartons of ball-point pens one week and 65 cartons the next. Each carton had a mass of 7.2 kg. What was the total mass of the cartons shipped?

★**28.** The school supply store received $42.12 for 100 ball-point pens. This included $3.12 tax. What was the price of each pen without tax?

THINK!

### Logical Reasoning

Mr. Rich has $1,000, all in one-dollar bills. He divided the money into 10 bundles. Now if Mr. Rich is asked for any number of dollars from $1 to $1,000, he can give one or more bundles to make the exact amount without opening any of the bundles. How many dollars did Mr. Rich put in each bundle?

1. 5,369.2 4. .002357



Homework page 464

# 3-10 Decimals for Divisors

**A.** These examples show that multiplying both divisor and dividend by the same number does not change the quotient.

| $8\overline{)5.6}$ | $80\overline{)56.0}$ | $800\overline{)560.0}$ | $8{,}000\overline{)5{,}600.0}$ |
|---|---|---|---|
| quotient .7 | quotient .7 | quotient .7 | quotient .7 |
| 5 6 | 56 0 | 560 0 | 5 600 0 |
| 0 | 0 | 0 | 0 |

| | | | | |
|---|---|---|---|---|
| *Divisor:* | 8 | $80 = 10 \times 8$ | $800 = 100 \times 8$ | $8{,}000 = 1{,}000 \times 8$ |
| *Dividend:* | 5.6 | $56 = 10 \times 5.6$ | $560 = 100 \times 5.6$ | $5{,}600 = 1{,}000 \times 5.6$ |

**B.** Replace divisions with decimal divisors by divisions with whole number divisors.

Divide 1.702 by .37.

**Step 1** To get a whole number divisor, multiply .37 by 100.

**Step 2** Multiply the dividend, 1.702, by the same number, 100.

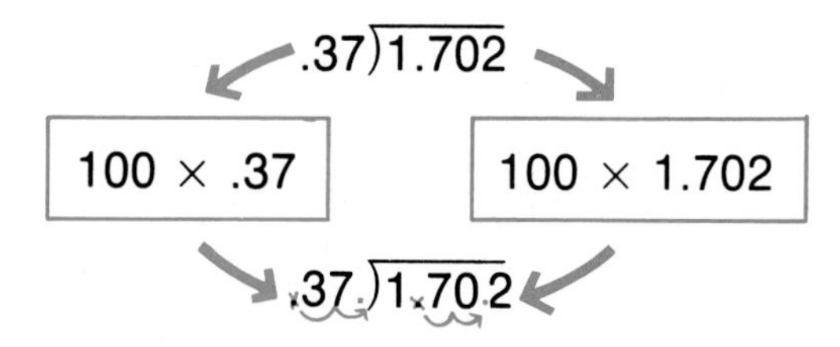


**Step 3** Divide.

$$
\begin{array}{r}
4.6 \\
.37.\overline{)1.70.2} \\
\underline{148\phantom{.2}} \\
22\ 2 \\
\underline{22\ 2} \\
0
\end{array}
$$

**Step 4** Check, using the original divisor.

$$
\begin{array}{r}
.37 \\
\underline{\times 4.6} \\
222 \\
\underline{1480} \\
1.702
\end{array}
$$

1.702, the original dividend ✓

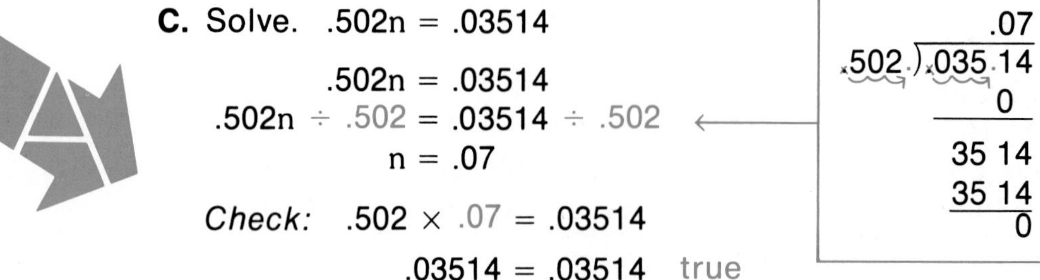

**C.** Solve. $.502n = .03514$

$$.502n = .03514$$
$$.502n \div .502 = .03514 \div .502$$
$$n = .07$$

*Check:* $.502 \times .07 = .03514$

$.03514 = .03514$ true

$$
\begin{array}{r}
.07 \\
.502.\overline{).035.14} \\
\underline{0\phantom{5.14}} \\
35\ 14 \\
\underline{35\ 14} \\
0
\end{array}
$$

## CLASS EXERCISES

*Divide. Check your answers.*

**1.** $.5\overline{)14.35}$ **2.** $.04\overline{)2.468}$ **3.** $.006\overline{)1.824}$ **4.** $5.2\overline{)19.24}$

**5.** $.36\overline{).3024}$ **6.** $.041\overline{).3239}$ **7.** $6.75\overline{)2.9025}$ **8.** $.592\overline{).028416}$

*Solve each equation.*

**9.** $8x = 103.44$ **10.** $\frac{z}{14.3} = 1.106$ **11.** $.029m = .02146$

## EXERCISES

*Divide.*

**1.** $.3\overline{).2841}$ **2.** $.09\overline{)76.14}$ **3.** $.007\overline{).02471}$ **4.** $.2\overline{).01614}$

**5.** $.92\overline{).8464}$ **6.** $019\overline{)1.425}$ **7.** $.038\overline{).2850}$ **8.** $4.6\overline{).0414}$

**9.** $.62\overline{).5394}$ **10.** $9.7\overline{)31.04}$ **11.** $.024\overline{).02376}$ **12.** $7.7\overline{).6622}$

**13.** $2.84\overline{)8.804}$ **14.** $3.56\overline{).14952}$ **15.** $.803\overline{)2.7302}$ **16.** $72.5\overline{).018850}$

**17.** $.827\overline{).52928}$ **18.** $9.36\overline{).12168}$ **19.** $.0652\overline{)5.4116}$ **20.** $.447\overline{).014751}$

*Solve, then check in the original equation.*

**21.** $\frac{x}{30.5} = 4.7$ **22.** $11w = .0616$ **23.** $\frac{a}{26} = 8.99$

**24.** $.006n = .0027$ **25.** $5.3t = .04346$ **26.** $\frac{y}{.06} = 1.5$

**27.** $\frac{p}{3.07} = .0017$ **28.** $.42v = .3906$ **29.** $.31m = .001767$

**30.** $.84c = .01428$ **31.** $\frac{z}{.0008} = 9.06$ **★32.** $10{,}000r + 7.4 = 66.77$

## PROBLEMS

**33.** A tank truck is leaking oil at a rate of 3.26 liters per hour. At this rate, how long will it take to leak 24.124 liters of oil?

**34.** An auto supply company packaged 67.5 liters of oil into 1.5-liter cans. If each can is sold for $.98, how much will the company receive?

### Logical Reasoning

Find two consecutive whole numbers whose sum is 295.

1. .947 5. .92 21. 143.35 24. .458



Homework page 465

## 3-11 More Decimals for Divisors

**A.** To replace a division with a decimal divisor by a division with a whole number divisor, you may have to write zeros in the dividend.

Divide 105 by 1.5.

105 ÷ 2 ≐ 50
105 ÷ 1 ≐ 100
105 ÷ 1.5 ≐ 75

```
                       70
1.5)105  --× 10-->  15.)1050.
                        105
                         00
                          0
                          0
```

**B.** Divide 2.6 by .427. Plan to round to the nearest hundredth.

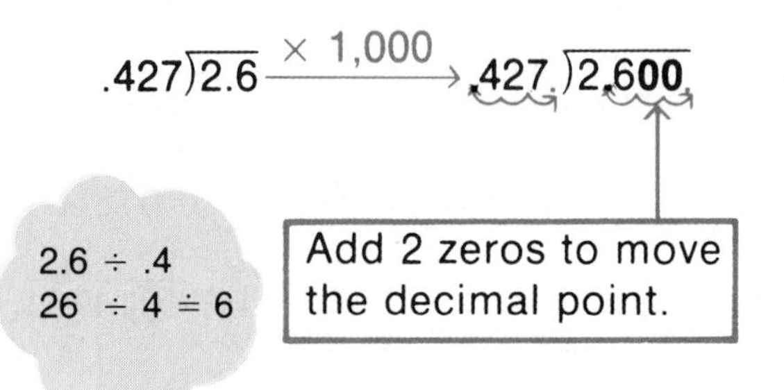


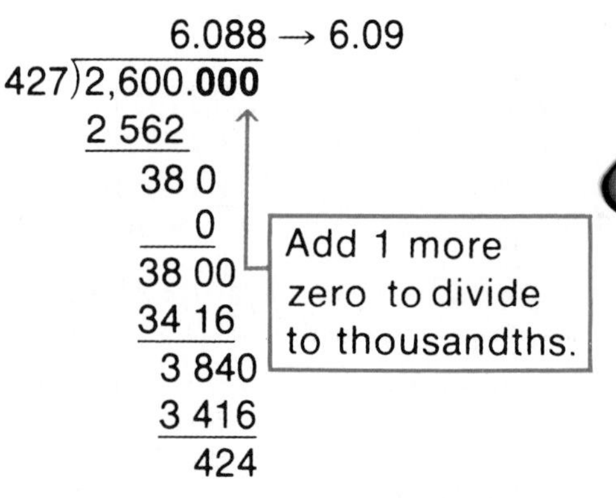


2.6 ÷ .427 ≐ 6.09

**C.** Ms. Inis earns $6.40 for each hour she works. One week she earned a total of $240. How many hours did she work that week?

Divide to find how many hours. $240 ÷ 6 = $40

```
        37.5
640.)24000.00   <-- Plan to round to the nearest tenth.
     192 0
      48 00
      44 80
       3 20 0
       3 20 0
            0
```

She worked 37.5 hours that week.

## CLASS EXERCISES

*Divide. Round to the nearest hundredth.*

**1.** .9)32.85 **2.** .4)2.5924 **3.** .95)79.5 **4.** .62)967.2

**5.** .28)1,572.8 **6.** 4.27)256.2 **7.** .044)2,121.6 **8.** .795)2,527.68

## EXERCISES

*Divide. Round to the nearest tenth.*

**1.** .6)9.36 **2.** .7)95 **3.** .9)49.73 **4.** .003).0019 **5.** .45)18.9

**6.** .3)4.18 **7.** .21)165.9 **8.** 3.16)1,485.7 **9.** .971)757.41 **10.** .004)16

**11.** .05)25.5 **12.** .3654)292.37 **13.** .2)8.64 **14.** 51.9)8.829 **15.** .793)143.81

*Divide.*

**16.** 3.14)415.9 **17.** .057)34.77 **18.** 2.7)947.7 **19.** 51.9)378.93 **20.** .4).03109

**21.** .03)35.6 **22.** .0007)531.3 **23.** 629.7)4.4081 **24.** .5).0175 **25.** 1.1)5.569

**26.** .47)98.9 **27.** .275).065 **28.** .8)4.076 **29.** .063)298.8 **30.** 3.1).1736

*Simplify. Round to the nearest hundredth.*

**31.** $1.58 + (2.65 \div 1.7)$ **32.** $(1.58 + 2.65) \div 1.7$ ★**33.** $7.65 \div 1.9 \div 1.1$

## PROBLEMS

**34.** An oil truck can pump 143.5 liters of fuel oil per minute. How long will it take to pump 1,200 liters? (Plan to round to the nearest tenth.)

★**35.** Mr. Smythe paid $83.80 for 285.7 liters of fuel oil one month and $147.12 for 476.3 liters of fuel oil the next month. What was the average price per liter of that fuel oil? (Plan to round to the nearest .001 dollar.)

## THINK!

### Make It Magic

Change just one number in the figure below to make a magic square. Write the magic sum.

| | | | | |
|---|---|---|---|---|
| 23.75 | 25.4 | 35.3 | 4.15 | 13.85 |
| 11.65 | 22.1 | 32.2 | 33.65 | 2.3 |
| .85 | 10.55 | 20.45 | 30.35 | 40.25 |
| 38.6 | 7.45 | 8.9 | 18.8 | 28.7 |
| 27.05 | 36.95 | 5.6 | 15.5 | 17.35 |

**1.** 15.6 **6.** 13.9 **16.** 132.452

Homework page 465

# 3-12 More Estimation

**A.** Estimates are very useful to check calculations done on a calculator.

Mr. Chambers bought a television set for \$372. The state sales tax was $6\frac{1}{2}\%$ or .065. How much sales tax did he pay? How much did he pay in all?

Round each factor to its first **non-zero digit.**

$$\begin{array}{r} \$372 \\ \times .065 \\ \hline \end{array} \qquad \begin{array}{r} \$400 \\ \times \quad .07 \\ \hline \$28.00 \end{array}$$

The sales tax should be about \$28.00.

$\$372 + \$28 = \$400$

The total price is about \$400.

Use a calculator.

$372 \times .065 =$ [24.18] $\qquad 372 + 24.18 =$ [396.18]

The calculator answer is close to the estimate.

**B.** In an expression you can round each number to the first non-zero digit to get a rough estimate.

Give a rough estimate of $.836 + (19.42 \div 3.7)$.

$.836 + (19.42 \div 3.7)$

$\downarrow \qquad \downarrow \qquad \downarrow$

$.8 + (20 \div 4)$ is about $.8 + 5 = 5.8$.

**C.** Often using rough estimates can help you check the placement of the decimal point in an answer.

Use a rough estimate to select the correct answer.

$(6.75 \times 24.9) - 4.235 = ■$ **a.** 16.384 **b.** 163.84 **c.** 1,638.4

$\downarrow \qquad \downarrow \qquad \downarrow$

$(7 \times 20) - 4$ is about $140 - 4 = 136$.

Choose **b.**

## CLASS EXERCISES

*Estimate. Use your calculator.*

**1.** $\begin{array}{r} .003426 \\ -.000219 \\ \hline \end{array}$ **2.** $\begin{array}{r} 83.75 \\ +\quad .5849 \\ \hline \end{array}$ **3.** $74\overline{).092637}$ **4.** $\begin{array}{r} 64.382 \\ \times \quad .093 \\ \hline \end{array}$

**5.** $.0078 \times 3.1867 = ■$ **6.** $.049\overline{).00931}$ **7.** $.093 + .85 + 24.6951 = ■$

*Use a rough estimate to select the correct answer.*

**8.** $5.28 \times (4.61912 \div .724) = ■$ **a.** 33.6864 **b.** 336.864 **c.** 3,368.64

## EXERCISES

*Estimate. Use your calculator.*

**1.** $\begin{array}{r} 10.3542 \\ -\ \ .8421 \\ \hline \end{array}$

**2.** $\begin{array}{r} 914.8 \\ \times .0056 \\ \hline \end{array}$

**3.** $.009\overline{).006138}$

**4.** $7.94\overline{)4{,}843.7}$

**5.** $\begin{array}{r} .0534 \\ \times\ \ .86 \\ \hline \end{array}$

**6.** $\begin{array}{r} 53.2197 \\ +\ \ .0825 \\ \hline \end{array}$

**7.** $\begin{array}{r} .013485 \\ -.0073 \\ \hline \end{array}$

**8.** $\begin{array}{r} .00694 \\ +.0837 \\ \hline \end{array}$

**9.** $.82\overline{)43.46}$

**10.** $.218 \times \$392.46 = ■$

**11.** $.0073 + 14.92 + 7.075 = ■$

**12.** $63\overline{)4}$

**13.** $.0789 - .001306 = ■$

**14.** $.08\overline{).1}$

*Use a rough estimate to select the correct answer.*

| | | | | |
|---|---|---|---|---|
| **15.** | $(31.1422 - 24.3504) \div 2.9 = ■$ | **a.** .02342 | **b.** .2342 | **c.** 2.342 |
| **16.** | $(874.3 \times .546) + 62.89 = ■$ | **a.** 540.2578 | **b.** 54.02578 | **c.** 5.402578 |
| **17.** | $7.3924 + (17.8 - .143) = ■$ | **a.** 250,494 | **b.** 25.0494 | **c.** 2,504.94 |
| **18.** | $(261.1812 \div 82.6) \div .93 = ■$ | **a.** 34 | **b.** .34 | **c.** 3.4 |

## PROBLEMS

*Estimate. Then use a calculator.*

**19.** Ms. Ruiz's salary is $28,750 annually. If the rate for social security is 7.15%, how much social security does she pay?

**20.** Ms. Ruiz saves 7.5% or .075 of her salary. How much does she save annually?

★ **21.** If Ms. Ruiz pays .13 of her salary in federal income tax, .03 of her salary in state income tax, and .006 in city income tax, how much does she pay in income taxes all together?

## THINK!

### Work Backwards

A man goes into a store and says to the owner, "Give me as much money as I have now, and I will spend $10 in your store." The owner agrees, and the man spends the money. The man goes into a second store and says, "Give me as much money as I have now, and I will spend $10 in your store." The same thing happens. He goes into a third store and repeats the question, after which he has no money left.
How much money did the man start with?

1. 9.6 5. .045 9. 50 15. c

Homework page 465

# Problem Solving READ • PLAN • DO • ANSWER • CHECK

## 3-13 Unit Pricing

**A.** Sometimes you may want to buy one item, when a store advertises the price for several of the items.

Cereal is advertised at 3 boxes for $2. How much would you pay for 1 box?

$3 \times \quad = \$2$
$3 \times \$.70 = \$2.10$

Divide to find the cost per box.

$$\begin{array}{r} \$.66 \\ 3\overline{)\$2.00} \\ \underline{1\,8} \\ 20 \\ \underline{18} \\ 2 \end{array}$$

Stores always round up if there is a remainder in the hundredths step.

You would pay $.67 for 1 box of cereal.

**B.** To compare the prices of similar items, find their ***unit prices***—their prices per kilogram or per liter. **You will need an exact answer.**

Which is the best buy: 1.75 liters of bleach for $1.94,
2 liters of bleach for $2.19,
or 2.5 liters of bleach for $2.79?

Find the unit prices. Plan to round to the nearest thousandth.

*For 1.75 liters:*

$$\begin{array}{r} \$1.1085 \rightarrow \$1.109 \\ 1.75\overline{)\$1.94\,0000} \end{array}$$

*Unit price:* $1.109/liter

*For 2 liters:*

$$\begin{array}{r} \$1.095 \\ 2\overline{)\$2.1900} \end{array}$$

*Unit price:* $1.095/liter

*For 2.5 liters:*

$$\begin{array}{r} \$1.116 \\ 2.5\overline{)\$2.7.9000} \end{array}$$

*Unit price:* $1.116/liter

2 liters of bleach for $2.19 is the best buy.

## CLASS EXERCISES

1. 6 cans of tomato soup cost $2.25. How much will 1 can cost? How much for 4 cans?

2. Which is the better buy: 2 kg of ground beef for $4.19 or 3.5 kg of ground beef for $7.39?

## PROBLEMS

*How much would one cost?*

1. 5 jars of peanut butter for $7.99
2. 3 bunches of carrots for $.89
3. 4 cans of peas for $2.09
4. 12 bottles of grape juice for $7
5. 10 green peppers for $2.14
6. 7 bags of frozen corn for $6
7. 8 boxes of soup mix cost $6.54. How much do 3 boxes cost?
8. 9 cans of tuna fish cost $15. How much do 5 cans cost?

*Which is the best buy?*

9. Milk:
   2 liters for $1.45
   or 3 liters for $2.15

10. Potatoes:
    5 kg for $.98
    or 8 kg for $1.55

11. Cheese:
    1 kg for $4.98,
    1.5 kg for $7.49,
    or 2.25 kg for $10.99

12. Tomato juice:
    1 liter for $.96,
    1.3 liters for $1.23,
    or 2 liters for $1.95

13. Detergent:
    2.1 liters for $2.69,
    2.4 liters for $3.09,
    or 3 liters for $3.85

14. Apples:
    2 kg for $1.31,
    3.5 kg for $2.30,
    or 5 kg for $2.99

15. Macaroni:
    2.25 kg for $2.75,
    3 kg for $3.65,
    or 4.5 kg for $5.49

16. Olive oil:
    1.8 liters for $3.74,
    2.25 liters for $4.69,
    or 2.7 liters for $5.64

★ 17. A 500-gram box of raspberries costs $2.49. What is the price per 100 grams (to the nearest .001 dollar)?

★ 18. A 750-milliliter jar of juice costs $.98. What is the price per 100 milliliters (to the nearest .001 dollar)?

## ON YOUR OWN

### Data Search

Check newspaper ads or prices in your local supermarket to find the costs of three different-size packages of the same product. Which size is the best buy?

Homework page 466

## 3-14 Installment Plans

An **installment** is a part of a purchase price that is paid at regular intervals until the entire purchase price has been paid.

**A.** The **cash price**—the price, if paid immediately—of a car is \$6,500. If paid in installments, the total cost is \$8,060.40. How much is saved by paying cash?

**Amount saved** = Installment price − Cash price
= \$8,060.40 − \$6,500
= **\$1,560.40**

8,000 − 6,500 = 1,500

\$1,560.40 is saved by paying cash.

**B.** A station wagon can be purchased through an **installment plan** of \$500 cash and 24 monthly payments of \$430.45 each. What is the total cost of the station wagon?

**Step 1** **Total cost** = Cash + Installment payments

**Step 2** Installment payments = Number of payments × Amount of each
= 24 × \$430.45
= \$10,330.80

25 × 400 = 10,000

Now you can use the result of Step 2 to complete Step 1.

**Total cost** = Cash + Installment payments
= \$500 + \$10,330.80
= **\$10,830.80**

The total cost of the station wagon is \$10,830.80.

**C.** The total cost of a sports car, including a cash payment of \$750, is \$16,423.50. Installments are paid monthly for 18 months. How much is each installment?

**Step 1** **Amount of installment** = Installment payments ÷ Number of payments

**Step 2** Installment payments = Total cost − Cash
= \$16,423.50 − \$750
= \$15,673.50

Now you can use the result of Step 2 to complete Step 1.

**Amount of installment** = \$15,673.50 ÷ 18
= **\$870.75**

16,000 ÷ 18 is a little less than 1,000.

Each installment is \$870.75.

## CLASS EXERCISES

1. A pick-up truck can be purchased for $8,750 cash or through an installment plan of $2,000 cash plus 36 monthly payments of $214.15. How much would be saved by paying cash?

2. For the installment plan in Exercise 1, what is the balance owed on the total cash price after the $2,000 is paid? What part of this amount is added to give the total installment payment? (Plan to round to the nearest thousandth.)

## PROBLEMS

1. A snowblower can be purchased through an installment plan of $25 cash and 12 monthly payments of $32.95 each. What is the total cost of the snowblower?

2. The total cost of a riding lawn mower, including a $150 cash payment, is $1,296. The monthly installments are $47.75. For how many months must installments be paid?

3. A motorcycle can be purchased for $500 cash and 24 monthly payments of $177.95 or for 30 monthly payments of $161.50. Which plan costs less? How much less?

4. The 36 monthly payments for a recreational vehicle are $399.89 each. The total cost of the vehicle is $19,396.04. What is the amount of the cash payment?

★5. The cash price of a snowmobile is $4,250. To determine installment payments, the dealer adds .18 of the balance owed. What would be the total installment payment on the snowmobile if $1,500 cash were paid? If 30 monthly installments were paid, what would be the amount of each? (Plan to round to the nearest cent.)

★6. When the Feingolds bought a boat and trailer, they were allowed $1,500 off the cash price for trading in a motorcycle. They also made a cash payment of $1,000. After adding .22 of the balance owed, the dealer determined that each of the 18 monthly installments would be $589.67. What was the cash price of the boat and trailer? (Plan to round to the nearest dollar.)

## ON YOUR OWN

### Decision Making

Discuss what factors other than total cost might influence a person's decision to buy an item through an installment plan. Why might buying through an installment plan be less expensive than paying cash?

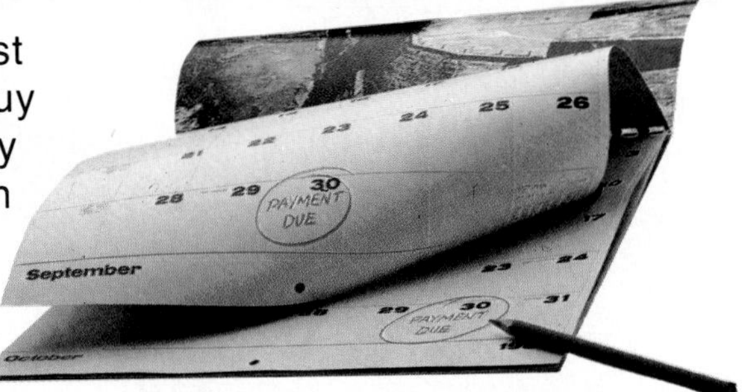




Homework page 466

# TECHNOLOGY

## Division with Remainders on a Calculator

A calculator will not show you a whole number remainder for division. You can find the remainder by following the steps below.

A factory has 59,273 bolts in stock. It uses 862 bolts each day. For how many full days can the factory operate before running out of bolts? How many bolts will be left over after the last full day's operation?

60,000 ÷ 900 = ■
60 +

**Plan.** Find the quotient and remainder for 862)59,273.

**Step 1** Divide. Record the whole number part of the quotient shown. 59,273 ÷ 862 =

```
      68     Quotient
862)59,273
```

68.762181

**Step 2** Multiply quotient and divisor. Record this product. Subtract the product from the dividend to find the remainder. 59,273 − 58,616 =

```
      68  R657
862)59,273
   − 58,616
       657    Remainder
```

657

**Check.** (Quotient × Divisor) + Remainder
= (68 × 862) + 657
= 59,273 ← Dividend

59273

The factory can operate for 68 full days. There will be 657 bolts left after the last full day's operation.

*Use your calculator to find the quotients and remainders. Check.*

**1.** 65)396,402 **2.** 246)792,538 **3.** 8,960)485,211

**4.** 49)7,682,510 **5.** 718)96,003 **6.** 5,084)2,906,738

**7.** 95)34,672 **8.** 471)8,493,726 **9.** 2,709)948,573

# Problem Solving Strategy

READ **PLAN** DO • ANSWER • CHECK

## Logical Reasoning with Clues

Bert, Cindy, Don, and Ellen sell refreshments at their school football games. Each sells only one kind of food or drink. Use the clues to find the type of refreshment each sells.

1. Don does not sell juice.
2. One of the girls sells yogurt.
3. Bert gives each customer a drinking straw.
4. Ellen offers a choice of salted or unsalted.

To solve these kinds of logic problems, read all the clues more than once. Then use a table to organize the information. Use x when the information does not match. Use ✓ when the information does match.

| Refreshments | Bert | Cindy | Don | Ellen |
|---|---|---|---|---|
| Juice | ✓ (clue 3) | X | X (clue 1) | |
| Peanuts | X | X | X | ✓ (clue 4) |
| Fruit | X | X | ✓ | X |
| Yogurt | X (clue 2) | ✓ | X (clue 2) | X |

Bert sells juice, Cindy sells yogurt, Don sells fruit, and Ellen sells peanuts.

---

*Solve.*

1. Alan, Brenda, Carl, and Donna live in four adjacent apartments. The jobs they hold are: teacher, scientist, banker, and computer programmer. Use the clues to find each person's occupation.
   - **a.** The scientist picks up Carl's mail when he is on vacation.
   - **b.** The teacher rings Alan's bell when his television is too loud.
   - **c.** Alan and Brenda have the banker help them with investments.
   - **d.** Donna is not the banker.
   - **e.** Alan is not the programmer.
   - **f.** Brenda takes homework home to grade.

2. Four teachers, Mr. Green, Ms. Hull, Mr. Ives, and Ms. Jones had lunch in the school cafeteria. Each person teaches a different subject—biology, math, French, and history. Each ordered a different sandwich—tuna, chicken, egg, and ham. Use the clues to find each teacher's subject and sandwich.
   - **a.** Mr. Green does not teach French or math.
   - **b.** The biology teacher did not have tuna or egg.
   - **c.** Mr. Ives teaches history.
   - **d.** Ms. Jones had chicken.
   - **e.** Ms. Hull had just given her class a test on number theory.
   - **f.** Mr. Ives is allergic to eggs.

Challenge Problems page 518

## Finding Total Earnings

**A.** Mrs. Ortega is paid at the **regular rate** of \$5.60 per hour (\$5.60/h) for the first 37.5 h she works each week. She is paid at the **overtime rate** of 1.5 times her regular rate for any hours over 37.5 h each week.

Overtime rate = 1.5 × Regular rate
= 1.5 × \$5.60
= \$8.40/h

**B.** Mrs. Ortega's employer keeps a **payroll record.** It shows how much each employee earns each week. This record shows the hours Mrs. Ortega worked during the week ending October 28.

| Payroll Record | Week Ending October 28 | | | | |
|---|---|---|---|---|---|
| EMPLOYEE | HOURS WORKED | | PAY/HOUR | PAY | TOTAL PAY |
| Ortega, V. | TOTAL | REG 37.5 | \$5.60 | \$210.00 | |
| | 41 | OT 3.5 | \$8.40 | | |

How much did Mrs. Ortega earn during the week ending October 28?

Total earned = Regular pay + Overtime pay
= \$210.00 + Overtime pay

Overtime pay = Overtime hours × Overtime rate
= 3.5 × \$8.40
= \$29.40

Total earned = \$210.00 + \$29.40
= \$239.40

*Copy and complete the payroll record for these employees. (OT = 1.5 times REG.)*

| EMPLOYEE | HOURS WORKED | | PAY/HOUR | PAY | TOTAL PAY |
|---|---|---|---|---|---|
| Maxwell, T. | TOTAL | REG 37.5 | \$5.80 | **2.** | **4.** |
| | 42 | OT **1.** | 8.70 | **3.** | |
| Barnes, C. | TOTAL | REG **5.** | 4.90 | **8.** | **10.** |
| | 43.5 | OT **6.** | **7.** | **9.** | |
| Ambrose, B. | TOTAL | REG. **11.** | 6.40 | **14.** | **16.** |
| | 39 | OT **12.** | **13.** | **15.** | |
| Whyte, S. | TOTAL | REG **17.** | 6.20 | **20.** | **22.** |
| | 43 | OT **18.** | **19.** | **21.** | |

*Find the total earnings of these employees. The overtime rate is 1.5 times the regular rate.*

**23.** *J. Foster:* Regular rate is $4.80/h for the first 35 h. Worked 41.5 h.

**24.** *W. Stein:* Regular rate is $5.50/h for the first 38.75 h. Worked 42.25 h.

*Sometimes employees are paid a special overtime rate of 2 times the regular rate for any time more than 45 h each week. Use this rule to find the total earnings of these employees.*

**25.** *L. Giancola:* Regular rate is $6.00/h for the first 37.5 h. Worked 48 h.

**26.** *D. Harris:* Regular rate is $5.20/h for the first 35 h. Worked 50 h.

*Part-time employees may have a* ***time card*** *which shows starting time, ending time, and earnings for each day. Use the time card for Paula Jones.*

**27.** Copy the time card. Find Paula's pay for each day.

★ **28.** There are *two* ways to find Paula's total earnings. Use one way to find her total earnings and the other way to check.

NAME Paula Jones
WEEK ENDING October 28
HOURLY PAY $ 2.80

| DAY | IN | OUT | HOURS WORKED | DAILY PAY |
|---|---|---|---|---|
| M | 4:30 P.M. | 6:06 P.M. | 1.6 | |
| TU | 4:15 P.M. | 6:21 P.M. | 2.1 | |
| W | — | — | — | — |
| TH | 3:56 P.M. | 7:14 P.M. | 3.3 | |
| F | 4:10 P.M. | 7:40 P.M. | 3.5 | |
| SA | 9:40 A.M. | 2:04 P.M. | 4.4 | |
| TOTAL FOR WEEK → | | | | |

## ON YOUR OWN

1. Make up your own set of data, then ask a classmate to complete a time card such as the one above. Be sure to include the employee's name, regular and overtime rates, and the number of hours worked each day.

2. Obtain examples of payroll records and/or time cards used by local businesses. Bring the material to class and discuss the different types of information each includes.

# Unit Review

*What does the digit 9 mean in each decimal?* *(pages 78–79)*

**1.** 4.695207 **2.** .003849 **3.** 21.347951 **4.** 8.930007

*Write a decimal for each.* *(pages 78–79)*

**5.** eighty-two and fifty-one thousandths

**6.** two hundred ninety-six hundred-thousandths

*Compare. Write >, <, or = for ●.* *(pages 80–81)*

**7.** .00628 ● .00641 **8.** .45861 ● .4582 **9.** 2.070 ● 2.07000

*Order from greatest to least.* *(pages 80–81)*

**10.** .062; .0026; 206; .602 **11.** .419; 3.2; .05819; .4164

*Add, subtract, or multiply.* *(pages 84–85, 86–87)*

**12.** $\begin{array}{r} .0689 \\ +.00758 \\ \hline \end{array}$ **13.** $\begin{array}{r} 2.6 \\ -1.943 \\ \hline \end{array}$ **14.** $\begin{array}{r} 8.435 \\ \times\ .09 \\ \hline \end{array}$ **15.** $\begin{array}{r} .06731 \\ \times\ 4.5 \\ \hline \end{array}$ **16.** $\begin{array}{r} .070009 \\ -.00526 \\ \hline \end{array}$

**17.** $\begin{array}{r} 9.0507 \\ +\ .86985 \\ \hline \end{array}$ **18.** $\begin{array}{r} .042 \\ \times .069 \\ \hline \end{array}$ **19.** $\begin{array}{r} 13.04 \\ -13.0396 \\ \hline \end{array}$ **20.** $\begin{array}{r} \$102.40 \\ \times\ .0375 \\ \hline \end{array}$ **21.** $\begin{array}{r} .648007 \\ +.0923 \\ \hline \end{array}$

**22.** .008 × 4.065 = ■ **23.** 600 − .91745 = ■ **24.** 8.7 + .009 + .65 + .8 = ■

*Divide. Round to the nearest thousandth.* *(pages 90–93, 96–99)*

**25.** $8\overline{).631}$ **26.** $25\overline{).096}$ **27.** $.7\overline{).1384}$ **28.** $.053\overline{)2.7}$ **29.** $4.8\overline{).80215}$

**30.** \$325 ÷ 4 = ■ **31.** .14287 ÷ .65 = ■ **32.** 22 ÷ 80 = ■

*Complete.* *(pages 94–95)*

**33.** 100 × 4.2 = ■ **34.** 8,604 ÷ 10 = ■ **35.** 10 × .00713 = ■

**36.** .9432 ÷ 1,000 = ■ **37.** 1,000 × 61 = ■ **38.** 158 ÷ 100 = ■

*Round with decimals to the nearest tenth; round amounts to the nearest cent.* *(pages 82–83)*

**39.** 5.23467 **40.** \$46.8275 **41.** .38196 **42.** \$.595 **43.** 471.952

*Estimate.* *(pages 100–101)*

44. $\begin{array}{r} .0352 \\ +.007481 \\ \hline \end{array}$

45. $\begin{array}{r} 6.738 \\ \times\ .043 \\ \hline \end{array}$

46. $\begin{array}{r} .896 \\ -.06375 \\ \hline \end{array}$

47. $84\overline{).06294}$

48. $\begin{array}{r} .0917 \\ \times\ .56 \\ \hline \end{array}$

49. $\begin{array}{r} 7.01348 \\ -\ .0067 \\ \hline \end{array}$

50. $\begin{array}{r} .00614 \\ \times\ 7.3 \\ \hline \end{array}$

51. $\begin{array}{r} .004965 \\ +.00468 \\ \hline \end{array}$

52. $.6\overline{)89.345}$

53. $.016\overline{).004}$ **.2**

*Solve.* *(pages 84–85, 96–97)*

54. $x + .049 = .3021$

55. $.7k = .035$

56. $n - .096 = .0078$

57. $\frac{m}{.56} = 3.4$

58. $.0687 + y = .07$

59. $4.5z = .315$

*Solve the problems.* *(pages 88–89, 102–105)*

60. Of the taxes paid to the Federal Government, .10125 supports health programs and .112 pays interest on borrowed money. For which purpose is a greater part of the taxes used? How much greater? **interest;**

61. A dishwasher costs $745. The McArtleys paid $150 cash deposit for the dishwasher. The store added a service charge of .14 of the balance due. What will be the amount of each installment, if the McArtleys pay for the dishwasher in 15 installments?

62. A salesperson earns a salary of $150/week, plus a commission of .04 of her sales over $10,000. How much would she earn in all for a week in which her sales totaled $27,000?

63. Find the prices per liter for milk. Which is the better buy?

2.5 L for $1.81
3.5 L for $2.56

64. At which store would you pay less for 4 L of milk, 2 L of tomato juice, and 1 L of fruit juice?

65. How much would you pay for 3.5 L of milk, 1.5 L of tomato juice, and 2 L of fruit juice, buying each item where it costs less?

| Item | Price per Liter | |
|---|---|---|
| | Store I | Store II |
| milk | $ .72 | $ .77 |
| tomato juice | .96 | .94 |
| fruit juice | 1.30 | 1.23 |

# Enrichment

## Truth Tables

**A.** An important part of logical reasoning deals with **statements.** Statements are true or false.

Statement: Today is Monday.

The statement is true sometimes (on Mondays) and false sometimes (on all other days of the week). However, it is always true or false. It is never both true and false, and it is never neither true nor false.

1. Write a statement that is always true.
2. Write a statement that is always false.
3. Write a statement that is sometimes true and sometimes false. Tell when it is true and when it is false.

**B.** Use the letters p, q, and r as names for statements.

Statement p: Today is Monday.
Statement q: Yesterday was Sunday.

Statement p and Statement q are **equivalent statements** because each is true when the other is true and false when the other is false.

4. Write two statements equivalent to "Next month will be April."

**C.** "Today is not Monday" is the **negation** of "Today is Monday." In symbols, the negation of p is "not p."

Rule for not p

When p is true (T), not p is false (F). When p is false, not p is true. This relation is shown in the **truth table** at the right.

Truth table for not p

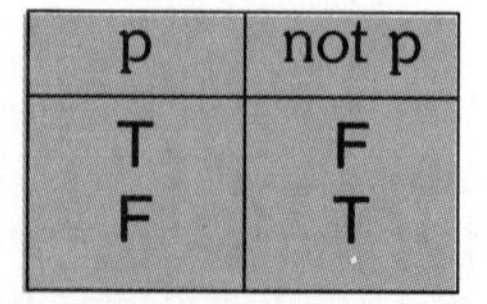

| p | not p |
|---|---|
| T | F |
| F | T |

5. Write the negation of "The book is red."
6. If "The book is red" is false, is "The book is not red" true or false?
7. Write the negation of "I have 5 dollars.'
8. Why is "I have 4 dollars" not the negation of "I have 5 dollars"?

**D.** Rule for 'p and r'

The **compound statement** 'p and r' is true whenever p is true and r is true. In any other case, 'p and r' is false. This relation is shown in the truth table at the right.

Truth table for 'p and r'

| p | r | p and r |
|---|---|---|
| T | T | T |
| T | F | F |
| F | T | F |
| F | F | F |

*If* p *is 'Today is Monday' and* r *is 'It is raining,' tell whether* 'p and r' *is true or false on:*

**9.** a sunny Tuesday
**10.** a rainy Wednesday
**11.** a sunny Monday
**12.** a rainy Friday
**13.** a rainy Monday
**14.** a snowy Saturday

**E.** Rule for 'p or r'

The compound statement 'p or r' is true in every case except the case in which p is false and r is false. This relation is shown in the truth table at the right.

Truth table for 'p or r'

| p | r | p or r |
|---|---|---|
| T | T | T |
| T | F | T |
| F | T | T |
| F | F | F |

**15.** For which days in Exercises 9-14 is 'p or r' true?

*Copy and complete the truth tables.*

| p | q | p and q | not (p and q) | not p | not q | not p and not q | not p and q |
|---|---|---|---|---|---|---|---|
| T | T | T | **16.** | F | F | **20.** | **24.** |
| T | F | F | **17.** | F | T | **21.** | **25.** |
| F | T | F | **18.** | T | F | **22.** | **26.** |
| F | F | F | **19.** | T | T | **23.** | **27.** |

True only when p and q is false.

| p | q | p or q | not (p or q) | not p | not q | not p or not q | p or not q |
|---|---|---|---|---|---|---|---|
| T | T | T | **28.** | F | F | **32.** | **36.** |
| T | F | T | **29.** | F | T | **33.** | **37.** |
| F | T | T | **30.** | T | F | **34.** | **38.** |
| F | F | F | **31.** | T | T | **35.** | **39.** |

**40.** Are 'not (p and q)' and 'not p or not q' equivalent?

# Cumulative Review

**1.** $\begin{array}{r} 4{,}716 \\ \times\ 300 \\ \hline \end{array}$

**a.** 141,480
**b.** 1,414,800
**c.** 1,213,800
**d.** Not given

**2.** Solve.
$\frac{3x}{4} = 15$

**a.** 20
**b.** 60
**c.** 8
**d.** Not given

**3.** $3.2\overline{)9.92}$

**a.** .31
**b.** 31
**c.** 3.1
**d.** Not given

**4.** Round to the nearest hundredth.
6.0451

**a.** 6.04
**b.** 6.05
**c.** 6.045
**d.** Not given

**5.** $7\overline{)42{,}281}$

**a.** 604 R1
**b.** $64\frac{1}{7}$
**c.** $6{,}040\frac{1}{7}$
**d.** Not given

**6.** Compare .0096 and .02.

**a.** $.0096 < .02$
**b.** $.0096 > .02$
**c.** $.0096 = .02$

**7.** Solve.
$4x + 6 = 42$

**a.** 12
**b.** 36
**c.** 48
**d.** Not given

**8.** $\begin{array}{r} 3.26 \\ \times\ 5.3 \\ \hline \end{array}$

**a.** 1,727.8
**b.** 17.278
**c.** 172.78
**d.** Not given

**9.** Show how to read 2.0006.

**a.** two and six thousandths
**b.** two and six ten-thousandths
**c.** two and six hundredths
**d.** Not given

**10.** $9.36 + 841 + 17.6 = \blacksquare$

**a.** 867.96
**b.** 19.53
**c.** 35.37
**d.** Not given

**11.** Dom's mother is 34 years old. This is 6 years less than 5 times Dom's age. How old is Dom?

**a.** 40 years old
**b.** 28 years old
**c.** 8 years old
**d.** Not given

**12.** Which is a better buy: 3.6 kg of butter for $25.74, or 3.25 kg of butter for $23.27?

**a.** 3.6 kg for $25.74
**b.** 3.25 kg for $23.27
**c.** They are equally good.

**13.** Plants are advertised, "On sale—6 for $8.96." What does one plant cost?

**a.** $1.49
**b.** $1.50
**c.** $1.48
**d.** Not given

**14.** A grocer is packaging oranges with 6 oranges in each sack. When she has filled 35 sacks she has 128 oranges left. How many sacks can she fill in all?

**a.** 21 sacks
**b.** 153 sacks
**c.** 56 sacks
**d.** Not given

**WORLD OCEANS**

| Name | Area (square miles) | Average Depth (feet) | Deepest Trench (feet) |
|---|---|---|---|
| Arctic Ocean | 5,105,700 | 3,407 | 17,800 |
| Atlantic Ocean | 33,420,000 | 11,730 | 28,374 |
| Indian Ocean | 28,350,500 | 12,598 | 25,344 |
| Pacific Ocean | 64,186,300 | 12,925 | 36,198 |

# 4-1 Exponents

**A.** During the growth period of bears, body cells multiply at a fast rate. Cells in some tissues may double every hour. If we were to start with one cell, how many cells would there be after 5 hours?

$$\text{Cells after 5 hours} = 2 \cdot 2 \cdot 2 \cdot 2 \cdot 2$$
$$= 32$$

The number of cells after 5 hours can also be expressed using an **exponent** to show the product of equal factors.

Exponent is 5.

There are 5 factors.

$$2^5 = 2 \cdot 2 \cdot 2 \cdot 2 \cdot 2$$

**Base** is 2.

Each factor is 2.

**B.** Exponents name **powers** of the base.

**Example 1** $4^3 = 4 \cdot 4 \cdot 4 = 64$ is the **third power** of 4.

**Example 2** $3^5 = 3 \cdot 3 \cdot 3 \cdot 3 \cdot 3 = 243$ is the **fifth power** of 3.

**C.** 0 and 1 are also used as exponents. The first power of any number is that number, and the zero power of any number except 0 is 1.

$6^1 = 6$ $\quad 8^0 = 1$ $\quad 37^1 = 37$ $\quad 71^0 = 1$

**D.** To simplify an expression having exponents, write its standard numeral.

**Example 1**
$(3 \cdot 5)^2 = 15^2$
$= 15 \cdot 15$
$= 225$

**Example 2**
$3 \cdot 5^2 = 3 \cdot 5 \cdot 5$
$= 3 \cdot 25$
$= 75$

**Example 3**
$(3 + 4)^2 = 7^2$
$= 7 \cdot 7$
$= 49$

**Example 4**
$3 + 4^2 = 3 + 4 \cdot 4$
$= 3 + 16$
$= 19$

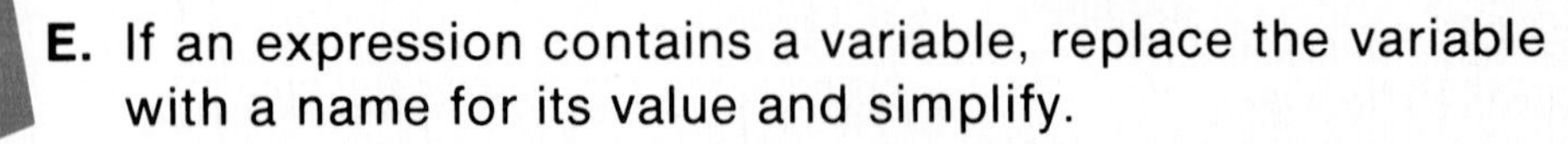

**E.** If an expression contains a variable, replace the variable with a name for its value and simplify.

**Example 1**
When x has the value 4, $(2x)^2 = (2 \cdot 4)^2$
$= 64$

**Example 2**
When x has the value 4, $2x^2 = 2 \cdot 4^2$
$= 32$

## CLASS EXERCISES

*Write the standard numeral.*

**1.** $4^3$ **2.** $3^4$ **3.** $8^0$ **4.** $9^1$ **5.** $10^2$

**6.** the fifth power of 2 **7.** the second power of 11 **8.** the third power of 5

*Simplify.*

**9.** $(2 \cdot 3)^2$ **10.** $2 \cdot 3^2$ **11.** $(6 - 2)^2$ **12.** $6 - 2^2$ **13.** $4 \cdot 10^2$

## EXERCISES

*Write the standard numeral.*

**1.** $2^2$ **2.** $4^4$ **3.** $2^4$ **4.** $4^2$ **5.** $12^0$

**6.** $5^3$ **7.** $2^5$ **8.** $8^2$ **9.** $6^3$ **10.** $38^1$

**11.** the sixth power of 3 **12.** the second power of 12 **13.** the third power of 9

*Simplify.*

**14.** $4 \cdot 5^2$ **15.** $4 + 5^2$ **16.** $4^2 \cdot 5$ **17.** $(4 \cdot 5)^2$ **18.** $(4 + 5)^2$

**19.** $6 \cdot 10^3$ **20.** $(2 \cdot 10)^2$ **21.** $9^0 \cdot 10^1$ **22.** $(8 + 10)^0$ **23.** $8 + 10^0$

*Find the value of each expression for the given value of x.*

| | x=0 | x=1 | x=2 | x=3 | x=4 | x=5 |
|---|---|---|---|---|---|---|
| $3x^2$ | **24.** | **25.** | **26.** | **27.** | **28.** | **29.** |
| $(3x)^2$ | **30.** | **31.** | **32.** | **33.** | **34.** | **35.** |
| $(5x)^3$ | **36.** | **37.** | **38.** | **39.** | **40.** | **41.** |
| $5x^3$ | **42.** | **43.** | **44.** | **45.** | **46.** | **47.** |
| $2x^2 + 1$ | ★**48.** | ★**49.** | ★**50.** | ★**51.** | ★**52.** | ★**53.** |
| $(2x + 1)^2$ | ★**54.** | ★**55.** | ★**56.** | ★**57.** | ★**58.** | ★**59.** |

## THINK!

### Using a Pattern

Continue the pattern to $10^9$.

$10^0 = 1$
$10^1 = 10$
$10^2 = 100$
$10^3 = 1{,}000$
$10^4 = 10{,}000$

Exponent is 4.

4 zeros

1. 4 11. 729 14. 100



Homework page 467

## 4-2 Greatest Common Factor (GCF)

**A.** Sometimes it is necessary to find factors of numbers.

$18 = 18 \times 1$ $\quad 18 = 2 \times 9$ $\quad 18 = 3 \times 6$

| Number | Factorizations | Factors |
|---|---|---|
| 18 | $1 \times 18$, $2 \times 9$, $3 \times 6$ | 1, 2, 3, 6, 9, 18 |

Each whole number has 1 and the number itself as factors.

**B.** Find the **greatest common factor (GCF)** of 48 and 36.

DO **Step 1** Find all factors of 48.
You know that 1 and 48 are factors. $48 = 1 \times 48$

Use division to find other factors.

Try 2. $2\overline{)48}$ = 24
$48 = 2 \times 24$
2 and 24 are factors.

Try 3. $3\overline{)48}$ = 16
$48 = 3 \times 16$
3 and 16 are factors.

Try 4. $4\overline{)48}$ = 12
$48 = 4 \times 12$
4 and 12 are factors.

Try 5. $5\overline{)48}$ = 9 R3
$48 = 5 \times 9 + 3$
5 is not a factor.

Try 6. $6\overline{)48}$ = 8
$48 = 6 \times 8$
6 and 8 are factors.

Try 7. $7\overline{)48}$ = 6 R6
$48 = 7 \times 6 + 6$
7 is not a factor.

Quotient is less than or equal to divisor. Stop!

Factors of 48 are 1, 2, 3, 4, 6, 8, 12, 16, 24, and 48.

**Step 2** Find all factors of 36.
1 and 36 are factors. Use the same method as in Step 1 to find all of the other factors.
Factors of 36 are 1, 2, 3, 4, 6, 9, 12, 18, and 36.

**Step 3** Compare the factors.
Factors of 48: 1, 2, 3, 4, 6, 8, 12, 16, 24, and 48.
Factors of 36: 1, 2, 3, 4, 6, 9, 12, 18, and 36.

The numbers 1, 2, 3, 4, 6, and 12 are **common factors** of 48 and 36.
The **greatest common factor** (GCF) of 48 and 36 is 12.

## CLASS EXERCISES

*List all factors.*

**1.** 16 **2.** 54 **3.** 45 **4.** 75 **5.** 91 **6.** 126

*List all common factors and name the GCF.*

**7.** 16 and 54 **8.** 45 and 75 **9.** 91 and 45 **10.** 91 and 126

## EXERCISES

*List all factors.*

**1.** 18 **2.** 24 **3.** 77 **4.** 22 **5.** 35 **6.** 44

**7.** 57 **8.** 14 **9.** 63 **10.** 49 **11.** 21 **12.** 28

**13.** 111 **14.** 441 **15.** 144 ★**16.** 1,013 ★**17.** 1,118 ★**18.** 1,111

*List all common factors and name the GCF.*

**19.** 18 and 24 **20.** 77 and 22 **21.** 22 and 35 **22.** 35 and 44

**23.** 57 and 14 **24.** 63 and 49 **25.** 21 and 28 **26.** 111 and 21

**27.** 243 and 111 ★**28.** 1,013 and 1,118 ★**29.** 1,001 and 1,053

★**30.** What whole numbers are factors of every *even* whole number?

★**31.** List all common factors of 243, 512, and 101.

★**32.** List all common factors of 1,000, 550, 1025, and 1,115.

## PROBLEMS

**33.** Two walls are to be covered by shelves. One wall is 120 inches high, and the other has 96 inches available above the radiator. The shelves are to be spaced evenly. What spacings, 10 inches or greater, could be used?

**34.** Sam has two pieces of shelving, one 72 inches long and the other 108 inches long. He cut shelves of the same size, as large as possible, without waste. How long were the shelves he made?

## THINK!

### Math Riddle

There are 12 four-cent stamps in a dozen.
How many six-cent stamps are there in a dozen?

**1.** 1, 2, 3, 6, 9, 18 **19.** 1, 2, 3, 6; 6



Homework page 467

## 4-3 Divisibility Tests

**A.** If a division gives a zero remainder, the divisor is a factor of the dividend and the dividend is **divisible by** the divisor.

$4\overline{)12}$ with quotient 3

4 is a factor of 12. 12 is divisible by 4.

**B.** Divisibility tests are shortcuts for determining if a number is divisible by certain numbers. Some divisibility tests can be done by looking only at the ones digit.

Numbers divisible by 2 are **even numbers.**

A number is:

**divisible by 2** if the ones digit is 0, 2, 4, 6, or 8. *Example:* 346 ÷ 2 = 173

**divisible by 5** if the ones digit is 0 or 5. *Example:* 250 ÷ 5 = 50

**divisible by 10** if the ones digit is 0. *Example:* 420 ÷ 10 = 42

**C.** All of these numbers are divisible by 3. Those in red are divisible by 9.

0, 3, 6, 9, 12, 15, 18, 21, 24, 27, 30, 33, 36, 39, 42 . . .

A number is:

**divisible by 3** if the sum of the digits is divisible by 3. *Example:* 261 ÷ 3 = 87

2 + 6 + 1 = 9
9 ÷ 3 = 3

**divisible by 9** if the sum of the digits is divisible by 9. *Example:* 396 ÷ 9 = 44

**D.** To be divisible by 6 a number must be divisible by 2 *and* by 3. Therefore, a number is:

**divisible by 6** if its ones digit is 0, 2, 4, 6, or 8 *and* the sum of its digits is divisible by 3. *Example:* 726 ÷ 6 = 121

**E.** A number is **divisible by 4** if the 2-digit number formed by its tens and ones digits is divisible by 4. *Example:* 648 ÷ 4 = 162

A number is **divisible by 8** if the 3-digit number formed by its hundreds, tens, and ones digits is divisible by 8. *Example:* 31,112 ÷ 8 = 3,889

### CLASS EXERCISES

*Tell whether the number is divisible by 2, 3, 5, or 10. Check by dividing.*

**1.** 625 **2.** 4,280 **3.** 166 **4.** 825 **5.** 1,008

*Tell whether the number is divisible by 4, 6, 8, or 9. Check by dividing.*

**6.** 426 **7.** 5,656 **8.** 9,486 **9.** 88,888 **10.** 129,456

## EXERCISES

*Tell whether the number is divisible by 2, 3, 5, or 10.*

**1.** 36 **2.** 100 **3.** 99 **4.** 135 **5.** 144 **6.** 150

**7.** 54 **8.** 32,424 **9.** 10,500 **10.** 2,505 **11.** 4,105 **12.** 31,608

**13.** 10,800 **14.** 1,494 **15.** 76,830 **16.** 41,052 **17.** 555,555 **18.** 2,180

*Tell whether the number is divisible by 4, 6, 8, or 9.*

**19.** 963 **20.** 7,832 **21.** 86,664 **22.** 1,980 **23.** 77,884 **24.** 28,408

**25.** 3,444 **26.** 99,810 **27.** 1,720 **28.** 24,516 **29.** 4,448 **30.** 2,008

**31.** 70,488 **32.** 95,319 **33.** 9,476 **34.** 34,848 **35.** 181,827 **36.** 28,144

*Fill in the missing digits to make the numbers divisible by the given number. (There may be more than one answer.)*

**37.** 7,894,6■8: divisible by 8.

**38.** 12■,519: divisible by 3 and 9.

★ **39.** 467,76■: divisible by 3 and 5.

★ **40.** 1■5,24■: divisible by 6 and 10.

## PROBLEMS

*Fresh Vegetable Preserves, Inc., packs cans in cartons of 6, 8, or 9 cans. For each order, determine what sizes of cartons could be used.*

**41.** 6,072 cans of corn

**42.** 3,402 cans of peas

**43.** 5,643 cans of beets

★ **44.** 5,256 cans of tomatoes

## THINK!

### Number Patterns

439,756 ← Divide sum of digits by 9, record remainder.

+258,417 ← Divide sum of digits by 9, record remainder.

■■■,■■■ ← Divide sum of digits by 9, record remainder.

What relationship do you find among these three remainders?
Try other sums.
How can this method be used as a "rough" check of addition exercises?
Find a similar method for multiplication. Make up your own example.

**1.** 2, 3 **13.** 2, 3, 5, 10 **19.** 9

Homework page 468

# 4-4 Least Common Multiple (LCM)

**A.** To find a **multiple** of a number, multiply the number by a whole number.

Zero is a multiple of every number. $0 \times n = 0$

The ten smallest **non-zero multiples** of 12 and 15 are shown below.

| Whole number $n$ | 1 | 2 | 3 | 4 | 5 | 6 | 7 | 8 | 9 | 10 |
|---|---|---|---|---|---|---|---|---|---|---|
| Multiples of 12 $n \cdot 12$ | 12 | 24 | 36 | 48 | 60 | 72 | 84 | 96 | 108 | 120 |
| Multiples of 15 $n \cdot 15$ | 15 | 30 | 45 | 60 | 75 | 90 | 105 | 120 | 135 | 150 |

**B.** A number that is a multiple of each of two numbers is a **common multiple** of these numbers.

From the table in A, 60 and 120 are non-zero common multiples of 12 and 15.

The smallest non-zero common multiple of two numbers is their **least common multiple (LCM).**
60 is the smallest non-zero common multiple of 12 and 15.
60 is the least common multiple of 12 and 15.

**C.** **To find the least common multiple (LCM) of two numbers, divide the multiples of the larger number by the smaller number until you get a remainder of 0.**

Find the least common multiple of 6 and 14.

$6\overline{)14}$ = 2 R2 ← Multiples of 14: 14, 28, 42, . . . Start with the smallest.

$6\overline{)28}$ = 4 R4

$6\overline{)42}$ = 7 R0

$7 \times 6 = 42$
42 is a multiple of 6.
42 is the LCM of 6 and 14.

## CLASS EXERCISES

*List the five smallest non-zero multiples.*

**1.** 7 **2.** 11 **3.** 44 **4.** 35 **5.** 27 **6.** 32

*Find the least common multiple (LCM).*

**7.** 5 and 15 **8.** 12 and 16 **9.** 45 and 36 **10.** 7 and 28

## EXERCISES

*List the five smallest non-zero multiples.*

**1.** 16 **2.** 31 **3.** 15 **4.** 41 **5.** 52 **6.** 22

**7.** 12 **8.** 26 **9.** 45 **10.** 39 **11.** 51 **12.** 13

**13.** 23 **14.** 33 **15.** 56 **16.** 75 **17.** 82 **18.** 61

*Find the least common multiple (LCM).*

**19.** 6 and 9 **20.** 3 and 5 **21.** 4 and 18 **22.** 8 and 20

**23.** 24 and 8 **24.** 25 and 20 **25.** 10 and 14 **26.** 15 and 8

**27.** 30 and 36 **28.** 16 and 15 **29.** 8 and 18 **30.** 9 and 24

★**31.** 6, 10, and 15 ★**32.** 8, 14, and 56 ★**33.** 7, 9, and 10

*Find the GCF and the LCM of each pair of numbers.*

**34.** 6 and 8 **35.** 10 and 30 **36.** 8 and 9 **37.** 7 and 21

## PROBLEMS

★**38.** A jeweler designed bead necklaces in three lengths: 35 beads, 56 beads, and 70 beads. Before she had decided which length to make, the bead salesperson called for her order. What is the least number of beads the jeweler should order so that she will have no beads left over, no matter which length necklace she finally decides to make?

### Visual Reasoning

*Draw the missing figures for I, II, III, and IV.*

**1.** 16, 32, 48, 64, 80 **19.** 18

Homework page 468

# 4-5 Prime and Composite Numbers

**A.** A **prime number** is a whole number that has exactly two factors: 1 and the number itself. The twelve smallest prime numbers are:

2, 3, 5, 7, 11, 13, 17, 19, 23, 29, 31, and 37.

**B.** **Composite numbers** are whole numbers that have more than two whole number factors. The ten smallest composite numbers and their factors are shown in the table.

| composite number | factors |
|---|---|
| 4 | 1, 2, 4 |
| 6 | 1, 2, 3, 6 |
| 8 | 1, 2, 4, 8 |
| 9 | 1, 3, 9 |
| 10 | 1, 2, 5, 10 |
| 12 | 1, 2, 3, 4, 6, 12 |
| 14 | 1, 2, 7, 14 |
| 15 | 1, 3, 5, 15 |
| 16 | 1, 2, 4, 8, 16 |
| 18 | 1, 2, 3, 6, 9, 18 |

Every **even number** greater than 2 is a composite number. Even numbers greater than 2 have at least three factors: 1, 2, and the number itself.

Many **odd numbers** are also composite numbers.

**C.** The number 1 has only *one* factor ($1 \times 1 = 1$). It is neither prime nor composite.

Only non-zero numbers are called prime or composite, so 0 is neither prime nor composite.

**D.** Determine if 41 is a prime number or a composite number. Use division to find the factors of 41. Start with 2 and try all numbers until you get a quotient less than or equal to the divisor.

$$2\overline{)41} = 20 \text{ R1} \quad 3\overline{)41} = 13 \text{ R2} \quad 4\overline{)41} = 10 \text{ R1} \quad 5\overline{)41} = 8 \text{ R1} \quad 6\overline{)41} = 6 \text{ R5} \quad 7\overline{)41} = 5 \text{ R6}$$

$5 < 7$ Stop!

None of the divisors tried is a factor of 41.
The only factors of 41 are 1 and 41. 41 is a prime number.

## CLASS EXERCISES

*Determine which are prime and which are composite numbers.*

**1.** 43 **2.** 51 **3.** 59 **4.** 61 **5.** 69 **6.** 71

## EXERCISES

*Determine which are prime and which are composite numbers.*

| | | | | | |
|---|---|---|---|---|---|
| **1.** 39 | **2.** 47 | **3.** 49 | **4.** 53 | **5.** 57 | **6.** 63 |
| **7.** 67 | **8.** 70 | **9.** 73 | **10.** 75 | **11.** 79 | **12.** 81 |
| **13.** 87 | **14.** 89 | **15.** 92 | **16.** 97 | **17.** 101 | **18.** 103 |
| **19.** 105 | **20.** 106 | **21.** 109 | **22.** 111 | **23.** 113 | **24.** 115 |
| **25.** 119 | **26.** 121 | **27.** 124 | **28.** 127 | **29.** 129 | **30.** 131 |
| **31.** 139 | **32.** 149 | **33.** 153 | **34.** 163 | **35.** 167 | **36.** 173 |

★**37.** Name the prime numbers between 1 and 50.

★**38.** Name the prime numbers between 50 and 100.

★**39.** Name two consecutive numbers that are prime numbers.

★**40.** Name three consecutive odd prime numbers.

★**41.** List all of the **prime twins** (pairs of prime numbers that differ by 2) less than 100.

## PROBLEMS

A toy dealer can package 12 cubic blocks of the same size in boxes with 4 different shapes:

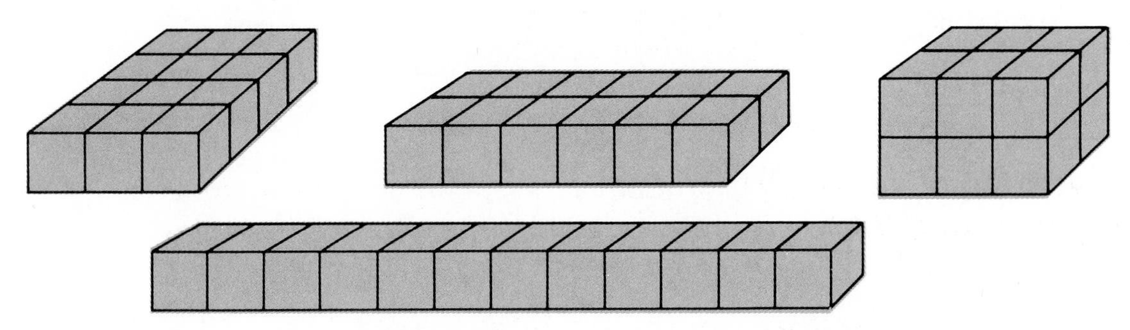

Draw the different shaped boxes that the toy dealer could use to package these numbers of cubic blocks.

**42.** 7 **43.** 8 **44.** 9 **45.** 16 **46.** 18

## THINK!

### Divisibility

How many four-digit numbers which contain a 5, 4, 3, and 0 are divisible by 3?

1. composite 31. prime

Homework page 469

# 4-6 Prime Factorization

**A.** Every composite number is a product of prime numbers. This product is the **prime factorization** of the number.

| Number | Prime factorization |
|---|---|
| 12 | $2 \times 2 \times 3 = 2^2 \times 3$ |
| 32 | $2 \times 2 \times 2 \times 2 \times 2 = 2^5$ |
| 45 | $3 \times 3 \times 5 = 3^2 \times 5$ |
| 105 | $3 \times 5 \times 7$ |

**B.** Find the prime factorization of 2,156. Start with a list of prime numbers. Use them in order as divisors. Use divisibility tests for 2, 3, and 5.

Prime numbers: 2, 3, 5, 7, 11, 13, 17, . . .

Try 2. 2,156 is divisible by 2.

$2{,}156 \div 2 = 1{,}078$ 2 is a factor. $2{,}156 = 2 \times 1{,}078$

Work with 1,078. Try 2 again. 1,078 is divisible by 2.

$1{,}078 \div 2 = 539$ 2 is a factor again. $2{,}156 = 2 \times 2 \times 539$

Work with 539. Try 2 again. 539 is *not* divisible by 2.

Try 3. 539 is not divisible by 3.

Try 5. 539 is not divisible by 5.

Try 7. $7\overline{)539}$ = 77 R0 7 is a factor. $2{,}156 = 2 \times 2 \times 7 \times 77$

Work with 77. Try 7 again.

$7\overline{)77}$ = 11 R0 7 is a factor again. $2{,}156 = 2 \times 2 \times 7 \times 7 \times 11$

Prime. Stop!

The prime factorization of 2,156 is $2^2 \times 7^2 \times 11$.

**C.** You can also use a factor tree to find the prime factorization of a number.

Find the prime factorization of 260.
Start with any two factors. Continue until all branches end with prime numbers.

260
26 × 10
2 × 13 × 2 × 5

The prime factorization of 260 is $2^2 \times 5 \times 13$.

## CLASS EXERCISES

*Write **P** for each prime number. Find the prime factorization of each composite number. Use exponents.*

**1.** 80 **2.** 126 **3.** 512 **4.** 111 **5.** 149 **6.** 441 **7.** 1,000

*Use a factor tree to find the prime factorization of each number.*

**8.** 25 **9.** 78 **10.** 121 **11.** 150 **12.** 200

## EXERCISES

*Write **P** for each prime number. Find the prime factorization of each composite number. Use exponents.*

**1.** 35 **2.** 57 **3.** 16 **4.** 72 **5.** 96 **6.** 81

**7.** 71 **8.** 45 **9.** 75 **10.** 100 **11.** 216 **12.** 243

**13.** 91 **14.** 85 **15.** 102 **16.** 133 **17.** 341 **18.** 99

**19.** 225 **20.** 135 **21.** 147 **22.** 435 **23.** 151 **24.** 343

**25.** 228 **26.** 253 **27.** 336 **28.** 157 **29.** 161 **30.** 90

*Use a factor tree to find the prime factorization of each number.*

**31.** 888 **32.** 390 **33.** 378 **34.** 282 **35.** 160 **36.** 218

**37.** 409 **38.** 222 **39.** 375 **40.** 303 ★**41.** 10,000 ★**42.** 1,024

*Use two different factor trees for each number to find the prime factorization.*

★**43.** 552 ★**44.** 144 ★**45.** 308 ★**46.** 270

*Use a calculator to find the prime factorization of each number.*

**47.** 18,183 **48.** 23,368 **49.** 384,408 **50.** 111,222 **51.** 77,832

## THINK!

### Make a Table

A carpenter makes three-legged tables and four-legged chairs. One day, the carpenter counted that 41 legs had been used for the day's completed furniture. How many tables and chairs were made that day?

1. 5 × 7 7. P



Homework page 469

# 4-7 Using Prime Factorization to Find GCF and LCM

**A.** You can list all factors of two numbers to find their GCF (greatest common factor). With large numbers it is easier to use their prime factorizations. Find the GCF of 1,500 and 350.

**Step 1** Find the prime factorizations of both numbers.

$1{,}500 = 2^2 \times 3 \times 5^3$ $\quad 350 = 2 \times 5^2 \times 7$

**Step 2** Find the prime factors common to these numbers.

$1{,}500 = 2 \times 2 \times 3 \times 5 \times 5 \times 5$

$350 = 2 \times 5 \times 5 \times 7$

**Step 3** Multiply the common prime factors. $2 \times 5 \times 5 = 50$

The GCF of 1,500 and 350 is 50.

**B.** To find the LCM (least common multiple) of two numbers, you can use their prime factorizations. Find the LCM of 126 and 210.

**Step 1** Find the prime factorizations of the numbers.

$126 = 2 \times 3^2 \times 7$ $\quad 210 = 2 \times 3 \times 5 \times 7$

**Step 2** Multiply to find the *smallest* product. Include the common prime factors only once.

$126 = 2 \times 3 \times 3 \times 7$

$210 = 2 \times 3 \times 5 \times 7$

$= 2 \times 3 \times 3 \times 5 \times 7 = 630$

The LCM of 126 and 210 is 630.

**C.** You can find the GCF and LCM of three or more numbers. Find the GCF and LCM of 30, 72, and 66. Find the prime factorizations of the three numbers.

$30 = 2 \times 3 \times 5$

$72 = 2 \times 2 \times 2 \times 3 \times 3$

$66 = 2 \times 3 \times 11$

*To find the GCF:*
Find the common prime factors and multiply.
*Common prime factors:* 2 and 3

$GCF = 2 \times 3$
$= 6$

*To find the LCM:*
Multiply the prime factors, but include common factors only once.

$LCM = 2 \times 2 \times 2 \times 3 \times 3 \times 5 \times 11$
$= 3{,}960$

## CLASS EXERCISES

*Use prime factorization to find the GCF of the numbers.*

**1.** 84; 24 **2.** 54; 27 **3.** 78; 95 **4.** 18; 30; 42

*Use prime factorization to find the LCM of the numbers.*

**5.** 27; 36 **6.** 30; 48 **7.** 45; 105 **8.** 42; 20; 90

## EXERCISES

*Use prime factorization to find the GCF of the numbers.*

**1.** 48; 80 **2.** 70; 96 **3.** 44; 24 **4.** 200; 216

**5.** 77; 182 **6.** 144; 216 **7.** 175; 300 **8.** 280; 728

**9.** 441; 693 **10.** 325; 426 **11.** 221; 323 **12.** 2,856; 3,060

**13.** 1,653; 2,223 **14.** 42; 56; 84 **15.** 210; 224; 238 **16.** 35; 77; 90

**17.** 91; 182; 455 **18.** 315; 480; 615 ★**19.** 1,260; 5,544; 7,200 ★**20.** 798; 1,045; 1,155

*Use prime factorization to find the LCM of the numbers.*

**21.** 40; 60 **22.** 78; 117 **23.** 210; 315 **24.** 45; 100

**25.** 54; 189 **26.** 70; 175 **27.** 108; 150 **28.** 180; 21

**29.** 72; 225 **30.** 99; 726 **31.** 90; 315 **32.** 39; 104

**33.** 15; 18; 21 **34.** 38; 39; 55 **35.** 63; 105; 135 **36.** 142; 202; 90

**37.** 251; 71; 209 **38.** 99; 121; 495 ★**39.** 513; 247; 1,160 ★**40.** 1,002; 1,023; 762

## PROBLEMS

*Compare the product of the GCF and the LCM with the product of the given numbers.*

**41.** 15 and 21 **42.** 22 and 30

**43.** Can you say the same thing about the product of the GCF and LCM of 3 numbers?

### Number Names

If the value of ADAMS is 3.8 and the value of LINCOLN is 7.9, what is the value of WASHINGTON?

1. 16 9. 63

Homework page 470

# 4-8 Fractions and Equivalent Fractions

**A.** Fractions name parts of objects or sets.

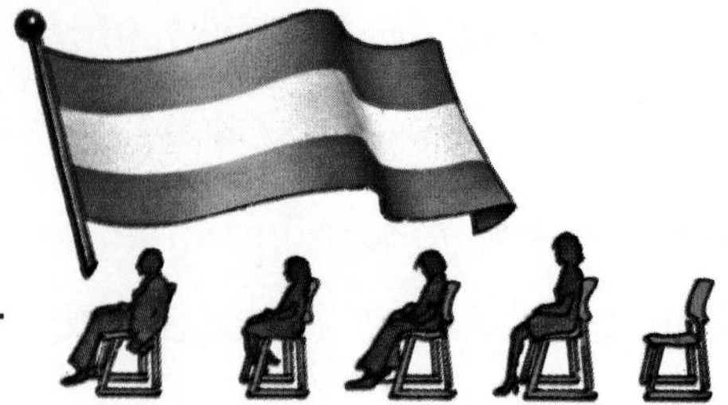

**Numerator** → $\frac{2}{3}$ of the flag is red.
**Denominator** →

$\frac{4}{5}$ of the chairs are filled.

Fractions also name quotients of whole numbers.

A scout cut 5 pieces of equal length from a rope 3 ft long. From the picture, the length of each piece was:

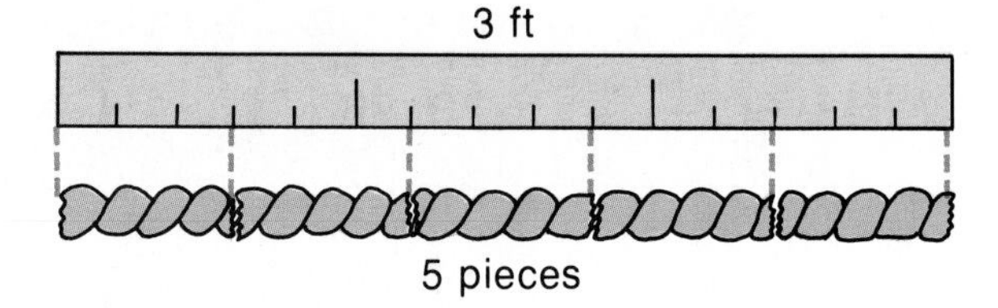


$$3 \div 5 = \frac{3}{5} \text{ ft}$$

Quotients of whole numbers are **fractional numbers.**

**B.** These **fractional number lines,** or **rulers,** show that **equivalent fractions** name the same number.

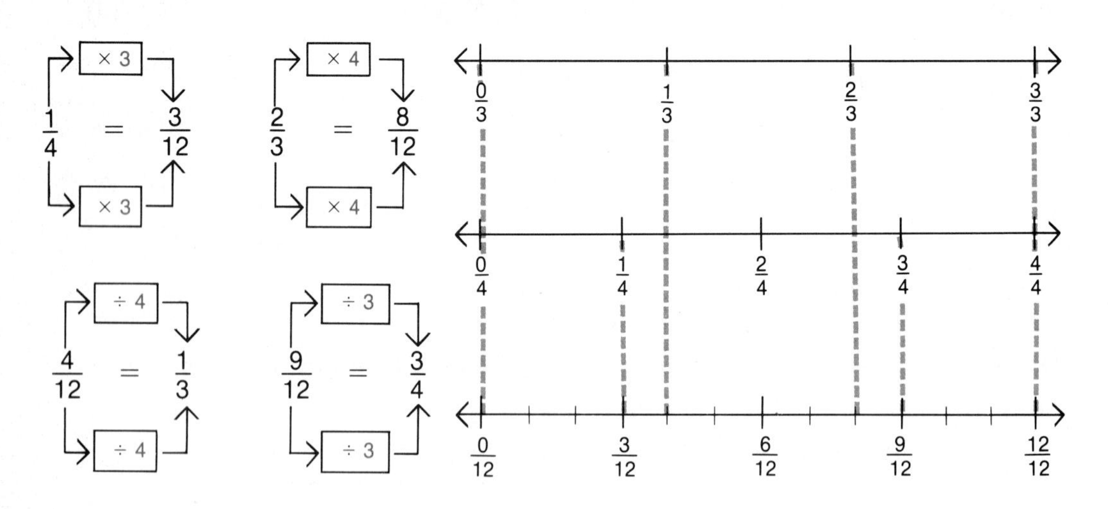


**To find an equivalent fraction, multiply or divide both numerator and denominator by the same non-zero number.**

**C.** A **lowest terms fraction** has a numerator and denominator with 1 as greatest common factor (GCF).

Find the lowest terms fraction equivalent to $\frac{24}{30}$.

The GCF of 24 and 30 is 6.
Divide both 24 and 30 by 6.

$$\frac{24}{30} = \frac{24 \div 6}{30 \div 6} = \frac{4}{5} \leftarrow \text{lowest terms fraction}$$

## CLASS EXERCISES

*Find the missing numbers.*

**1.** $\frac{5}{6} = \frac{\blacksquare}{18}$ **2.** $\frac{15}{20} = \frac{\blacksquare}{4}$ **3.** $\frac{2}{3} = \frac{18}{\blacksquare}$ **4.** $\frac{32}{40} = \frac{\blacksquare}{5}$

*Write the lowest terms fractions.*

**5.** $\frac{16}{24}$ **6.** $\frac{8}{21}$ **7.** $\frac{27}{45}$ **8.** $\frac{9}{36}$ **9.** $\frac{16}{45}$

## EXERCISES

*Find the missing numbers.*

**1.** $\frac{4}{5} = \frac{\blacksquare}{35}$ **2.** $\frac{20}{30} = \frac{\blacksquare}{3}$ **3.** $\frac{2}{9} = \frac{\blacksquare}{36}$ **4.** $\frac{21}{24} = \frac{\blacksquare}{8}$

**5.** $\frac{1}{4} = \frac{5}{\blacksquare}$ **6.** $\frac{18}{27} = \frac{2}{\blacksquare}$ **7.** $\frac{8}{11} = \frac{\blacksquare}{33}$ **8.** $\frac{35}{42} = \frac{\blacksquare}{6}$

**9.** $\frac{7}{12} = \frac{21}{\blacksquare}$ **10.** $\frac{12}{39} = \frac{\blacksquare}{13}$ **11.** $\frac{40}{72} = \frac{\blacksquare}{9}$ **12.** $\frac{3}{8} = \frac{\blacksquare}{56}$

**13.** $\frac{6}{5} = \frac{\blacksquare}{55}$ **14.** $\frac{54}{63} = \frac{6}{\blacksquare}$ **15.** $\frac{81}{90} = \frac{\blacksquare}{10}$ **16.** $\frac{20}{60} = \frac{\blacksquare}{3}$

**17.** $\frac{25}{30} = \frac{5}{\blacksquare}$ **18.** $\frac{48}{90} = \frac{\blacksquare}{15}$ **19.** $\frac{5}{17} = \frac{\blacksquare}{102}$ **20.** $\frac{625}{1{,}000} = \frac{\blacksquare}{8}$

*Write the lowest terms fractions.*

**21.** $\frac{12}{32}$ **22.** $\frac{8}{20}$ **23.** $\frac{15}{18}$ **24.** $\frac{36}{48}$ **25.** $\frac{22}{33}$

**26.** $\frac{16}{35}$ **27.** $\frac{12}{18}$ **28.** $\frac{13}{52}$ **29.** $\frac{51}{34}$ **30.** $\frac{17}{18}$

**31.** $\frac{24}{36}$ **32.** $\frac{8}{18}$ **33.** $\frac{20}{35}$ **34.** $\frac{15}{51}$ **35.** $\frac{30}{34}$

**36.** $\frac{30}{35}$ **37.** $\frac{30}{36}$ **38.** $\frac{21}{77}$ ★ **39.** $\frac{253}{299}$ ★ **40.** $\frac{322}{391}$

## PROBLEMS

★ **41.** The numerator of the lowest terms fraction equivalent to $\frac{45}{60}$ is 21 less than a number. Find the number.

★ **42.** The sum of twice a number and 12 is the denominator of the lowest term fraction equivalent to $\frac{36}{64}$. Find the number.

## THINK!

### Stamp Arrangements

Here are two ways in which 4 stamps may be attached. How many ways are there in all? Draw them.

1. 28 21. $\frac{3}{8}$

Homework page 470

# 4-9 Fractions, Mixed Numerals, and Standard Numerals

**A.** You can use a number line to compare numbers.
On the number line below you can see that:

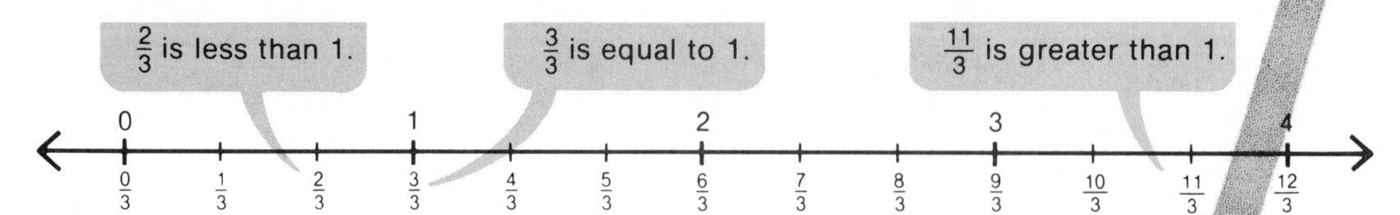


To decide whether a fraction names a number less than 1, equal to 1, or greater than 1, compare the numerator and denominator.

$2 < 3$, so $\frac{2}{3}$ is less than 1.

$3 = 3$, so $\frac{3}{3}$ is equal to 1.

$11 > 3$, so $\frac{11}{3}$ is greater than 1.

**B.** To find a **mixed numeral** or a **standard numeral** equivalent to a fraction, divide.

**Example 1**

$\frac{8}{5} = 8 \div 5 = 1\frac{3}{5}$

mixed numeral

**Example 2**

$\frac{15}{3} = 15 \div 3 = 5$

**Example 3**

$\frac{7}{7} = 7 \div 7 = 1$

standard numerals

**C.** A **lowest terms mixed numeral** contains a standard numeral and a lowest terms fraction less than 1.

Find the lowest terms mixed numeral for $7\frac{6}{24}$.

$$7\frac{6}{24} = 7\frac{1}{4}$$

> The **simplest form** equivalent to a fraction is a lowest terms fraction, a lowest terms mixed numeral, or a standard numeral.

**D.** To **simplify** a fraction means to replace it by its simplest form.

Simplify $\frac{15}{20}$, $\frac{46}{8}$, and $\frac{18}{6}$.

$\frac{15}{20} = \frac{3}{4}$ $\quad$ $\frac{46}{8} = 5\frac{6}{8} = 5\frac{3}{4}$ $\quad$ $\frac{18}{6} = 3$

## CLASS EXERCISES

*Find the lowest terms mixed numeral or standard numeral for each.*

**1.** $\frac{17}{3}$ **2.** $\frac{22}{7}$ **3.** $\frac{42}{7}$ **4.** $\frac{41}{6}$ **5.** $\frac{19}{2}$ **6.** $\frac{51}{3}$

*Tell whether each is less than 1, greater than 1, or equal to 1. Simplify.*

**7.** $\frac{19}{3}$ **8.** $\frac{20}{20}$ **9.** $\frac{23}{21}$ **10.** $\frac{7}{9}$ **11.** $\frac{33}{51}$ **12.** $\frac{9}{9}$

## EXERCISES

*Find the lowest terms mixed numeral or standard numeral for each.*

**1.** $\frac{23}{5}$ **2.** $\frac{25}{25}$ **3.** $\frac{43}{15}$ **4.** $\frac{93}{10}$ **5.** $\frac{52}{9}$ **6.** $\frac{48}{5}$

**7.** $\frac{97}{8}$ **8.** $\frac{20}{7}$ **9.** $\frac{133}{8}$ **10.** $\frac{82}{25}$ **11.** $\frac{303}{50}$ **12.** $\frac{97}{20}$

**13.** $\frac{267}{89}$ **14.** $\frac{397}{100}$ **15.** $\frac{57}{32}$ **16.** $\frac{167}{64}$ **17.** $\frac{6{,}217}{1{,}000}$ **18.** $\frac{0}{2{,}001}$

*Simplify.*

**19.** $\frac{102}{100}$ **20.** $\frac{25}{45}$ **21.** $\frac{15}{31}$ **22.** $\frac{40}{11}$ **23.** $\frac{8}{8}$ **24.** $\frac{17}{34}$

**25.** $\frac{51}{94}$ **26.** $\frac{21}{21}$ **27.** $\frac{66}{65}$ **28.** $\frac{36}{12}$ **29.** $\frac{84}{18}$ **30.** $\frac{125}{11}$

**31.** $\frac{144}{24}$ **32.** $\frac{36}{432}$ **33.** $\frac{255}{34}$ **34.** $\frac{1{,}173}{51}$ ★**35.** $\frac{514}{7{,}710}$ ★**36.** $\frac{0}{1{,}001}$

## PROBLEMS

**37.** Spools of thread are packed 12 in each box. A tailor used 8 spools in one week. What part of the box was used? What part of the box was not used?

**38.** A dressmaker cut 215 feet of ribbon into 30 pieces of equal length. How long is each piece?

## MIXED REVIEW

*What does the digit 3 mean in each decimal?*

**1.** 4.0356 **2.** .000293 **3.** .001346 **4.** 87.302 **5.** .04053

*Add, subtract, multiply, or divide.*

**6.** $30.974 + .835$ **7.** $8.652 \times .09$ **8.** $71 - .942$ **9.** $.0386 \times .15$ **10.** $4.6\overline{).7268}$

*Round to the nearest hundredth; to the nearest one.*

**11.** 7.09561 **12.** 3.9847 **13.** .86342 **14.** 19.9976 **15.** .742985

1\. $4\frac{3}{5}$ 19. $1\frac{1}{50}$

Homework page 471

# 4-10 Least Common Denominator

If you are given two or more fractions, you can find fractions with a **common denominator** equivalent to them.

**A.** A common denominator for two or more fractions is a common multiple of their denominators.

**Example 1**
Find fractions with a common denominator equivalent to $\frac{3}{8}$ and $\frac{11}{24}$.

Look at the denominators. 24 is a multiple of 8, so 24 is a common denominator.

$\frac{3}{8} = \frac{■}{24}$  $\frac{3 \times 3}{8 \times 3} = \frac{9}{24}$

$24 = 8 \times 3$

$\frac{9}{24}$ and $\frac{11}{24}$ have a common denominator.

**Example 2**
Find fractions with a common denominator equivalent to $\frac{1}{2}$, $\frac{2}{3}$, and $\frac{4}{5}$.

**The product of the denominators is always a common denominator.**

$2 \times 3 \times 5 = 30$  so 30 is a common denominator.

$\frac{1}{2} = \frac{■}{30}$  $\frac{2}{3} = \frac{■}{30}$  $\frac{4}{5} = \frac{■}{30}$

$\frac{1}{2} = \frac{15}{30}$  $\frac{2}{3} = \frac{20}{30}$  $\frac{4}{5} = \frac{24}{30}$

$\frac{15}{30}$, $\frac{20}{30}$, and $\frac{24}{30}$ have a common denominator.

**B.** The **least common denominator** (LCD) for two or more fractions is the least common multiple of their denominators.

Find fractions with a LCD equivalent to $\frac{2}{9}$, $\frac{4}{11}$, and $\frac{5}{33}$.

The LCM of 9, 11, and 33 is 99.
99 is the LCD.

$\frac{2}{9} = \frac{2 \times 11}{9 \times 11} = \frac{22}{99}$  $\frac{4}{11} = \frac{4 \times 9}{11 \times 9} = \frac{36}{99}$  $\frac{5}{33} = \frac{5 \times 3}{33 \times 3} = \frac{15}{99}$

$\frac{22}{99}$, $\frac{36}{99}$, and $\frac{15}{99}$ are equivalent to $\frac{2}{9}$, $\frac{4}{11}$, and $\frac{5}{33}$.

## CLASS EXERCISES

*Find equivalent fractions with the LCD.*

1. $\frac{5}{6}, \frac{7}{10}$
2. $\frac{5}{4}, \frac{4}{5}$
3. $\frac{11}{15}, \frac{17}{12}$
4. $\frac{3}{5}, \frac{13}{20}$

## EXERCISES

*Find equivalent fractions with the LCD.*

1. $\frac{1}{6}, \frac{2}{9}$
2. $\frac{4}{3}, \frac{3}{5}$
3. $\frac{5}{18}, \frac{3}{4}$
4. $\frac{17}{20}, \frac{13}{8}$
5. $\frac{5}{24}, \frac{3}{8}$
6. $\frac{7}{15}, \frac{4}{9}$
7. $\frac{1}{25}, \frac{1}{20}$
8. $\frac{19}{10}, \frac{23}{14}$
9. $\frac{4}{15}, \frac{7}{20}$
10. $\frac{7}{4}, \frac{7}{16}$
11. $\frac{14}{15}, \frac{7}{8}$
12. $\frac{11}{24}, \frac{17}{30}$
13. $\frac{7}{6}, \frac{8}{5}$
14. $\frac{5}{8}, \frac{11}{18}$
15. $\frac{1}{9}, \frac{5}{24}$
16. $\frac{9}{16}, \frac{8}{15}$
17. $\frac{13}{40}, \frac{7}{20}$
18. $\frac{9}{25}, \frac{1}{4}$
19. $\frac{25}{48}, \frac{3}{288}$

★20. $\frac{7}{18}, \frac{4}{9}, \frac{5}{12}$

★21. $\frac{4}{30}, \frac{1}{40}, \frac{2}{50}$

★22. $\frac{2}{121}, \frac{1}{55}, \frac{3}{11}$

★23. $\frac{7}{130}, \frac{2}{65}, \frac{9}{10}$

★24. $\frac{5}{27}, \frac{6}{36}, \frac{7}{54}$

## PROBLEMS

★25. An automobile dealer received $\frac{1}{8}$ of the cars ordered on Monday and $\frac{5}{6}$ on Wednesday. What is the fewest number of cars that could have been ordered? How many were received on Monday? on Wednesday?

★26. Car salespeople were scheduled to work on different days. $\frac{1}{3}$ of the staff worked on Monday, Wednesday, and Friday. $\frac{4}{7}$ of the staff worked on Tuesday, Thursday, and Saturday. The rest of the staff worked Monday to Friday. What is the least number of people that could be on the sales staff?

## THINK!

### Lengths of Paths

What is the length of the red path if the small squares are .5 cm on each side?

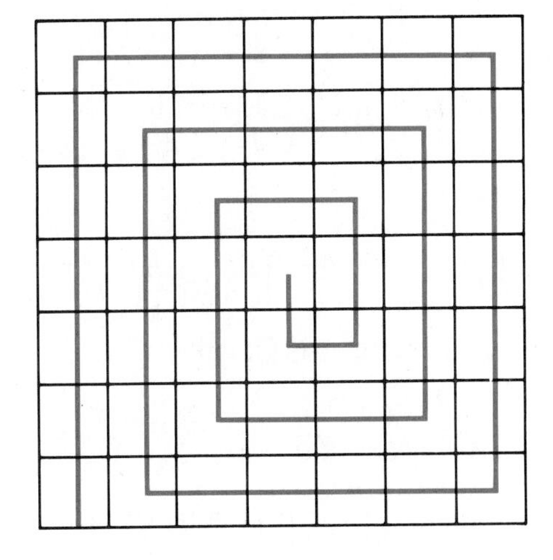

1. $\frac{3}{18}, \frac{4}{18}$ 13. $\frac{35}{30}, \frac{48}{30}$

Homework page 471

# 4-11 Comparing with Fractions

**A.** Most of the earth's surface is covered with water. The Pacific Ocean forms $\frac{3}{8}$ of the earth's water surface and the Indian Ocean forms $\frac{1}{8}$. Which ocean is larger?

$3 > 1 \quad \text{so } \frac{3}{8} > \frac{1}{8}$

The Pacific Ocean is larger.

**To compare with fractions having a common denominator, compare the numerators.**

**B.** Compare $\frac{2}{3}$ and $\frac{7}{12}$.

**Step 1** Find equivalent fractions with a common denominator.
Use 12 as the LCD. $\frac{2}{3} = \frac{■}{12}$ $\qquad \frac{2 \times 4}{3 \times 4} = \frac{8}{12}$

**Step 2** Compare numerators.

$8 > 7 \quad \text{so } \frac{8}{12} > \frac{7}{12} \rightarrow \frac{2}{3} > \frac{7}{12}$ $\qquad 7 < 8 \quad \text{so } \frac{7}{12} < \frac{8}{12} \rightarrow \frac{7}{12} < \frac{2}{3}$

**C.** Write >, < or = for ●. $\quad \frac{5}{8}$ ● $\frac{5}{6}$

24 is the LCD.

$\frac{5}{8} = \frac{■}{24} \qquad \frac{5 \times 3}{8 \times 3} = \frac{15}{24} \qquad \frac{5}{6} = \frac{■}{24} \qquad \frac{5 \times 4}{6 \times 4} = \frac{20}{24}$

$15 < 20 \quad \text{so } \frac{15}{24} < \frac{20}{24} \rightarrow \frac{5}{8} < \frac{5}{6}$

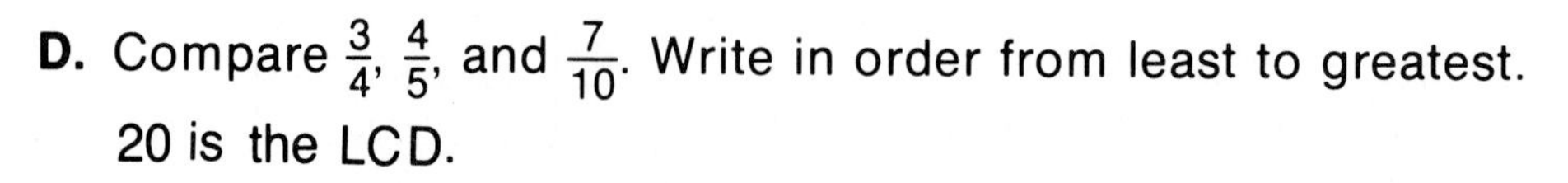

**D.** Compare $\frac{3}{4}$, $\frac{4}{5}$, and $\frac{7}{10}$. Write in order from least to greatest.

20 is the LCD.

$\frac{3}{4} = \frac{■}{20} = \frac{15}{20} \qquad \frac{4}{5} = \frac{■}{20} = \frac{16}{20} \qquad \frac{7}{10} = \frac{■}{20} = \frac{14}{20}$

$\frac{14}{20} < \frac{15}{20} < \frac{16}{20}$ $\qquad$ So $\frac{7}{10} < \frac{3}{4} < \frac{4}{5}$, from least to greatest.

## CLASS EXERCISES

*Write >, < or = for ●.*

1. $\frac{7}{11}$ ● $\frac{3}{11}$
2. $\frac{17}{20}$ ● $\frac{7}{8}$
3. $\frac{2}{3}$ ● $\frac{3}{5}$
4. $\frac{4}{5}$ ● $\frac{5}{4}$
5. $\frac{5}{9}$ ● $\frac{5}{11}$

*List in order, from least to greatest.*

6. $\frac{2}{5}$; $\frac{1}{2}$; $\frac{1}{10}$
7. $\frac{5}{12}$; $\frac{5}{13}$; $\frac{11}{24}$
8. $\frac{4}{9}$; $\frac{1}{8}$; $\frac{7}{15}$

## EXERCISES

*Write >, <, or = for ●.*

1. $\frac{5}{12}$ ● $\frac{7}{12}$
2. $\frac{1}{2}$ ● $\frac{2}{5}$
3. $\frac{9}{10}$ ● $\frac{5}{6}$
4. $\frac{3}{4}$ ● $\frac{11}{12}$
5. $\frac{5}{4}$ ● $\frac{7}{6}$
6. $\frac{7}{20}$ ● $\frac{1}{4}$
7. $\frac{7}{8}$ ● $\frac{5}{6}$
8. $\frac{5}{8}$ ● $\frac{2}{3}$
9. $\frac{5}{12}$ ● $\frac{3}{8}$
10. $\frac{4}{3}$ ● $\frac{9}{10}$
11. $\frac{3}{4}$ ● $\frac{9}{14}$
12. $\frac{7}{4}$ ● $\frac{5}{2}$
13. $\frac{11}{6}$ ● $\frac{16}{9}$
14. $\frac{4}{5}$ ● $\frac{5}{6}$
15. $\frac{13}{16}$ ● $\frac{9}{16}$
16. $\frac{2}{3}$ ● $\frac{3}{4}$
17. $\frac{13}{8}$ ● $\frac{7}{5}$
18. $\frac{3}{2}$ ● $\frac{13}{10}$
19. $\frac{7}{10}$ ● $\frac{5}{8}$
20. $\frac{3}{5}$ ● $\frac{9}{10}$
21. $\frac{10}{9}$ ● $\frac{17}{15}$
22. $\frac{11}{4}$ ● $\frac{9}{4}$
23. $\frac{8}{5}$ ● $\frac{21}{16}$
24. $\frac{18}{25}$ ● $\frac{3}{4}$
25. $\frac{3}{10}$ ● $\frac{4}{15}$
26. $\frac{5}{12}$ ● $\frac{7}{16}$
27. $\frac{3}{25}$ ● $\frac{13}{100}$
28. $\frac{16}{9}$ ● $\frac{17}{10}$
29. $\frac{11}{20}$ ● $\frac{13}{15}$
30. $\frac{5}{63}$ ● $\frac{2}{50}$

*List in order, from least to greatest.*

31. $\frac{9}{2}$; $\frac{7}{10}$; $\frac{2}{3}$
32. $\frac{4}{5}$; $\frac{1}{17}$; $\frac{2}{11}$
33. $\frac{5}{7}$; $\frac{5}{24}$; $\frac{7}{8}$
34. $\frac{9}{10}$; $\frac{6}{5}$; $\frac{5}{4}$
35. $\frac{1}{9}$; $\frac{1}{10}$; $\frac{1}{15}$
36. $\frac{3}{5}$; $\frac{5}{17}$; $\frac{2}{9}$

★ 37. $\frac{11}{20}$; $\frac{49}{50}$; $\frac{2}{25}$; $\frac{7}{40}$

★ 38. $\frac{1}{19}$; $\frac{5}{18}$; $\frac{8}{9}$; $\frac{3}{3}$

★ 39. $\frac{21}{7}$; $\frac{8}{15}$; $\frac{75}{63}$; $\frac{22}{45}$

## PROBLEM

★ 40. The gravitational pull of planets varies. If a man visited Mercury, his weight would be $\frac{7}{25}$ of his Earth weight. On Mars his weight would be $\frac{19}{50}$ of his Earth weight. On Venus it would be $\frac{17}{20}$ of his Earth weight. On which planet would he be the heaviest? the lightest?

## THINK!

### Logical Reasoning

A certain substance doubles its size every 5 minutes. At 2:00 P.M. some of this substance was placed in a quart-sized container. At 3:00 P.M. the container was full. At what time did the container hold exactly one pint of the substance?

1. < 16. < 31. $\frac{2}{3}$; $\frac{7}{10}$; $\frac{9}{2}$

Homework page 472

# Problem Solving READ • PLAN • DO • ANSWER • CHECK

## 4-12 Using Equivalent Fractions

**A.** During October, a mountain climber climbed 5,100 meters of Tup Peak in the Andes Mountains. This is $\frac{3}{4}$ of its total height. What is the total height of Tup Peak?

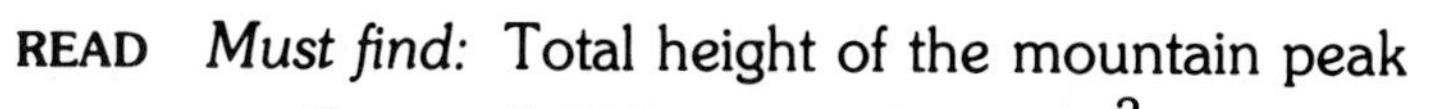

**READ** *Must find:* Total height of the mountain peak

*Know:* 5,100 meters climbed; $\frac{3}{4}$ of height climbed

**PLAN** Write equivalent fractions for the part climbed.

$$\text{Part climbed} = \frac{\text{height climbed}}{\text{total height}}$$

$$\frac{3}{4} = \frac{5{,}100}{\text{total height}}$$

**DO** $\frac{3}{4} = \frac{5{,}100}{\blacksquare}$

5,100 ÷ 3 = 1,700
so 3 × 1,700 = 5,100

$\frac{3 \times 1{,}700}{4 \times 1{,}700} = \frac{5{,}100}{6{,}800}$

**ANSWER** The total height of Tup Peak is 6,800 meters.

**CHECK** $\frac{5{,}100}{6{,}800} = \frac{5{,}100 \div 1{,}700}{6{,}800 \div 1{,}700} = \frac{3}{4}$ ✓

**B.** A construction company built two housing developments. Of the 30 houses in development A, 17 had solar heating systems. In development B, 14 of the 45 houses had solar heating systems. Did a larger part of houses in development A or in development B have solar heating?

*Must find:* Which development had solar heating in a larger part of the houses?

*Know:* $\frac{17}{30}$ of the houses in development A had solar heating.

$\frac{14}{45}$ of the houses in development B had solar heating.

Compare $\frac{17}{30}$ and $\frac{14}{45}$. Use 90 as the LCD.

$\frac{17}{30} = \frac{51}{90}$ and $\frac{14}{45} = \frac{28}{90}$

$\frac{51}{90} > \frac{28}{90}$ So $\frac{17}{30} > \frac{14}{45}$

A larger part of the houses in development A had solar heating.

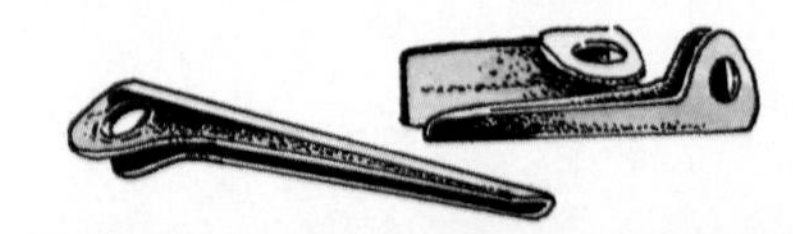

## CLASS EXERCISES

1. During a blood donor drive 78 of the employees of Continental Paper Company pledged to give blood. This was $\frac{3}{5}$ of the total number of employees. How many people were employed by the Continental Paper Company?

2. At Kennedy High School, 88 of the 224 entering freshmen elected to take German. At Jefferson High School, 68 of the 140 freshmen chose to study German. In which freshman class did a larger part of the students take German?

## PROBLEMS

1. The Brown family spent \$130 of their \$390 weekly income on food. The Stein family spent \$110 of their \$260 weekly income on food. Which family spent the greater part of their income on food?

2. Laurey decided to take a bicycle trip from New York to Pittsburgh. After bicycling 154 miles, which was $\frac{2}{5}$ of the distance, her bicycle broke down. How far is it from New York to Pittsburgh?

3. While playing a game of golf, Sue lost 11 of her 27 golf balls and Ed lost 9 of his 21 golf balls. Sue claimed to have lost a larger part of her golf balls. Was she correct?

4. In July, Jack's air conditioner used 400 kilowatt-hours of electricity. This was $\frac{4}{7}$ of his total usage for the month. How many kilowatt-hours of electricity did Jack use during July?

★ 5. During a 400-mile drive from Los Angeles to San Francisco, a small car used 10 gallons, or $\frac{5}{8}$ of a full tank of gasoline. How many gallons does the gasoline tank of the car hold? How many miles can this car travel on a full tank?

★ 6. Doug dieted for two months. At the end of one month he had lost 25 lb, which was $\frac{1}{10}$ of his weight at the start of the diet. How much did he weigh at the start of his diet? If he lost 20 lb during the second month, how much did he weigh at the end of the diet?

## ON YOUR OWN

**Visual Reasoning**

How can the figures at right be arranged to show a logical order?

Homework page 472

## Algorithms and Flowcharts

Below is an algorithm for finding the sale price of any item. It is given both as a **list of numbered steps** and as a **flowchart.** (The steps are numbered by tens so more can be added.)

10 Get the regular price from the price tag.
20 Decide what **discount rate** to use.
30 Multiply the discount rate (decimal form) by the regular price.
40 Round the **discount** (product) to the nearest cent.
50 Subtract the discount from the regular price to find the sale price.
60 Record the sale price.
70 If there is another sale price to find, go to step 10. Otherwise, stop.

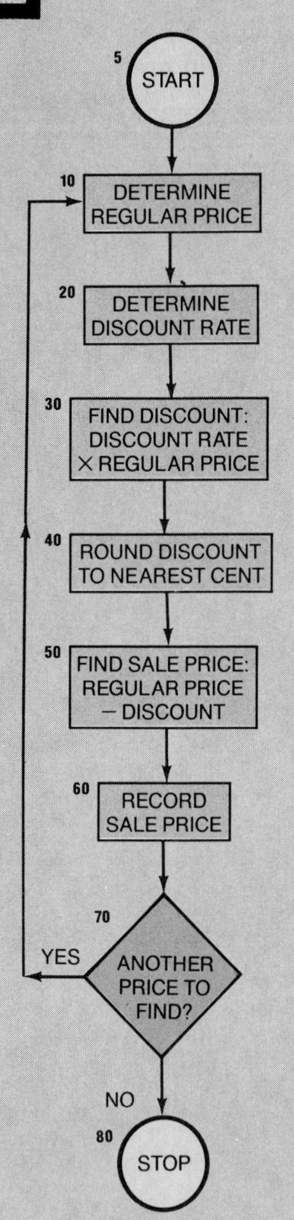


In a flowchart, instructions are given in different-shaped boxes, joined by arrows.

| Shape | Name of Box | Meaning |
|---|---|---|
| circle | **alert** | start or stop |
| rectangle | **instruction** | do something |
| diamond | **decision** | answer yes or no and follow that arrow |

**1.** Use the algorithm to find the sale price:
regular price: \$49.50 discount rate: .10

**2.** Which boxes in the flowchart are
**a.** alert boxes? **b.** decision boxes? **c.** instruction boxes?

**3.** One step from the list has been split into two boxes in the flowchart. Give the number of the step in the list and the numbers of the matching boxes in the flowchart.

**4.** Discount rates are often given as percents. Add this step before step 30 of the algorithm above: Put the discount rate in decimal form. What step number can you use? What shape of box should be added to the flowchart for the new step?

# Problem Solving Strategy

READ PLAN DO • ANSWER • CHECK

## Mixed Strategies

| Logical Reasoning | Logical Reasoning with Clues |
| --- | --- |
| Draw a Diagram | Multiple-Step Problems |

**1.** A truck driver left the depot and drove west for 3 hours at 40 miles per hour. The driver stopped for lunch, then continued driving north for 2 hours at 50 miles per hour. The driver made a delivery, then drove east 65 miles, south 60 miles, then east again for 55 miles. In what direction must the driver go to get back to the depot? If the driver is going 40 miles per hour, how long will it take?

**2.** Mr. Lopez, Ms. Chan, Mrs. Nevins, and Mr. Agretti are managers at the Supertown Market. Each manages a different department: bakery, dairy, frozen foods, and produce, but not necessarily in that order. From the clues below, find each person's department.

a. Mrs. Nevins does not manage the bakery or the dairy.
b. Mr. Agretti returned a shipment of spoiled melons today.
c. Mr. Lopez goes to lunch at the same time as the bakery manager.

**3.** Three men on an island had a pile of bananas. At night one of the men came to the pile of bananas and, finding that there was just one more banana than could be divided exactly by 3, ate the extra banana and took his third of the rest. Later, the second man went to the banana pile. He also found just one too many to be divided evenly by 3, so he ate the extra and took his third of the remainder. Finally the third man awoke, went to the banana pile, ate one banana and took his third of the bananas that remained. In the morning all three men went to the pile, found one banana too many which they cut into 3 pieces, and divided the rest evenly. What is the least number of bananas with which this can be done?

**4.** The first five students who finished the walkathon were Joel, Marta, Hal, Kevin, and Sylvia, but not necessarily in that order. Each student wore a different color T-shirt: red, blue, green, yellow, orange. Use the clues below to find the color of each student's shirt and the order in which he or she finished the Walkathon.

a. Marta, in her green shirt, was the third one to cross the finish line.
b. Joel beat the student in the blue shirt by three places and beat Kevin by one.
c. Hal placed fourth, just ahead of the student in the yellow shirt.
d. The winner said he was glad he wore his red shirt.

# Problem Solving Project

READ • PLAN • DO • ANSWER • CHECK

## Computing the Electric Bill

**A.** As an electric appliance operates, it uses energy. A **kilowatt-hour** (kwh) is a unit of measurement for electric energy. When an electric appliance is in use, the amount of electric energy it uses is recorded on a meter in kilowatt-hours.

The power that is needed by an appliance is given in watts. You can usually find the number of watts listed somewhere on the appliance. The following formula can be used to calculate how many kilowatt-hours an appliance in your home or school uses:

| Model No. 417 | |
|---|---|
| Volts | Watts |
| 120 | 15 |

$$\frac{\text{Watts} \times \text{Hours Used}}{1{,}000} = \text{Kilowatt-hours}$$

**Example 1**

A 200-watt light bulb is in use for 8 hours. How many kilowatt-hours are used?

$$\frac{200 \times 8}{1{,}000} = \frac{1{,}600}{1{,}000}$$
$$= 1.6$$

The light bulb used 1.6 kwh.

Complete. Assume a month has 30 days.

| | Appliance | Watts | Average Hours Used Daily | Average Daily kwh | Average Monthly kwh |
|---|---|---|---|---|---|
| 1. | Hair dryer | 900 | 0.5 | | |
| 2. | Toaster | 1,100 | 0.3 | | |
| 3. | Stereo | 280 | 2.5 | | |
| 4. | Vacuum Cleaner | 630 | 1 | | |
| 5. | Electric Clock | 2.5 | 24 | | |
| 6. | Color Television | 95 | 4 | | |

**B.** Electric companies bill their customers by measuring the number of kilowatt-hours of electricity used, and then multiplying this number by the rate per kilowatt-hour.

| Union Electric Company | | | | |
|---|---|---|---|---|
| Reading Date | Meter Previous | Meter Present | Usage Kwh | Current Charges |
| 10/19 | 6118 | 6310 | 192 | $37.48 |

Usage = Meter Present − Meter Previous

An electric company may have a fixed rate per kwh or a rate that varies depending upon how many kwh are used. The table at right gives the rate schedule for one electric company.

| Rate Schedule | |
|---|---|
| First 20 kwh or less | $4.59 |
| Over 20 kwh | $ .1912 per kwh |

**Example 2**

The present meter reading is 8739. The previous meter reading was 8325. Use the given rate schedule to compute the electric bill to the nearest cent.

Usage = 8739 − 8325 = 414 kwh

First 20 kwh = $4.59
Remaining kwh = 414 − 20 = 394
394 × .1912 = 75.33
Total bill = $4.59 + $75.33 = $79.92

*Use the meter readings and the rate schedule above to compute each bill.*

| Meter Previous | **7.** 1296 | **8.** 2337 | **9.** 7690 | **10.** 5614 |
|---|---|---|---|---|
| Meter Present | 2108 | 4111 | 8315 | 5766 |
| Total Bill | | | | |

**ON YOUR OWN**

Take a home energy check. Prepare a chart similar to the one on page 142. List the electric appliances in your home and estimate the average number of hours used daily. Include all lighting fixtures. Calculate the average monthly kilowatt-hours.

# Unit Review

*Write a standard numeral.* *(pages 116–117)*

**1.** $3^3$ **2.** $6^2$ **3.** $5^4$ **4.** $7^0$ **5.** $9^1$

*Simplify.* *(pages 116–117)*

**6.** $2 \cdot 6^2$ **7.** $(2 \cdot 6)^2$ **8.** $5 + 3^2$ **9.** $(5 + 3)^2$ **10.** $5^2 + 3$

*Find the greatest common factor.* *(pages 118–119, 128–129)*

**11.** 21 and 56 **12.** 18 and 64 **13.** 15 and 26 **14.** 24 and 72

**15.** 180 and 336 **16.** 357 and 693 **17.** 1,368 and 1,836 **18.** 969 and 1,196

*Tell whether the number is divisible by 2, 3, 4, 5, 6, 8, 9, or 10.* *(pages 120–121)*

**19.** 1,656 **20.** 1,430 **21.** 638 **22.** 5,115 **23.** 3,599

*Find the least common multiple.* *(pages 122–123, 128–129)*

**24.** 6 and 9 **25.** 15 and 20 **26.** 27 and 54 **27.** 7 and 23

**28.** 44 and 52 **29.** 126 and 132 **30.** 825 and 385 **31.** 273 and 845

*Write P for each prime number. Find the prime factorization of each composite number. Use exponents.* *(pages 126–127)*

**32.** 208 **33.** 891 **34.** 399 **35.** 563 **36.** 2,520

*Write the lowest terms fractions.* *(pages 130–131)*

**37.** $\frac{4}{22}$ **38.** $\frac{16}{64}$ **39.** $\frac{40}{50}$ **40.** $\frac{23}{46}$ **41.** $\frac{14}{30}$

**42.** $\frac{12}{20}$ **43.** $\frac{9}{16}$ **44.** $\frac{15}{26}$ **45.** $\frac{76}{100}$ **46.** $\frac{104}{156}$

*Find the lowest terms mixed numeral or standard numeral.* *(pages 132–133)*

**47.** $\frac{11}{3}$ **48.** $\frac{18}{6}$ **49.** $\frac{37}{5}$ **50.** $\frac{42}{4}$ **51.** $\frac{52}{6}$

*Simplify.* *(pages 132–133)*

**52.** $\frac{16}{56}$ **53.** $\frac{30}{5}$ **54.** $\frac{62}{8}$ **55.** $\frac{16}{27}$ **56.** $\frac{240}{72}$

**57.** $\frac{48}{3}$ **58.** $\frac{14}{52}$ **59.** $\frac{189}{45}$ **60.** $\frac{256}{32}$ **61.** $\frac{46}{4}$

*Find equivalent fractions with the least common denominator.* *(pages 134–135)*

**62.** $\frac{2}{3}$ and $\frac{3}{4}$ **63.** $\frac{1}{2}$ and $\frac{5}{6}$ **64.** $\frac{5}{8}$ and $\frac{7}{12}$ **65.** $\frac{1}{4}$ and $\frac{3}{5}$

**66.** $\frac{1}{8}$ and $\frac{9}{10}$ **67.** $\frac{4}{9}$ and $\frac{7}{36}$ **68.** $\frac{4}{9}$ and $\frac{5}{12}$ **69.** $\frac{7}{20}$ and $\frac{3}{25}$

*Compare. Write >, <, or = for ●.* *(pages 136–137)*

**70.** $\frac{5}{7}$ ● $\frac{3}{7}$ **71.** $\frac{7}{12}$ ● $\frac{5}{8}$ **72.** $\frac{18}{24}$ ● $\frac{3}{4}$ **73.** $\frac{5}{6}$ ● $\frac{5}{9}$

**74.** $\frac{4}{5}$ ● $\frac{5}{8}$ **75.** $\frac{15}{27}$ ● $\frac{5}{9}$ **76.** $\frac{7}{10}$ ● $\frac{3}{4}$ **77.** $\frac{11}{12}$ ● $\frac{13}{16}$

*Find the value of each expression if the value of* x *is 2.* *(pages 116–117)*

**78.** $4x^2$ **79.** $(4x)^2$ **80.** $3x^2 + 2$ **81.** $(3x + 2)^2$

**82.** $7x^2 - 5$ **83.** $(7x - 5)^2$ **84.** $8 + 4x^2$ **85.** $8 + (4x)^2$

*Solve the problems.* *(pages 138–139)*

**86.** Kim has over 100 stamps. She found she could use them to make full pages in her album that holds 18 stamps per page or in her album that holds 12 stamps per page. What is the fewest stamps Kim could have?

**87.** Each box contains 36 stamp albums. A store sold 17 albums from a full box. What part of the box of albums was sold? What part of this box of albums was left?

**88.** Loni has completed $\frac{7}{12}$ of her homework. Jean has completed $\frac{9}{16}$ of her homework. Who has the greater part of her homework completed?

**89.** Tom sold 64 tickets. This was $\frac{2}{3}$ of the total he had promised to sell. How many tickets had he promised to sell in all? How many more must he sell?

# Enrichment

## Numeration Systems

**A.** You can write **expanded forms** for standard numerals. This is an expanded form for 6,032,705:

$6 \times 10^6 + 0 \times 10^5 + 3 \times 10^4 + 2 \times 10^3 + 7 \times 10^2 + 0 \times 10^1 + 5 \times 10^0$

The expanded form shows that the value of each place in a standard numeral is a **power of ten.** For this reason ten is called the **base** of our numeration system.

*Write an expanded form for each standard numeral.*

1. 2,409
2. 581,457
3. 45,003
4. 9,750,240
5. 311,311
6. 9,562
7. 7,235,810
8. 4,065,370

**B.** In our base ten system, the ten digits 0, 1, 2, 3, 4, 5, 6, 7, 8, and 9 are used to form all numerals. In a **base seven system,** the seven digits 0, 1, 2, 3, 4, 5, and 6. would be used to form all numerals. The value of each place in a base seven numeral would be a **power of seven.**

$463502_{seven} = 4 \times 7^5 + 6 \times 7^4 + 3 \times 7^3 + 5 \times 7^2 + 0 \times 7^1 + 2 \times 7^0$

base

To find the base ten numeral for $463502_{seven}$, multiply and add.

$463502_{seven} = 4 \times 7^5 + 6 \times 7^4 + 3 \times 7^3 + 5 \times 7^2 + 0 \times 7^1 + 2 \times 7^0$
$= 4 \times 16{,}807 + 6 \times 2{,}401 + 3 \times 343 + 5 \times 49 + 0 \times 7 + 2 \times 1$
$= 67{,}228 + 14{,}406 + 1{,}029 + 245 + 0 + 2$
$= 82{,}910_{ten}$

can be omitted

*What digits would be used in each system?*

9. a base five system
10. a base two system
11. a base twelve system
12. a base eight system **0, 1, 2, 3, 4, 5, 6, 7**
13. a base three system **0, 1, 2**

2 new digits needed

*Find the base ten numeral.*

14. $43065_{seven}$
15. $32401_{five}$
16. $40526_{eight}$
17. $1011011_{two}$
18. $105304_{six}$
19. $2301230_{four}$
20. $80075_{nine}$
21. $10221_{three}$

**C.** Find the base seven numeral for $59{,}043_{ten}$.

List powers of seven until you reach a number greater than 59,043.

$7^0 = 1$ $\quad 7^2 = 49$ $\quad 7^4 = 2{,}401$ $\quad 7^6 = 117{,}649$

$7^1 = 7$ $\quad 7^3 = 343$ $\quad 7^5 = 16{,}807$

Too big.

Start with $7^5$. Plan to have a digit in the base seven numeral for each place value from $7^5$ to $7^0$.

| $7^5$ | $7^4$ | $7^3$ | $7^2$ | $7^1$ | $7^0$ |
|---|---|---|---|---|---|
| | | | | | |

Divide to find how many $7^5$ in 59,043. The answer is 3 R8,622. The quotient, 3, gives the digit in the $7^5$ place.

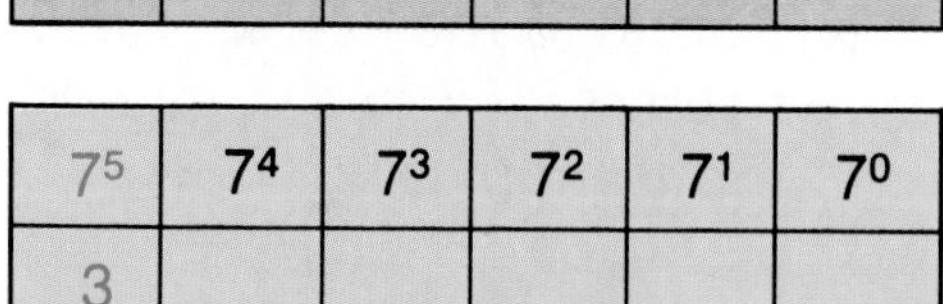

| $7^5$ | $7^4$ | $7^3$ | $7^2$ | $7^1$ | $7^0$ |
|---|---|---|---|---|---|
| 3 | | | | | |

The remainder 8,622 is greater than $7^4$, so divide by $7^4$. The answer is 3 R1,419. The quotient, 3, gives the digit in the $7^4$ place.

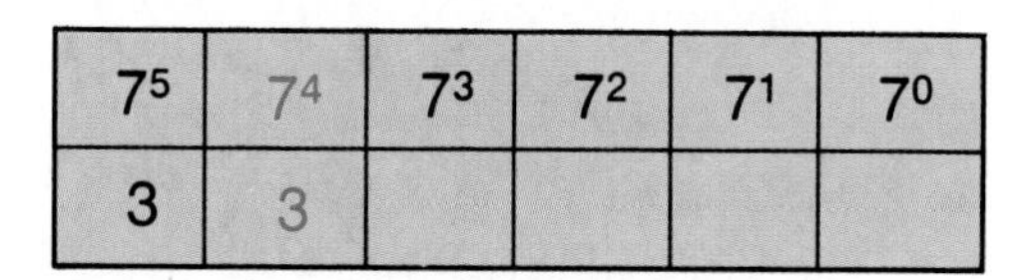

| $7^5$ | $7^4$ | $7^3$ | $7^2$ | $7^1$ | $7^0$ |
|---|---|---|---|---|---|
| 3 | 3 | | | | |

The remainder 1,419 is greater than $7^3$, so divide by $7^3$. The answer is 4 R47. The quotient, 4, gives the digit in the $7^3$ place.

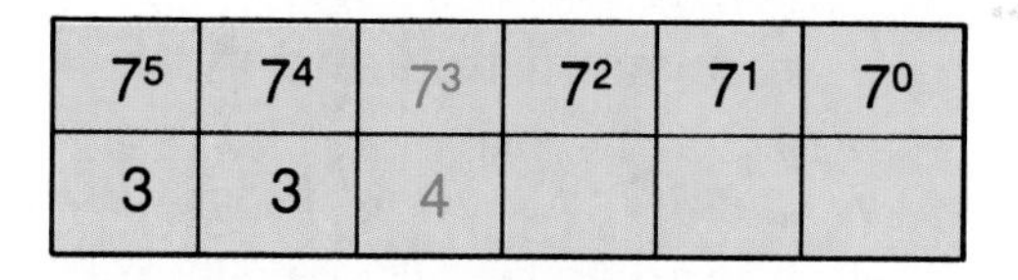

| $7^5$ | $7^4$ | $7^3$ | $7^2$ | $7^1$ | $7^0$ |
|---|---|---|---|---|---|
| 3 | 3 | 4 | | | |

The remainder 47 is less than $7^2$. Write 0 in the $7^2$ place.

| $7^5$ | $7^4$ | $7^3$ | $7^2$ | $7^1$ | $7^0$ |
|---|---|---|---|---|---|
| 3 | 3 | 4 | 0 | | |

47 is greater than $7^1$, so divide by $7^1$. The answer is 6 R5. The quotient, 6 gives the digit in the $7^1$ place. The remainder, 5, gives the digit in the $7^0$ place.

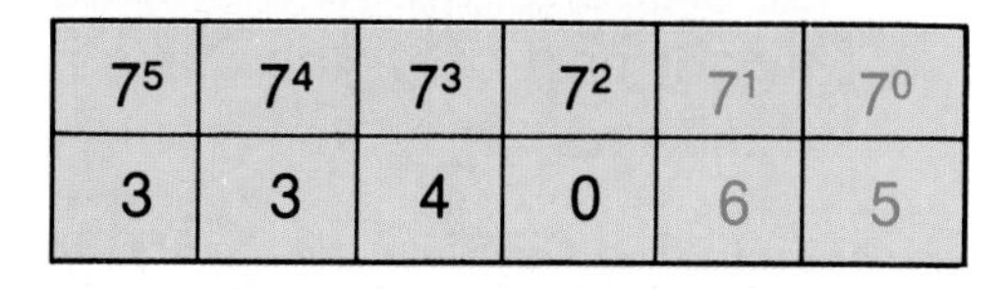

| $7^5$ | $7^4$ | $7^3$ | $7^2$ | $7^1$ | $7^0$ |
|---|---|---|---|---|---|
| 3 | 3 | 4 | 0 | 6 | 5 |

$$59{,}043_{ten} = 334065_{seven}$$

*Find the base seven numeral and the base four numeral for each.*

**22.** $5{,}000_{ten}$ **23.** $14{,}802_{ten}$ **24.** $53{,}670_{ten}$ **25.** $86{,}009_{ten}$

**26.** Using t for ten and e for eleven, find the base twelve numeral for each number in Exercises **22–25**.

# Cumulative Review

1. Estimate.
$$\begin{array}{r} .0269 \\ \times .0034 \\ \hline \end{array}$$
**a.** .0009 **b.** .000009 **c.** .03 **d.** .00009

2. Find the lowest terms fraction for $\frac{16}{24}$.
**a.** $\frac{8}{12}$ **b.** $\frac{2}{3}$ **c.** $\frac{4}{6}$ **d.** $\frac{1}{24}$

3. Simplify.
$.3 \times (.63 + .2)$
**a.** .195 **b.** .389 **c.** .249 **d.** 1.13

4. Find the LCM of 18 and 30.
**a.** 18 **b.** 30 **c.** 540 **d.** 90

5. Round to the nearest thousandth.
$5.2\overline{).0869}$
**a.** .167
**b.** .002
**c.** .017
**d.** 16.712

6.
$$\begin{array}{r} 52.8 \\ \times 2.04 \\ \hline \end{array}$$
**a.** 1,077.12
**b.** 107.712
**c.** 12.670
**d.** 1,267.2

7. Find the prime factorization of 585.
**a.** $3^2 \cdot 5 \cdot 13$
**b.** $3 \cdot 5 \cdot 39$
**c.** $3 \cdot 5 \cdot 13$
**d.** $5 \cdot 117$

8.
$$\begin{array}{r} \$964 \\ -\quad 5.87 \\ \hline \end{array}$$
**a.** $377
**b.** $3.77
**c.** $961.87
**d.** $958.13

9. Find fractions with LCD equivalent to $\frac{3}{8}$ and $\frac{5}{12}$.
**a.** $\frac{3}{24}$ and $\frac{5}{24}$ **b.** $\frac{9}{24}$ and $\frac{10}{24}$
**c.** $\frac{6}{24}$ and $\frac{15}{24}$ **d.** $\frac{36}{96}$ and $\frac{40}{96}$

10. Find the value of $3x - 5y$ for the value 6 of $x$ and the value 2 of $y$.
**a.** 8 **b.** 2
**c.** 18 **d.** 28

11. 8 of Ms. Daniel's 28 students are in the band. 9 of Mr. Case's 30 students are in the band. A larger part of which class is in the band?
**a.** Daniel's class **b.** Case's class
**c.** They are equal. **d.** 17 students

12. A bicycle can be purchased for $40 down payment and 10 equal installments of $14.96 each. What is the total cost of this bicycle?
**a.** $54.96 **b.** $414.96
**c.** $64.96 **d.** $189.60

13. The populations of three cities (to the nearest 100 thousand) are 1.6 million, 1.9 million, and 1.7 million. How much larger than the smallest city is the largest one?
**a.** 2,000,000 **b.** 5,200,00
**c.** 300,000 **d.** 100,000

14. Tommie spent $35.80 for shoes and $19.65 for shirts. She gave the clerk $60. How much change should she receive?
**a.** $55.45 **b.** $120.45
**c.** $29.20 **d.** $4.55

# Fractions and Mixed Numerals

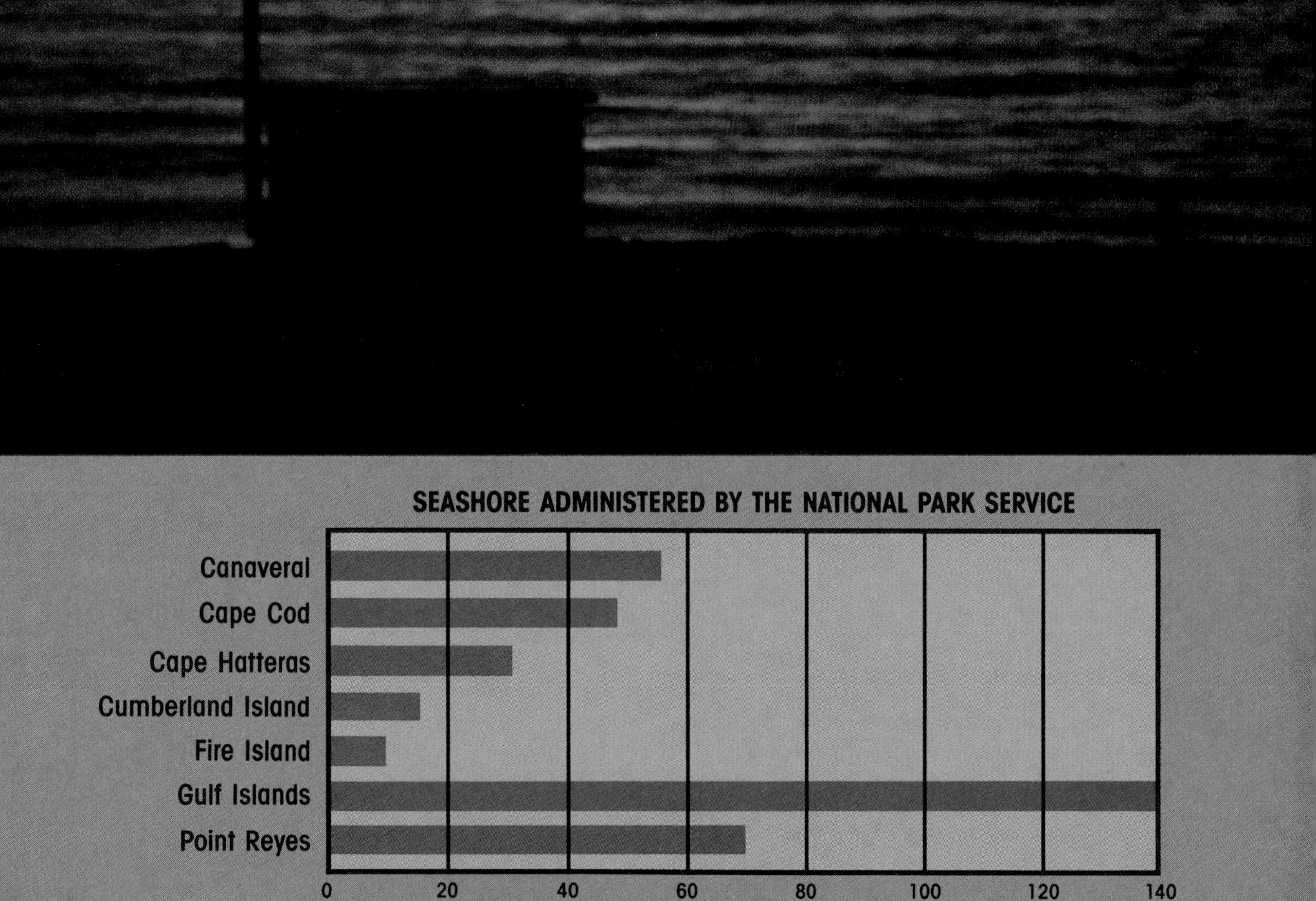

# 5-1 Addition and Subtraction: Common Denominators

**A.** In July, Phoenix had $\frac{9}{10}$ inch of rain. In August, Phoenix had $\frac{4}{10}$ inch of rain. What was the combined rainfall for the two months?

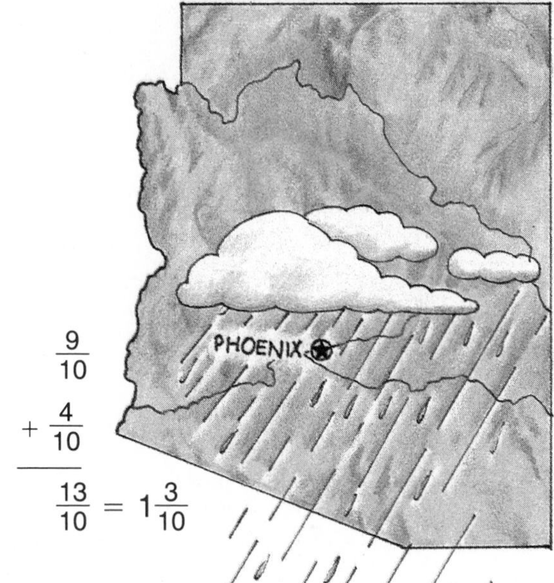


Add to find the total rainfall.

**To add with fractions that have a common denominator, add the numerators and use the same denominator.**

$$\frac{9}{10} + \frac{4}{10} = \frac{13}{10} = 1\frac{3}{10}$$

The total rainfall for the two months was $1\frac{3}{10}$ inches.

**B.** How much more rain did Phoenix have in July than in August? Subtract to find how much more.

**To subtract with fractions that have a common denominator, subtract the numerators and use the same denominator.**

$$\frac{9}{10} - \frac{4}{10} = \frac{5}{10} = \frac{1}{2}$$

Phoenix had $\frac{1}{2}$ inch more rainfall in July than in August.

**C.** Add or subtract.

**Example 1**

$\frac{5}{8} + \frac{3}{8} = $ ▪

$$\frac{5}{8} + \frac{3}{8} = \frac{8}{8} = 1$$

**Example 2**

$1 - \frac{3}{5} = $ ▪

$1 \longrightarrow \frac{5}{5}$

$-\frac{3}{5} \longrightarrow -\frac{3}{5}$

$$\frac{5}{5} - \frac{3}{5} = \frac{2}{5}$$

## CLASS EXERCISES

*Give the simplest form for each.*

**1.** $\frac{9}{16} + \frac{1}{16} = ■$  **2.** $1 - \frac{3}{4} = ■$  **3.** $\frac{4}{7} + \frac{3}{7} = ■$  **4.** $\frac{9}{10} - \frac{3}{10} = ■$

*Find the value of each expression.*

**5.** $\left(\frac{13}{20} - \frac{3}{20}\right) + \frac{7}{20}$  **6.** $\frac{11}{12} - \left(\frac{7}{12} - \frac{5}{12}\right)$  **7.** $\left(\frac{27}{40} + \frac{9}{40}\right) - \left(\frac{21}{40} + \frac{3}{40}\right)$

## EXERCISES

*Add or subtract.*

**1.** $\frac{5}{6} - \frac{1}{6} = ■$  **2.** $\frac{4}{5} + \frac{3}{5} = ■$  **3.** $\frac{7}{4} - \frac{3}{4} = ■$  **4.** $\frac{9}{10} + \frac{8}{10} = ■$

**5.** $\frac{17}{18} + \frac{7}{18} = ■$  **6.** $\frac{2}{3} - \frac{2}{3} = ■$  **7.** $1 - \frac{5}{8} = ■$  **8.** $\frac{7}{10} + 0 = ■$

**9.** $\frac{5}{8} + \frac{7}{8}$  **10.** $\frac{7}{8} + \frac{5}{8}$  **11.** $\frac{11}{12} - \frac{5}{12}$  **12.** $\frac{7}{16} + \frac{5}{16}$  **13.** $\frac{3}{2} - \frac{1}{2}$  **14.** $\frac{7}{6} - \frac{1}{6}$  **15.** $\frac{12}{25} + \frac{13}{25}$

**16.** $\frac{17}{10} - \frac{13}{10}$  **17.** $\frac{11}{15} + \frac{13}{15}$  **18.** $\frac{7}{12} - \frac{7}{12}$  **19.** $\frac{17}{20} + \frac{13}{20}$  **20.** $\frac{23}{20} - \frac{11}{20}$  **21.** $\frac{37}{100} + \frac{23}{100}$  **22.** $\frac{17}{50} + \frac{28}{50}$

*Find the value of each expression.*

**23.** $\left(\frac{5}{6} + \frac{1}{6}\right) + \frac{7}{6}$  **24.** $\frac{5}{6} + \left(\frac{1}{6} + \frac{7}{6}\right)$  **25.** $\left(\frac{3}{8} + \frac{7}{8}\right) + \left(\frac{11}{8} - \frac{5}{8}\right)$

**26.** $\left(\frac{9}{16} + \frac{11}{16}\right) - \frac{13}{16}$  **★27.** $\left(\frac{1}{30} + \frac{23}{30} - \frac{19}{30}\right) + \frac{17}{30} - \frac{7}{30}$  **★28.** $\frac{61}{48} - \left(\frac{13}{48} + \frac{17}{48}\right) - \frac{31}{48}$

## PROBLEMS

The chart shows the monthly rainfall in Phoenix for four months.

**29.** Find the total rainfall for the four months.

| Rainfall in Phoenix | |
|---|---|
| January $\frac{73}{100}$ in. | February $\frac{56}{100}$ in. |
| March $\frac{19}{100}$ in. | April $\frac{32}{100}$ in. |

## THINK!

### Joining Corners

One way of joining the corners of the square below without lifting your pencil and without crossing or retracing a line, is ABCD. In how many distinct ways can this be done? List the ways.

B C A D

1. $\frac{2}{3}$ 5. $\frac{1}{3}$

Homework page 473

# 5-2 Addition: Unlike Denominators

**A.** Jared has an aquarium filled with tropical fish. $\frac{1}{3}$ of the fish are angelfish and $\frac{7}{15}$ of the fish are swordtails. What part of the total number of fish in the aquarium are angelfish or swordtails?

Add. $\frac{1}{3} + \frac{7}{15} = ▒$

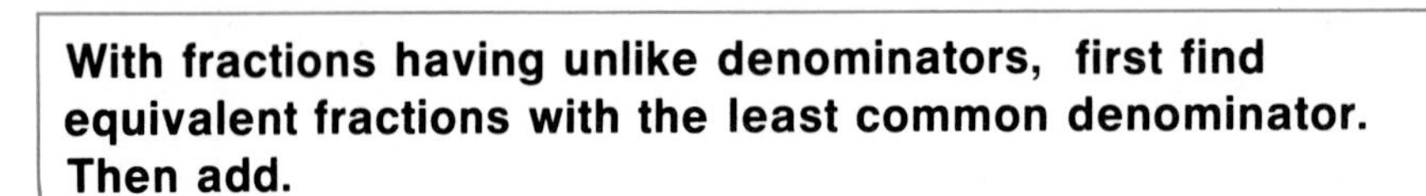

**With fractions having unlike denominators, first find equivalent fractions with the least common denominator. Then add.**

> 15 is the least common multiple of 3 and 15. Use 15 as the least common denominator.

$$\begin{array}{rcr} \frac{1}{3} & \rightarrow & \frac{5}{15} \\ +\frac{7}{15} & \rightarrow & +\frac{7}{15} \\ \hline & & \frac{12}{15} = \frac{4}{5} \end{array}$$

lowest terms

$\frac{4}{5}$ of the fish in the aquarium are angelfish or swordtails.

**B.** Sometimes both fractions must be replaced by equivalent fractions.

**Example 1** $\frac{5}{6} + \frac{4}{9} = ▒$

> 18 is the LCM of 6 and 9. Use 18 as the LCD.

$$\frac{5}{6} + \frac{4}{9} = ▒$$

$$\downarrow \qquad \downarrow$$

$$\frac{15}{18} + \frac{8}{18} = \frac{23}{18}, \text{ or } 1\frac{5}{18}$$

**Example 2** Find the sum of $\frac{8}{10}$ and $\frac{2}{3}$.

> Use 30 as the LCD.

$$\frac{8}{10} + \frac{2}{3} = ▒$$

$$\downarrow \qquad \downarrow$$

$$\frac{24}{30} + \frac{20}{30} = \frac{44}{30} = \frac{22}{15}, \text{ or } 1\frac{7}{15}$$

## CLASS EXERCISES

*Give the simplest form for each sum.*

**1.** $\frac{5}{8} + \frac{1}{2} = \blacksquare$ **2.** $\frac{2}{3} + \frac{1}{4} = \blacksquare$ **3.** $\frac{3}{4} + \frac{9}{10} = \blacksquare$ **4.** $\frac{3}{8} + \frac{17}{50} = \blacksquare$

*Simplify.*

**5.** $\left(\frac{3}{4} + \frac{5}{6}\right) + \frac{5}{12}$ **6.** $\frac{3}{4} + \left(\frac{5}{6} + \frac{5}{12}\right)$ **7.** $\left(\frac{7}{15} + \frac{2}{3}\right) + \left(1 + \frac{3}{5}\right)$

## EXERCISES

*Add.*

**1.** $\frac{3}{10} + \frac{1}{2} = \blacksquare$ **2.** $\frac{5}{6} + \frac{3}{4} = \blacksquare$ **3.** $\frac{3}{2} + \frac{2}{5} = \blacksquare$ **4.** $\frac{5}{8} + \frac{7}{12} = \blacksquare$

**5.** $\frac{1}{6} + \frac{7}{10} = \blacksquare$ **6.** $\frac{8}{15} + \frac{8}{15} = \blacksquare$ **7.** $\frac{4}{9} + \frac{5}{12} = \blacksquare$ **8.** $\frac{2}{3} + \frac{4}{9} = \blacksquare$

**9.** $\frac{2}{5} + \frac{3}{10}$ **10.** $\frac{3}{10} + \frac{2}{5}$ **11.** $\frac{1}{8} + \frac{1}{6}$ **12.** $\frac{3}{4} + \frac{2}{5}$ **13.** $\frac{4}{5} + \frac{2}{3}$ **14.** $\frac{11}{10} + \frac{1}{8}$ **15.** $\frac{14}{15} + \frac{5}{6}$

**16.** $\frac{1}{3} + \frac{7}{8}$ **17.** $\frac{5}{6} + \frac{6}{5}$ **18.** $\frac{11}{20} + \frac{12}{25}$ **19.** $\frac{5}{12} + \frac{7}{18}$ **20.** $\frac{2}{9} + \frac{9}{10}$ **21.** $\frac{5}{16} + \frac{1}{6}$ **22.** $\frac{4}{9} + \frac{5}{8}$

*Simplify.*

**23.** $\left(\frac{2}{3} + \frac{3}{7}\right) + \frac{1}{2}$ **24.** $\frac{3}{4} + \left(\frac{2}{9} + \frac{1}{2}\right)$ **25.** $\left(\frac{1}{2} + \frac{2}{5}\right) + \left(\frac{2}{7} + \frac{3}{10}\right)$

*Find the value of each expression if the value of* $x$ *is* $\frac{1}{2}$, $y$ *is* $\frac{3}{4}$, *and* $z$ *is* $\frac{4}{5}$.

**26.** $x + (y + z)$ **★27.** $(z + x) + \left(y + \frac{1}{4}\right)$ **★28.** $x + \left(\frac{7}{4} - y\right)$

## PROBLEMS

**29.** $\frac{3}{8}$ of the swordtails in the aquarium are black and $\frac{1}{4}$ are red. What part of the total number of swordtails are black or red?

**30.** $\frac{1}{4}$ of Jared's fish are angelfish and $\frac{1}{3}$ are swordtails. Does Jared have more angelfish or swordtails?

## THINK!

### Making Change

What is the greatest amount of money you can have and still be unable to make change for a dollar?

1. $\frac{4}{5}$ 9. $\frac{7}{10}$

Homework page 473

## 5-3 Subtraction: Unlike Denominators

**A.** The gasoline tank of Tom's moped was $\frac{9}{10}$ full when he left home. When he returned home the tank was $\frac{1}{2}$ full. What part of a tank of gasoline did Tom use?

**With fractions having unlike denominators, first find equivalent fractions with the least common denominator. Then subtract.**

Subtract. $\frac{9}{10} - \frac{1}{2} = \blacksquare$

10 is the least common multiple of 10 and 2. Use 10 as the least common denominator.

$$\frac{9}{10} \longrightarrow \frac{9}{10}$$
$$-\frac{1}{2} \longrightarrow -\frac{5}{10}$$
$$\frac{4}{10} = \frac{2}{5}$$

lowest terms

Tom used $\frac{2}{5}$ of a tank of gasoline.

**B.** Sometimes both fractions must be replaced by equivalent fractions.

**Example 1** $\frac{5}{3} - \frac{1}{5} = \blacksquare$

15 is the LCM of 3 and 5. Use 15 as the LCD.

$$\frac{5}{3} - \frac{1}{5} = \blacksquare$$
$$\frac{25}{15} - \frac{3}{15} = \frac{22}{15} = 1\frac{7}{15}$$

**Example 2** Find the difference of $\frac{5}{6}$ and $\frac{2}{15}$.

Use 30 as the LCD.

$$\frac{5}{6} - \frac{2}{15} = \blacksquare$$
$$\frac{25}{30} - \frac{4}{30} = \frac{21}{30} = \frac{7}{10}$$

### CLASS EXERCISES

*Find the difference. Simplify.*

**1.** $\frac{4}{5} - \frac{1}{10} = \blacksquare$ **2.** $\frac{2}{3} - \frac{1}{4} = \blacksquare$ **3.** $\frac{5}{6} - \frac{1}{9} = \blacksquare$ **4.** $\frac{8}{7} - \frac{11}{14} = \blacksquare$

*Simplify.*

**5.** $\left(\frac{11}{12} - \frac{1}{2}\right) - \frac{1}{3}$ **6.** $\frac{11}{12} - \left(\frac{1}{2} - \frac{1}{3}\right)$ **7.** $\left(\frac{7}{6} - \frac{3}{4}\right) + \left(\frac{13}{10} - \frac{5}{6}\right)$

## EXERCISES

*Subtract.*

1. $\frac{11}{16} - \frac{5}{8} = ■$
2. $\frac{4}{5} - \frac{2}{3} = ■$
3. $\frac{9}{10} - \frac{3}{4} = ■$
4. $\frac{5}{8} - \frac{7}{12} = ■$
5. $\frac{3}{2} - \frac{2}{5} = ■$
6. $\frac{5}{6} - \frac{7}{10} = ■$
7. $\frac{14}{9} - \frac{5}{6} = ■$
8. $\frac{17}{20} - \frac{17}{20} = ■$

9. $\frac{5}{6} - \frac{3}{8}$
10. $\frac{7}{8} - \frac{1}{2}$
11. $\frac{13}{15} - \frac{13}{15}$
12. $\frac{2}{5} - \frac{1}{4}$
13. $\frac{5}{14} - \frac{4}{21}$
14. $\frac{11}{12} - \frac{5}{9}$
15. $\frac{14}{15} - \frac{5}{6}$
16. $\frac{16}{17} - \frac{37}{51}$
17. $\frac{17}{12} - \frac{17}{18}$
18. $\frac{13}{15} - \frac{5}{8}$
19. $\frac{7}{10} - \frac{11}{25}$
20. $\frac{3}{4} - \frac{13}{25}$
21. $\frac{7}{12} - \frac{7}{15}$
22. $\frac{7}{10} - \frac{3}{8}$

*Simplify.*

23. $\left(\frac{7}{8} - \frac{1}{2}\right) - \frac{1}{4}$
24. $\frac{11}{12} - \left(\frac{5}{6} - \frac{1}{4}\right)$
25. $\left(\frac{7}{10} - \frac{1}{3}\right) + \left(\frac{3}{5} - \frac{7}{15}\right)$

*Find the value of each expression if the value of* $x$ *is* $\frac{7}{8}$, $y$ *is* $\frac{5}{6}$, *and* $z$ *is* $\frac{3}{10}$.

26. $(x - z) + y$
★27. $(1 - x) + (1 - y)$
★28. $(x + y) + z - \frac{241}{120}$

## PROBLEMS

29. Tom rode his moped for $\frac{2}{3}$ of an hour during the weekend. He rode for $\frac{1}{4}$ of an hour on Saturday. How long did Tom ride on Sunday?

30. The moped used $\frac{1}{3}$ gallon of gasoline Saturday and $\frac{1}{2}$ gallon on Sunday. How much gasoline did it use in all?

## THINK!

### Use Algebra

A restaurant manager needed many pounds of potatoes. The first supplier she called charged $.22 a pound, but the manager calculated she would be $16.80 over her budget for the number of pounds she needed. Another supplier charged $.16 a pound, and the restaurant manager calculated she would be $9.60 under her budget after placing the order. How many pound of potatoes did the manager need?

1. $\frac{1}{16}$ 9. $\frac{11}{24}$



Homework page 474

## 5-4 Comparing with Mixed Numerals

**A.** You have used division to replace fractions by equivalent mixed numerals. You can also replace mixed numerals by equivalent fractions.

Find a fraction equivalent to $5\frac{3}{4}$. Use division to check.

$$5\frac{3}{4} = 5 + \frac{3}{4}$$
$$= \frac{5}{1} + \frac{3}{4}$$
$$= \frac{5 \times 4}{1 \times 4} + \frac{3}{4}$$
$$= \frac{(5 \times 4) + 3}{4}$$
$$= \frac{23}{4}$$

**Shortcut** $5\frac{3}{4} = \frac{(5 \times 4) + 3}{4}$

$$= \frac{23}{4}$$

*Check:*

$$\begin{array}{r} 5\frac{3}{4} \checkmark \\ 4\overline{)23} \\ \underline{20} \\ 3 \end{array}$$

**B.** To compare with mixed numerals, make sure the fractional parts name numbers less than 1. Then look at the whole number parts.

**Example 1** Compare $2\frac{4}{5}$ and $3\frac{1}{3}$.

Both $\frac{4}{5}$ and $\frac{1}{3}$ are less than 1.

Compare the whole number parts.

$2 < 3$,

so $2\frac{4}{5} < 3\frac{1}{3}$.

**Example 2** Compare $4\frac{3}{4}$ and $4\frac{7}{10}$.

Both $\frac{3}{4}$ and $\frac{7}{10}$ are less than 1.

**Step 1** Compare the whole number parts. $4 = 4$

**Step 2** Compare the fractional parts.

$$\frac{3}{4} \quad \frac{7}{10}$$
$$\downarrow \quad \downarrow$$
$$\frac{15}{20} > \frac{14}{20},$$

so $4\frac{3}{4} > 4\frac{7}{10}$.

**C.** Write >, <, or = for ●. $2\frac{1}{8}$ ● $1\frac{5}{4}$

$\frac{1}{8} < 1$, but $\frac{5}{4} > 1$. $1\frac{5}{4} = 1 + \frac{5}{4} = 1 + 1\frac{1}{4} = 2\frac{1}{4}$

Compare $2\frac{1}{8}$ and $2\frac{1}{4}$. $\frac{1}{8} < \frac{1}{4}$ so $2\frac{1}{8} < 2\frac{1}{4}$

and $2\frac{1}{8} < 1\frac{5}{4}$.

## CLASS EXERCISES

*Find an equivalent fraction for each.*

**1.** $6\frac{1}{3}$ **2.** $5\frac{3}{8}$ **3.** $6\frac{1}{6}$ **4.** $7\frac{1}{2}$ **5.** $3\frac{1}{4}$ **6.** $4\frac{4}{5}$

*Write >, <, or = for ●.*

**7.** $3\frac{7}{10}$ ● $2\frac{9}{10}$ **8.** $4\frac{1}{2}$ ● $4\frac{3}{5}$ **9.** $16\frac{10}{21}$ ● $16\frac{15}{32}$ **10.** $4\frac{1}{4}$ ● $3\frac{7}{5}$

## EXERCISES

*Find an equivalent fraction for each. Then divide to check.*

**1.** $5\frac{2}{3}$ **2.** $3\frac{1}{7}$ **3.** $6\frac{5}{6}$ **4.** $9\frac{1}{2}$ **5.** $2\frac{5}{7}$ **6.** $5\frac{1}{4}$

**7.** $4\frac{3}{5}$ **8.** $2\frac{13}{15}$ **9.** $9\frac{3}{10}$ **10.** $5\frac{7}{9}$ **11.** $15\frac{3}{5}$ **12.** $12\frac{1}{8}$

**13.** $2\frac{6}{7}$ **14.** $16\frac{5}{8}$ **15.** $3\frac{7}{25}$ **16.** $6\frac{3}{50}$ **17.** $4\frac{17}{20}$ **18.** $2\frac{19}{35}$

**19.** $3\frac{97}{100}$ **20.** $1\frac{25}{32}$ **21.** $2\frac{39}{64}$ **22.** $3\frac{13}{100}$ **23.** $6\frac{218}{1000}$ **24.** $4\frac{7}{500}$

*Write >, <, or = for ●.*

**25.** $2\frac{3}{8}$ ● $2\frac{5}{8}$ **26.** $3\frac{1}{3}$ ● $2\frac{11}{12}$ **27.** $5\frac{1}{2}$ ● $5\frac{7}{8}$ **28.** $10\frac{3}{10}$ ● $10\frac{1}{4}$

**29.** $6\frac{1}{2}$ ● $5\frac{7}{4}$ **30.** $1\frac{2}{5}$ ● $1\frac{1}{3}$ **31.** $8\frac{1}{100}$ ● $7\frac{99}{100}$ **32.** $2\frac{1}{6}$ ● $2\frac{7}{48}$

**33.** $1\frac{14}{39}$ ● $1\frac{26}{75}$ **34.** $5\frac{7}{15}$ ● $5\frac{7}{16}$ **35.** $3\frac{1}{7}$ ● $3\frac{14}{100}$ **36.** $14\frac{1}{3}$ ● $14\frac{6}{17}$

## PROBLEMS

**37.** Ms. Stinett wants to do a task in $1\frac{1}{2}$ hours. She worked for $\frac{5}{6}$ hour in the morning and $\frac{3}{4}$ hour after lunch. Did she meet her goal?

**38.** Mr. Wooster worked $37\frac{2}{3}$ hours one week, while Mr. Foster worked $37\frac{3}{5}$ hours. Who worked longer?

## THINK!

### A Colorful Quilt

The colors of a quilt are brown, orange, white, tan, and yellow. One half of the quilt is brown, and one half this amount is orange. For the part of the quilt that remains, one third is white and one fourth is tan. The rest of the quilt is yellow. What fraction of the quilt is each color?

**1.** $\frac{17}{3}$ **25.** <

## 5-5 Addition with Mixed Numerals

**A.** Find the sum of $2\frac{3}{11}$ and $1\frac{4}{11}$.

**Step 1** Add the fractional parts.

**Step 2** Add the whole numbers.

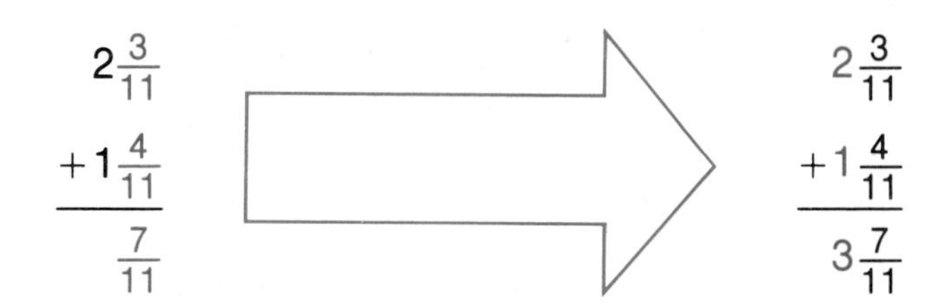

$$\begin{array}{r} 2\frac{3}{11} \\ +1\frac{4}{11} \\ \hline \frac{7}{11} \end{array} \qquad \begin{array}{r} 2\frac{3}{11} \\ +1\frac{4}{11} \\ \hline 3\frac{7}{11} \end{array}$$

**B.** You may need to rename the fractional parts before adding.

**Example 1** $4\frac{1}{4} + \frac{2}{3} = \blacksquare$

$$\begin{array}{r} 4\frac{1}{4} \\ +\ \frac{2}{3} \\ \hline \end{array} \longrightarrow \begin{array}{r} 4\frac{3}{12} \\ +\ \frac{8}{12} \\ \hline 4\frac{11}{12} \end{array}$$

**Example 2** $8\frac{1}{2} + 7\frac{3}{10} = \blacksquare$

$$\begin{array}{r} 8\frac{1}{2} \\ +7\frac{3}{10} \\ \hline \end{array} \longrightarrow \begin{array}{r} 8\frac{5}{10} \\ 7\frac{3}{10} \\ \hline 15\frac{8}{10} \end{array} = 15\frac{4}{5}$$

**C.** You may need to regroup to simplify the sum.

**Example 1** Find the sum of $4\frac{3}{7}$ and $6\frac{5}{7}$.

**Step 1** Add.

$$\begin{array}{r} 4\frac{3}{7} \\ +\ 6\frac{5}{7} \\ \hline 10\frac{8}{7} \end{array}$$

**Step 2** Simplify the sum.

$$10\frac{8}{7} = 10 + 1\frac{1}{7} = 11\frac{1}{7}$$

**Example 2**

$$\begin{array}{r} 4\frac{3}{8} \\ +1\frac{5}{8} \\ \hline 5\frac{8}{8} \end{array} = 5 + 1 = 6$$

**Example 3**

$$\begin{array}{r} 2\frac{6}{7} \\ +1\frac{9}{14} \\ \hline \end{array} \longrightarrow \begin{array}{r} 2\frac{12}{14} \\ +1\frac{9}{14} \\ \hline 3\frac{21}{14} \end{array} = 3\frac{3}{2} = 3 + 1\frac{1}{2} = 4\frac{1}{2}$$

## CLASS EXERCISES

*Add.*

1. $1\frac{3}{5} + 4\frac{4}{5}$
2. $3\frac{5}{8} + 4\frac{1}{8}$
3. $5\frac{1}{6} + 7\frac{5}{6}$
4. $6 + 9\frac{3}{4}$
5. $1\frac{7}{15} + 3\frac{17}{20}$
6. $1\frac{3}{5} + 4\frac{3}{7}$

## EXERCISES

*Add.*

1. $9\frac{1}{2} + 6\frac{1}{2}$
2. $8\frac{4}{5} + 3\frac{2}{5}$
3. $5\frac{5}{8} + 4\frac{3}{8}$
4. $7\frac{1}{3} + 6\frac{1}{3}$
5. $3\frac{7}{10} + 12\frac{1}{10}$
6. $8\frac{11}{12} + \frac{7}{12}$
7. $5\frac{5}{6} + 6\frac{2}{5}$
8. $9\frac{2}{3} + 9$
9. $16\frac{7}{8} + 32\frac{3}{4}$
10. $\frac{1}{12} + 5\frac{1}{4}$
11. $12\frac{2}{3} + 9\frac{4}{5}$
12. $19\frac{3}{8} + 5\frac{7}{12}$
13. $28\frac{4}{5} + 18\frac{3}{10} = ■$
14. $8\frac{5}{6} + 6\frac{7}{8} = ■$
15. $7\frac{1}{3} + 13\frac{1}{6} = ■$
16. $6\frac{3}{4} + 19\frac{5}{6} = ■$
17. $8\frac{7}{10} + 9\frac{9}{10} = ■$
18. $7\frac{3}{4} + 6\frac{1}{2} = ■$
19. $3\frac{4}{5} + 4\frac{5}{6} = ■$
20. $1\frac{1}{3} + 2\frac{3}{4} = ■$
21. $6\frac{3}{4} + 7\frac{3}{8} + 17\frac{11}{12}$
22. $2\frac{1}{2} + 13\frac{1}{6} + 9\frac{11}{12}$
23. $5\frac{1}{3} + 22\frac{11}{12} + 8\frac{5}{18}$
24. $14\frac{3}{5} + 36\frac{9}{10} + 13$

★25. $2\frac{5}{6} + 8\frac{1}{12} + 7\frac{5}{8}$

★26. $19\frac{5}{6} + 16\frac{5}{8} + 24\frac{2}{9}$

## PROBLEMS

27. Mr. Jones is a carpenter. It took him $3\frac{5}{6}$ hours, $4\frac{1}{4}$ hours, and $1\frac{1}{2}$ hours to do three jobs. How long did he work in all?

28. Last week Mr. Jones worked 4 days. He worked $8\frac{1}{2}$ hours, $10\frac{1}{4}$ hours, $11\frac{1}{4}$ hours, and $11\frac{3}{4}$ hours. How long did he work in all?

## THINK!

**Work Backwards**

It was raining for one fifth of the drive. It was snowing for one fourth of the drive. It was sunny along the remaining 22 km. How long was the drive?

1. 16 7. $12\frac{7}{30}$



Homework page 475

## 5-6 Subtraction with Mixed Numerals

**A.** $6\frac{8}{9} - 2\frac{5}{9} = \blacksquare$

$$\begin{array}{r} 6\frac{8}{9} \\ -2\frac{5}{9} \\ \hline 4\frac{3}{9} = 4\frac{1}{3} \end{array}$$

**B.** Subtract $1\frac{11}{15}$ from $7\frac{5}{6}$.

$$\begin{array}{rcr} 7\frac{5}{6} & \longrightarrow & 7\frac{25}{30} \\ -1\frac{11}{15} & \longrightarrow & -1\frac{22}{30} \\ \hline & & 6\frac{3}{30} = 6\frac{1}{10} \end{array}$$

**C.** It is sometimes necessary to regroup when subtracting with mixed numerals.

**Example 1** Subtract. $5\frac{2}{13} - 3\frac{8}{13} = \blacksquare$

**Step 1** $\frac{2}{13} < \frac{8}{13}$ Regroup.

$$\begin{array}{r} 5\frac{2}{13} \longrightarrow 4 + 1\frac{2}{13} \longrightarrow 4\frac{15}{13} \\ -3\frac{8}{13} \end{array}$$

**Step 2** Subtract.

$$\begin{array}{r} 4\frac{15}{13} \\ -3\frac{8}{13} \\ \hline 1\frac{7}{13} \end{array}$$

**Example 2** Find the difference. $8\frac{1}{4} - 7\frac{5}{6}$

$$\begin{array}{rcrcr} 8\frac{1}{4} & \xrightarrow{\text{Rename}} & 8\frac{3}{12} & \xrightarrow{\text{Regroup}} & 7\frac{15}{12} \\ -7\frac{5}{6} & \xrightarrow{\text{Rename}} & -7\frac{10}{12} & \longrightarrow & -7\frac{10}{12} \\ \hline & & & & \frac{5}{12} \end{array}$$

**Example 3** $10 - 4\frac{3}{7} = \blacksquare$

**Step 1** Regroup.

$$\begin{array}{r} 10 \longrightarrow 9\frac{7}{7} \\ -\ 4\frac{3}{7} \end{array}$$

**Step 2** Subtract.

$$\begin{array}{rcr} 10 & \longrightarrow & 9\frac{7}{7} \\ -\ 4\frac{3}{7} & \longrightarrow & -4\frac{3}{7} \\ \hline & & 5\frac{4}{7} \end{array}$$

## CLASS EXERCISES

*Subtract.*

**1.** $6\frac{4}{5} - 3\frac{2}{5}$ **2.** $7\frac{1}{10} - 5\frac{9}{10}$ **3.** $3\frac{3}{4} - 1\frac{1}{8}$ **4.** $2 - 1\frac{1}{7}$ **5.** $6\frac{1}{9} - 3$ **6.** $7\frac{2}{5} - 5\frac{3}{5}$ **7.** $9\frac{1}{3} - 3\frac{7}{9}$

**8.** $7 - 3\frac{7}{8} = ■$ **9.** $4\frac{7}{8} - 3\frac{1}{12} = ■$ **10.** Subtract $3\frac{1}{2}$ from $7\frac{3}{8}$.

## EXERCISES

*Subtract.*

**1.** $7\frac{3}{4} - 6\frac{1}{4}$ **2.** $5\frac{4}{5} - 2\frac{2}{5}$ **3.** $12\frac{1}{2} - 9\frac{3}{4}$ **4.** $16 - 4\frac{5}{9}$ **5.** $12\frac{4}{5} - 9\frac{3}{10}$ **6.** $8 - 2\frac{5}{8}$ **7.** $6\frac{1}{8} - 4\frac{3}{8}$

**8.** $4\frac{5}{6} - 2\frac{3}{8}$ **9.** $20\frac{1}{3} - 5\frac{1}{6}$ **10.** $5\frac{3}{8} - 4\frac{11}{12}$ **11.** $11 - 3\frac{1}{4}$ **12.** $5\frac{5}{8} - 4\frac{2}{9}$ **13.** $5\frac{1}{12} - 2\frac{5}{8}$ **14.** $13\frac{1}{6} - 8\frac{3}{4}$

**15.** $4\frac{2}{5} - 4\frac{1}{3} = ■$ **16.** $7\frac{4}{7} - 5\frac{2}{3} = ■$ **17.** Subtract $3\frac{3}{8}$ from $11\frac{1}{24}$.

**18.** $3\frac{5}{6} - 1\frac{7}{8} = ■$ **19.** $5\frac{11}{16} - 2\frac{11}{12} = ■$ **20.** Subtract $4\frac{1}{6}$ from $9\frac{5}{9}$.

**21.** $6\frac{3}{4} - 2\frac{9}{16} = ■$ **22.** $9\frac{2}{7} - 7\frac{1}{5} = ■$ **23.** Subtract $4\frac{5}{12}$ from $4\frac{3}{4}$.

## THINK!

### Making a Logical Choice

All cards in a stack have a red dot or a black dot. Each of 3 players selects a card and without looking at it holds it so the other 2 players can see its dot. All players who see at least 1 black dot raise their hands. Then, the first player to guess correctly the color of the dot on her or his card wins the game.

On one play of the game all 3 players raised their hands. Then, after a short time Player A was sure of the color of the dot on her or his card. What was the color of the dot and how did Player A know the color?

1. $1\frac{1}{2}$ 8. $2\frac{11}{24}$

Homework page 475

# Problem Solving

READ PLAN DO • ANSWER • CHECK

## 5-7 Related Problems

It is sometimes possible to use one plan to solve several related problems. If one of the problems is a whole-number problem, use it to write a plan.

Find how much of each product a store sold during a week.

| Product | Amount at start | Amount received | Amount at end |
|---|---|---|---|
| Eggs | 426 dozen | 509 dozen | 453 dozen |
| Butter | 152.6 kilograms (kg) | 209.8 kg | 183.7 kg |
| Milk | $102\frac{3}{4}$ cases | $205\frac{1}{2}$ cases | $198\frac{1}{2}$ cases |

*Must find:* Amount sold

*Know:* Amount at start
Amount received
Amount at end

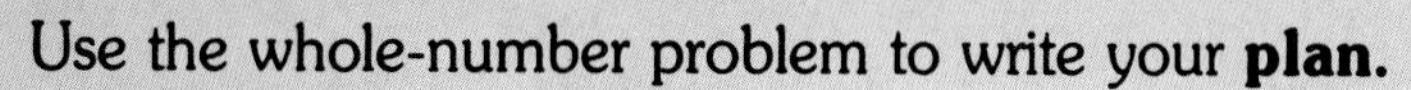

Use the whole-number problem to write your **plan.**

**Step 1** Amount sold = Amount in all − Amount at end
**Step 2** Amount in all = Amount at start + Amount received

Use this plan to do all three problems.

Eggs: Amount in all = 426 + 509 = 935
Amount sold = 935 − 453 = 482

Butter: Amount in all = 152.6 + 209.8 = 362.4
Amount sold = 362.4 − 183.7 = 178.7

Milk: Amount in all = $102\frac{3}{4} + 205\frac{1}{2} = 308\frac{1}{4}$
Amount sold = $308\frac{1}{4} - 198\frac{1}{2} = 109\frac{3}{4}$

The amounts of different products sold were:

482 dozen eggs
178.7 kg of butter
$109\frac{3}{4}$ cases of milk

## CLASS EXERCISES

**1.** How much canned corn did a store have if it had:

i) 379 cases, then received 468 cases?

ii) 126.9 kg, then received 378.6 kg?

iii) $208\frac{7}{8}$ cases, then received $104\frac{11}{12}$ cases?

**2.** How many days were left in a 12-day cruise after:

i) 3 days, then 6 days more?

ii) 2.5 days, then 4.6 days more?

iii) $5\frac{1}{3}$ days, then $5\frac{1}{6}$ days more?

## PROBLEMS

**1.** How much fuel was left at the boat dock if:

i) 305 of 410 cans were used?

ii) 216.7 of 308.3 liters were used?

iii) $145\frac{1}{2}$ of $306\frac{1}{4}$ cans were used?

**2.** How much paint did a painter use in all if he:

i) had 38 of 73 cans left?

ii) had 56.4 of 93.2 liters left?

iii) had $73\frac{2}{3}$ of 89 cans left?

**3.** How many rolls of wire did a store have left if it had 75 rolls:

i) then bought 42 rolls, sold 27 rolls?

ii) then bought 56.8 rolls, sold 39.3 rolls?

iii) then bought $67\frac{1}{2}$ rolls, sold $51\frac{3}{4}$ rolls?

**4.** How much floor tile did a store have left if it had 100 crates, then:

i) bought 87 crates, sold 69 crates?

ii) bought 165 crates, sold 92.6 crates?

iii) bought 93 crates, sold $74\frac{1}{4}$ crates?

**5.** How far did a marathoner run in all if she:

i) ran 36 km, then 45 km more?

ii) ran 14.5 km, then 17.3 km more?

iii) ran $23\frac{1}{10}$ laps, then ran $31\frac{6}{10}$ laps more?

**6.** A store sold 120 boxes of peaches. How many boxes of fruit were sold in all if it had left:

i) 30 of 100 boxes of peaches?

ii) 51.75 of 80 boxes of peaches?

iii) $41\frac{1}{2}$ of 76 boxes of peaches?

## MIXED REVIEW

*Divide. Plan to round to the nearest thousandth.*

**1.** $6\overline{)3.45}$ **2.** $.3\overline{)5.69}$ **3.** $.041\overline{)2.9}$ **4.** $.19\overline{).70414}$

*Write prime or composite. If composite, give the prime factorization.*

**5.** 39 **6.** 51 **7.** 97 **8.** 121 **9.** 255 **10.** 301 **11.** 349

Homework page 476

## TECHNOLOGY

### Prime Factorization with a Calculator

**A.** A calculator can help you find the prime factorization of a number quickly. Use what you know about divisibility. Find the prime factorization of 5,040.

**Examine the last digit.**

5,040

5,040 is divisible by 2 and by 5.

**Examine the sum of the digits.**

$5+0+4+0=9$

5,040 is divisible by 3.

Now use your calculator. Divide by each prime factor you know.

Press
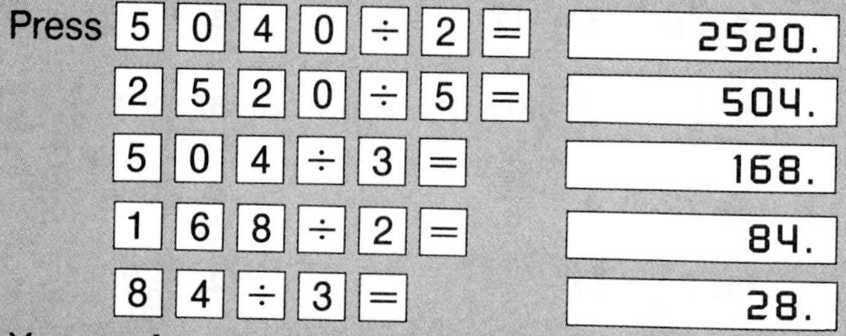


You can factor 28 into primes easily: $28=2\times2\times7$.
So $5{,}040=2\times2\times7\times3\times2\times3\times5\times2=2^4\times3^2\times5\times7$

**B.** You can use prime factorization to find the GCF and LCM of two numbers on a calculator. Find the GCF and LCM of 5,040 and 15,300.

$5{,}040=2^4\times3^2\times5\times7$
GCF $=2^2\times3^2\times5$

2 × 2 × 3 × 3 × 5 =

180.

The GCF of 5,040 and 15,300 is 180.

$15{,}300=2^2\times3^2\times5^2\times17$
LCM $=2^4\times3^2\times5^2\times7\times17$

2 × 2 × 2 × 2 × 3 × 3 × 5 × 5 × 7 × 1 7 =

42,8400.

The LCM of 5,040 and 15,300 is 428,400.

**C.** Find fractions equivalent to $\frac{5}{33}$ and $\frac{17}{25}$ with the LCD.

$\frac{5}{33}=\frac{■}{825}$ $\frac{17}{25}=\frac{■}{825}$

825 is the LCD.

Press 8 2 5 ÷ 3 3 × 5 = 125.

Press 8 2 5 ÷ 2 5 × 1 7 = 561.

$\frac{5}{33}=\frac{125}{825}$ $\frac{17}{25}=\frac{561}{825}$

*Use a calculator to find the prime factorization of each number. Then find the GCF and the LCM.*

1. 455; 1,750
2. 36,414; 945
3. 520; 3,640
4. 396; 450; 990
5. Find fractions equivalent to $\frac{200}{396}$, $\frac{38}{450}$ and $\frac{621}{990}$ with the LCD.

# Problem Solving Strategy

READ **PLAN** DO • ANSWER • CHECK

## Work a Simpler Problem

Sometimes the best way to solve a problem is by working similar problems that are easier, and then trying to discover a pattern. By looking at the pattern, you may be able to discover a general rule.

Suppose you are asked to find the sum:

$$\frac{1}{2} + \frac{1}{2^2} + \frac{1}{2^3} + \frac{1}{2^4} + \frac{1}{2^5} + \frac{1}{2^6} + \frac{1}{2^7} + \frac{1}{2^8}$$

You can solve the problem by finding a common denominator, writing equivalent fractions, and then adding. This will take you a long time. (Try it.) Or, you can look for a pattern.

$$\frac{1}{2} + \frac{1}{2^2} = \frac{1}{2} + \frac{1}{4} = \frac{3}{4}$$

$$\frac{1}{2} + \frac{1}{2^2} + \frac{1}{2^3} = \underbrace{\frac{1}{2} + \frac{1}{4}} = \frac{1}{8}$$

$$= \frac{3}{4} + \frac{1}{8} = \frac{7}{8}$$

$$\frac{1}{2} + \frac{1}{2^2} + \frac{1}{2^3} + \frac{1}{2^4} = \underbrace{\frac{1}{2} + \frac{1}{4} + \frac{1}{8}} + \frac{1}{16}$$

$$\frac{7}{8} + \frac{1}{16} = \frac{15}{16}$$

Now you should see a pattern. In each case, the denominator is equal to $2^n$, where $n$ is the number of terms being added. The numerator is 1 less than the denominator, so the numerator is $2^n - 1$. The fraction that gives the sum is $\frac{2^n - 1}{2^n}$.

---

**1.** Using the formula found above, find the sum:

$$\frac{1}{2} + \frac{1}{2^2} + \frac{1}{2^3} + \frac{1}{2^4} + \frac{1}{2^5} + \frac{1}{2^6} + \frac{1}{2^7} + \frac{1}{2^8} + \frac{1}{2^9}$$

**2.** If the sequence of fractions is continued, what is the sum when $n = 12$?

**3.** Complete the table. Look for a pattern.

| Fraction Sequence | Sum |
|---|---|
| $\frac{1}{1 \times 3}$ | $\frac{1}{3}$ |
| $\frac{1}{1 \times 3} + \frac{1}{3 \times 5}$ | $\frac{2}{5}$ |
| $\frac{1}{1 \times 3} + \frac{1}{3 \times 5} + \frac{1}{5 \times 7}$ | ■ |
| $\frac{1}{1 \times 3} + \frac{1}{3 \times 5} + \frac{1}{5 \times 7} + \frac{1}{7 \times 9}$ | ■ |

**4.** What do you notice about the numerators? What do you notice about the denominators?

**5.** Use the pattern in the table. Find the sum.

$$\frac{1}{1 \times 3} + \frac{3}{5}$$

# Problem Solving Project

READ • PLAN **DO** ANSWER • CHECK

**A.** Navigators use **latitude** and **longitude** to locate places on the earth.

**Parallels of Latitude**

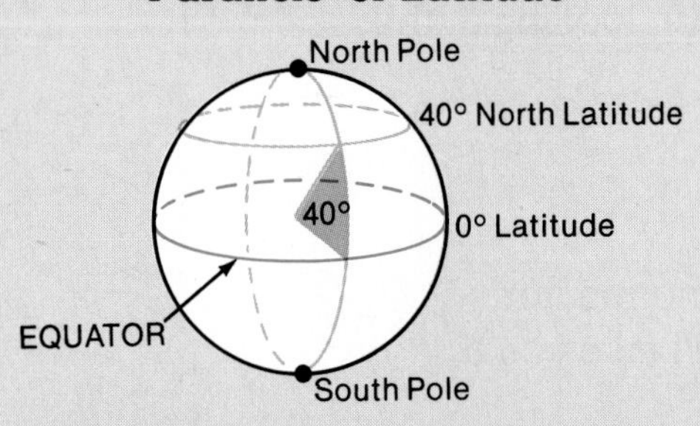


**Meridians of Longitude**

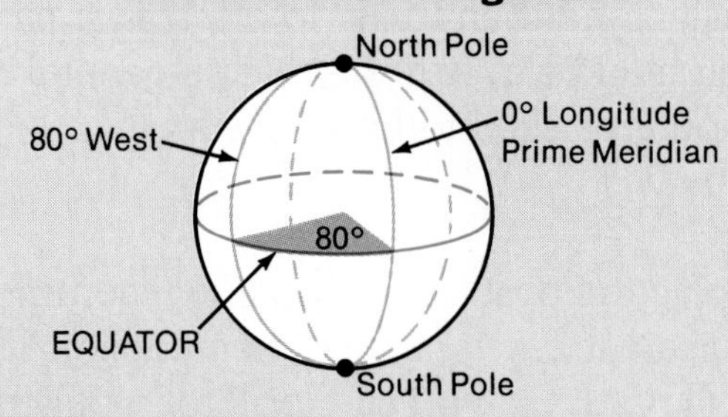


The east-west lines on a globe are **parallels of latitude.** Their names, in degrees, give the measures of central angles north or south of the **equator.** The north-south lines are **meridians of longitude.** Their names give the measures of central angles east or west of the **prime meridian** that passes through Greenwich, England.

**B.** The map of Europe below shows some of the parallels of latitude from 35°N ("thirty-five degrees north") to 70°N ("seventy degrees north") and some of the meridians of longitude from 25°W ("twenty-five degrees west) to 60°E ("sixty degrees east").

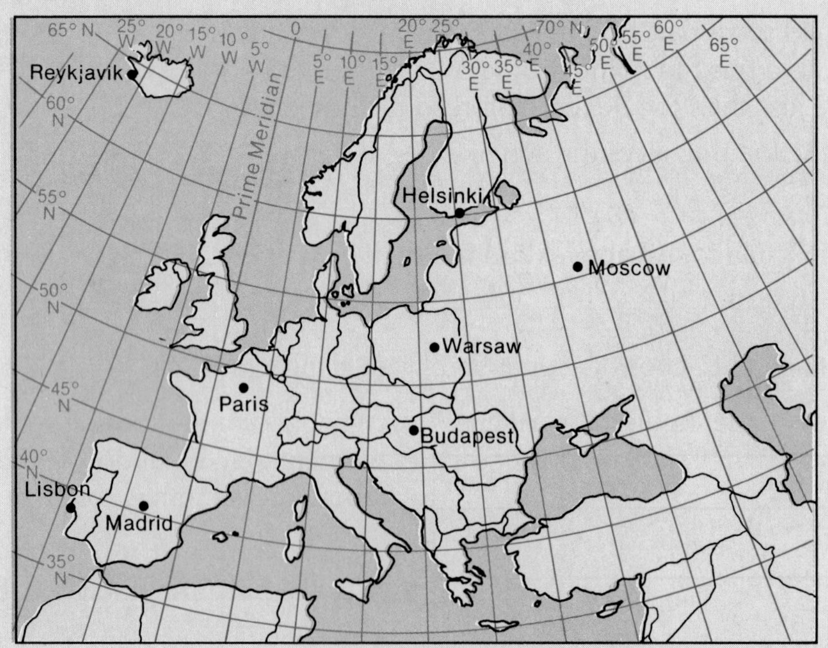


*What city is located at each of these places?*

**1.** 52°N, 21°E **2.** 56°N, 38°E **3.** 49°N, 2°E **4.** 39°N, 9°W

*Estimate the latitude and longitude of each city.*

**5.** Reykjavik **6.** Budapest **7.** Madrid **8.** Helsinki

**C. Meteorologists** forecast the weather. They use parallels of latitude and meridians of longitude to track the movement of **hurricanes** and other storms. Meteorologists use the speed and direction of movement of storms to predict where and when the storms will reach land.

*Trace a map of the southern United States and the islands in the Caribbean Sea. Show some of the parallels of latitude and meridians of longitude.* ***Plot the path*** *of each hurricane.*

**9.** *Hurricane Jonah:* 20°N, 83° W at noon, Tuesday
22°N, 87° W at 4:00 A.M., Wednesday
24°N, 90°W at 8:00 P.M., Wednesday
At about what time will it reach Galveston, Texas?

**10.** *Hurricane Kate:* 24°N, 80°W at 6:00 P.M., Monday
26°N, 83°W at 7:00 P.M., Tuesday
28°N, 87°W at 8:00 P.M., Wednesday
At about what time will it reach New Orleans, Louisana?

## ON YOUR OWN

**1.** Use a globe. Estimate the longitude and latitude of ten capital cities that are not in Europe or the United States.

**2.** Find articles in your local newspaper about different towns or cities in the United States. Estimate the longitude and latitude of each place. Bring the articles to class and make a bulletin board showing a map of the United States. Draw arrows from the articles to the places on the map.

**3.** Plan a summer vacation to places around the world you would most like to visit. Use a map to find the longitude and latitude of each place.

**4.** Pretend an imaginary hurricane is heading to Key West, Florida. Describe a path for the storm using the latitude and longitude of different places along the path.

# Unit Review

*Add or subtract. (pages 150–155)*

**1.** $\frac{2}{5} + \frac{1}{5} = \blacksquare$ **2.** $\frac{5}{6} - \frac{3}{4} = \blacksquare$ **3.** $\frac{7}{8} + \frac{5}{12} = \blacksquare$ **4.** $\frac{9}{10} - \left(\frac{2}{3} + \frac{1}{5}\right) = \blacksquare$

**5.** $\frac{1}{2} + \frac{4}{9}$ **6.** $\frac{17}{20} - \frac{3}{5}$ **7.** $\frac{11}{12} - \frac{7}{16}$ **8.** $\frac{7}{10} + \frac{1}{4}$ **9.** $\frac{2}{3} + \frac{3}{8}$ **10.** $\frac{6}{7} - \frac{15}{28}$

*Add or subtract. (pages 158-161)*

**11.** $4\frac{2}{3} - 1\frac{1}{3}$ **12.** $2\frac{1}{8} + 3\frac{1}{2}$ **13.** $1\frac{2}{5} + 2\frac{9}{10}$ **14.** $4 - 2\frac{2}{3}$ **15.** $5\frac{1}{6} - 1\frac{3}{8}$ **16.** $2\frac{5}{12} + 3\frac{3}{4}$

**17.** $6\frac{1}{5} - 4\frac{2}{3} = \blacksquare$ **18.** $8 + 5\frac{7}{12} = \blacksquare$ **19.** $3\frac{1}{4} - 2\frac{1}{2} = \blacksquare$ **20.** $6\frac{7}{8} + 3\frac{11}{12} = \blacksquare$

*Write a fraction for each. (pages 156–157)*

**21.** $1\frac{5}{16}$ **22.** $3\frac{2}{7}$ **23.** $6\frac{1}{2}$ **24.** $2\frac{5}{12}$ **25.** $4\frac{1}{9}$ **26.** $7\frac{23}{100}$

*Compare. Write $>$, $<$, or $=$ for $\bullet$. (pages 156–157)*

**27.** $2\frac{1}{10} \bullet 1\frac{7}{8}$ **28.** $3\frac{3}{4} \bullet 3\frac{4}{5}$ **29.** $4\frac{9}{18} \bullet 4\frac{1}{2}$ **30.** $2\frac{8}{5} \bullet 3\frac{1}{4}$

*Multiply or divide. (pages 164–167)*

**31.** $\frac{3}{5} \times \frac{2}{3} = \blacksquare$ **32.** $\frac{3}{5} \div \frac{2}{3} = \blacksquare$ **33.** $\frac{7}{12} \times 4 = \blacksquare$ **34.** $5 \div \frac{5}{8} = \blacksquare$

**35.** $\frac{13}{16} \div \frac{3}{4} = \blacksquare$ **36.** $\frac{9}{10} \div 3 = \blacksquare$ **37.** $\frac{5}{9} \times \frac{2}{5} = \blacksquare$ **38.** $\frac{7}{16} \div \left(\frac{7}{8} \times 2\right) = \blacksquare$

*Multiply or divide. (pages 168–169)*

**39.** $1\frac{2}{3} \times 2\frac{1}{4} = \blacksquare$ **40.** $8 \div 1\frac{1}{2} = \blacksquare$ **41.** $5\frac{2}{3} \div 17 = \blacksquare$ **42.** $4\frac{1}{2} \times 1\frac{5}{8} = \blacksquare$

**43.** $3\frac{1}{5} \div 4\frac{2}{5} = \blacksquare$ **44.** $2\frac{5}{6} \times 3\frac{3}{4} = \blacksquare$ **45.** $9\frac{1}{2} \div 4\frac{3}{4} = \blacksquare$ **46.** $20 \times 6\frac{1}{5} = \blacksquare$

*Write a decimal for each.* *(pages 170–171)*

**47.** $\frac{7}{8}$ **48.** $\frac{5}{12}$ **49.** $\frac{7}{16}$ **50.** $2\frac{3}{4}$ **51.** $6\frac{1}{30}$ **52.** $3\frac{8}{9}$

*Write a fraction for each.* *(pages 170–171)*

**53.** .27 **54.** .313 **55.** 2.67 **56.** 4.219 **57.** 1.965

*Solve.* *(pages 176–177)*

**58.** $\frac{1}{2}x - 4 = 7$ **59.** $\frac{2}{3}x + 4 = 6$ **60.** $\frac{1}{4}y - \frac{1}{2} = \frac{1}{2}$

**61.** $\frac{3}{5}z + \frac{7}{10} = 2$ **62.** $4m - \frac{2}{3} = \frac{5}{6}$ **63.** $\frac{3}{8}x + \frac{1}{5} = \frac{5}{12}$

*Solve the problems.* *(pages 162–165, 172–175)*

**64.** How much more white paint than red paint did a painter have if he had:

**i)** 49 gal of white, 37 gal of red?

**ii)** 43.6 gal of white, 26.9 of red?

**iii)** $37\frac{1}{4}$ gal of white, $19\frac{7}{8}$ of red?

**65.** Mr. Laino drove $\frac{2}{5}$ of the total distance he had to go the first day and $\frac{3}{8}$ of the total the second day. What part of the total distance did he still have to go after 2 days?

**66.** What was the average speed of a plane that flew:

**i)** 1,900 mi in 4 h?

**ii)** 2,494 mi in 5.8 h?

**iii)** 1,725 mi in $3\frac{3}{4}$ h?

**67.** An airline charges $\frac{1}{2}$ fare for children. It also gives .3 off for traveling on weekends. How much does a child's ticket for a Saturday flight cost if the regular fare is $280?

**68.** What is the sale price of a shirt with a regular price of $22.40 if the shirt was sold for $\frac{2}{5}$ off during the sale?

**69.** Ms. Flores earned $8.70/h for the $37\frac{1}{2}$ h she worked last week. What were her total earnings for the week?

**70.** A store charges $\frac{1}{8}$ more for a late payment of a bill. How much must be paid in all if a bill for $128.56 is paid late?

**71.** Which taxi company charges less for a 3-mi trip?

A: $1.60 for first mile; $.20 for each additional $\frac{1}{4}$mile

B: $1.40 for the first mile; $.25 for each additional $\frac{1}{5}$ mile

# Enrichment

## Mental Math

### Methods for Squaring Numbers

**A.** To **square** a number means to multiply the number by itself. It is easy to square a number that is a multiple of a power of ten.

$800^2 = ■$ $(8 \times 100) \times (8 \times 100) = (8 \times 8) \times (100 \times 100)$

$= 640{,}000$

**B.** For any number $x$, it is easy to show that $(x - 5) \cdot (x + 5) + 25 = x^2$.

$(x - 5) \cdot (x + 5) + 25 = (x - 5) \cdot x + (x - 5) \cdot 5 + 25$

$= x \cdot x - 5 \cdot x + 5 \cdot x - 5 \cdot 5 + 25$

$0 \qquad 0$

$= x^2$

When squaring numbers with ones digit 5, this relationship gives numbers that are easy to handle mentally.

$45^2 = (45 - 5) \cdot (45 + 5) + 25$
$= 40 \cdot 50 + 25$
$= 2{,}025$

$205^2 = (205 - 5) \cdot (205 + 5) + 25$
$= 200 \cdot 210 + 25$
$= 42{,}025$

*Use the methods in **A** or **B** to find:*

**1.** $90^2$ **2.** $700^2$ **3.** $55^2$ **4.** $85^2$ **5.** $155^2$ **6.** $250^2$

**C.** For any numbers $x$ and $y$ it is easy to show that $(x + y)^2 = x^2 + 2xy + y^2$.

You can use this relationship to square numbers mentally.

$43^2 = ■$ *Think:* $43 = 40 + 3$

$(40 + 3)^2 = 40^2 + 2 \cdot 40 \cdot 3 + 3^2$

$= 1600 + 240 + 9$

$= 1849$

*Use method **C** to find:*

**7.** $64^2$ **8.** $29^2$ **9.** $46^2$ **10.** $51^2$ **11.** $123^2$ **12.** $503^2$

**D.** If $x$ and $y$ are any two numbers, $x > y$, and if $a$ is their average or mean, the two distances, $d$, shown on the number line are equal.

$$x \cdot y = (a + d) \cdot (a - d)$$
$$= a \cdot (a - d) + d \cdot (a - d)$$
$$= a \cdot a - a \cdot d + d \cdot a - d \cdot d$$
$$= a^2 - d^2$$

0

For any numbers $x$ and $y$, $x > y$, with average $a$, and distance $d$ from each to the average, $x \cdot y = a^2 - d^2$.

**E.** The result in **D** can be used to find the product of any two numbers. For two numbers with ones digit 5, the result in **D** is especially useful.

$65 \times 35 = ■$

*Think:* $a = (65 + 35) \div 2 = 50$

$d = 65 - 50 = 50 - 35 = 15$

$65 \times 35 = 50^2 - 15^2$

$= 2{,}500 - 225$

$= 2{,}275$

**F.** When the average of two factors is a multiple of ten, the result in **D** is easy to apply mentally.

$27 \times 33 =$

*Think:* $a = 30$ $d = 3$

$27 \times 33 = 30^2 - 3^2$

$= 900 - 9$

$= 891$

*Use the result in **D** as a shortcut. Use mental arithmetic when you can.*

**13.** $55 \times 45$ **14.** $95 \times 75$ **15.** $105 \times 95$

**16.** $36 \times 24$ **17.** $82 \times 78$ **18.** $49 \times 31$

# Cumulative Review

**1.** Multiply.
$\frac{2}{7} \times \frac{3}{4}$

**a.** $\frac{5}{11}$ **b.** $\frac{8}{21}$
**c.** $\frac{3}{14}$ **d.** Not above

**2.** Write a standard numeral for $2^5$.

**a.** 64 **b.** 32
**c.** 10 **d.** Not above

**3.** $\frac{5}{6} + \frac{3}{8}$

**a.** $1\frac{5}{12}$ **b.** $1\frac{5}{24}$
**c.** $1\frac{9}{24}$ **d.** Not above

**4.** Find the greatest common factor of 72 and 120.

**a.** 24
**b.** 12
**c.** 36
**d.** Not above

**5.** $.053 \times .046$

**a.** .003428
**b.** .0002438
**c.** .002438
**d.** Not above

**6.** $5\frac{1}{4} - 2\frac{1}{2}$

**a.** $2\frac{3}{4}$ **b.** $2\frac{1}{4}$
**c.** $3\frac{3}{4}$ **d.** Not above

**7.** Complete.
$3w - 9 = 3(w - \blacksquare)$

**a.** 6 **b.** 3
**c.** 9 **d.** Not above

**8.** Write a decimal for $2\frac{5}{8}$.

**a.** 2.875
**b.** 2.625
**c.** 2.265
**d.** Not above

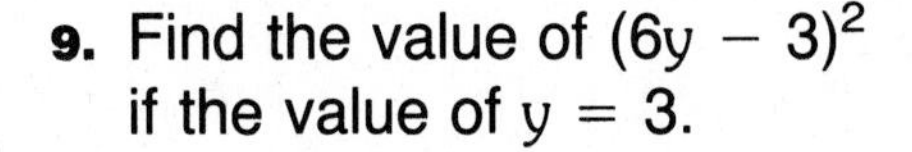

**9.** Find the value of $(6y - 3)^2$ if the value of $y = 3$.

**a.** 225 **b.** 30
**c.** 321 **d.** Not above

**10.** Solve.
$\frac{3}{4}m + 7 = 10$

**a.** $m = 12$ **b.** $m = 32\frac{2}{3}$
**c.** $m = 4$ **d.** Not above

**11.** A clock radio costs $24.95 and a record player costs $65.39. Joni saved $32.50. How much more does she need for the record player?

**a.** $57.84 **b.** $32.89
**c.** $33.89 **d.** Not above

**12.** An automatic washer-dryer set can be purchased for $2,195 cash, or through an installment plan of $500 cash plus 18 monthly payments of $101.70. How much would be saved by paying cash?

**a.** $135.60 **b.** $364.40
**c.** $1,695 **d.** Not above

**13.** Clara is 4 years younger than twice Barry's age. Clara is 28. How old is Barry?

**a.** 24 years **b.** 12 years
**c.** 16 years **d.** Not above

**14.** Mr. Evans had 1,200 rolls of film. He packed 60 rolls in each carton. He sold 9.8 cartons. How many cartons did Mr. Evans have left?

**a.** 190.2 cartons **b.** 10.2 cartons
**c.** 50.2 cartons **d.** Not above

# Problem Solving Situations

## Black and White or Color Film?

You are an amateur photographer. Your photography club asks you to take a total of 212 pictures. Some pictures require special flashcubes. You have a choice of film size as well as black and white film (B & W) or color film. What type of film will you choose?

means 26 millimeter (mm) film with 12 pictures or exposures

**Your Notes**

| Size | B & W film | Color film | B & W processing | Color processing |
|---|---|---|---|---|
| 126-12 | $1.29 | $1.98 | $1.02 | $1.23 |
| 110-20 | $1.75 | $2.40 | $1.55 | $1.65 |
| 135-36 | $2.34 | $3.72 | $2.21 | $3.48 |

**Other Conditions**

- Black and white prints from negatives are $.27 each.
- Color prints from negatives are $.49 each.
- Package of 3 flashcubes is $2.37.
- Enlargements of B & W prints are $\frac{3}{8}$ the cost of color enlargements.

*Work in small groups to find answers and make decisions.*

**1.** To take all the pictures, you decide to buy 2 rolls of 126-12 B & W film, twice as many rolls of 110-20 color film, and some rolls of 135-36 color film. How many rolls of 135-36 color film do you buy? Write an equation and solve. Let x represent the number of rolls of 135-36 color film.

**2.** What is the total cost of all the film above?

**3.** You have to buy a dozen packages of flashcubes. What is the total cost of the flashcubes and all the film processing?

**4.** You order 8 black and white prints from negatives and one more than three times this amount of color prints from negatives. You also order the same number of enlargements of color prints as enlargements of black and white prints. The cost of your color enlargements is $20.72. What is the total cost of prints and enlargements?

**5.** What other things should you think about?

**6.** What type of film will you choose? Explain.

## Train or Plane?

You are planning a trip from Newark to Boston. The distance between the two cities is about 300 miles. You have a choice of taking a train or a plane. What type of transportation will you choose?

**Your Notes**

**Rates**

The train travels 60 miles per hour.
The plane travels 500 miles per hour.

**Costs**

A one-way train ticket costs $30.
A one-way plane ticket costs $50.

**Schedules**

The train leaves at 10 A.M.
The plane leaves every hour.

**Other Conditions**

- The plane provides a free meal.
- The plane flies direct from Boston to Newark.
- The train makes seven 15-minute stops.

*Work in small groups to find answers and make decisions.*

1. If the train leaves Newark at 10 A.M., what time will you arrive in Boston?

2. How many minutes is the plane trip?

3. How much money would you save by taking the train round-trip instead of the plane?

4. If you traveled to Boston by plane and returned by train for 6 round trips, how much money would you spend on transportation?

5. What other things should you think about?

6. Will you take the train or the plane? Explain.

## Renting a Fishing Boat

You and two friends are planning a fishing trip. You want to begin the fishing trip at 6:15 A.M. and return at 2:30 P.M. There are two types of boat rentals available: by the hour or by the day. Which type of rental will you and your friends choose?

**Your Notes**

| **Rates** | **Other Conditions** |
|---|---|
| *Boat rentals by the hour:*<br>$7.50 each hour for the first $3\frac{1}{2}$ hours<br>$6.25 for each additional hour or fraction of an hour<br>*Boat rentals by the day:*<br>$69.99 all day | • Fishing tackle is free when you rent by the day.<br>• Fishing tackle is $3.75 per person when you rent by the hour.<br>• Larger boats are rented by the day.<br>• Newer boats are rented by the hour. |

*Work in small groups to find answers and make decisions.*

1. How many hours do you want to rent the fishing boat?

2. If you rent the boat by the hour and also buy fishing tackle for yourself and your friends, what will the total cost be?

3. How much is saved per person on just the boat rental cost if you rent by the hour instead of by the day?

4. Suppose you and your 2 friends agree to pay just the boat rental cost in the ratio of 1:2:2. How much would each person pay if you rent by the hour?

5. What other things should you think about?

6. Will you rent by the hour or by the day? Explain.

## Taking a Taxi

You are planning to take a taxi to the museum. You have a choice of two taxis: Express Cab and Ray's Taxi Service. Both taxis have different rates. Which taxi will you take?

**Your Notes**

**Rates**

*Express Cab*

\$1.00 1st $\frac{1}{8}$ mile
\$.10 each additional $\frac{1}{8}$ mile

*Ray's Taxi Service*

\$1.25 1st $\frac{1}{5}$ mile
\$.15 each additional $\frac{1}{5}$ mile

**Other Conditions**

- Both taxis charge an additional \$.75 for each suitcase.
- Both taxis are of the same make, year, and condition.

*Work in small groups to find answers and make decisions.*

1. One day you took Express Cab for 3 miles. The next day you took Ray's Taxi Service for the same distance. How much was the fare for each ride?

2. The next day you took Express Cab for 5 miles. The following day you took Ray's Taxi Service for the same distance. How much was the fare for each ride?

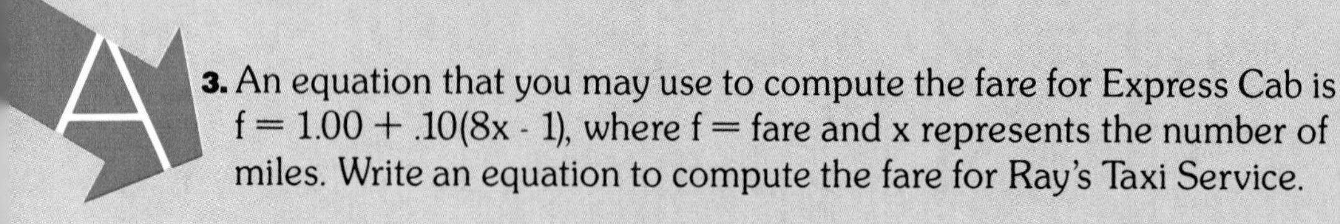

3. An equation that you may use to compute the fare for Express Cab is $f = 1.00 + .10(8x - 1)$, where $f$ = fare and $x$ represents the number of miles. Write an equation to compute the fare for Ray's Taxi Service.

4. For what value of $x$ would the fares for both taxi services be the same?

5. What other things should you think about?

6. Which taxi will you take?

## Competing in a Triathlon

You are planning to run in a triathlon. You must swim $1\frac{1}{2}$ miles, bicycle 25 miles, and run $6\frac{1}{5}$ miles. The winning time for such a triathlon is about $2\frac{1}{2}$ hours. What strategy should you use to compete in the triathlon?

**Your Notes**

**Your Range of Training Times**

Swimming: $\frac{3}{4}$ hour–$\frac{7}{8}$ hour

Bicycling: $1\frac{1}{4}$ hours– $1\frac{1}{2}$ hours

Running: $\frac{3}{5}$ hour–$\frac{7}{10}$ hour

**Other Conditions**

- You clock your best times under ideal conditions.
- You clock your worst times when it is raining or cold.
- You risk serious injury when you try to do better than your best times.
- 624 athletes start the race at 8:20 A.M.
- $\frac{5}{8}$ of the starters finish the triathlon.

*Work in small groups to find answers and make decisions.*

1. What time do you expect the winner to cross the finish line? How many starters do you expect will finish?
2. What are your speeds for swimming, bicycling, and running, assuming your best times?
3. What is your best training time under ideal conditions?
4. Suppose that on the day of the triathlon it is overcast with a slight drizzle. Consequently, you clock your average time (avg. time = (best time + worst time) ÷ 2). At approximately what time can you expect to cross the finish line?
5. What other things should you think about?
6. What strategy should you use to compete in the triathlon?

# Choice of Carpenters

You want to do some carpentry work for your family. You have the tools, but you would need to buy all the materials. Your family has offered to pay you an hourly rate for labor, plus the cost of the materials. A professional carpenter can do the entire job for $420 (labor and materials). What should you and your family consider?

### Your Notes

You will be paid $7.35 per hour for labor.

**Materials Needed**

Tiles and paint for an 8 ft by 12 ft ceiling

Four pieces of lumber. Each piece is 2 in. by 4 in. by 12 ft.

**Costs**

Paint costs $8.95 per gallon.

12 in. by 12 in. ceiling tile costs $.39 per tile.

Lumber costs $.65 per board foot. (A board foot is a piece of lumber 1 in. thick and 1 ft square.)

**Other Conditions**

- One gallon of paint covers 50 sq ft.
- You could complete the job by working the following hours over a 4-day period: $6\frac{1}{2}$, $5\frac{3}{4}$, $10\frac{1}{4}$, and $7\frac{3}{5}$.
- You are not an experienced painter.
- The professional carpenter has an excellent reputation.

*Work in small groups to find answers and make decisions.*

1. How much would your labor cost?
2. What is the cost of lumber and paint?
3. How many tiles do you need to cover the ceiling?
4. What is the total cost of materials?
5. What percent of the paint will not be used?
6. How much money will your family save if you do the carpentry job?
7. What other things should you and your family consider?
8. Should your family hire you or the professional carpenter for the job?

# 6 Integers and Rational Numbers

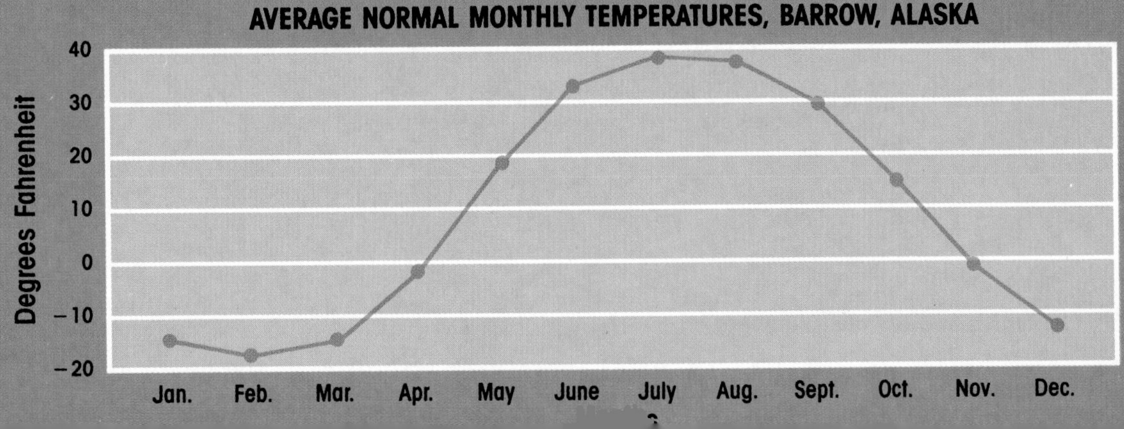

# 6-1 Integers

**A.** Integers can be used to name points on a number line. Whole numbers other than 0 are **positive integers** and name points to the right of 0. **Negative integers** name points to the left of 0. Zero is an integer which is neither positive nor negative.

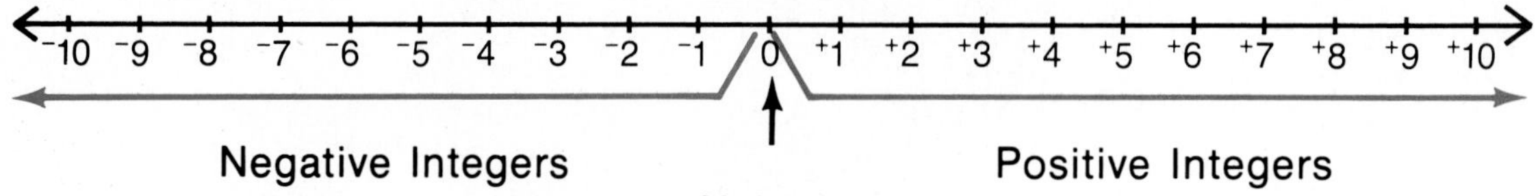


Neither
positive nor negative

$^-6$ is read "negative 6." It names the point 6 units to the left of 0. $^+6$ is read "positive 6." It names the point 6 units to the right of 0. You can write either $^+6$ or 6 for positive 6.

**B.** The **absolute value** of an integer is the number of units from 0 to the point named by the integer.

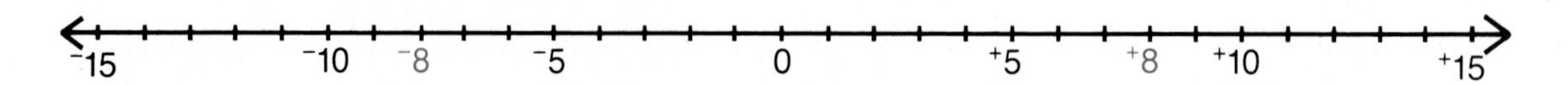


$^-8$ names a point 8 units from 0. $^+8$ names a point 8 units from 0. The absolute value of $^-8$ is 8. The absolute value of $^+8$ is 8.

$$|^-8| = 8 \qquad |^+8| = 8$$
$$|^-8| = |^+8| = 8$$

Since the absolute value of an integer is the distance between the integer and 0, the absolute value of 0 is 0. $|0| = 0$

**C.** Add. $|^+12| + |^-9| = ■$
$\downarrow \quad \downarrow$
$12 + 9 = 21$

**D.** Subtract. $|^-8| - |^+5| = ■$
$\downarrow \quad \downarrow$
$8 - 5 = 3$

**E.** Write >, <, or = for ●.

**Example 1**
$|^+3|$ ● $|^-9|$
$\downarrow \quad \downarrow$
3 ● 9
$3 < 9$
So $|^+3| < |^-9|$

**Example 2**
$|^-9|$ ● $|^+9|$
$\downarrow \quad \downarrow$
9 ● 9
$9 = 9$
So $|^-9| = |^+9|$

**Example 3**
$|^+9|$ ● $|^-3|$
$\downarrow \quad \downarrow$
9 ● 3
$9 > 3$
So $|^+9| > |^-3|$

## CLASS EXERCISES

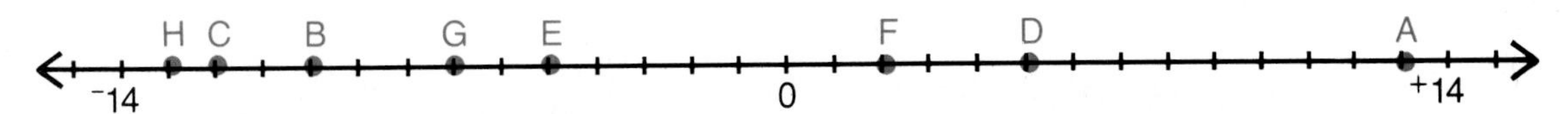


*Give the integer for each point.*

**1.** A  **2.** B  **3.** C  **4.** D  **5.** E  **6.** F  **7.** G  **8.** H

*Find each absolute value.*

**9.** $|^-8|$  **10.** $|9|$  **11.** $|^-6|$  **12.** $|0|$  **13.** $|^-21|$  **14.** $|51|$  **15.** $|^-98|$

## EXERCISES

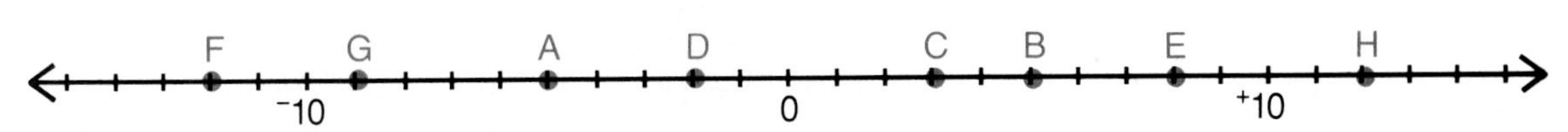


*Give the integer for each point.*

**1.** A  **2.** B  **3.** C  **4.** D  **5.** E  **6.** F  **7.** G  **8.** H

*Find each absolute value.*

**9.** $|^-1|$  **10.** $|1|$  **11.** $|^-16|$  **12.** $|16|$  **13.** $|32|$  **14.** $|^-83|$  **15.** $|^-75|$

**16.** $|125|$  **17.** $|^-216|$  **18.** $|^-59|$  **19.** $|^-22|$  **20.** $|236|$  **21.** $|^-715|$  **22.** $|800|$

*Complete.*

**23.** $|^-6| + |3| =$ ■  **24.** $|^-6| - |3| =$ ■  **25.** $|^-5| \times |4| =$ ■

**26.** $|^-6| \times |^-7| =$ ■  **27.** $|^-15| - |^-10| =$ ■  **28.** $|^-24| \div |^-4| =$ ■

**29.** $|24| \div |^-4| =$ ■  **30.** $|0| \times |^-62| =$ ■  **31.** $|^-42| - |0| =$ ■

*Write $>$, $<$, or $=$ for ●.*

**32.** $|6|$ ● $|^-12|$  **33.** $|^-10|$ ● $|^-9|$  **34.** $|14|$ ● $|20|$  **35.** $|14|$ ● $|^-20|$

**36.** $|^-5|$ ● $|0|$  **37.** $|7|$ ● $|^-7|$  **38.** $|^-8|$ ● $|^-14|$  ★**39.** $|^-8| - 5$ ● $|^-(1 + 4)|$

## PROBLEMS

Temperatures above 0 can be written as positive integers. 15 degrees above 0 is written $^+15°$. Temperatures below 0 can be written as negative integers.

*Write an integer for each temperature.*

**40.** 99 degrees above 0  **41.** 13 degrees below 0  **42.** 2 degrees below 0

1. $^-5$ 9. 1

Homework page 480

# 6-2 Rational Numbers

**A.** **Rational numbers** can be used to name points on a number line. **Positive rational numbers** name points to the right of 0. **Negative rational numbers** name points to the left of 0. Zero is a rational number which is neither positive nor negative.

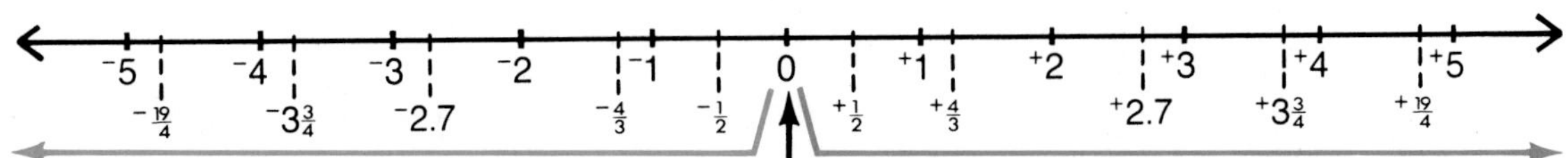


Negative rational numbers

Neither positive nor negative

Positive rational numbers

$^{-}2.7$ is read "negative 2.7." It names the point 2.7 units to the left of 0.
$^{+}2.7$ is read "positive 2.7." It names the point 2.7 units to the right of 0.
You can write either $^{+}2.7$ or 2.7 for positive 2.7.

**B.** The **absolute value** of a rational number is the distance from 0 to the point named by the rational number.

The absolute value of $|^{-}3\frac{3}{4}|$ is $3\frac{3}{4}$. The absolute value of $|^{+}3\frac{3}{4}|$ is $3\frac{3}{4}$.

$$|^{-}3\tfrac{3}{4}| = 3\tfrac{3}{4} \qquad\qquad |^{+}3\tfrac{3}{4}| = 3\tfrac{3}{4}$$

**C.** Add. $|\frac{^{-}3}{8}| + |\frac{^{+}1}{4}| = \blacksquare$

$$|\tfrac{^{-}3}{8}| \rightarrow \tfrac{3}{8} \rightarrow \tfrac{3}{8}$$
$$+|\tfrac{^{+}1}{4}| \rightarrow +\tfrac{1}{4} \rightarrow +\tfrac{2}{8}$$
$$\tfrac{5}{8}$$

**D.** Subtract. $|\frac{^{+}5}{6}| - |\frac{^{-}1}{4}| = \blacksquare$

$$|\tfrac{^{+}5}{6}| \rightarrow \tfrac{5}{6} \rightarrow \tfrac{10}{12}$$
$$-|\tfrac{^{-}1}{4}| \rightarrow -\tfrac{1}{4} \rightarrow -\tfrac{3}{12}$$
$$\tfrac{7}{12}$$

**E.** When you are comparing two numbers on a number line, the number to the right is greater.

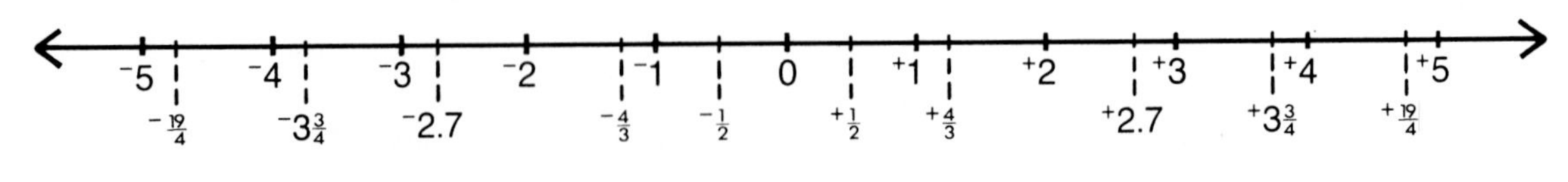


$\frac{^{-}19}{4} < {}^{-}2.7$ $\qquad$ $0 > \frac{^{-}1}{2}$ $\qquad$ $^{-}3\frac{3}{4} > {}^{-}4$

$^{-}5 < \frac{^{+}1}{2}$ $\qquad$ $\frac{^{+}19}{4} > {}^{+}2.7$ $\qquad$ $\frac{^{+}4}{3} < {}^{+}2$

## CLASS EXERCISES

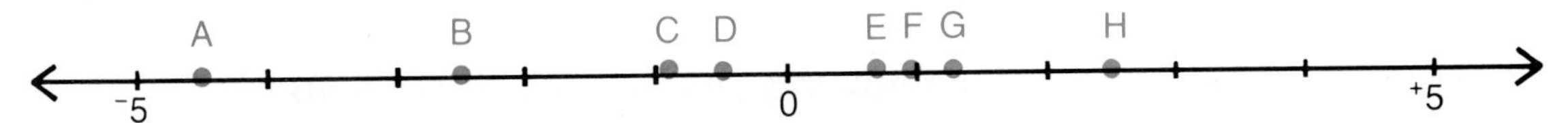


*Name the point for each rational number.*

**1.** $2.5$ **2.** $\frac{3}{4}$ **3.** $\frac{^-1}{2}$ **4.** $^-.9$ **5.** $1\frac{1}{4}$ **6.** $^-2.5$ **7.** $.9$ **8.** $^-4\frac{1}{2}$

*Write >, <, or = for ●.*

**9.** $^-9$ ● $2$ **10.** $\frac{2}{7}$ ● $\frac{5}{7}$ **11.** $|^-7|$ ● $|3|$ **12.** $\frac{9}{1}$ ● $^-9$

## EXERCISES

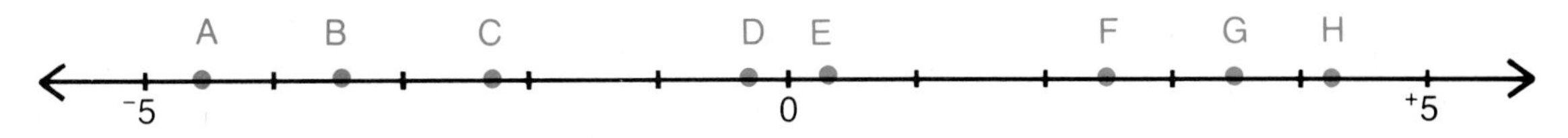


*Name the point for each rational number.*

**1.** $^-3\frac{1}{2}$ **2.** $\frac{1}{4}$ **3.** $\frac{7}{2}$ **4.** $^-2.25$ **5.** $\frac{17}{4}$ **6.** $2\frac{1}{2}$ **7.** $^-4\frac{1}{2}$ **8.** $^-.25$

*Find each absolute value.*

**9.** $|^-.8|$ **10.** $|\frac{^-3}{4}|$ **11.** $|3\frac{2}{5}|$ **12.** $|^-6.8|$ **13.** $|^-5\frac{2}{3}|$ **14.** $|4.3|$ **15.** $|\frac{5}{6}|$ **16.** $|^-.75|$

*Write >, <, or = for ●.*

**17.** $10$ ● $^-6$ **18.** $.8$ ● $.80$ **19.** $\frac{^-1}{7}$ ● $\frac{^-3}{7}$ **20.** $^-7$ ● $^-6$

**21.** $\frac{^-5}{1}$ ● $^-2\frac{1}{2}$ **22.** $\frac{1}{6}$ ● $\frac{^-5}{6}$ **23.** $^-.6$ ● $^-.1$ **24.** $.8$ ● $^-.80$

*Complete.*

**25.** $|^-.7| + |.2| =$ ■ **26.** $|\frac{1}{5}| + |\frac{^-1}{5}| =$ ■ **27.** $|3.7| + |^-1.5| =$ ■

**28.** $|^-1\frac{3}{5}| + |4\frac{1}{5}| =$ ■ **29.** $|.9| - |^-.8| =$ ■ **30.** $|\frac{7}{9}| - |\frac{^-5}{9}| =$ ■

**31.** $|6.3| - |^-6.2| =$ ■ **32.** $|^-9\frac{7}{8}| - |^-6\frac{7}{8}| =$ ■ **33.** $|^-.3| \times |^-.3| =$ ■

**34.** $|\frac{^-1}{4}| \times |\frac{^-1}{4}| =$ ■ **35.** $|^-2.1| \times |3 \times 1|$ ■ **36.** $|^-1\frac{1}{2}| \times |5\frac{1}{2}| =$ ■

THINK!

### Logical Reasoning

A rabbit ate 100 carrots in five days. Each day the rabbit ate 6 more carrots than on the day before. How many carrots did the rabbit eat each day?

1. B 9. .8

Homework page 480

# 6-3 Addition

**A.** To add integers, think of combining charges. Each positive charge **cancels** the effect of one negative charge.

Find the **net charge** for each combination.

$^{+}5 + {}^{+}8 = ■$

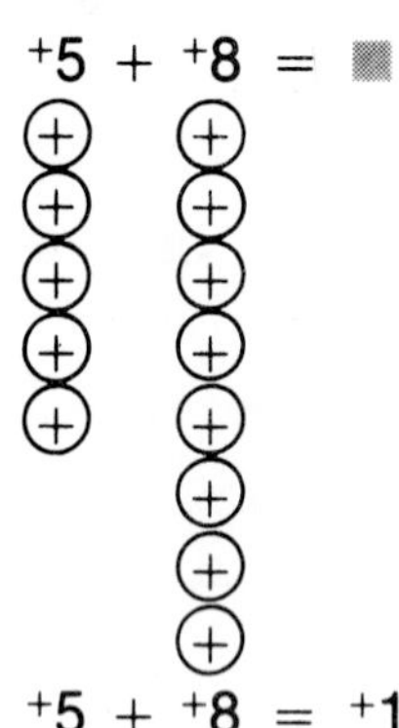

$^{+}5 + {}^{+}8 = {}^{+}13$

$^{-}5 + {}^{-}8 = ■$

$^{-}5 + {}^{-}8 = {}^{-}13$

$^{-}5 + {}^{+}8 = ■$

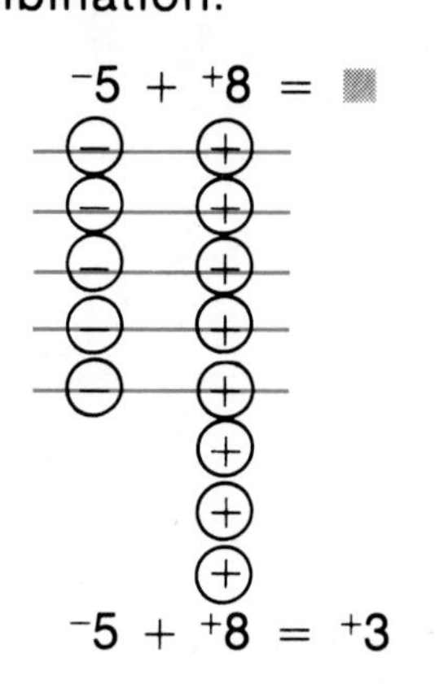

$^{-}5 + {}^{+}8 = {}^{+}3$

$^{+}5 + {}^{-}8 = ■$

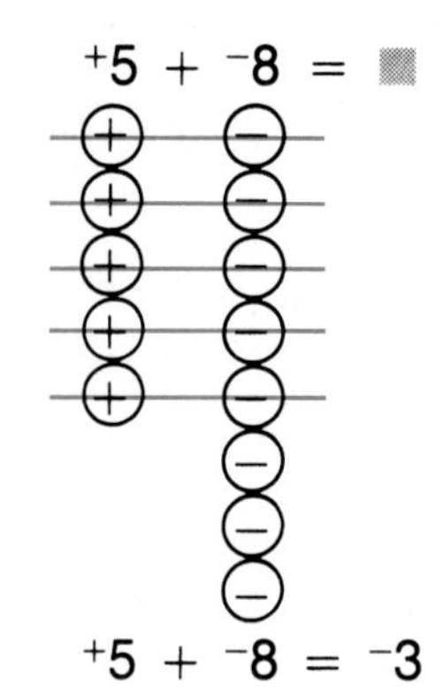

$^{+}5 + {}^{-}8 = {}^{-}3$

**B.** $^{+}7 + {}^{-}7 = ■$

$^{+}7 + {}^{-}7 = 0$

$^{-}7 + {}^{+}7 = ■$

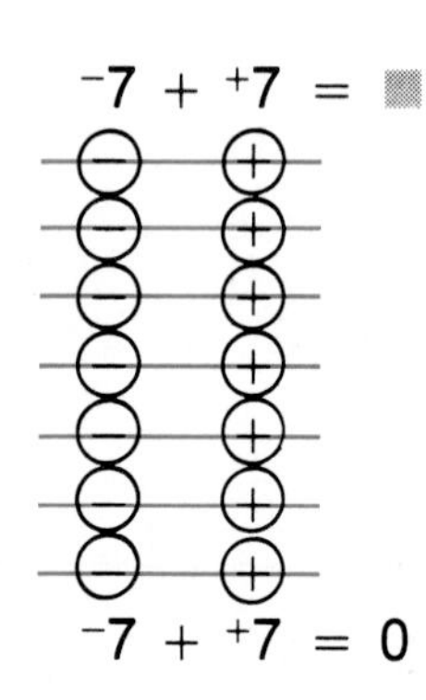

$^{-}7 + {}^{+}7 = 0$

**When the sum of two integers is 0, each is the additive inverse, or opposite, of the other.**

The additive inverse, or opposite, of $^{+}7$ is $^{-}7$.
*Write:* $- {}^{+}7 = {}^{-}7$
The additive inverse, or opposite, of $^{-}7$ is $^{+}7$.
*Write:* $- {}^{-}7 = {}^{+}7$
Since $0 + 0 = 0$, 0 is its own additive inverse.

**C.** Complete.

**Example 1**

$- {}^{+}16 = ■$

$^{+}16 + {}^{-}16 = 0$

So, $- {}^{+}16 = {}^{-}16$

**Example 2**

$- {}^{-}25 = ■$

$^{-}25 + {}^{+}25 = 0$

So, $- {}^{-}25 = {}^{+}25$

## CLASS EXERCISES

*Add.*

1. $6 + {}^{-}2 =$ ■
2. ${}^{-}6 + 2 =$ ■
3. ${}^{-}6 + {}^{-}2 =$ ■
4. $6 + 2 =$ ■
5. ${}^{-}5 + 0 =$ ■
6. $0 + {}^{-}5 =$ ■
7. ${}^{-}5 + 5 =$ ■
8. ${}^{-}5 + {}^{-}5 =$ ■

*Complete.*

9. $-{}^{+}5 =$ ■
10. $-{}^{-}8 =$ ■
11. $-{}^{-}16 =$ ■ **$^{+}16$**
12. $-{}^{+}23 =$ ■

## EXERCISES

*Add.*

1. ${}^{-}8 + 2 =$ ■
2. ${}^{-}4 + {}^{-}3 =$ ■
3. ${}^{-}3 + 7 =$ ■
4. ${}^{-}3 + {}^{-}5 =$ ■
5. ${}^{-}9 + 0 =$ ■
6. $12 + {}^{-}5 =$ ■
7. $2 + {}^{-}6 =$ ■
8. ${}^{-}7 + {}^{-}3 =$ ■
9. $9 + {}^{-}9 =$ ■
10. ${}^{-}9 + {}^{-}9 =$ ■
11. ${}^{-}9 + 9 =$ ■
12. $9 + 9 =$ ■
13. ${}^{-}10 + 7 =$ ■
14. ${}^{-}10 + {}^{-}7 =$ ■
15. $10 + {}^{-}7$ ■

*Complete.*

16. $-{}^{-}10 =$ ■
17. $-{}^{+}7 =$ ■
18. $-{}^{-}12 =$ ■
19. $-{}^{+}27 =$ ■
20. $-{}^{-}11 =$ ■
★21. ${}^{+}8 + (-{}^{-}3) =$ ■
★22. ${}^{-}5 + (-{}^{+}3) =$ ■
★23. $6 + (-{}^{+}8) =$ ■
★24. $16 + (-{}^{-}4) =$ ■

## PROBLEMS

25. The temperature reading at 6:30 A.M. was ${}^{-}8°$. During the next hour and a half there was a temperature change of ${}^{+}10°$. What was the temperature reading at 8:00 A.M.?

26. The temperature reading at 9:30 P.M. was ${}^{-}5°$. During the next hour and a half there was a temperature change of ${}^{-}4°$. What was the temperature reading at 11:00 P.M.?

## THINK!

**Integer Magic Square**

The sum of the numbers in each row, column, and diagonal is ${}^{-}35$. Complete the magic square.

| | | | | |
|---|---|---|---|---|
| | | $^{-}18$ | $^{-}9$ | |
| 3 | | | $^{-}15$ | $^{-}6$ |
| | | $^{-}7$ | | $^{-}14$ |
| $^{-}8$ | 1 | | $^{-}1$ | |
| $^{-}19$ | $^{-}5$ | 4 | | $^{-}3$ |

1. $^{-}6$ 16. $^{+}10$

Homework page 480

# 6-4 More Addition

**A.** You can add integers without combining charges.

$^{-}5 + ^{-}3 = \blacksquare$

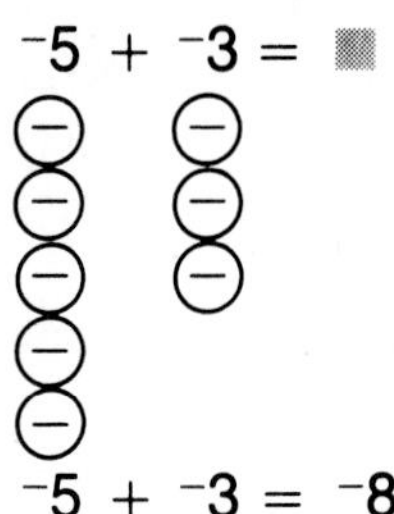

$^{-}5 + ^{-}3 = ^{-}8$

Notice: $|^{-}5| + |^{-}3| = 8$

$^{-}5 + ^{-}3 = ^{-}8$

Both negative. Sum is negative.

$^{+}3 + ^{+}5 = \blacksquare$

$^{+}3 + ^{+}5 = ^{+}8$

Notice: $|^{+}3| + |^{+}5| = 8$

$^{+}3 + ^{+}5 = ^{+}8$

Both positive. Sum is positive.

> **To find the sum of two positive or two negative integers, add their absolute values.**
>
> **If the two integers are positive, the sum is positive.**
> **If the two integers are negative, the sum is negative.**

**B.** $^{+}3 + ^{-}5 = \blacksquare$

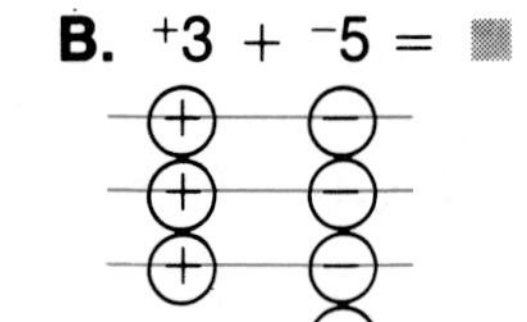

$^{+}3 + ^{-}5 = ^{-}2$

$^{-}5 + ^{+}3 = \blacksquare$

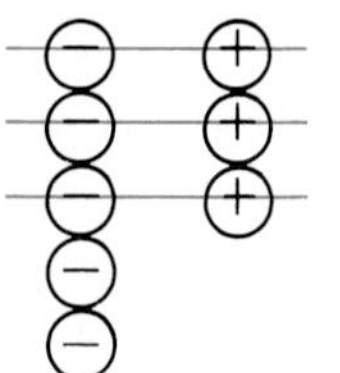

$^{-}5 + ^{+}3 = ^{-}2$

$^{-}3 + ^{+}5 = \blacksquare$

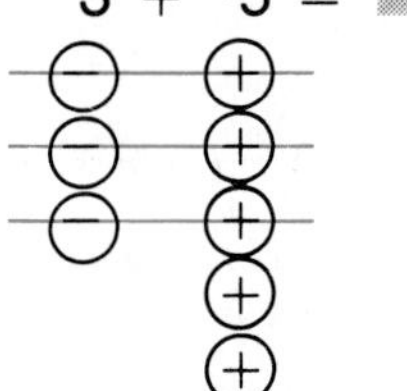

$^{-}3 + ^{+}5 = ^{+}2$

$^{+}5 + ^{-}3 = \blacksquare$

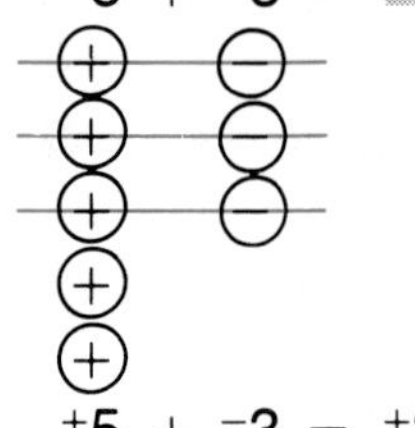

$^{+}5 + ^{-}3 = ^{+}2$

Subtract the smaller absolute value from the larger in each example.

$^{+}3 + ^{-}5 = ^{-}2$ and $^{-}5 + ^{+}3 = ^{-}2$

$|^{-}5| - |^{+}3| = 2$

|Negative| larger ⟶ Sum negative

$^{+}3 + ^{-}5 = ^{-}2$ $\quad$ $^{-}5 + ^{+}3 = ^{-}2$

$^{-}3 + ^{+}5 = ^{+}2$ and $^{+}5 + ^{-}3 = ^{+}2$

$|^{+}5| - |^{-}3| = 2$

|Positive| larger ⟶ Sum positive

$^{-}3 + ^{+}5 = ^{+}2$ $\quad$ $^{+}5 + ^{-}3 = ^{+}2$

> **To find the sum of a positive integer and a negative integer, subtract the smaller absolute value from the larger.**
>
> **If |positive integer| > |negative integer|, the sum is positive.**
> **If |negative integer| > |positive integer|, the sum is negative.**

## CLASS EXERCISES

*Add.*

1. ${}^{-}8 + {}^{-}7 =$ ■
2. ${}^{-}8 + 7 =$ ■
3. $8 + {}^{-}7 =$ ■
4. ${}^{-}8 + 8 =$ ■
5. ${}^{-}9 + 4 =$ ■
6. ${}^{-}9 + {}^{-}4 =$ ■
7. $9 + {}^{-}4 =$ ■
8. ${}^{-}9 + 9 =$ ■

## EXERCISES

*Add.*

1. $12 + {}^{-}9 =$ ■
2. ${}^{-}3 + {}^{-}8 =$ ■
3. ${}^{-}6 + 13 =$ ■
4. ${}^{-}20 + 8 =$ ■
5. $16 + {}^{-}10 =$ ■
6. $14 + 12 =$ ■
7. ${}^{-}11 + {}^{-}7 =$ ■
8. ${}^{-}14 + 15 =$ ■
9. $17 + {}^{-}6 =$ ■
10. $8 + {}^{-}12 =$ ■
11. ${}^{-}2 + {}^{-}13 =$ ■
12. ${}^{-}7 + 15 =$ ■
13. ${}^{-}12 + 17 =$ ■
14. $20 + {}^{-}10 =$ ■
15. $78 + {}^{-}78 =$ ■
16. ${}^{-}50 + 23 =$ ■
17. $48 + {}^{-}60 =$ ■
18. ${}^{-}24 + {}^{-}30 =$ ■
19. ${}^{-}89 + 89 =$ ■
20. ${}^{-}58 + 92 =$ ■
21. $43 + {}^{-}57 =$ ■
22. ${}^{-}80 + 197 =$ ■
23. ${}^{-}27 + {}^{-}19 =$ ■
24. $93 + 6 =$ ■
25. $60 + {}^{-}100 =$ ■
26. $26 + 114 =$ ■
27. $378 + 543 =$ ■
28. ${}^{-}214 + 502 =$ ■
29. $200 + {}^{-}319 =$ ■
30. $1{,}162 + {}^{-}1{,}621 =$ ■

★ 31. ${}^{-}1\frac{1}{4} + 3\frac{1}{4} =$ ■

★ 32. $8.7 + {}^{-}7.4 =$ ■

★ 33. $-(52 + 60) + {}^{-}93 =$ ■

**THINK!**

### Number Patterns

A certain worker asked for the following wages during the month of February (it was not a leap year): 1¢ the first day, 2¢ the second day, 4¢ the third day, and so on, each day's pay being double that of the day before. How much would the worker be paid on the last day of February? What would the total wages for the month be? (Use your calculator to find the answers.)

1. ${}^{+}3$ 7. ${}^{-}18$

Homework page 481

# 6-5 Subtraction

**A.** The coach of a football team records a positive integer when his team gains yardage and a negative integer when his team loses yardage. When a play ended, his team was on their own 25-yard line and the coach recorded ${}^{-}12$. On what yard line was the team prior to that play?

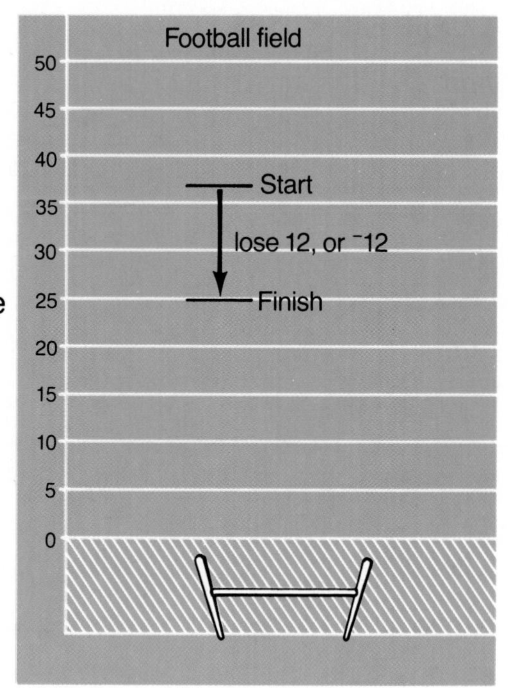


Subtract to find the yard line.

From the picture: ${}^{+}25 - {}^{-}12 = {}^{+}37$

Note that ${}^{+}25 + {}^{+}12 = {}^{+}37$

Also, ${}^{+}12 = -\,{}^{-}12$

So, ${}^{+}25 - {}^{-}12 = {}^{+}25 + {}^{+}12 = {}^{+}37$

The team was on their own 37-yard line prior to the play.

**B.** **To find the difference of two integers, add the first integer and the additive inverse of the second integer.**

**Example 1**

${}^{+}7 - {}^{-}15 = ■$

$\downarrow \quad \downarrow$

${}^{+}7 + (-\,{}^{-}15)$

$\downarrow \quad \downarrow$

${}^{+}7 + {}^{+}15 = {}^{+}22$

**Example 2**

${}^{-}20 - {}^{-}9 = ■$

$\downarrow \quad \downarrow$

${}^{-}20 + (-\,{}^{-}9)$

$\downarrow \quad \downarrow$

${}^{-}20 + {}^{+}9 = {}^{-}11$

**Example 3**

${}^{+}29 - {}^{+}38 = ■$

$\downarrow \quad \downarrow$

${}^{+}29 + {}^{-}38 = {}^{-}9$

**Example 4**

${}^{-}16 - {}^{+}13 = ■$

$\downarrow \quad \downarrow$

${}^{-}16 + {}^{-}13 = {}^{-}29$

**C.** Solve. $x + {}^{-}2 = 7$

Subtract ${}^{-}2$ from both sides.

$x + {}^{-}2 = 7$

$x + {}^{-}2 - {}^{-}2 = 7 - {}^{-}2$

$x = 7 + 2$

$x = 9$

*Solution:* 9

*Check:* $9 + {}^{-}2 = 7$

$7 = 7$ true

Solve. $y - {}^{-}4 = {}^{-}3$

Add ${}^{-}4$ to both sides.

$y - {}^{-}4 = {}^{-}3$

$y - {}^{-}4 + {}^{-}4 = {}^{-}3 + {}^{-}4$

$y = {}^{-}3 + {}^{-}4$

$y = {}^{-}7$

*Solution:* ${}^{-}7$

*Check:* ${}^{-}7 - {}^{-}4 = {}^{-}3$

${}^{-}3 = {}^{-}3$ true

## CLASS EXERCISES

*Complete.*

**1.** $9 - {}^{-}3 = 9 + \blacksquare$ **2.** ${}^{-}8 - {}^{-}4 = {}^{-}8 + \blacksquare$ **3.** $5 - 18 = 5 + \blacksquare$

*Find the difference.*

**4.** $13 - 15 = \blacksquare$ **5.** ${}^{-}26 - {}^{-}40 = \blacksquare$ **6.** ${}^{-}5 - 17 = \blacksquare$ **7.** $2 - 16 = \blacksquare$

## EXERCISES

*Subtract.*

**1.** $2 - {}^{-}5 = \blacksquare$ **2.** $6 - 15 = \blacksquare$ **3.** ${}^{-}7 - {}^{-}10 = \blacksquare$

**4.** ${}^{-}9 - 4 = \blacksquare$ **5.** ${}^{-}8 - {}^{-}2 = \blacksquare$ **6.** $9 - 10 = \blacksquare$

**7.** ${}^{-}11 - 14 = \blacksquare$ **8.** $8 - {}^{-}12 = \blacksquare$ **9.** ${}^{-}15 - {}^{-}15 = \blacksquare$

**10.** $24 - 16 = \blacksquare$ **11.** ${}^{-}3 - 8 = \blacksquare$ **12.** $10 - 40 = \blacksquare$

**13.** ${}^{-}60 - {}^{-}10 = \blacksquare$ **14.** ${}^{-}50 - 40 = \blacksquare$ **15.** $20 - {}^{-}30 = \blacksquare$

**16.** ${}^{-}16 - {}^{-}20 = \blacksquare$ **★17.** $7 - {}^{-}.6 = \blacksquare$ **★18.** ${}^{-}8\frac{1}{2} - {}^{-}5\frac{1}{2} = \blacksquare$

**★19.** ${}^{-}5.9 - {}^{+}1.3 = \blacksquare$ **★20.** $\frac{3}{7} - \frac{{}^{-}1}{7} = \blacksquare$ **★21.** ${}^{-}\frac{1}{2} - {}^{-}\frac{3}{8} = \blacksquare$

*Solve.*

**22.** $y + {}^{-}9 = 13$ **23.** $m - {}^{-}12 = {}^{-}5$ **24.** $s + 20 = 12$ **25.** $a + {}^{-}7 = 10$

**26.** $u - 9 = {}^{-}5$ **27.** $w + {}^{-}20 = 0$ **28.** $x - {}^{-}16 = 16$ **29.** $b - 6 = {}^{-}8$

## PROBLEMS

**30.** After a play that ended on the team's own 40-yard line the coach recorded ⁻8. On what yard line was the football team prior to that play?

**31.** After a play that began on the team's own 30-yard line the coach recorded ⁻16. On what yard line was the football team after the play?

## THINK!

### Logical Reason

If you have a balance scale and the following weights—1 lb, 2 lb, 4 lb, 8 lb—you can weigh every package with a whole number weight from 1 to 15 lb. Which packages could not be weighed if the 1-lb weight were missing? If the 4-lb weight were missing?

Homework page 481

# 6-6 Multiplication

**A.** A diver descended at a rate of $^-3$ meters per minute. If she started at the surface, how far from the surface was she after 4 minutes?

From the picture:
$4 \times {}^-3 = {}^-12$

The diver was $^-12$ meters from the surface.

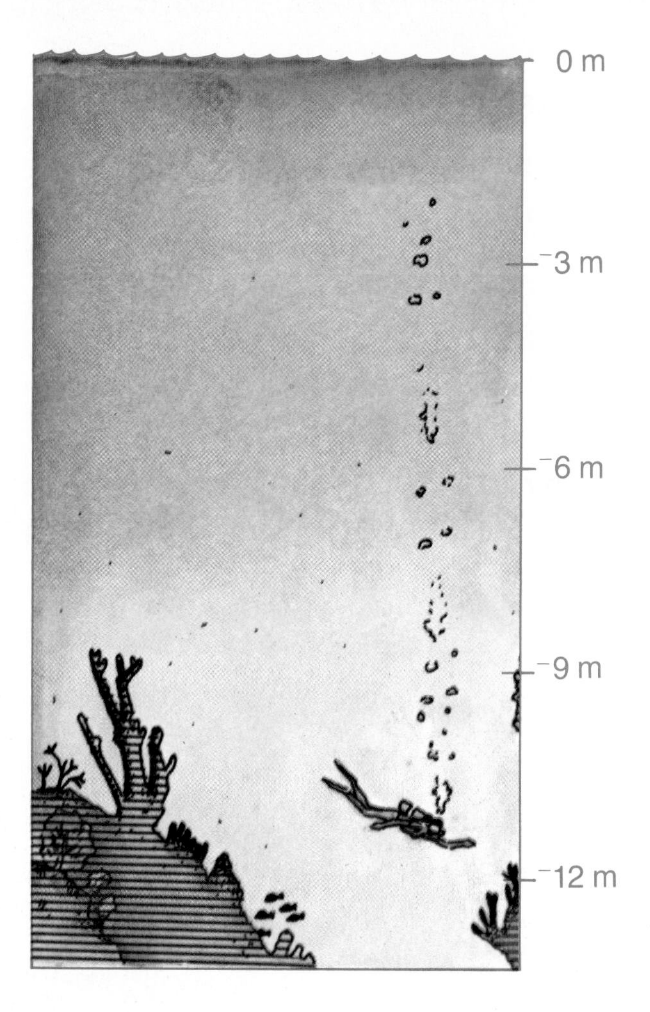


**B.**

> **To multiply integers, multiply their absolute values.**
>
> **If one integer is positive and the other is negative, the product is negative.**
>
> **If both integers are positive or both are negative, the product is positive.**

**Example 1**

$^+7 \times {}^-6 = \blacksquare$

$|^+7| \times |^-6| = 42$

| One positive, one negative. Product is negative. |
|---|

$^+7 \times {}^-6 = {}^-42$

**Example 2**

$^-8 \times {}^+7 = \blacksquare$

$|^-8| \times |^+7| = 56$

| One negative, one positive. Product is negative. |
|---|

$^-8 \times {}^+7 = {}^-56$

**Example 3**

$^+8 \times {}^+75 = \blacksquare$

$|^+8| \times |^+75| = 600$

| Both positive. Product is positive. |
|---|

$^+8 \times {}^+75 = {}^+600$

**Example 4**

$^-11 \times {}^-9 = \blacksquare$

$|^-11| \times |^-9| = 99$

| Both negative. Product is positive. |
|---|

$^-11 \times {}^-9 = {}^+99$

## CLASS EXERCISES

*Multiply.*

**1.** $^-3 \times 8 = ■$ **2.** $^-5 \times {}^-4 = ■$ **3.** $6 \times {}^-2 = ■$ **4.** $9 \times 60 = ■$

**5.** $^-98 \times 0 = ■$ **6.** $^-20 \times {}^-8 = ■$ **7.** $75 \times {}^-3 = ■$ **8.** $^-7 \times {}^-80 = ■$

## EXERCISES

*Multiply.*

**1.** $^-5 \times {}^-8 = ■$ **2.** $^-7 \times {}^-9 = ■$ **3.** $^-3 \times 6 = ■$

**4.** $^-9 \times {}^-6 = ■$ **5.** $8 \times 7 = ■$ **6.** $8 \times {}^-4 = ■$

**7.** $3 \times 26 = ■$ **8.** $10 \times {}^-16 = ■$ **9.** $^-12 \times {}^-20 = ■$

**10.** $^-80 \times 50 = ■$ **11.** $42 \times 100 = ■$ **12.** $^-3{,}651 \times 0 = ■$

*Add, subtract, or multiply.*

**13.** $^-31 - 45 = ■$ **14.** $^-16 \times 20 = ■$ **15.** $^-82 + 100 = ■$

**16.** $^-79 + {}^-34 = ■$ **17.** $^-47 - {}^-60 = ■$ **18.** $^-51 \times {}^-14 = ■$

**19.** $197 + {}^-108 = ■$ **20.** $92 - 300 = ■$ **21.** $^-16 \times {}^-1{,}000 = ■$

**22.** $^-418 + {}^-563 = ■$ **23.** $^-2{,}416 \times 1 = ■$ **24.** $^-6{,}107 \times 0 = ■$

**25.** $96 \times 2{,}004 = ■$ **26.** $^-200 \times {}^-714 = ■$ **27.** $73 - 568 = ■$

**28.** $^-8 \times ({}^-20 + 10) = ■$ **29.** $^-12 + ({}^-10 \times {}^-5) = ■$ **30.** $(16 - 50) \times {}^-7 = ■$

★ **31.** $9 \times {}^-.9 = ■$ ★ **32.** $^-3 \times \frac{1}{2} = ■$ ★ **33.** $^-.6 \times {}^-.6 = ■$

## PROBLEMS

**34.** Jill descended from the surface at a rate of $^-4$ meters per minute. Where was Jill at the end of 5 minutes? 7 minutes?

★ **35.** Harry descended from the surface at a rate of $^-3.5$ meters per minute. Where was Harry at the end of 6 minutes?

## THINK!

**Guess and Check**

Find three consecutive even integers whose sum is $^-36$.

**1.** $^+40$ **13.** $^-76$



Homework page 481

# 6-7 Division

**A.** Multiplication and division of integers are related in the same way as multiplication and division of whole numbers.

**Example 1** $^{+}56 \div {}^{+}8 = \blacksquare$

$^{+}7 \times {}^{+}8 = {}^{+}56$

So, $^{+}56 \div {}^{+}8 = {}^{+}7$

**Example 2** $^{+}56 \div {}^{-}8 = \blacksquare$

$^{-}7 \times {}^{-}8 = {}^{+}56$

So, $^{+}56 \div {}^{-}8 = {}^{-}7$

**Example 3** $^{-}56 \div {}^{+}8 = \blacksquare$

$^{-}7 \times {}^{+}8 = {}^{-}56$

So, $^{-}56 \div {}^{+}8 = {}^{-}7$

**Example 4** $^{-}56 \div {}^{-}8 = \blacksquare$

$^{+}7 \times {}^{-}8 = {}^{-}56$

So, $^{-}56 \div {}^{-}8 = {}^{+}7$

**B.** **To divide integers, divide their absolute values.**

**If both integers are positive or both are negative, the quotient is positive.**

**If one integer is positive and one is negative, the quotient is negative.**

**Example 1**

$^{+}40 \div {}^{-}5 = \blacksquare$

$|^{+}40| \div |^{-}5| = 8$

One positive, one negative.
Quotient is negative.

So, $^{+}40 \div {}^{-}5 = {}^{-}8$

**Example 2**

$^{-}39 \div {}^{+}6 = \blacksquare$

$|^{-}39| \div |^{+}6| = 6.5$, or $6\frac{1}{2}$

One negative, one positive.
Quotient is negative.

So, $^{-}39 \div {}^{+}6 = {}^{-}6.5$, or $^{-}6\frac{1}{2}$

**Example 3**

$^{-}63 \div {}^{-}7 = \blacksquare$

$|^{-}63| \div |^{-}7| = 9$

Both integers negative.
Quotient is positive.

$^{-}63 \div {}^{-}7 = {}^{+}9$

**Example 4**

$^{+}25 \div {}^{+}3 = \blacksquare$

$|^{+}25| \div |^{+}3| = 8.\overline{3}$, or $8\frac{1}{3}$

Both integers positive.
Quotient is positive.

$^{+}25 \div {}^{+}3 = {}^{+}8.\overline{3}$, or $^{+}8\frac{1}{3}$

**C.** Solve. $^{-}4x = 32$

Divide both sides by $^{-}4$.

$$^{-}4x = 32$$
$$^{-}4x \div {}^{-}4 = 32 \div {}^{-}4$$
$$x = {}^{-}8$$

*Solution:* $^{-}8$

Solve. $\frac{x}{^{-}5} = {}^{-}30$

Multiply both sides by $^{-}5$.

$$\frac{x}{^{-}5} \cdot {}^{-}5 = {}^{-}30 \cdot {}^{-}5$$
$$x = 150$$

*Solution:* 150

## CLASS EXERCISES

*Divide.*

1. $24 \div {}^{-}8 =$ ■
2. ${}^{-}15 \div 7 =$ ■
3. ${}^{-}20 \div 4 =$ ■
4. ${}^{-}19 \div {}^{-}2 =$ ■
5. $110 \div 7 =$ ■
6. ${}^{-}12 \div {}^{-}3 =$ ■
7. $0 \div {}^{-}8 =$ ■
8. ${}^{-}63 \div 8 =$ ■

## EXERCISES

*Divide.*

1. ${}^{-}36 \div {}^{-}4 =$ ■
2. $72 \div {}^{-}8 =$ ■
3. ${}^{-}42 \div 7 =$ ■
4. ${}^{-}81 \div 9 =$ ■
5. $54 \div {}^{-}6 =$ ■
6. ${}^{-}63 \div {}^{-}7 =$ ■
7. $35 \div {}^{-}7 =$ ■
8. ${}^{-}24 \div {}^{-}3 =$ ■
9. ${}^{-}56 \div 8 =$ ■
10. $0 \div 16 =$ ■
11. ${}^{-}82 \div {}^{-}2 =$ ■
12. $64 \div {}^{-}4 =$ ■
13. ${}^{-}84 \div {}^{-}6 =$ ■
14. ${}^{-}40 \div 40 =$ ■
15. $48 \div {}^{-}3 =$ ■
16. $51 \div {}^{-}1 =$ ■
17. ${}^{-}32 \div 4 =$ ■
18. ${}^{-}96 \div 1 =$ ■
19. $57 \div 8 =$ ■
20. ${}^{-}15 \div 2 =$ ■
21. ${}^{-}41 \div {}^{-}3 =$ ■
22. $94 \div {}^{-}5 =$ ■
23. ${}^{-}73 \div 9 =$ ■
24. ${}^{-}80 \div {}^{-}6 =$ ■

★25. ${}^{-}8.4 \div 4 =$ ■

★26. ${}^{-}6.08 \div .02 =$ ■

★27. $\frac{{}^{-}1}{3} \div \frac{{}^{-}1}{6} =$ ■

*Solve.*

28. ${}^{-}5x = {}^{-}20$
29. $\frac{t}{7} = {}^{-}3$
30. $\frac{w}{{}^{-}4} = 8$
31. $9m = {}^{-}63$
32. $\frac{y}{{}^{-}2} = {}^{-}15$

★33. $2x - 6 = {}^{-}10$

★34. $\frac{s}{{}^{-}3} + {}^{-}2 = 1$

★35. $\frac{{}^{-}2f}{5} - {}^{-}3 = 7$

## PROBLEMS

36. The price of gold on the commodities market changed ${}^{-}\$75$ during a 5-day period. What was the average daily change in the value of gold during the period?

37. The price of silver during the same 5-day period changed ${}^{+}\$.18$ each day. What was the total change in value for the 5-day period?

## THINK!

**True or False**

Write T if you think the statement is always true. Write F if the statement is not always true. If x is a positive rational number and y is a negative rational number, then:

1. $x + y < x$ and $x + y > y$
2. $x \cdot y < x$ and $x \cdot y > y$
3. $x^2 > y^2$
4. $(x \cdot y) \cdot (x \cdot y) > 0$

1. +9 5. −9

Homework page 482

# Problem Solving READ • PLAN • DO • ANSWER • CHECK

## 6-8 Using Number Scales

When numbers are used as measures, it is often important to label some important time or position "zero" and give other measures as "below or before zero" and "above or after zero." A **number scale** can be used to show numbers that are measures.

**Example 1**
The opening value of one share of stock on Wednesday was $36.70. The graph shows the stock's change in value during the day on Wednesday. What was the closing value of the stock on Wednesday?

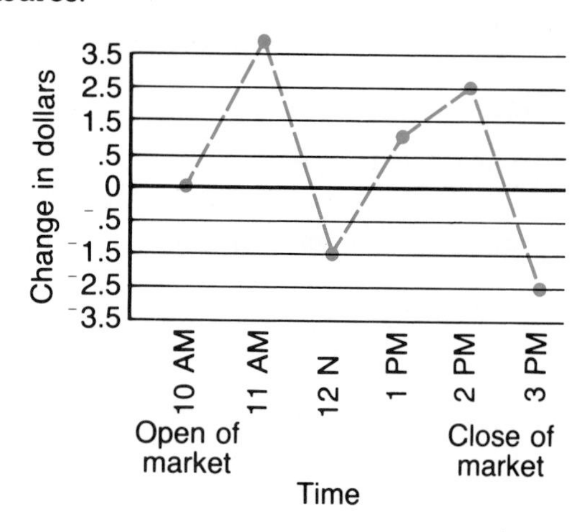


$\$36.70 + {}^{-}\$2.50 = \$34.20$

The stock's closing value was $34.20.

**Example 2** Temperature

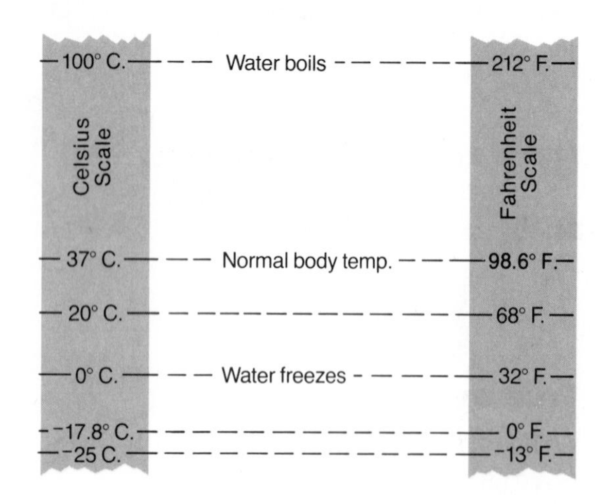


From a temperature of 12°C there was a temperature change of ⁻16°C. What was the temperature after the change?

$$12 + {}^{-}16 = {}^{-}4$$

The temperature was ⁻4°C after the change.

**Example 3** Altitudes above and below sea level

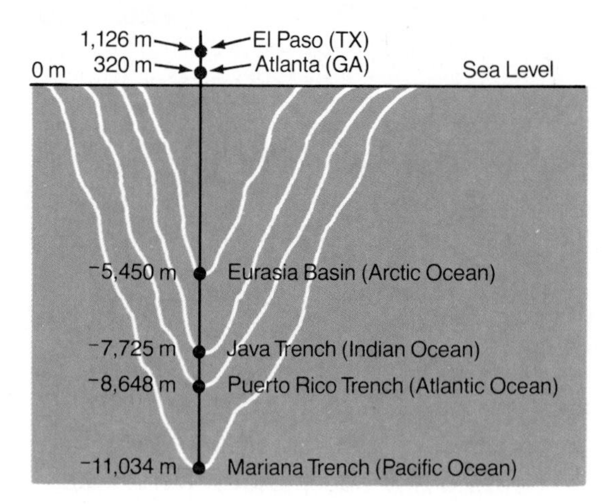


Find the difference in altitudes between El Paso, Texas and the Java Trench.

$$1{,}126 - {}^{-}7{,}725 = 1{,}126 + 7{,}725 = 8{,}851 \text{ m}$$

The difference in altitudes is 8,851 m.

## CLASS EXERCISES

1. On Thursday, the stock shown in Example 1 closed with a change in value of $^-$1.75 from Wednesday's closing. What was its closing value on Thursday?

2. After a change of $^-12$°C the temperature was $^-5$°C. What was the temperature before this change?

## PROBLEMS

1. The altitude of the highest mountain on Earth is 8,848 m. How far above the bottom of the Mariana Trench is the top of this mountain?

2. After a change in mass of $^-3.6$ kg, Mr. Tim's mass was 80.9 kg. What was his mass before this change?

3. The Sears Tower, the world's tallest building, has a height of 443 m. If it were "moved" to sit in the Puerto Rico Trench, what would be the altitude of its top?

4. The highest temperature recorded on Earth was 136°F, in northern Africa. The lowest was $^-126.9$°F in Siberia. How great is the difference of these record temperatures?

5. The altitude of Death Valley is $^-86$ m. The CN Tower is 555 m high. If the CN Tower were moved to Death Valley, what would be the altitude of its top?

6. The closing value of a share of stock was $189.70. During that day its change in value was $^-$12.25. What was its opening value that day?

7. To rocket engineers, $^-3$ h means 3 hours before the launching time of a rocket. 5 h means 5 h after launching. 0 h names the exact time of the launch. What is the total time from $^-$(3 h 2 min) to 2 h 10 min?

★ 8. A rocket was to be launched at 1:40 P.M. The countdown started at $^-$(9 h 50 min) and continued until 1 h 30 min. At what time did the countdown start? At what time did it end?

★ 9. Suppose Sears Tower buildings, each 443 m tall, were stacked on top of each other, starting at the bottom of the Mariana Trench. How many Sears Towers would have to be used in order to see part of the last one above the surface of the Pacific Ocean? How much of the tower could be seen?

## ON YOUR OWN

### Data Search

Find the height in meters of the tallest building in your state. Use that information along with any information you choose from Example 3 on page 208 to create three word problems. Give them to a classmate to solve.

Homework page 482

# 6-9 Integers as Exponents

**A.** You have already used 0 and positive integers as exponents. You can use $^-1$ as an exponent to show the reciprocal of a number.

$2^{-1} = \frac{1}{2}$ $\quad 10^{-1} = \frac{1}{10}$ $\quad 100^{-1} = \frac{1}{100}$

**B.** These examples show how other negative integers are used as exponents.

$2^{-3} = \frac{1}{2^3} = \frac{1}{2 \cdot 2 \cdot 2} = \frac{1}{8}$ $\quad 10^{-4} = \frac{1}{10^4} = \frac{1}{10 \cdot 10 \cdot 10 \cdot 10} = \frac{1}{10{,}000}$

**C.** You can multiply powers of the same base by adding exponents.

$3^5 \times 3^2 = \underbrace{(3 \cdot 3 \cdot 3 \cdot 3 \cdot 3) \cdot (3 \cdot 3)}_{\text{7 factors}} = 3^7$ — $7 = 5 + 2$

$5^4 \times 5^{-2} = 5^4 \times \frac{1}{5^2} = \frac{\overset{1}{\cancel{5}} \cdot \overset{1}{\cancel{5}} \cdot 5 \cdot 5}{\underset{1}{\cancel{5}} \cdot \underset{1}{\cancel{5}}} = \underbrace{5 \cdot 5}_{\text{2 factors}} = 5^2$ — $2 = 4 + {}^-2$

$6^{-4} \times 6^{-3} = \frac{1}{6^4} \times \frac{1}{6^3} = \frac{1}{6^4 \times 6^3} = \frac{1}{\underbrace{6 \cdot 6 \cdot 6 \cdot 6 \cdot 6 \cdot 6 \cdot 6}_{\text{7 factors}}} = \frac{1}{6^7} = 6^{-7}$ — ${}^-7 = {}^-4 + {}^-3$

**D.** You can divide powers of the same base by subtracting exponents.

$4^5 \div 4^2 = \frac{4^5}{4^2} = \frac{\overset{1}{\cancel{4}} \cdot \overset{1}{\cancel{4}} \cdot 4 \cdot 4 \cdot 4}{\underset{1}{\cancel{4}} \cdot \underset{1}{\cancel{4}}} = 4 \cdot 4 \cdot 4 = 4^3$ — $3 = 5 - 2$

$3^2 \div 3^4 = \frac{3^2}{3^4} = \frac{\overset{1}{\cancel{3}} \cdot \overset{1}{\cancel{3}}}{\underset{1}{\cancel{3}} \cdot \underset{1}{\cancel{3}} \cdot 3 \cdot 3} = \frac{1}{\underbrace{3 \cdot 3}_{\text{2 factors}}} = \frac{1}{3^2} = 3^{-2}$ — ${}^-2 = 2 - 4$

$5^6 \div 5^{-2} = 5^6 \div \frac{1}{5^2} = 5^6 \times \frac{5^2}{1} = 5^6 \times 5^2 = 5^8$ — $8 = 6 - {}^-2$

**E.** You can use the laws of exponents only when the bases are equal.

$2^3 \cdot 2^2 \cdot 3^4 = (2 \cdot 2 \cdot 2) \cdot (2 \cdot 2) \cdot (3 \cdot 3 \cdot 3 \cdot 3)$

$= 2^5 \cdot 3^4$

Bases are different.
Cannot be simplified using exponents.

## CLASS EXERCISES

*Complete. Use exponents.*

**1.** $3^2 \times 3^5 = ■$ **2.** $5^3 \div 5^{-4} = ■$ **3.** $\frac{7^{-5}}{7^{-3}} = ■$ **4.** $6^{-7} \times 6^4 = ■$

*Simplify. Use exponents.*

**5.** $(2 \cdot 2) \cdot (2 \cdot 2 \cdot 2) \cdot (7 \cdot 7)$ **6.** $3^5 \cdot 2^{-4} \cdot 3^2 \cdot 2^7$ **7.** $\frac{5^2 \cdot 7^{-3}}{7^2}$

## EXERCISES

*Complete. Use exponents.*

**1.** $2^3 \times 2^5 = ■$ **2.** $4^{-2} \times 4^8 = ■$ **3.** $10^{-3} \times 10^{-5} = ■$

**4.** $5^4 \times 5^{-6} = ■$ **5.** $\frac{5^7}{5^4} = ■$ **6.** $\frac{6^3}{6^8} = ■$

**7.** $\frac{2^{-4}}{2^3} = ■$ **8.** $\frac{7^{-5}}{7^{-2}} = ■$ **9.** $10^{-2} \div 10^{-4} = ■$

**10.** $5^3 \div 5^{-4} = ■$ **11.** $3^9 \times 3^{-6} = ■$ **12.** $7^{-2} \div 7^{10} = ■$

**13.** $\frac{8^{-4}}{8^{-9}} = ■$ **14.** $10^5 \times 10^4 = ■$ **15.** $6^4 \div 6^{-1} = ■$

**16.** $\frac{2^5}{2^0} = ■$ **17.** $3^4 \times 3^1 = ■$ **18.** $\frac{9^{-3}}{9^{-4}} = ■$

**19.** $12^{-5} \times 12^7 = ■$ **20.** $2^{-4} \div 2^{-6} = ■$ **21.** $8^{-2} \div 8^{-6} = ■$

*Simplify. Use exponents.*

**22.** $(2 \cdot 2) \cdot (2 \cdot 2 \cdot 2 \cdot 2)$ **23.** $(6 \cdot 6 \cdot 6) \cdot (6 \cdot 6 \cdot 6)$

**24.** $(4 \cdot 4 \cdot 4) \cdot (4 \cdot 4 \cdot 4) \cdot (9 \cdot 9)$ **25.** $(2 \cdot 2) \cdot (2 \cdot 2) \cdot (3 \cdot 3) \cdot (3 \cdot 3)$

*Complete. Use exponents.*

**26.** $\frac{2^5 \cdot 2^4}{2^3} = ■$ **27.** $5^4 \cdot 5^3 \cdot 5^5 = ■$ **28.** $3^4 \cdot 3^3 \cdot 5^{-5} = ■$

**29.** $\frac{2^2 \cdot 2^3 \cdot 3^2}{2^3} = ■$ **30.** $\frac{3^4 \cdot 4^3}{3^2} = ■$ **31.** $\frac{2^4 \cdot 2^{-2} \cdot 3^2}{2^2} = ■$

**32.** $(7^{-6} \cdot 5^3) \cdot (7^3 \cdot 5^{-2}) = ■$ **33.** $(5^{-3} \cdot 5^{-2}) \cdot (3^2 \cdot 3^{-4}) \cdot (7^4 \cdot 7^2) = ■$

★ **34.** $(3^4)^2 = 3^4 \cdot 3^4 = 3^{■}$ ★ **35.** $(4^{■})^2 = 4^{10}$ ★ **36.** $[(2^3)^2]^0 = ■$

THINK!

**Sum of Squares**

Find two consecutive negative integers such that the sum of their squares is 85.

1. $2^8$ 22. $2^6$

Homework page 483

## 6-10 Scientific Notation

**A.** In **scientific notation,** a number is shown as the product of two factors. The first factor is a number 1 or greater, but less than 10. The second factor is a power of ten.

Some examples of scientific notation are:

$6 \times 10^3$ $2.16 \times 10^4$ $7 \times 10^{-2}$ $3.9 \times 10^{-5}$

**B.** To find standard numerals or decimals for numbers given in scientific notation, use the shortcut for multiplying or dividing by powers of ten.

**Example 1** $6 \times 10^3 = ■$

$6 \times 10^3 = 6{,}000$ (3 places)

$= 6{,}000$

**Example 2** $3.9 \times 10^{-5} = ■$

$3.9 \times 10^{-5} = 3.9 \times \frac{1}{10^5}$

$= 3.9 \div 10^5$

$= 00003.9$ (5 places)

$= .000039$

**C.** To find scientific notation when you are given a standard numeral or decimal, use two steps.

**Example 1** $.0053 = ■$

**Step 1** Find the first factor.

$.0053 = 5.3 \times 10^{■}$

1 or greater, but less than 10.

**Step 2** Find the power of 10.

$.0053 = .005.3$ (3 places)

$.0053 = 5.3 \div 10^3$

$= 5.3 \times 10^{-3}$

**Example 2** $16{,}400 = ■$

**Step 1** $16{,}400 = 1.64 \times 10^{■}$

**Step 2** $16{,}400 = 1.6400. = 1.64 \times 10^4$ (4)

**D.** Find scientific notation for $.036 \times 10^5$.

Work with .036 first.
$.036 = 3.6 \times 10^{-2}$

Multiply powers of ten.
$.036 \times 10^5 = 3.6 \times 10^{-2} \times 10^5$
$= 3.6 \times 10^3$

## CLASS EXERCISES

*Write scientific notation for each number.*

**1.** 7,394 **2.** 1,600,000 **3.** .0005 **4.** .0000069

*Write a standard numeral or decimal for each number.*

**5.** $3.45 \times 10^3$ **6.** $5.16 \times 10^{-4}$ **7.** $4.07 \times 10^5$ **8.** $7.6 \times 10^{-3}$

**9.** Write scientific notation for $68.3 \times 10^{-4}$.

## EXERCISES

*Write scientific notation for each number.*

**1.** 357 **2.** 37,000 **3.** .000896 **4.** 25,000,000

**5.** 82.4 **6.** .00493 **7.** 867,000,000 **8.** .469

**9.** .0147 **10.** .000046 **11.** 6,240,000 **12.** .0924

**13.** 16.25 **14.** .4836 **15.** 7.394 **16.** 295,000

★ **17.** 6,350,000,000,000,000,000 ★ **18.** .000000000000017

★ **19.** 493,000,000,000,000 ★ **20.** .0000000000000666

*Write a standard numeral or decimal for each number.*

**21.** $7.3 \times 10^2$ **22.** $8.2 \times 10^{-4}$ **23.** $9.32 \times 10^{-6}$ **24.** $1.414 \times 10^{-0}$

**25.** $2.4 \times 10^1$ **26.** $4 \times 10^{-6}$ **27.** $6.87 \times 10^5$ **28.** $1.663 \times 10^{-5}$

**29.** $6 \times 10^7$ **30.** $4.7 \times 10^{-2}$ **31.** $7.95 \times 10^{-4}$ **32.** $8.96 \times 10^8$

**33.** $5.1 \times 10^{16}$ **34.** $5.9 \times 10^{-20}$ **35.** $2.13 \times 10^{-12}$ **36.** $6.73 \times 10^{25}$

*Write scientific notation for each number.*

**37.** $.059 \times 10^8$ **38.** $683 \times 10^{-7}$ **39.** $.002 \times 10^{-10}$ **40.** $6,000 \times 10^{11}$

THINK!

### Digit Patterns

Pick any 2-digit number. Multiply it by 111. Multiply the product by 91. What do you notice? Try the same thing with other 2-digit numbers. Explain.

**1.** $3.57 \times 10^2$ **21.** 730



Homework page 483

## 6-11 Using Scientific Notation

This table gives the maximum distance (to the nearest $10^7$ km) of other planets from Earth.

| Planet | Distance |
|---|---|
| Jupiter | $9.6 \times 10^8$ km |
| Mars | $4.0 \times 10^8$ km |
| Saturn | $1.66 \times 10^9$ km |
| Venus | $2.6 \times 10^8$ km |

**A.** To compare two numbers given in scientific notation, first look at the exponents.

**Example 1**
Is Mars or Saturn farther from Earth?

Compare $4.0 \times 10^8$ and $1.66 \times 10^9$.

**Step 1** Compare the exponents.

$8 < 9$, so $4.0 \times 10^8 < 1.66 \times 10^9$

You do not need to compare the first factors in this case.

Saturn is farther from Earth.

**Example 2**
Is Jupiter or Venus nearer to Earth?

Compare $9.6 \times 10^8$ and $2.6 \times 10^8$.

**Step 1** Compare the exponents.

$8 = 8$

**Step 2** Compare the first factors.

$9.6 > 2.6$, so $9.6 \times 10^8 > 2.6 \times 10^8$.

Venus is nearer to Earth.

**B.** Light travels about $3.0 \times 10^5$ kilometers per second. About how much time does it take light to travel from Earth to Saturn? Round the answer to show 2 digits in the first factor.

Divide. $\frac{1.66 \times 10^9}{3.0 \times 10^5} = \frac{1.66}{3.0} \times \frac{10^9}{10^5}$

$\doteq .55 \times 10^4$

$\doteq (5.5 \times 10^{-1}) \times 10^4$

$\doteq 5.5 \times 10^3 \leftarrow$ $10^{-1} \times 10^4 = 10^3$

It takes light about $5.5 \times 10^3$ seconds to travel from Earth to Saturn.

**C.** One millisecond is $10^{-3}$ seconds. How far will light travel in 5 milliseconds?

Multiply. $(5 \times 10^{-3}) \times (3 \times 10^5) = (5 \times 3) \times (10^{-3} \times 10^5)$

$= 15 \times 10^2 \leftarrow$ $10^{-3} \times 10^5 = 10^2$

$= 1.5 \times 10^3$

Light will travel about $1.5 \times 10^3$ km in 5 milliseconds.

## CLASS EXERCISES

*Write >, <, or = for ●.*

1. $7.3 \times 10^{-6}$ ● $5.9 \times 10^{-6}$

2. $8.5 \times 10^{4}$ ● $3.1 \times 10^{6}$

*Give scientific notation for each answer.*

3. $(1.6 \times 10^{-2}) \div (2 \times 10^{3}) =$ ■

4. $(8.1 \times 10^{-6}) \times (4 \times 10^{8}) =$ ■

## PROBLEMS

*Give scientific notation for answers. Round to keep 3 digits in first factors.*

1. About how many seconds does it take light to travel from Earth to Venus?

2. There are $3.6 \times 10^{3}$ seconds in 1 hour. How many hours does it take light to travel from Earth to Saturn?

3. The maximum distance of Earth from the sun is $1.52 \times 10^{8}$ km. About how many seconds does it take light to travel from the sun to Earth? About how many hours? Give a standard numeral for the number of hours.

4. The maximum distance of Pluto from the sun is $7.32 \times 10^{9}$ km. How many times the maximum distance from the sun to Earth is this distance? About how many hours does it take light from the sun to reach Pluto?

5. The mass of an atom of iron is about $9.2 \times 10^{-23}$ g. A hydrogen atom has a mass of about $1.7 \times 10^{-24}$ g. About how many hydrogen atoms would have a mass equal to the mass of one atom of iron?

6. The mass of 1 liter of hydrogen at 0°C under normal pressure is about $8.98 \times 10^{-2}$ g. About how many hydrogen atoms are there in 1 liter of hydrogen?

7. The mass of a uranium atom is about 238 times that of a hydrogen atom. Find the mass of a uranium atom. How many atoms are there in 100 g of uranium?

★ 8. A molecule of water has a mass of about $3.1 \times 10^{-23}$ g. How many molecules of water are there in 1 liter of water? (Mass of 1 liter of water is 1 kg.)

## MIXED REVIEW

*Express each fraction or mixed numeral as a decimal; express each decimal as a lowest terms fraction or mixed numeral.*

1. $\frac{3}{8}$
2. .026
3. .00815
4. $9\frac{2}{3}$
5. 8.55
6. $3\frac{13}{40}$

*Complete.*

7. $4.9 \div 1{,}000 =$ ■
8. $1{,}000 \times .074 =$ ■
9. $5{,}760 \div 100 =$ ■

Homework page 484

# 6-12 Real Numbers

**A.** Every rational number can be named by a terminating or a repeating decimal. Some rational numbers are:

$4.0$ $\qquad ^-.35$ $\qquad 6.\bar{3}$ $\qquad 7.\overline{253}$

The decimal .1010010001 . . . is a non-terminating and non-repeating decimal.

.1010010001 . . . represents an **irrational number.**

**B.** **Real numbers** can be used to name all points of the number line. The set of real numbers contains:

All integers (such as $^-1, 2, \ldots$)
All rational numbers (quotients of integers)
All irrational numbers (such as $\pi$, .1010010001 . . .)

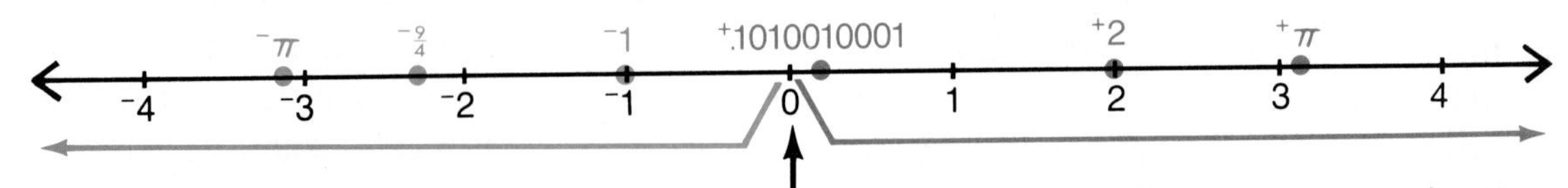


Negative real numbers

$^-\pi$ is read "negative pi."

Neither positive nor negative

Positive real numbers

$^+\pi$ is read "positive pi."

The point each number names is the **graph** of the number. Each number is the **coordinate** of its graph.

**C.** You can find absolute values, sums, differences, products, and quotients of real numbers just as you have for integers.

**Example 1** $^-.3 \times .4 = ▩$

$|^-.3| \times |.4|$

$\downarrow \qquad \downarrow$

$.3 \times .4 = .12$

So, $^-.3 \times .4 = ^-.12$

**Example 2** $^-5.2 + 3.8 = ▩$

$|^-5.2| - |3.8|$

$\downarrow \qquad \downarrow$

$5.2 - 3.8 = 1.4$

So, $^-5.2 + 3.8 = ^-1.4$

**Example 3** $\frac{3}{5} \div \frac{^-4}{5} = ▩$

$|\frac{3}{5}| \div |\frac{^-4}{5}|$

$\downarrow \qquad \downarrow$

$\frac{3}{5} \div \frac{4}{5} = \frac{3}{5} \times \frac{5}{4}$

$= \frac{3}{4}$

So $\frac{3}{5} \div \frac{^-4}{5} = \frac{^-3}{4}$

**Example 4** $^-\pi - 2.121121112\ldots = ▩$

Since $^-\pi \doteq ^-3.14$ and $2.121121112\ldots \doteq 2.12$,

$^-\pi - 2.121121112 \doteq ^-3.14 - 2.12$

$\doteq ^-3.14 + ^-2.12$

$|^-3.14| + |^-2.12|$

$\downarrow \qquad \downarrow$

$3.14 + 2.12 = 5.26$

So, $^-\pi - 2.121121112\ldots \doteq ^-5.26$

## CLASS EXERCISES

C D G E F B A H

$^{-}7$ $^{-}5$ $^{-}3$ $^{-}1$ 0 1 3 5 7

*Give the letter of the point named by each real number.*

**1.** $^{-}5.1$ **2.** 1.61161116 . . . **3.** $4\frac{2}{5}$ **4.** $\frac{^{-}5}{3}$ **5.** $^{-}3\frac{1}{2}$ **6.** $^{-}2.323323332$ . . .

*Add, subtract, or multiply.*

**7.** $^{-}2.3 + {^{-}1.6} = \blacksquare$ **8.** $\frac{^{-}3}{4} \times \frac{1}{2} = \blacksquare$ **9.** $^{-}5 - 3.7 = \blacksquare$

## EXERCISES

**1.** $^{-}6 \times {^{-}12} = \blacksquare$ **2.** $9 - 17 = \blacksquare$ **3.** $^{-}10 + {^{-}8} = \blacksquare$

**4.** $9.2 - {^{-}1.5} = \blacksquare$ **5.** $^{-}.3 \times 12 = \blacksquare$ **6.** $^{-}.7 + .3 = \blacksquare$

**7.** $^{-}.8 - {^{-}1.2} = \blacksquare$ **8.** $^{-}.5 \times {^{-}7} = \blacksquare$ **9.** $50 + {^{-}16} = \blacksquare$

**10.** $^{-}5.09 + {^{-}4.63} = \blacksquare$ **11.** $11 \times {^{-}80} = \blacksquare$ **12.** $^{-}3.6 \div 4 = \blacksquare$

**13.** $^{-}34 \times {^{-}2.6} = \blacksquare$ **14.** $2 + {^{-}4.7} = \blacksquare$ **15.** $10.14 - 7.02 \quad \blacksquare$

**16.** $^{-}41.7 \times 0 = \blacksquare$ **17.** $^{-}6.94 \div {^{-}20} = \blacksquare$ **18.** $^{-}12.7 - 15.1 = \blacksquare$

**19.** $900 \div {^{-}90} = \blacksquare$ **20.** $^{-}20.1 + 20.1 = \blacksquare$ **21.** $^{-}27.9 \div {^{-}.3} = \blacksquare$

**22.** $^{-}8 - 1.4 = \blacksquare$ **23.** $7.6 \times 8.1 = \blacksquare$ **24.** $23.6 - 30 = \blacksquare$

**25.** $\frac{^{-}1}{8} \div \frac{^{-}5}{8} = \blacksquare$ **26.** $\frac{^{-}3}{10} \times \frac{^{-}2}{3} = \blacksquare$ **27.** $\frac{7}{9} + \frac{^{-}2}{9} = \blacksquare$

**28.** $^{-}3 + \frac{4}{5} = \blacksquare$ **29.** $\frac{^{-}4}{5} \div 4 = \blacksquare$ **30.** $\frac{^{-}5}{8} + \frac{^{-}1}{6} = \blacksquare$

**31.** $^{-}2\frac{3}{4} + {^{-}.8} = \blacksquare$ **32.** $^{-}2\frac{1}{3} - 4\frac{5}{6} = \blacksquare$ **33.** $^{-}1\frac{1}{8} \times {^{-}2\frac{1}{2}} = \blacksquare$

*Solve.*

**34.** $t + {^{-}.2} = {^{-}5}$ **35.** $2m = {^{-}1.2}$ **36.** $u + 7.7 =$

**37.** $w - {^{-}.9} = 0$ **38.** $x - 16.7 = {^{-}16.7}$ **39.** $z + {^{-}8.1} =$

**40.** $n + 11.4 = 9$ **41.** $\frac{y}{^{-}3} = .33$ **42.** $s + {^{-}1.2} =$

1. $^{+}72$ 4. $^{+}10.7$

Homework page 484

## 6-13 Using a Square-Root Table

**A.** If one number is the second power of some other number, you can write this relationship in two ways.

Since $10^2 = 100$, 100 is the **square** of 10.
Also, 10 is a **square root** of 100, or $10 = \sqrt{100}$.

Some square roots are whole numbers.

$0^2 = 0$, so $0 = \sqrt{0}$

$1^2 = 1$, so $1 = \sqrt{1}$

$2^2 = 4$, so $2 = \sqrt{4}$

$3^2 = 9$, so $3 = \sqrt{9}$

$4^2 = 16$, so $4 = \sqrt{16}$

The only other whole numbers 100 or less that have whole number square roots are 25 ($5^2$), 36 ($6^2$), 49 ($7^2$), 64 ($8^2$), 81 ($9^2$), and 100 ($10^2$).

**B.** All other whole numbers less than 100 have square roots that are irrational numbers. Square roots can be estimated and rounded to any place. In the table below, irrational roots are rounded to the nearest hundredth. If you need a more accurate estimation, you can use a calculator.

**C.** Find $\sqrt{2} \times \sqrt{7}$. Round to the nearest hundredth. Compare with $\sqrt{14}$.

$\sqrt{2} \times \sqrt{7} \doteq 1.41 \times 2.65$
$\doteq 3.7365$
$\doteq 3.74$
Also, $\sqrt{14} \doteq 3.74$
So, both $\sqrt{14}$ and $\sqrt{2} \times \sqrt{7}$ are about 3.74.

**D.** Find $\sqrt{3} + \sqrt{10}$. Round to the nearest hundredth. Compare with $\sqrt{13}$.

$\sqrt{3} + \sqrt{10} \doteq 1.73 + 3.16$
$\doteq 4.89$
Also, $\sqrt{13} \doteq 3.61$
So, $\sqrt{13}$ does not equal $\sqrt{3} + \sqrt{10}$.

| n | $\sqrt{n}$ | n | $\sqrt{n}$ |
|---|---|---|---|
| 1 | 1.00 | 20 | 4.47 |
| 2 | 1.41 | 25 | 5.00 |
| 3 | 1.73 | 27 | 5.20 |
| 4 | 2.00 | 30 | 5.48 |
| 5 | 2.24 | 36 | 6.00 |
| 6 | 2.45 | 40 | 6.32 |
| 7 | 2.65 | 49 | 7.00 |
| 8 | 2.83 | 64 | 8.00 |
| 9 | 3.00 | 81 | 9.00 |
| 10 | 3.16 | 100 | 10.00 |
| 11 | 3.32 | 121 | 11.00 |
| 12 | 3.46 | 125 | 11.18 |
| 13 | 3.61 | 144 | 12.00 |
| 14 | 3.74 | 169 | 13.00 |
| 15 | 3.87 | 196 | 14.00 |

## CLASS EXERCISES

*Use the table on page 218. Round to the nearest hundredth.*

**1.** $\sqrt{2} \times \sqrt{15}$ (Compare with $\sqrt{30}$)

**2.** $\sqrt{7} + \sqrt{13}$ (Compare with $\sqrt{20}$)

**3.** $\frac{\sqrt{30}}{\sqrt{5}}$ (Compare with $\sqrt{6}$)

**4.** $\sqrt{36} - \sqrt{6}$ (Compare with $\sqrt{30}$)

## EXERCISES

*Use the table on page 218. Round to the nearest hundredth.*

**1.** $\sqrt{4} \times \sqrt{16}$ (Compare with $\sqrt{64}$)

**2.** $\sqrt{8} \times \sqrt{5}$ (Compare with $\sqrt{40}$)

**3.** $\sqrt{16} + \sqrt{4}$ (Compare with $\sqrt{20}$)

**4.** $\sqrt{8} - \sqrt{5}$ (Compare with $\sqrt{3}$)

**5.** $\sqrt{9} \times \sqrt{3}$ (Compare with $\sqrt{27}$)

**6.** $\sqrt{9} + \sqrt{3}$ (Compare with $\sqrt{12}$)

**7.** $\sqrt{5} \times \sqrt{4} \times \sqrt{5}$ (Compare with $\sqrt{100}$)

**8.** $\sqrt{3} \times \sqrt{4} \times \sqrt{12}$ (Compare with $\sqrt{144}$)

**9.** $\sqrt{2} \times \sqrt{3} \times \sqrt{5}$ (Compare with $\sqrt{30}$)

**10.** $\sqrt{2} \times \sqrt{4} \times \sqrt{5}$ (Compare with $\sqrt{40}$)

**11.** $\sqrt{2} \times \sqrt{8} \times \sqrt{9}$ (Compare with $\sqrt{144}$)

**12.** $\sqrt{2} \times \sqrt{5} \times \sqrt{10}$ (Compare with $\sqrt{100}$)

**13.** $\sqrt{2} \times \sqrt{3} \times \sqrt{6}$ (Compare with $\sqrt{36}$)

**14.** $\sqrt{5} \times \sqrt{4} \times \sqrt{1}$ (Compare with $\sqrt{20}$)

**15.** $\sqrt{2} \times \sqrt{4} \times \sqrt{8}$ (Compare with $\sqrt{64}$)

**16.** $\sqrt{2} \times \sqrt{7} \times \sqrt{14}$ (Compare with $\sqrt{196}$)

**17.** $\frac{\sqrt{10}}{\sqrt{2}}$ (Compare with $\sqrt{5}$)

**18.** $\frac{\sqrt{30}}{\sqrt{10}}$ (Compare with $\sqrt{3}$)

## THINK!

### Finding Cube Roots

If one number is the third power of some other number, you can write this relationship in two ways.

Since $10^3 = 1{,}000$,
1,000 is the **cube** of 10.

Also, 10 is the **cube root** of 1,000,
or $10 = \sqrt[3]{1{,}000}$.

Find these cube roots.

**a.** $\sqrt[3]{8}$ **b.** $\sqrt[3]{64}$ **c.** $\sqrt[3]{1}$ **d.** $\sqrt[3]{125}$ **e.** $\sqrt[3]{0}$ **f.** $\sqrt[3]{27}$

1. Both equal 8.00 3. $\sqrt{16} + \sqrt{4} = 6$; $\sqrt{20} \doteq 4.47$

Homework page 485

## -TECHNOLOGY-

### Computer Spreadsheets

A **spreadsheet** consists of cells (column and row) in which numbers, labels, and formulas are entered. Spreadsheets are very useful for keeping and updating a record of stocks. Mrs. Gianelli's stocks are shown in this spreadsheet.

| | A | B | C | D | E | F |
|---|---|---|---|---|---|---|
| 1 | Name of | No. of | Purchase | Total | Value | Total |
| 2 | Stock | Shares | Price | Paid | Now | Value Now |
| 3 | | | | | | |
| 4 | ALR | 100 | 22.75 | 2,275.00 | 19.75 | 1,975.00 |
| 5 | | | | | | |
| 6 | LuckyG | 250 | 11.25 | 2,812.50 | 12.00 | 3,000.00 |
| 7 | | | | | | |
| 8 | GenTek | 85 | 37.50 | 3,187.50 | 35.50 | 3,017.50 |
| 9 | | | | | | |
| 10 | Sangly | 115 | 48.25 | 5,548.75 | 57.25 | 6,583.75 |
| 11 | | | | | | |
| 12 | Totals | 550 | ______ | 13,823.75 | ______ | 14,576.25 |

Mrs. Gianelli enters the number of shares she owns, the price per share she paid, and the daily value per share. The spreadsheet program calculates the total amount paid for each stock and the total value of the stock each day. It also computes column totals.

From the spreadsheet you can easily see that Mrs. Gianelli paid a total of $2,812.50 for her LuckyG stock. The stock is now worth $3,000.00. The total amount she has spent to buy stock is $13,823.75.

Another very useful feature of spreadsheets is that they allow you to change values, and then they recalculate to show what results the change would have. Mrs. Gianelli might wonder about the total value of her GenTek stock if the price fell to $30.00 per share. All she needs to do is enter one new price and have the program calculate the total value. The program would place $2,550.00 in cell F8.

1. Which of Mrs. Gianelli's stocks increased in value since she bought them?
2. How many shares of stock does Mrs. Gianelli own?
3. How much more are all Mrs. Gianelli's stocks worth now ?
4. How much would all of Mrs. Gianelli's stocks be worth if GenTek fell to $30.00 per share and the other stocks stayed the same as now?

# Problem Solving Strategy

READ **PLAN** DO • ANSWER • CHECK

## Make a Table

Two 3,000-liter water tanks are being emptied. Tank A starts emptying 2 minutes before Tank B. Tank A empties at the rate of 200 L/min, and Tank B empties at the rate of 275 L/min. How long after Tank B starts emptying will it contain less water than Tank A?

A good method to use to solve this type of problem is to **make a table.** By showing the data given in the problem, you will see how to continue to find a solution.

To begin, note that Tank A empties for 2 minutes before Tank B starts. Therefore, when Tank B starts, Tank A contains only

$$3{,}000 - 2(200) = 2{,}600 \text{ L.}$$

Now, make your table.

| | Start | 1 min | 2 min | 3 min | 4 min | 5 min | 6 min |
|---|---|---|---|---|---|---|---|
| Tank A | 2,600 | 2,400 | 2,200 | 2,000 | 1,800 | 1,600 | 1,400 |
| Tank B | 3,000 | 2,725 | 2,450 | 2,175 | 1,900 | 1,625 | 1,350 |

The table shows that 6 min after Tank B starts emptying, it will contain less water than Tank A.

*Solve.*

1. A car and a van start from the same place and travel the same route. The van starts first and travels 60 km before the car starts. The van averages 68 km/h and the car averages 82 km/h. How long will it take the car to be 24 km ahead of the van?

2. Patti and Matti were trying to reduce. At the start of their diets Patti was 60 kg and Matti was 56 kg. Patti lost 1 kg a week and Matti lost 0.5 kg a week. The girls continued to reduce at this rate, and stopped dieting when their scales gave the same reading. How long were they on diets?

3. In January, 500 pairs of skis and 100 tennis rackets were sold. Each month thereafter, the number of pairs of skis sold decreased by 50 and the number of tennis rackets sold increased by 30. In which month were sales of both items equal? Can you find expressions for each item's sales after t months? How would you find when they are equal?

4. Alphonse and Zaida start from the clubhouse and jog along the same path. Zaida starts first and jogs for 3 min before Alphonse sets out. Zaida jogs an average of 120 m/min and Alphonse jogs an average of 150 m/min. How long after Alphonse starts will he meet up with Zaida? Can you find expressions for each jogger's distance after p minutes?

## Drawing and Using Graphs

**A.** A **bar graph** can be used to *compare* amounts. This double-bar graph shows the number of males and females in the United States by age group. Numbers have been rounded to the nearest million.

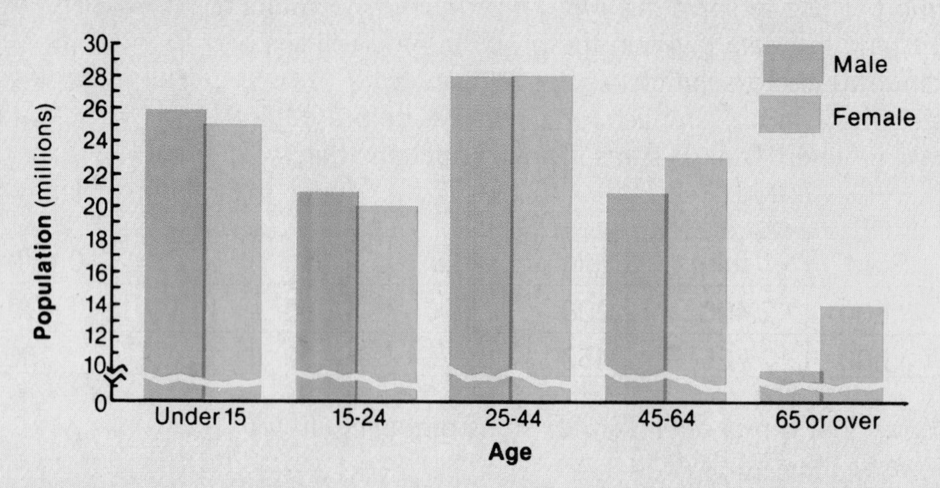


When drawing a double- or triple-bar graph, you must use a different color for each type of item. The **legend** at the side tells the meaning of each color. The break in the graph shows that parts of the bars have been left out.

1. In what age groups are there more females than males? more males than females?
2. In what age group is the difference between the number of males and the number of females the greatest?

**B.** To draw a bar graph, start by drawing horizontal and vertical scales.
**Step 1:** Choose the largest number on the vertical scale to be as large as the largest number being graphed.
**Step 2:** Mark off intervals on the vertical scale evenly.
**Step 3:** Draw and label vertical bars.

3. Draw a bar graph to show the information in the table. Round amounts to the nearest billion dollars.

| Trading Area | U.S Exports (millions) | U.S. Imports (millions) |
|---|---|---|
| Canada | $33,096 | $39,021 |
| Latin America | $26,257 | $26,085 |
| Western Europe | $54,331 | $44,448 |
| Africa | $ 6,299 | $26,014 |

4. Use your graph. Which area receives the most U.S. exports?

**C.** A **broken-line graph** can be used to show *change* or *growth* over time. Each point shows the amount at a given time. The line segments joining the points show increases and decreases. They also show how quickly the increases and decreases have happened.

This triple-line graph shows the average monthly temperatures of three cities. Temperatures have been rounded to the nearest degree Celsius.

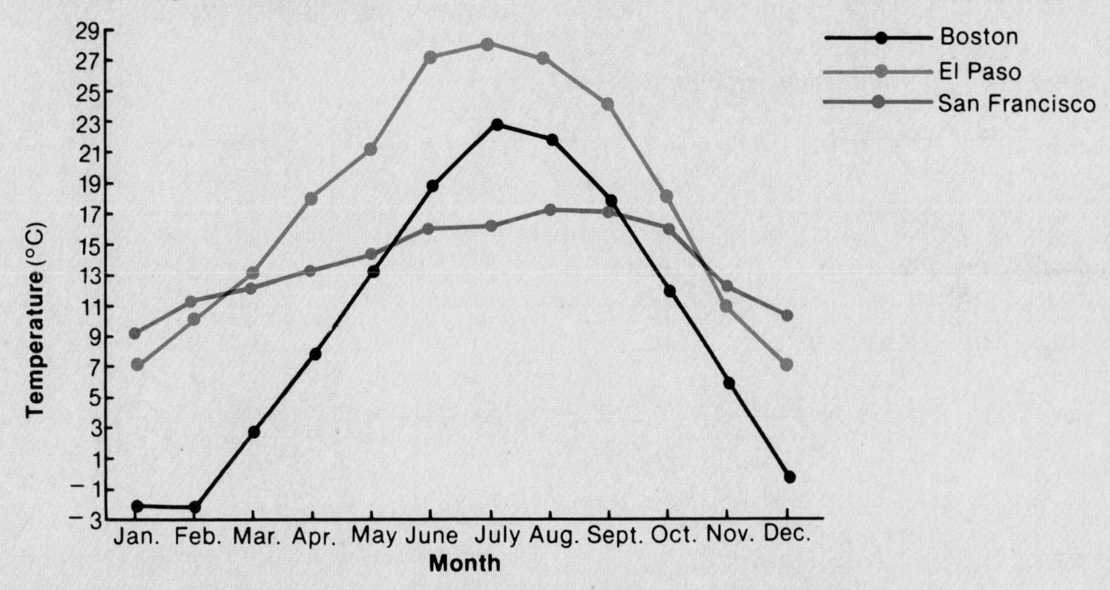


**5.** Which city has the greatest changes in temperature? the least?

**6.** In what months is San Francisco warmer than El Paso? cooler than Boston?

**7.** In what month does each city's temperature change the least from the previous month?

**8.** The average annual temperature for Boston is 10°C, for El Paso is 18°C, and for San Francisco is 13°C. In how many months does each city's temperature exceed its annual average?

## ON YOUR OWN

Select three cities for which daily weather information is given in your local newspaper. Record the daily low temperature in each of these cities for a two-week period. Draw a triple-line graph to show the data. Which city has the greatest changes in temperature? The least?

# Unit Review

*Name the point for each number. (pages 194–197)*

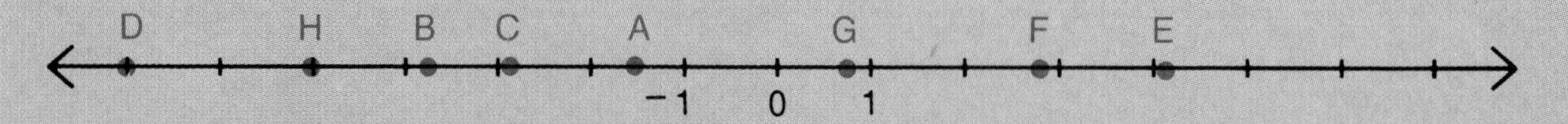


**1.** $^-5$ **2.** $^+4.2$ **3.** $^-1\frac{1}{2}$ **4.** $^-7$ **5.** $\frac{^+3}{4}$ **6.** $^-3.7$ **7.** $^+2\frac{7}{8}$ **8.** $^-2\frac{7}{8}$

*Find each absolute value. (pages 194–197)*

**9.** $|^-6|$ **10.** $|^+9|$ **11.** $|^-2.3|$ **12.** $|3\frac{1}{2}|$ **13.** $|0|$ **14.** $|^-6\frac{1}{3}|$ **15.** $|5.3|$

*Complete. (pages 194–197)*

**16.** $|^-5| + |^+9| =$ ■ **17.** $|^-16| - |3| =$ ■ **18.** $|^-8| \times |7| =$ ■

**19.** $|^-15| \div |^-5| =$ ■ **20.** $|\frac{^-2}{5}| + |\frac{1}{5}| =$ ■ **21.** $|^-9.8| \div |^-2| =$ ■

**22.** $|7.9| - |^-6.8| =$ ■ **23.** $|^-2| \times |1\frac{1}{3}| =$ ■

*Compare. Write >, <, or = for ●. (pages 194–197)*

**24.** $|^-10|$ ● $|7|$ **25.** $|^-2|$ ● $|^-3|$ **26.** $|\frac{^-5}{8}|$ ● $|\frac{3}{8}|$ **27.** $|6.1|$ ● $|^-4.3|$

**28.** $8$ ● $^-9$ **29.** $^-6$ ● $^-1$ **30.** $0$ ● $^-2\frac{2}{5}$ **31.** $^-8.3$ ● $1.6$

*Add or subtract. (pages 198–203)*

**32.** $9 + {^-6} =$ ■ **33.** $4 + 10 =$ ■ **34.** $^-11 + 18 =$ ■ **35.** $^-8 - {^-2} =$ ■

**36.** $14 - {^-3} =$ ■ **37.** $^-5 - {^-12} =$ ■ **38.** $4 + {^-10} =$ ■ **39.** $26 - 11 =$ ■

**40.** $^-43 - {^-9} =$ ■ **41.** $^-26 + 5 =$ ■ **42.** $^-30 - {^-10} =$ ■ **43.** $^+37 + {^+16} =$ ■

**44.** $^-19 + {^-11} =$ ■ **45.** $^-25 - {^-50} =$ ■ **46.** $^-82 + 93 =$ ■ **47.** $43 - 61 =$ ■

*Multiply or divide. (pages 204–207)*

**48.** $7 \times {^-4} =$ ■ **49.** $^-30 \div {^-6} =$ ■ **50.** $^-16 \div 1 =$ ■ **51.** $4 \times 12 =$ ■

**52.** $^-32 \div {^-8} =$ ■ **53.** $^-6 \times 7 =$ ■ **54.** $18 \div {^-2} =$ ■ **55.** $^-3 \times {^-6} =$ ■

**56.** $14 \div {^-3} =$ ■ **57.** $^+72 \div {^+8} =$ ■ **58.** $^-6 \times {^-10} =$ ■ **59.** $9 \div {^-2} =$ ■

**60.** $^-9 \times 10 =$ ■ **61.** $^-8 \div 5 =$ ■ **62.** $12 \times {^-20} =$ ■ **63.** $^-35 \times 0 =$ ■

*Complete. Use exponents.* *(pages 210–211)*

**64.** $2^3 \times 2^{-5} =$ ■ **65.** $5^{-4} \div 5^{-6} =$ ■ **66.** $6^{-2} \times 6^{-3} =$ ■ **67.** $8^2 \div 8 =$ ■

**68.** $\frac{2^2 \cdot 3^{-4}}{2^3 \cdot 3^{-5}} =$ ■ **69.** $\frac{2^4 \cdot 2^{-5} \cdot 3^4}{2^{-2} \cdot 3^{-3}} =$ ■ **70.** $(2^3 \cdot 2^{-2} \cdot 3^2) \cdot (2^{-1} \cdot 3^{-2}) =$ ■

*Write scientific notation for each number.* *(pages 212–213)*

**71.** 52,400 **72.** .0318 **73.** 695,000 **74.** .00047

*Write a decimal or standard numeral for each.* *(pages 212–213)*

**75.** $3.6 \times 10^{-4}$ **76.** $7.31 \times 10^6$ **77.** $5.24 \times 10^{-3}$ **78.** $7.25 \times 10^3$

*Complete.* *(pages 216–217)*

**79.** $^-3.8 \times {}^-8 =$ ■ **80.** $^-81.9 \div 9 =$ ■ **81.** $^-8.63 - {}^-10.79 =$ ■

*Use the table on page 218 or estimate to the nearest hundredth.* *(pages 218–221)*

**82.** $\sqrt{10} =$ ■ **83.** $\sqrt{40} =$ ■ **84.** $\sqrt{125} =$ ■ **85.** $\sqrt{196} =$ ■

*Solve.* *(pages 202–203, 206–207)*

**86.** $x - {}^-2 = {}^-5$ **87.** $y + {}^-6 = {}^-9$ **88.** $\frac{m}{^-8} = {}^-7$ **89.** $^-4t = {}^-9$

*Use a number line to graph each sentence.* *(pages 222–223)*

**90.** $|x| = 5$ **91.** $y \leq {}^-1$ **92.** $m > 0$ **93.** $w < 7$

*Solve the problems.* *(pages 208–209, 214–215)*

**94.** The temperature after a change of $^-12$°C was $^-5$°C. What was the temperature before this change?

**95.** The mass of an atom of iron is about $9.2 \times 10^{-23}$ g. About how many atoms are there in 32.2 g of iron?

**96.** The opening value of one share of stock was \$69.90. During that day the value changed $^-$\$3.95. What was the closing value that day?

**97.** One light-year is the distance light will travel in 1 year. About how many kilometers are there in 1 light-year? (1 year $\doteq 3.2 \times 10^7$ s, speed of light $\doteq 3.0 \times 10^5$ km/sec)

# Cumulative Review

1. Simplify $\frac{38}{4}$.
   - a. $9\frac{2}{4}$
   - b. $2\frac{3}{4}$
   - c. $9\frac{1}{2}$
   - d. Not given

2. $45.03 - 3.672$
   - a. 8.31
   - b. 41.358
   - c. 42.642
   - d. Not given

3. Simplify. $\frac{2^7 \cdot 2^{-3}}{2^2}$
   - a. $2^6$
   - b. $2^{12}$
   - c. $2^2$
   - d. Not given

4. $4 - {}^-16 = \blacksquare$
   - a. 20
   - b. $^-12$
   - c. 12
   - d. Not given

5. $\frac{3}{4} + \frac{5}{6} = \blacksquare$
   - a. $\frac{8}{10}$
   - b. $\frac{15}{24}$
   - c. $1\frac{7}{12}$
   - d. Not given

6. $11 + {}^-19 = \blacksquare$
   - a. $^-8$
   - b. 8
   - c. $^-30$
   - d. Not given

7. $4\frac{5}{8} + 3\frac{7}{8} = \blacksquare$
   - a. $8\frac{1}{2}$
   - b. $7\frac{3}{4}$
   - c. $7\frac{1}{2}$
   - d. Not given

8. $\frac{4}{5} \times \frac{2}{3} = \blacksquare$
   - a. $\frac{6}{8}$
   - b. $\frac{12}{10}$
   - c. $\frac{8}{5}$
   - d. Not given

9. $^-14 \div {}^-3 = \blacksquare$
   - a. $^-17$
   - b. 52
   - c. $4\frac{2}{3}$
   - d. Not given

10. Find the GCF of 14 and 35.
    - a. 70
    - b. 7
    - c. 35
    - d. Not given

11. Each can holds 2.25 gal of paint. How much paint in all is in $1\frac{3}{5}$ cans?
    - a. $3\frac{3}{5}$ or 3.6 gal
    - b. $3\frac{13}{20}$ or 3.65 gal
    - c. $3\frac{11}{20}$ or 3.55 gal
    - d. Not given

12. When 7 is added to the result of dividing a number by 5, the sum is 10. Find the number.
    - a. 22
    - b. 15
    - c. $^-2$
    - d. Not given

13. An auto traveled for 6.4 h at an average speed of 72.5 km/h. How far did the auto travel?
    - a. 4,640 km
    - b. 450.8 km
    - c. 464 km
    - d. Not given

14. A buyer had $1,000 to spend for lamps for the store. How many lamps could she buy at $38 each?
    - a. 26
    - b. 34
    - c. 263
    - d. Not given

# 7 Measurement Systems

| Name | Location | Latest Activity | Height (meters) |
|---|---|---|---|
| Stromboli | Italy | 1975 | 924 |
| Mt. St. Helens | United States | 1980 | 2,549 |
| Krakatoa | Indonesia | 1883 | 813 |
| El Chichon | Mexico | 1983 | 1,060 |
| Surtsey | Iceland | 1967 | 173 |
| Cotopaxi | Ecuador | 1975 | 6,959 |

## 7-1 Metric Units

**A.** The **meter (m)**, the **decimeter (dm)**, the **centimeter (cm)**, and the **millimeter (mm)** are units used to measure lengths or distances.

| 1 m = 10 dm | 1 m = 100 cm | 1 m = 1,000 mm |
|---|---|---|

The length of the small car is about 4 m.
The width of the car door is about 7 dm.
The height of the car bumper is about 18 cm.
The thickness of the windshield is about 5 mm.

**B.** The **kilometer (km)** is a unit used to measure large lengths or distances.

| 1 km = 1,000 m |
|---|

The car can travel about 90 km in an hour.
You can walk about 6.5 km in an hour.

**C.** The **liter (L)** and the **milliliter (mL)** are units used to measure the volume of liquids or the capacity of containers.

| 1 L = 1,000 mL |
|---|

The gas tank of a small car holds about 60 L of gasoline.
An eyedropper holds about 2 mL of water.

**D.** The **milligram (mg)**, the **gram (g)**, the **kilogram (kg)**, and the **metric ton (t)** are units used to measure the mass of objects.

| 1 g = 1,000 mg | 1 kg = 1,000 g | 1 t = 1,000 kg |
|---|---|---|

30 small flower seeds have a mass of about 1 mg.
An orange has a mass of about 100 g.
The mass of a Saint Bernard dog is about 70 kg.
A small car has a mass of about 1 t.

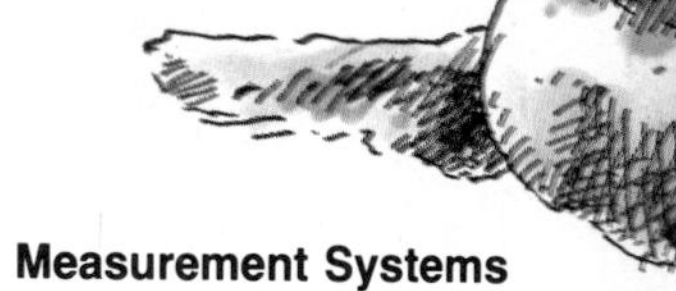

## CLASS EXERCISES

*What unit would you use to measure:*

1. the capacity of an eggcup?
2. the length of a river?
3. the mass of an egg?
4. the height of a building?
5. the width of a postage stamp?
6. the mass of a cat?

## EXERCISES

*Name several measures you would report using each unit.*

1. meter
2. decimeter
3. centimeter
4. millimeter
5. kilometer
6. milligram
7. gram
8. metric ton
9. kilogram
10. milliliter
11. liter

*Select the measure that seems reasonable.*

12. The capacity of a kitchen sink is about:
    a. 3 L b. 300 mL c. 30 L
13. The mass of a 1-year-old child is about:
    a. 8 kg b. 800 g c. 80 kg
14. The width of a two-lane street is about:
    a. 80 m b. 8 dm c. 8 m
15. The distance from San Francisco to Los Angeles is about:
    a. 6,500 m b. 650 km c. 65 km
16. The mass of a full truckload of gravel is about:
    a. 12 t b. 120 t c. 1,200 kg
17. The volume of orange juice in a small glass is about:
    a. 15 L b. 150 mL c. 1,500 mL
18. The length of a ball-point pen is about:
    a. 14 dm b. 14 cm c. 14 mm

## THINK!

### Logical Reasoning

The teacher said, "One half of my students study mathematics, one third study geometry, one seventh study chemistry, and 20 do not study at all." How many students does the teacher have? (Be careful, this is tricky.)

Homework page 486

## 7-2 The Metric System

**A.** The prefix used in the name of each unit of length describes its relation to the meter.

**Milli (m)** means thousandth.
**Centi (c)** means hundredth.
**Deci (d)** means tenth.
**Deka (da)** means ten.
**Hecto (h)** means hundred.
**Kilo (k)** means thousand.

| | | |
|---|---|---|
| 1 mm | = | 0.001 m |
| 1 cm | = | 0.01 m |
| 1 dm | = | 0.1 m |
| 1 dam | = | 10 m |
| 1 hm | = | 100 m |
| 1 km | = | 1,000 m |

You can use the same prefixes with liter (L) to name units of liquid volume or capacity and with gram (g) to name units of mass.

**B.** This table shows relations among metric units. You can use m, L, or g for ▽ to name units of length, liquid volume, or mass. The measures in each column are equal. Each measure is ten times the measure in the column to its right.

| | | | | | | |
|---|---|---|---|---|---|---|
| | | | 1,000 m▽ | 100 m▽ | 10 m▽ | 1 m▽ |
| | | | 100 c▽ | 10 c▽ | 1 c▽ | 0.1 c▽ |
| | | | 10 d▽ | 1 d▽ | 0.1 d▽ | 0.01 d▽ |
| 1,000 ▽ | 100 ▽ | 10 ▽ | 1 ▽ | 0.1 ▽ | 0.01 ▽ | 0.001 ▽ |
| 100 da▽ | 10 da▽ | 1 da▽ | 0.1 da▽ | | | |
| 10 h▽ | 1 h▽ | 0.1 h▽ | 0.01 h▽ | | | |
| 1 k▽ | 0.1 k▽ | 0.01 k▽ | 0.001 k▽ | | | |

**C.** You can use these relations to change a report using one unit to a report using any of the other units.

**Example 1** 40 hL = ■ L
Use 1 hL = 100 L.
40 hL = 40 · (100 L) = 4,000 L

**Example 2** 0.7 dg = ■ mg
Use 0.1 dg = 10 mg.
0.7 dg = 7 · (10 mg) = 70 mg

**Example 3** 9 mm = ■ m
Use 1 mm = 0.001 m.
9 mm = 9 · (0.001 m) = 0.009 m

**Example 4** 0.5 kL = ■ daL
Use 1 kL = 100 daL.
0.5 kL = 0.5 · (100 daL) = 50 daL

## CLASS EXERCISES

*Use the six prefixes to name:*

**1.** units of liquid volume

**2.** units of mass

*Complete.*

**3.** 5 km = ■ m **4.** 3 dL = ■ mL **5.** 0.4 hg = ■ g **6.** 0.09 dm = ■ mm

**7.** 60 mg = ■ g **8.** 0.3 kL = ■ daL **9.** 4 dam = ■ km **10.** 7,000 g = ■ hg

## EXERCISES

*Complete.*

| | | |
|---|---|---|
| **1.** 8 kg = ■ g | **2.** 7 m = ■ cm | **3.** 0.09 hL = ■ daL |
| **4.** 0.4 cm = ■ mm | **5.** 8 dL = ■ mL | **6.** 0.5 hL = ■ L |
| **7.** 4,000 mg = ■ dg | **8.** 0.7 km = ■ hm | **9.** 3,000 g = ■ hg |
| **10.** 70 cm = ■ m | **11.** 0.003 km = ■ dam | **12.** 0.006 g = ■ mg |
| **13.** 20 mL = ■ dL | **14.** 2 dam = ■ km | **15.** 0.9 cL = ■ L |
| **16.** 60 hg = ■ g | **17.** 400 m = ■ km | **18.** 0.07 dL = ■ mL |
| **19.** 0.8 dag = ■ kg | **20.** 400 cL = ■ dL | **21.** 20 daL = ■ L |
| **22.** 0.04 m = ■ mm | **23.** 0.2 g = ■ mg | **24.** 0.06 hm = ■ km |
| **25.** 40 kg = ■ g | **26.** 0.7 cm = ■ mm | **27.** 0.009 g = ■ mg |
| **28.** 0.02 hm = ■ km | **29.** 900 cL = ■ dL | **30.** 0.005 km = ■ dam |
| **31.** 4 dam = ■ km | **32.** 30 mL = ■ dL | **33.** 0.3 dag = ■ kg |
| **34.** 40 daL = ■ L | **35.** 0.07 m = ■ mm | **36.** 600 m = ■ km |

## PROBLEMS

**37.** The fuel tank of a car holds 0.07 kL of gasoline. How many liters of gasoline does it hold?

**38.** A 12-story building is 4 dam high. Report this height using hectometers.

**39.** A nickel has a mass of about 5 g. Report this mass using decigrams.

## THINK!

**Visual Perception**

How many squares can you find in the figure?

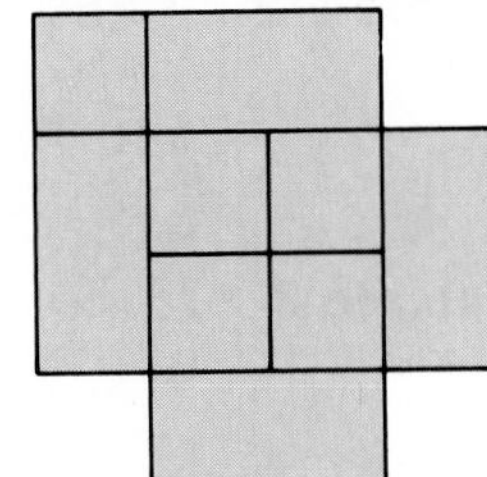

1. 8,000 g 4. 4 mm

# 7-3 Changing Units

**A.** This table shows relations among the principal unit (meter, liter, or gram) and its **submultiples**—the units named with the prefixes deci, centi, and milli. The measures in each column are equal.

| | | | |
|---|---|---|---|
| 1,000 m▽ | 100 m▽ | 10 m▽ | 1 m▽ |
| 100 c▽ | 10 c▽ | 1 c▽ | 0.1 c▽ |
| 10 d▽ | 1 d▽ | 0.1 d▽ | 0.01 d▽ |
| 1 ▽ | 0.1 ▽ | 0.01 ▽ | 0.001 ▽ |

**B.** You can show a measure like 5,432 m▽ in a table like the one above. The measures in each column are equal.

| | | | | |
|---|---|---|---|---|
| 5,000 m▽ | 400 m▽ | 30 m▽ | 2 m▽ | → 5,432. m▽ |
| 500 c▽ | 40 c▽ | 3 c▽ | 0.2 c▽ | → 543.2 c▽ |
| 50 d▽ | 4 d▽ | 0.3 d▽ | 0.02 d▽ | → 54.32 d▽ |
| 5 ▽ | 0.4 ▽ | 0.03 ▽ | 0.002 ▽ | → 5.432 ▽ |

The unit of the ones digit in each report in the table is the unit used in the report. Using m, L, or g for ▽:

5,432. mm = 543.2 cm = 54.32 dm = 5.432 m

5,432. mL = 543.2 cL = 54.32 dL = 5.432 L

5,432. mg = 543.2 cg = 54.32 dg = 5.432 g

**C.** These examples show how to change the unit used in the report of a measure without multiplying.

**Example 1** 4.9 cm = ▒ m

4.9 cm = 4.9 cm = 004.9 cm = 0.049 m = 0.049 m

**Example 2** 1,650 mL = ▒ L

1,650 mL = 1,650. mL = 1.650 L = 1.65 L

**Example 3** 78 dg = ▒ mg

78 dg = 78. dg = 78.00 dg = 7,800. mg = 7,800 mg

## CLASS EXERCISES

1. When you change a given report to one using a *larger* unit, will the new number be greater or less than the given number?
2. When you change a given report to one using a *smaller* unit, will the new number be greater or less than the given number?

*Complete using m, L, and g for ▽.*

3. 0.46 d▽ = ■ ▽
4. 1.9 ▽ = ■ c▽
5. 6 m▽ = ■ c▽

## EXERCISES

*Complete.*

1. 302 mm = ■ dm
2. 0.715 L = ■ mL
3. 38.2 cg = ■ dg
4. 0.45 m = ■ cm
5. 93 mL = ■ dL
6. 6.7 g = ■ mg
7. 65 dm = ■ cm
8. 18.4 cL = ■ mL
9. 29 cg = ■ g
10. 29.6 cm = ■ mm
11. 0.645 L = ■ dL
12. 43 mg = ■ dg
13. 8.35 m = ■ mm
14. 7.5 cL = ■ dL
15. 0.025 g = ■ dg
16. 0.3 cm = ■ dm
17. 3.7 dL = ■ mL
18. 7,320 mg = ■ g
19. 51 mm = ■ m
20. 67.1 cL = ■ L
21. 50 cg = ■ mg
22. 416 mm = ■ dm
23. 25.4 cL = ■ L
24. 57.4 cg = ■ dg
25. 35 dm = ■ cm
26. 0.835 L = ■ mL
27. 39 mg = ■ dg
28. 7.45 m = ■ mm
29. 31.2 dL = ■ cL
30. 4,510 mg = ■ g
31. 87 mm = ■ m
32. 6.5 dL = ■ mL
33. 0.038 g = ■ dg
34. 56.3 cm = ■ mm
35. 43.7 cL = ■ L
36. 80 cg = ■ mg

## PROBLEMS

37. A car is 4.85 m long. What is its length in decimeters?
38. An Irish wolfhound is 85 cm tall. What is its height in meters?
39. A fruit punch contains 0.25 g of Vitamin C. How many milligrams is that?

## THINK!

### Number Patterns

Multiply 123,456,789 by 8. Add 9. How is the result related to the original number?

1. 3.02 dm 4. 45 cm

Homework page 486

## 7-4 Changing Units—Multiples

**A.** This table shows relations among the principal unit (meter, liter, or gram) and its **multiples**—the units named with the prefixes deka, hecto, and kilo. The measures in each column are equal.

| | | | |
|---|---|---|---|
| 1,000 ▽ | 100 ▽ | 10 ▽ | 1 ▽ |
| 100 da▽ | 10 da▽ | 1 da▽ | 0.1 da▽ |
| 10 h▽ | 1 h▽ | 0.1 h▽ | 0.01 h▽ |
| 1 k▽ | 0.1 k▽ | 0.01 k▽ | 0.001 k▽ |

**B.** You can show a measure like 2,468 ▽ in a table like the one above. The measures in each column are equal.

| | | | | |
|---|---|---|---|---|
| 2,000 ▽ | 400 ▽ | 60 ▽ | 8 ▽ | ⟶ 2,468. ▽ |
| 200 da▽ | 40 da▽ | 6 da▽ | 0.8 da▽ | ⟶ 246.8 da▽ |
| 20 h▽ | 4 h▽ | 0.6 h▽ | 0.08 h▽ | ⟶ 24.68 h▽ |
| 2 k▽ | 0.4 k▽ | 0.06 k▽ | 0.008 k ▽ | ⟶ 2.468 k▽ |

The unit of the ones digit in each report in the table is the unit used in that report. Using m, L, or g for ▽:

km hm dam m

2,468. m = 246.8 dam = 24.68 hm = 2.468 km

kL hL daL L

2,468. L = 246.8 daL = 24.68 hL = 2.468 kL

kg hg dag g

2,468. g = 246.8 dag = 24.68 hg = 2.468 kg

**C.** The method used with submultiple units can be used with multiples.

**Example 1** 8.5 km = ■ dam

8.5 km = 8.5 km = 8.50 km = 850. dam = 850 dam

**Example 2** 36 L = ■ hL

36 L = 36. L = 036. L = 0.36 hL = 0.36 hL

**Example 3** 0.047 kg = ■ g

0.047 kg = 0.047 kg = 0047. g = 47 g

## CLASS EXERCISES

*Complete using m, L, and g for ▽.*

**1.** 18 ▽ = ■ k▽ **2.** 6.7 h▽ = ■ da▽ **3.** 71.5 da▽ = ■ k▽

## EXERCISES

*Complete.*

**1.** 4.75 km = ■ hm
**2.** 82.9 daL = ■ L
**3.** 91 g = ■ dag
**4.** 940 m = ■ dam
**5.** 0.07 kL = ■ hL
**6.** 0.3 hg = ■ g
**7.** 0.68 km = ■ m
**8.** 800 L = ■ daL
**9.** 4.68 kg = ■ hg
**10.** 27 m = ■ hm
**11.** 3.9 kL = ■ L
**12.** 1.2 dag = ■ hg
**13.** 0.39 hm = ■ km
**14.** 0.052 kL = ■ daL
**15.** 0.75 hg = ■ kg
**16.** 560 dam = ■ m
**17.** 3.4 daL = ■ hL
**18.** 260 dag = ■ g

## PROBLEMS

**19.** The Washington Monument is 1.69 hm high. What is its height in meters?

**20.** The fuel tank of a car holds 95 L of gasoline. How many dekaliters is that?

**21.** A recipe calls for 0.85 kg of hamburger meat. How many dekagrams is that?

**22.** A football field is 11 dam long. What is its length in kilometers?

## THINK!

### Logical Reasoning

A machinist, a nurse, and an electrician live on the same block in 3 adjoining houses. The nurse lives in the blue house. The red house is immediately to the right of the green house. The electrician used to live in the house on the right. The machinist lives next door to the nurse. Which house is in the middle?

1. 47.5 hm 4. 94 dam

Homework page 487

# Problem Solving

READ **PLAN** DO • ANSWER • CHECK

## 7-5 Using Metric Measures

An electrician cut eighteen 51-cm pieces of wire and twenty-five 242-mm pieces of wire from a 20.75-m roll. How many meters of wire were left?

**READ** *Must find:* How many meters of wire left.
*Know:* Had 20.75 m of wire to start.
Used eighteen 51-cm pieces and twenty-five 242-mm pieces.

**PLAN** **Step 1** Meters left = Meters to start − Meters used
= 20.75 m − Meters used

**Step 2** Meters used = Meters of 51-cm pieces + Meters of 242-mm pieces

**Step 3** Meters of 51-cm pieces
Number of pieces × Meters per piece
= 18 × ?

**Step 4** Meters of 242-mm pieces
Number of pieces × Meters per piece
= 25 × ?

**Step 5** To find Meters per piece, report 51 cm and 242 mm as meters.

**DO** Do Step 5 first: 51 cm = 0.51 m
242 mm = 0.242 m

Now do Steps 3 and 4:
Meters of 51-cm pieces
= 18 × 0.51 m
= 9.18 m

Meters of 242-mm pieces
= 25 × 0.242 m
= 6.05 m

Do Step 2: Meters used = Meters of 51-cm pieces + Meters of 242-mm pieces
= 9.18 m + 6.05 m
= 15.23 m

Do Step 1: Meters left = Meters to start − Meters used
= 20.75 m − 15.23 m
= 5.52 m

**ANSWER** There were 5.52 m of wire left on the roll.

**CHECK** Use estimation.

| | | | |
|---|---|---|---|
| Meters left | 5.52 m | ⟶ | 6 m |
| 51-cm pieces | 9.18 m | ⟶ | 9 m |
| 242-mm pieces | +6.05 m | ⟶ | +6 m |
| Total on roll | | | 21 m |

Near 20.75 m ✓

## CLASS EXERCISES

1. The electrician bought six 4.75-L bottles of distilled water to use in batteries. How many 20-cL bottles would be needed to store all of the distilled water?

2. The electrician has 12 bags of ivory faceplates and 9 bags of brown faceplates. Each faceplate has a mass of 25 g. If there are 30 faceplates in each bag, what is their total mass in kilograms?

## PROBLEMS

1. Mr. Kelvin walks at an average rate of 1.2 km/h. How many minutes does it take him to walk 3 km?

2. Ms. Harris' gas station has a 2.5-kL gas tank. She pays $.39/L for gasoline. What will it cost to fill the tank if it already contains 670 L?

3. The Acme Nail Co. packages nails in 20 dag boxes. How many boxes could be filled from a crate containing 18.75 kg of nails? Each nail has a mass of 8 g. How many nails are in each box?

4. A mixture contains three chemicals—A, B, and C. In 3.5 kg of the mixture there are 1.375 kg of chemical A and 5 hg of chemical B. How many grams of chemical C are in 3.5 kg of the mixture?

5. A supermarket received the following shipment of shampoo:
50 mL: 3 boxes of 25 bottles
200 mL: 2 boxes of 20 bottles
450 mL: 4 boxes of 12 bottles.
How many bottles of shampoo did the store receive? How many liters of shampoo were received?

6. Worker A used 1.2 m of ribbon on Monday, 90 cm on Tuesday, and 13.4 dm on Wednesday. Worker B used 83 cm, 13 dm, and 1.15 m of ribbon on those days. Who used more ribbon? How many meters more?

7. In a book, each line of print is 13 cm long. Each page has 42 lines of print. What is the total length of the lines of print on 464 pages in meters? in kilometers?

## MIXED REVIEW

*Add, subtract, multiply, or divide.*

1. $4 + {}^{-}9 = \blacksquare$
2. ${}^{-}3 - {}^{-}8 = \blacksquare$
3. $|{}^{-}4| \times |2| = \blacksquare$
4. $16 \div {}^{-}2 = \blacksquare$
5. ${}^{-}3 \times 6 = \blacksquare$
6. $|{}^{-}10| \div |5| = \blacksquare$
7. $13 - {}^{-}6 = \blacksquare$
8. $\frac{{}^{-}3}{4} \times \frac{{}^{-}5}{6} = \blacksquare$

*Write scientific notation for each.*

9. 71,200,000
10. .00000000593
11. 406,000,000,000

Homework page 487

# Problem Solving

READ • PLAN **DO** ANSWER • CHECK

## 7-6 Special Metric Relations

Volume of Water → Mass of Water

**A.**

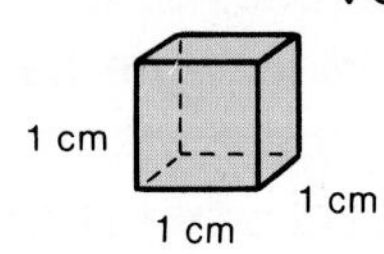


The volume of the water in this box is **1 cm³** (1 cubic centimeter).

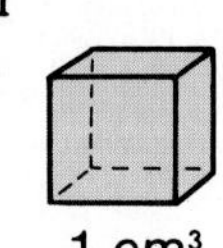

1 cm³

Another name for the volume is **1 mL.**

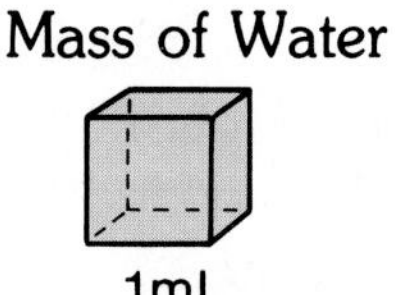

1mL

The mass of the water is **1 g.**

**B.**

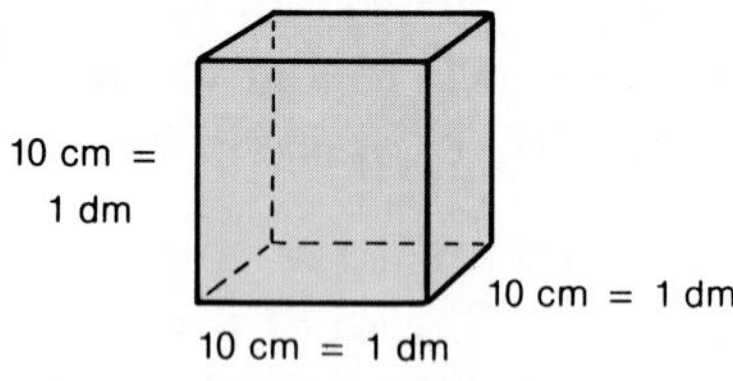


The volume of the water in this box is 1,000 cm³, or **1 dm³** (1 cubic decimeter).

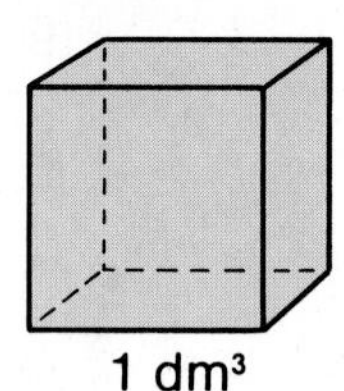

1 dm³

Another name for the volume is 1,000 mL, or **1 L.**

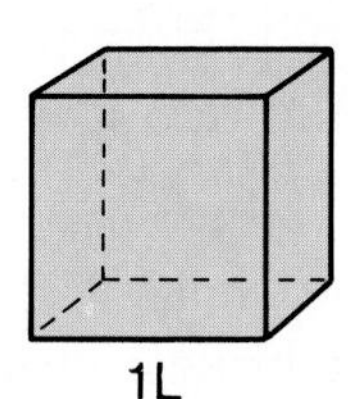

1L

The mass of the water is 1,000 g, or **1 kg.**

**C.**

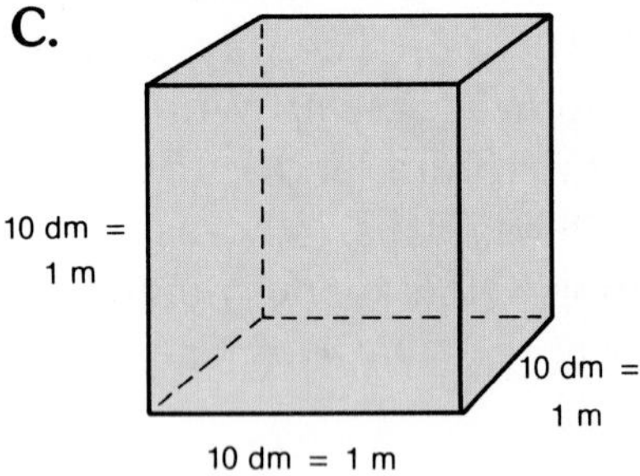


The volume of the water in this box is 1,000 dm³, or **1 m³** (1 cubic meter).

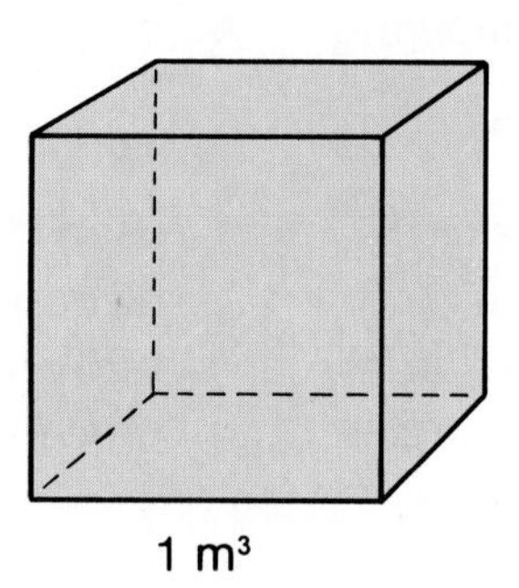

1 m³

Another name for the volume is 1,000 L, or **1 kL.**

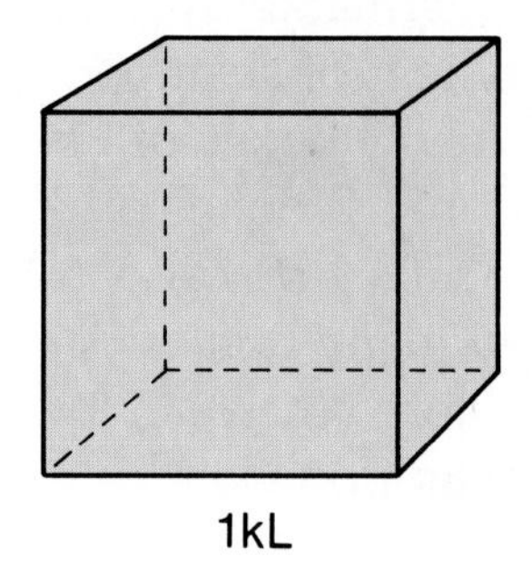

1kL

The mass of the water is 1,000 kg, or **1 t.**

**D.** Find the mass of the water that fills a swimming pool that is 10 m long, 5 m wide, and 3 m deep.

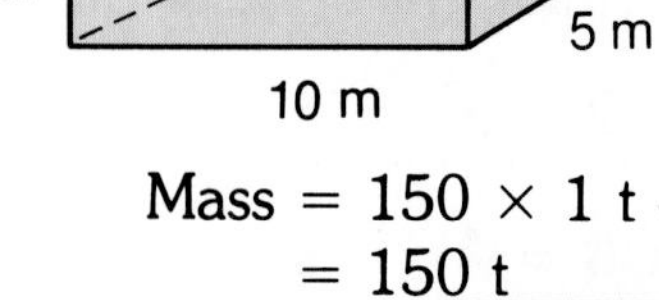


Volume = length × width × height
= 10 × 5 × 3
= 150 m³

Mass = 150 × 1 t
= 150 t

1 m³ of water has a mass of 1 t.

The water in the swimming pool has a mass of 150 t.

## CLASS EXERCISES

*Find the volume and mass of the water that fills each box.*

| length | 5 cm | 6 dm | 3 m | 100 mm | 80 cm | 1,200 cm |
|---|---|---|---|---|---|---|
| width | 4 cm | 4 dm | 3 m | 60 mm | 40 cm | 800 cm |
| height | 3 cm | 4 dm | 3 m | 50 mm | 20 cm | 700 cm |
| volume | **1.** ■ $cm^3$ | **4.** ■ $dm^3$ | **7.** ■ $m^3$ | **10.** ■ $cm^3$ | **13.** ■ $dm^3$ | **16.** ■ $m^3$ |
| | **2.** ■ mL | **5.** ■ L | **8.** ■ kL | **11.** ■ L | **14.** ■ L | **17.** ■ kL |
| mass | **3.** ■ g | **6.** ■ kg | **9.** ■ t | **12.** ■ g | **15.** ■ kg | **18.** ■ t |

## PROBLEMS

**1.** When empty, a water truck has a mass of 12.6 t. When full, its mass is 40 t. How many cubic meters of water can the truck carry?

**2.** A tray contains 12 ice cubes, each 3 cm long, 2.5 cm wide, and 2 cm high. How many milliliters of water are needed to fill this tray?

**3.** A recipe calls for 1.5 kg of chicken, 0.25 kg of mushrooms, and 125 mL of water. What is the total mass of these ingredients in kilograms?

**4.** A trough that is 16 dm long and 7dm wide contains 560 L of water. How deep is the water in the trough?

**5.** Kerry filled eighteen 15-L pails with water. What is the total mass of the water?

**6.** A water cooler holds 12 kg of water. What is the capacity of the water cooler in cubic decimeters?

**7.** A baking dish is 25 cm long, 25 cm wide, and 25 mm deep. How many grams of water will it hold?

**8.** A water reservoir is 12 m long, 3 m wide, and 7.5 m high. How many kiloliters of water will it hold?

★ **9.** A farmer's water tower holds 5,000 kL of water. The area of the bottom of the tower is 125 $m^2$. What is its height in decimeters?

### Logical Reasoning

How can you make $1.00 using exactly 50 coins?

Homework page 488

# 7-7 Units of Time

**A.** You can use the relations in this table to change units of time.

| | |
|---|---|
| 1 minute (min) = 60 seconds (s) | 1 week (wk) = 7 days |
| 1 hour (h) = 60 minutes | 1 year (yr) = 12 months (mo) |
| 1 day (d) = 24 hours | 1 century (cen) = 100 years |

**Example 1** It took Mr. Martin 6 days 18 hours to finish his project. How many hours was that?

**Step 1** Report days as hours.

1 d = 24 h

so 6 d = 6 × 24 h = 144 h

**Step 2** Add the hours.

144 h + 18 h = 162 h

It took Mr. Martin 162 h.

**Example 2** Ms. Watson worked 465 minutes on Monday. This can be reported as hours and minutes or as hours.

465 ÷ 60 = ■
about 480 ÷ 60 = 8
less than 8 h

*As hours and minutes.*

$$60\overline{)465}\quad 7\ \text{R}45$$

465 min is 7 h 45 min.

*As hours.*

$$60\overline{)465}\quad 7\tfrac{45}{60} \rightarrow 7\tfrac{3}{4}$$

465 min is $7\frac{3}{4}$ h.

**B.** When you do arithmetic with times you may have to change units.

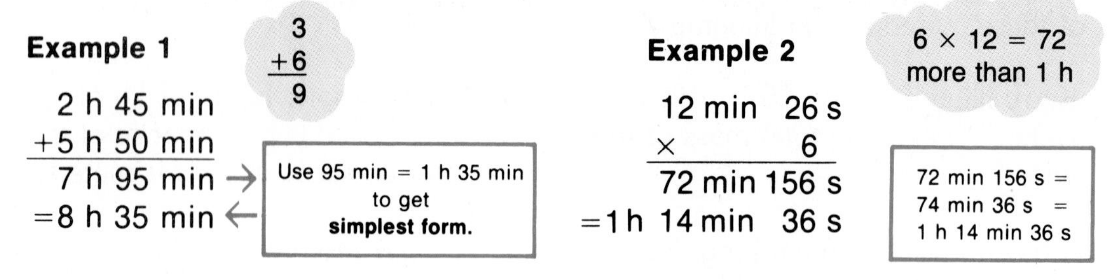


**Example 3**

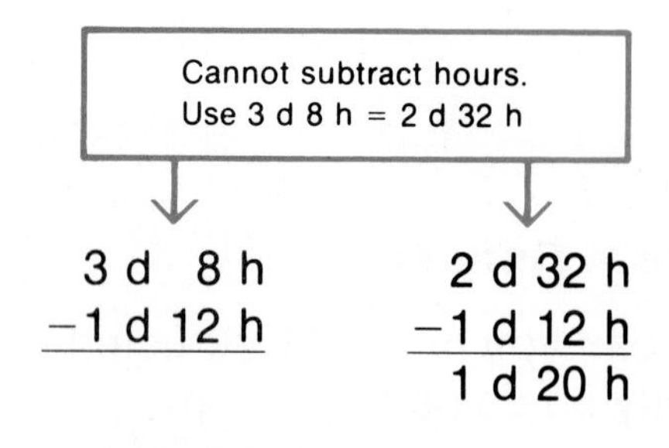


**Example 4**

140 ÷ 35 = 4

$$35\overline{)2\text{ h }30\text{ min}} \rightarrow 35\overline{)150\text{ min}}\quad 4\tfrac{10}{35} \rightarrow 4\tfrac{2}{7}\text{ min}$$

## CLASS EXERCISES

*Complete.*

**1.** 256 h = ■ d ■ h  **2.** 5 min 23 s = ■ s  **3.** 120 d = ■ wk ■ d

*Give the simplest form for the answers.*

**4.** 4 wk 3 d − 2 wk 6 d

**5.** 18 min 47 s + 35 min 29 s

**6.** 5 d 10 h × 18

**7.** 40)8 min 25 s

## EXERCISES

*Complete.*

**1.** 4 h 15 min = ■ min  **2.** 362 s = ■ min  **3.** $2\frac{3}{7}$ wk = ■ d

**4.** 90 d = ■ wk  **5.** 757 min = ■ h ■ min  **6.** 263 h = ■ d

**7.** 12 d 12 h = ■ h  **8.** 410 min = ■ h  **9.** 31 min 27 s = ■ s

*Add, subtract, multiply, or divide. Give the simplest form.*

**10.** 7 min 12 s − 3 min 56 s

**11.** 15 h 45 min + 12 h 45 min

**12.** 6 d − 2 d 8 h

**13.** 5 min 24 s × 5

**14.** 3 d 7 h × 12

**15.** 5 wk 6 d + 8 wk 5 d

**16.** 21)53 min 17 s

**17.** 6 d 12 h − 3 d 19 h

**18.** 13 wk 5 d × 9

**19.** 2 wk 3 d × 10

**20.** 10)40 min 35 s

**21.** 18 wk − 5 wk 4 d

**22.** 8 min 36 s × 8

**23.** 14 yr − 6 yr 5 mo

**24.** 5)16 wk 2 d

**25.** 15 h 37 min + 7 h 56 min

## PROBLEMS

**26.** Mr. Kress works 4 h 20 min before lunch. He works a total of 8 h during the day. How long does he work after lunch?

**27.** Erika can type a page in 12 min. At that rate, how many pages can she type in 5 h 30 min?

## THINK!

### Logical Reasoning

If it takes 1 minute to make each cut, how long will it take to cut a 20-meter pole into 20 equal pieces?

**1.** 255 min **10.** 3 min 16 s

Homework page 488

# 7-8 Clock Time

**A.** There are 24 hours in every day but most clocks have only 12 hour marks. When you look at a clock you must decide whether the time shown is A.M. or P.M.

After midnight and before noon:
4:30 A.M.

After noon and before midnight:
4:30 P.M.

12-hour clock

**B.** The United States Armed Forces and many airline and ship navigators use a 24-hour clock to avoid confusion between A.M. and P.M. times.

24-hour clock

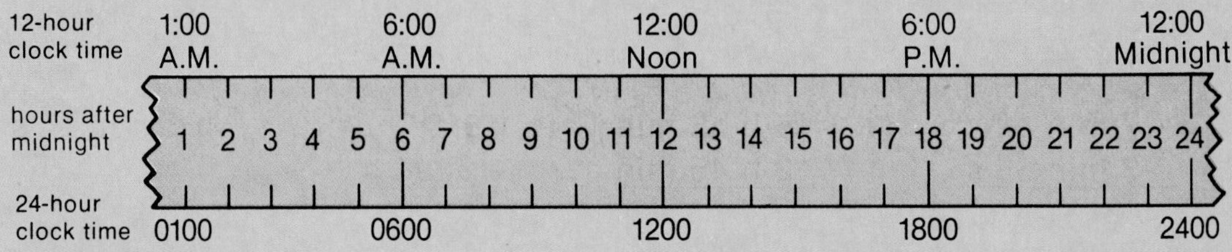


**C.** **To change from 12-hour time to 24-hour time,** write the time as ■ h ■ min.

For times:

1 P.M. or later, add 12 h. Then write 24-hour time.

Earlier than 1 A.M., subtract 12 h.

**Example 1** 8:30 A.M. → 8 h 30 min → 0830, 24-hour time

**Example 2** 2:45 P.M. → 2 h 45 min
+12 h
14 h 45 min → 1445, 24-hour time

**D.** **To change from 24-hour time to 12-hour time,** write the time as ■ h ■ min.

For times:

1300 or later, subtract 12 h. Then write the 12-hour time.

Earlier than 0100, add 12 h.

**Example 1** 0615 → 6 h 15 min → 6:15 A.M., 12-hour time

**Example 2** 1830 → 18 h 30 min
−12 h
6 h 30 min → 6:30 P.M., 12-hour time

## CLASS EXERCISES

*Give the 24-hour clock times.*

**1.** 7:10 A.M. **2.** 8:25 P.M. **3.** 2:15 A.M. **4.** 4:50 P.M.

*Give the 12-hour clock times.*

**5.** 0640 **6.** 1315 **7.** 2130 **8.** 0345

## EXERCISES

*Give the 24-hour clock times.*

**1.** 6:15 A.M. **2.** 11:42 P.M. **3.** 2:35 P.M. **4.** 10:50 A.M. **5.** 7:21 A.M.

**6.** 1:18 P.M. **7.** 3:55 P.M. **8.** 8:10 A.M. ★**9.** 12:01 A.M. ★**10.** 12:00 midnight

*Give the 12-hour clock times.*

**11.** 1638 **12.** 0400 **13.** 0705 **14.** 2035 **15.** 1810

**16.** 0143 **17.** 0917 **18.** 1140 **19.** 0040 **20.** 2400

Airline schedules usually give times using the 12-hour clock. However, pilots often use 24-hour clocks.

**21.** Copy this airline schedule using 24-hour clock times.

| LOS ANGELES TO NEW YORK | | |
|---|---|---|
| **Flight** | **Departure** | **Arrival** |
| 421 | 9:30 A.M. | 3:10 P.M. |
| 407 | 11:15 A.M. | 5:20 P.M. |
| 453 | 12:00 noon | 6:00 P.M. |
| 436 | 2:45 P.M. | 8:05 P.M. |

### On Time

A 24-hour digital clock has 4 "windows." How many sensible time combinations can it show? The clock shows a zero in the leftmost place when appropriate.

| sensible | not sensible |
|---|---|
| 0 7 : 3 9 | 4 3 : 9 9 |

1. 0615 11. 4:38 P.M.



Homework page 489

## 7-9 Elapsed Time

Sometimes you need to find an amount of time *before* an event, *after* an event, or *between* events.

**A.** One way to solve such problems is to think about a 12-hour clock.

A conference began at 8:30 A.M. and lasted 9 hours 45 minutes. At what time did it end?

Conference begins

8:30 A.M.

9 h later

5:30 P.M.

45 min later

6:15 P.M.

The conference ended at 6:15 P.M.

**B.** Another way to solve elapsed time problems is to think about hours after midnight on a 24-hour clock.

**Example 1** A conference session ended at 2:00 P.M. The meeting lasted 1 h 30 min. At what time did the meeting start?

Starting time = Ending time − Time worked
= 2:00 P.M. − 1 h 30 min
↓
14 h − 1 h 30 min
↓
= 13 h 60 min − 1 h 30 min
= 12 h 30 min
↓
12:30 P.M.

The meeting started at 12:30 P.M.

**Example 2** Another session started at 2:45 P.M. and ended at 4:30 P.M. How long did the session last?

Session time = Ending time − Starting time
= 4:30 P.M. − 2:45 P.M.
↓ ↓
16 h 30 min − 14 h 45 min
↓
= 15 h 90 min − 14 h 45 min
= 1 h 45 min

The session lasted 1 h 45 min.

## CLASS EXERCISES

*Report each time as hours after midnight.*

**1.** 6:35 A.M. **2.** 7:15 P.M. **3.** 11:20 P.M. **4.** 1:40 A.M. **5.** 8:00 P.M.

*Find the time or the time elapsed.*

**6.** 4 h 25 min before 1:30 P.M.

**7.** 6 h 5 min after 9:15 A.M.

**8.** between 5:45 A.M. and 2:30 P.M.

**9.** 11 h 40 min after 6:50 A.M.

## PROBLEMS

*Find the time or the time elapsed.*

**1.** 7 h 55 min before 3:30 P.M.

**2.** between 3:40 A.M. and 5:30 P.M.

**3.** 10 h 10 min after 4:50 P.M.

**4.** 8 h 15 min before 12:00 midnight

**5.** 2 h 20 min after 6:10 P.M.

**6.** 1 h 45 min before 7:15 A.M.

**7.** between 12:00 noon and 8:25 P.M.

**8.** between 0645 and 1915

**9.** 3 h 30 min after 4:40 A.M.

**10.** 6 h 5 min before 1:05 P.M.

*Complete this airline schedule for flight 365.*

| City | Arrives | On Ground | Departs | Flight Time |
|---|---|---|---|---|
| Los Angeles | —— | —— | 9:30 A.M. | **11.** |
| San Francisco | 10:40 A.M. | 35 min | **12.** | 2 h 5 min |
| Portland | 1:20 P.M. | **13.** | 1:45 P.M. | 45 min |
| Seattle | **14.** | —— | —— | —— |

**15.** Carol has to report for work at 10:00 A.M. on Saturday. It takes her 40 min to dress and eat breakfast and 50 min to get to work. At what time should she get up?

**16.** Ted worked from 8:30 A.M. to 4:15 P.M. on Saturday. He receives $6.15 per hour. How much did Ted earn on Saturday? (Round to the nearest cent.)

**17.** Janet earns $2.50 per hour. She starts her after-school job at 3:45 P.M. To earn $8.75, until what time will she have to work?

★ **18.** Al worked on a holiday from 8:45 A.M. to 3:30 P.M. for 1.5 times his usual pay of $3.50 per hour. How much did he earn? (Round to the nearest cent.)

## ON YOUR OWN

Find a train, bus, or plane schedule and use it to write three problems for your classmates.

1. 7:35 A.M. 3. 3:00 A.M.



Homework page 489

# 7-10 Customary Units

**A.** Some customary units of length or distance are the **inch (in.)**, the **foot (ft)**, the **yard (yd)**, and the **mile (mi)**.

| 1 ft = 12 in. | 1 yd = 3 ft<br>1 yd = 36 in. | 1 mi = 1,760 yd<br>1 mi = 5,280 ft |
|---|---|---|

The height of a car bumper is about 10 in.
The width of the glove compartment is about 1 ft.
The length of a compact car is about 5 yd.
The car can travel about 55 mi in an hour.
You can walk about 4 mi in an hour.

**B.** The **fluid ounce (fl oz)**, the **cup**, the **pint (pt)**, the **quart (qt)**, and the **gallon (gal)** are customary units used to measure volumes of liquids and the capacity of containers.

| 1 cup = 8 fl oz<br>1 pt = 2 cups<br>1 qt = 2 pt<br>1 gal = 4 qt |
|---|

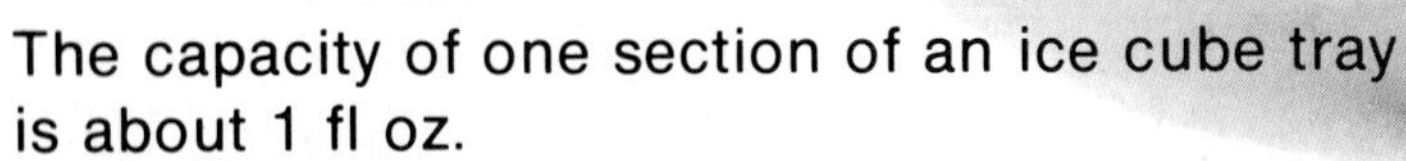

The capacity of one section of an ice cube tray is about 1 fl oz.
A thermos bottle holds about 2 cups or 1 pt of milk.
A large saucepan holds about 2 qt of soup.
The capacity of a pail is about 2 gal.

**C.** The **ounce (oz)**, **pound (lb)**, and **ton (tn)** are customary units used to measure weight.

| 1 lb = 16 oz<br>1 tn = 2,000 lb |
|---|

The weight of an orange is about 3 oz.
A Saint Bernard dog weighs about 150 lb.
An adult rhinoceros weighs about 4 tn.

## CLASS EXERCISES

*What unit would you use to measure:*

1. the capacity of an eggcup?
2. the length of a river?
3. the weight of an egg?
4. the width of an envelope?
5. the volume of gasoline in a fuel tank?
6. the weight of a transport truck?
7. the height of a building?
8. the capacity of a juice pitcher?

## EXERCISES

*Select the measure that seems reasonable.*

1. the capacity of a kitchen sink
   **a.** 8 qt **b.** 8 gal **c.** 8 pt
2. the volume of juice in a small glass
   **a.** 5 fl oz **b.** 5 cups **c.** 5 pt
3. the weight of a one-year-old child
   **a.** 18 oz **b.** 180 lb **c.** 18 lb
4. the length of a ball-point pen
   **a.** $5\frac{1}{2}$ in. **b.** 15 in. **c.** $5\frac{1}{2}$ ft
5. the width of a two-lane street
   **a.** 26 ft **b.** 26 yd **c.** 26 in
6. the weight of a bar of soap
   **a.** 40 oz **b.** 4 lb **c.** 4 oz
7. the weight of a full load of gravel
   **a.** 120 tn **b.** 12 tn **c.** 12 lb
8. the capacity of a garbage can
   **a.** 20 oz **b.** 20 gal **c.** 2 gal
9. the distance from Los Angeles to San Francisco
   **a.** 4,000 mi **b.** 400 yd **c.** 400 mi

### Space Race

It is 1,000 miles from space station I to space station II. During the Galaxy Races, Starship Delta averaged 500 mph each way on a round trip. Starship Omega averaged 400 mph going and 600 mph returning. Which starship won the race?

1. b. 8 gal



Homework page 490

## 7-11 Changing Customary Units

**A.** This table summarizes some relations among customary units.

| Length | Volume or Capacity | Weight |
|---|---|---|
| 1 ft = 12 in.<br>1 yd = 3 ft = 36 in.<br>1 mi = 1,760 yd<br>1 mi = 5,280 ft | 1 cup = 8 fl oz<br>1 pt = 2 cups<br>1 qt = 2 pt<br>1 gal = 4 qt | 1 lb = 16 oz<br>1 ton = 2,000 lb |

**B.** To solve problems with customary units, you often have to change a report using one unit to a report using another unit.

**Example 1** A small barbell weighs 8 lb 11 oz. How many ounces is this?

Find: 8 lb 11 oz = ■ oz

**Step 1** Report pounds as ounces.

| 1 lb = 16 oz<br>so 8 lb = 8 × 16 oz |
|---|

$$\begin{array}{r} 16 \text{ oz} \\ \times\ 8 \\ \hline 128 \text{ oz} \end{array}$$

**Step 2** Add ounces.

$$\begin{array}{r} 128 \text{ oz} \\ +\ 11 \text{ oz} \\ \hline 139 \text{ oz} \end{array}$$

The barbell weighs 139 oz.

**Example 2** A track team jogs 4,400 yd each morning. This can be reported as miles and yards or as miles.

*As miles and yards:*

$$1{,}760\overline{)4{,}400} \quad 2 \text{ R}880$$

4,400 yd is 2 mi 880 yd.

*As miles:*

$$1{,}760\overline{)4{,}400} \quad 2\frac{880}{1{,}760} = 2\frac{1}{2}$$

4,400 yd is $2\frac{1}{2}$ mi.

## CLASS EXERCISES

*Complete.*

1. 2 ft 8 in. = ■ in.
2. 39 qt = ■ gal ■ qt
3. 4 tn 1,150 lb = ■ lb
4. 85 in. = ■ yd ■ ft ■ in.
5. $14\frac{3}{4}$ lb = ■ oz
6. 24 pt = ■ qt = ■ gal

## EXERCISES

*Complete.*

1. 7,250 lb = ■ tn ■ lb
2. 3 pt 1 cup = ■ cups
3. 43 in. = ■ ft ■ in.
4. 7 qt 1 pt = ■ pt
5. 29 ft = ■ yd ■ ft
6. 2 mi 500 yd = ■ yd
7. $3\frac{1}{4}$ mi = ■ ft
8. 92 oz = ■ lb
9. $21\frac{3}{4}$ gal = ■ qt
10. 62 fl oz = ■ cups
11. 8 yd 7 in. = ■ in.
12. 30,000 ft = ■ mi ■ ft
13. 15 cups = ■ pt
14. 45 pt = ■ qt ■ pt
15. 100 ft = ■ yd
16. $5\frac{1}{2}$ yd = ■ in.
17. 19,600 lb = ■ tn
18. $11\frac{1}{2}$ ft = ■ in.
19. 8 mi 1,250 ft = ■ ft
20. $24\frac{2}{3}$ yd = ■ ft
21. 110 oz = ■ lb ■ oz
22. $6\frac{1}{10}$ tn = ■ lb
23. 98 in. = ■ yd
24. 98 in. = ■ ft

## PROBLEMS

25. A recipe calls for 20 fl oz of milk. How many cups and fluid ounces is that?
26. A football player jogs $1\frac{1}{4}$ mi each evening. How many yards is that?
27. A cement truck weighs $17\frac{1}{2}$ tn empty and 32 tn full. How many pounds of concrete does it hold?

## THINK!

**Visual Perception**

Squares ABCF and FCDE are the same size. Is the distance around the shaded area greater than, less than, or equal to the distance around the unshaded area?

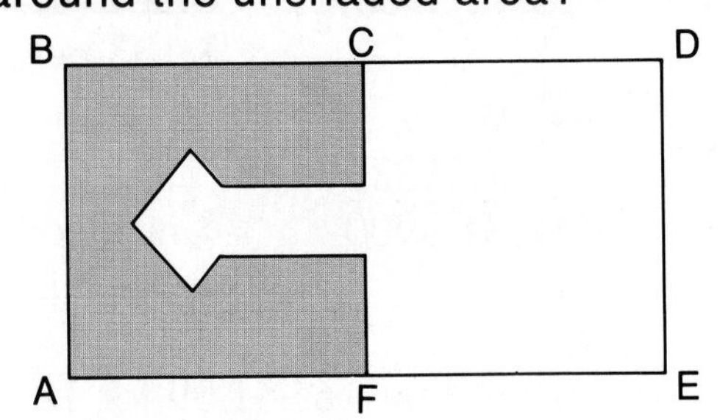


1. 3 tn 1,250 lb 3. 3 ft 7 in.

Homework page 490

## 7-12 Using Customary Units

**A.** Mrs. Forest had twins. One baby weighed 5 lb 14 oz and the other weighed 6 lb 10 oz. How much did the twins weigh all together? Give the simplest form for the answer.

**Step 1** Add.

```
  5 lb 14 oz
 +6 lb 10 oz
 11 lb 24 oz
```

**Step 2** Find the simplest form.

1 lb = 16 oz

11 lb 24 oz → 11 lb + 1 lb 8 oz = 12 lb 8 oz

The twins weighed 12 lb 8 oz all together.

**B.** Lauren wants to jog 7 mi. She has already jogged 2 mi 640 yd. How much farther does she have to jog?

Not enough yards to subtract. Regroup first.

```
  7 mi                     6     1,760 yd
 −2 mi 640 yd    ──→      7̸ mi
                         −2 mi    640 yd
                          4 mi  1,120 yd
```

She has to jog 4 mi 1,120 yd farther.

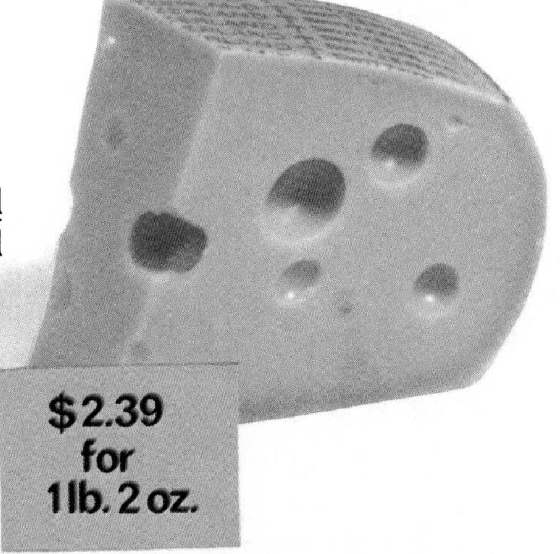


**C.** Erik wanted to buy cheese to make some sandwiches. One brand cost $2.39 for 1 lb 2 oz or $1.59 for 12 oz. Which was the better buy?

Find the unit prices and compare.

For 1 lb 2 oz:
1 lb 2 oz = 18 oz

$18\overline{)\$2.3900}$ = $ .1327 → $.133

Unit Price:
$.133 per ounce

For 12 oz:

$12\overline{)\$1.5900}$ = $ .1325

Unit Price:
$.1325 per ounce

The better buy was $1.59 for 12 oz.

## CLASS EXERCISES

1. Four runners on a relay team run distances of 220 yd, 440 yd, 880 yd, and 880 yd. What is the total distance run in miles and yards?

2. Bread costs $.95 for 1 lb or $.69 for 12 oz. Which is the better buy?

## PROBLEMS

1. Mr. Kelly bought 16 bags of feed for his chickens. Each bag weighed 5 lb 9 oz. What was the total weight of the 16 bags?

2. A recipe for a casserole that serves 6 calls for 2 cups 5 fl oz of milk. How much milk is there in each serving of this casserole?

3. A 4 lb 2 oz chicken cost $5.25 and a 7 lb 1 oz chicken cost $9.05. Which was the better buy?

4. Cottage cheese costs $.65 for 1 pt or $.40 for 6 fl oz. Which is the better buy?

5. Mark's dog weighs 22 lb 8 oz. Amy's dog weighs 9 lb 11 oz. How much more does Mark's dog weigh?

6. A carpenter used 15 ft of wood to make a table, 12 ft of wood to make a chest, and 7 ft of wood to make a chair. How much wood did he use all together?

7. A gravel truck contained 14 tn of gravel when full. After some gravel was used on a driveway, 9 tn 900 lb of gravel remained. How much gravel was used?

8. Alex made some fruit punch for the school picnic. He used 2 qt 1 pt of orange juice, 3 qt 1 pt of grape juice, and 1 qt of pineapple juice. How much juice did he use in all?

9. A gardener had 6 gal 3 qt of weed spray. He bought 4 gal 3 qt more. How much weed spray does he have all together?

## ON YOUR OWN

### Visual Perception

House A faces left, House B faces right. Can you remodel House A so it also faces right by moving exactly two of the lines. Tell what numbered lines you would move, and where you would place them.

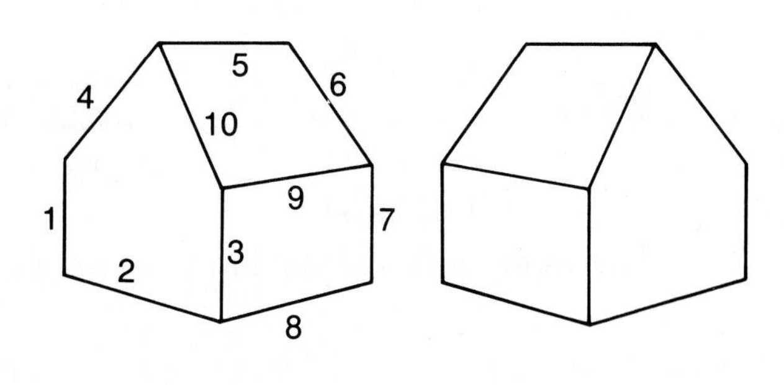

## 7-13 Special Customary Relations

Volume of Water → Weight of Water

**A.**

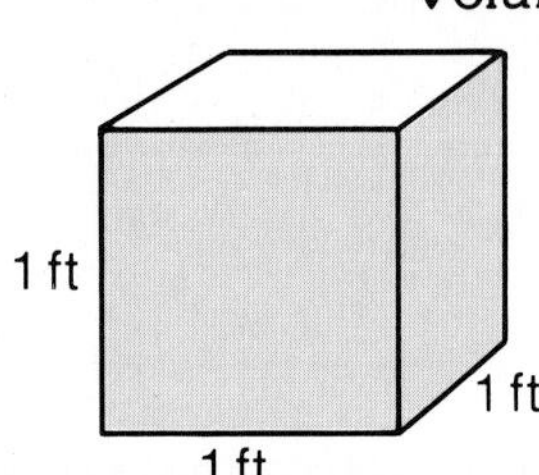


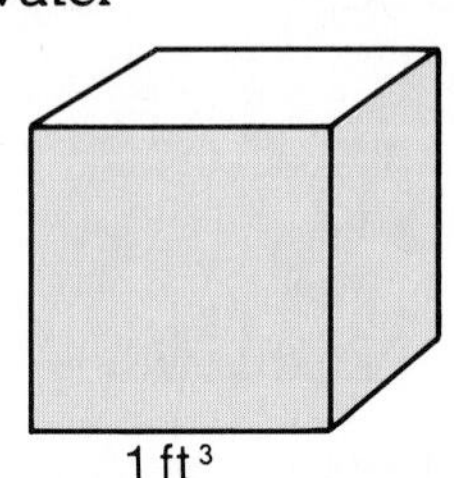


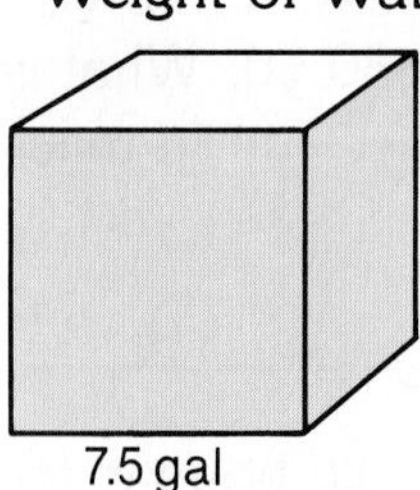


The volume of the water in a box this size is **1ft³** (1 cubic foot). The volume of the water is also about **7.5 gal.** The water weighs about **62.4 lb.**

**B.**

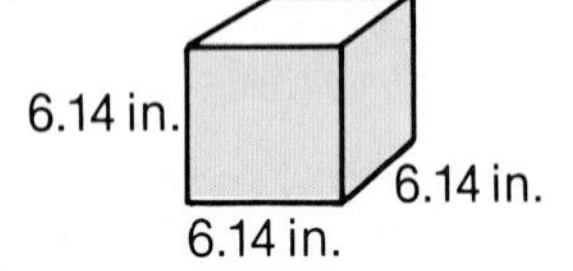


231 in.³

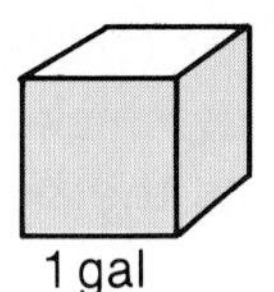


The volume of the water in this box is about **231 in.³** (cubic inches). The volume of the water is **1 gal.** The water weighs about **8.3 lb.**

**C.**

3.02 in. 3.02 in. 3.02 in.

27.5 in.³

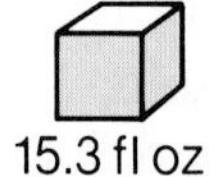


The volume of the water in this box is about **27.5 in.³** The volume of the water is also about **15.3 fl oz.** The water weighs **1 lb.**

**D.** Find the weight of the water that fills a swimming pool that is 30 ft long, 15 ft wide, and 8 ft deep.

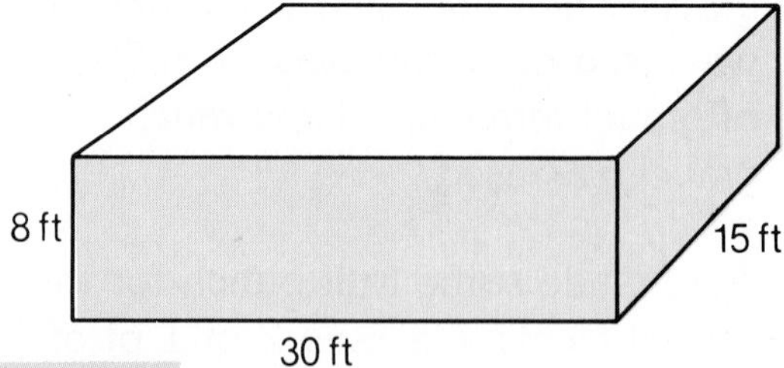


$$\begin{aligned}\text{Volume} &= \text{length} \times \text{width} \times \text{height}\\ &= 30 \times 15 \times 8\\ &= 3{,}600 \text{ ft}^3\end{aligned}$$

$$\begin{aligned}\text{Weight} &= 3{,}600 \times 62.4 \text{ lb}\\ &= 224{,}640 \text{ lb}\\ &= 112 \text{ tn } 640 \text{ lb}\end{aligned}$$

1 ft³ of water weighs 62.4 lb.

The water in the swimming pool weighs 112 tn 640 lb.

## CLASS EXERCISES

*Find the volume and weight of the water that fills each box.*

| length | 4 ft | 8 ft | 4 in. | 5 in. | 8 in. | 25 in. |
|---|---|---|---|---|---|---|
| width | 3 ft | 8 ft | 2 in. | 5 in. | 7 in. | 20 in. |
| height | 2 ft | 8 ft | 3 in. | 5 in. | 6 in. | 10 in. |
| volume | **1.** ▩ $ft^3$ | **4.** ▩ $ft^3$ | **7.** ▩ $in.^3$ | **10.** ▩ $in.^3$ | **13.** ▩ $in.^3$ | **16.** ▩ $in.^3$ |
| | **2.** ▩ gal | **5.** ▩ gal | **8.** ▩ fl oz | **11.** ▩ fl oz | **14.** ▩ gal | **17.** ▩ gal |
| weight | **3.** ▩ lb | **6.** ▩ lb | **9.** ▩ lb | **12.** ▩ lb | **15.** ▩ lb | **18.** ▩ lb |

## PROBLEMS

**1.** When empty, a water truck weighs 12 tn. When full, it weighs 40 tn. How many cubic feet of water can the truck carry?

**2.** Sean filled eighteen $3\frac{1}{3}$-gal pails with water from a reservoir. What was the total weight of the water?

**3.** A recipe calls for 3 lb of chicken, 0.5 lb of mushrooms, and 5 fl oz of water. What is the total weight of the ingredients?

**4.** A water cooler holds 25 lb of water. What is the capacity of the water cooler in cubic inches?

**5.** A water reservoir is 12 yd long, 3 yd wide, and 8 yd high. How many gallons of water will it hold?

**6.** A tray contains 12 ice cubes, each 1.25 in. long, 1 in. wide, and 0.75 in. high. How many fluid ounces of water are needed to fill this tray?

**7.** A baking dish is 12 in. long, 12 in. wide, and 1 in. deep. How many fluid ounces of water would it hold?

**8.** A trough that is 5 ft long and 2 ft wide contains 150 gal of water? About how deep is the water in the trough?

★ **9.** A farmer's water tower holds 1,350,000 gal of water. The area of the bottom of the tower is 3,600 $ft^2$. What is its height?

### ON YOUR OWN

**Use Algebra**

The lesser of two consecutive integers is 1 more than twice the greater. Find the numbers.

**Homework page 491**

TECHNOLOGY

## Volume, Mass, Time, and Weight on a Calculator

Your calculator can help you solve problems of volume, mass, time, and weight.

**A.** Find the mass of water that fills a pool 92 dm long, 77 dm wide, and 31 dm deep. Give the mass in metric tons.

First use a calculator to find the volume of water. Press:

100 × 70 × 30 = 210,000

[9] [2] [×] [7] [7] [×] [3] [1] [=] 219604.

The volume is 219,604 $dm^3$. Be sure to label answers carefully.

Since 1 $dm^3$ of water has a mass of 1 kg, the water in the pool has a mass of 219,604 kg.

219,604 kg = ■ t

Divide by 1,000. Use the calculator or mental math.

[2] [1] [9] [6] [0] [4] [÷] [1] [0] [0] [0] [=] 2196.04

The water has a mass of 219.604 t.

**B.** 14,827 min = ■ h ■ min

First find the number of whole hours. Press:

14,827 ÷ 60 = ■
12,000 ÷ 60 = 200

[1] [4] [8] [2] [7] [÷] [6] [0] [=] 247.11666

There are 247 whole hours.

Next find the number of minutes left over.

[2] [4] [7] [×] [6] [0] [=] [M+]

[1] [4] [8] [2] [7] [−] [RM] [=] 7.

There are 7 minutes.

14,827 min = 247 h 7 min

*Complete.*

1. 9,400 min = ■ h ■ min
2. 2,173 h = ■ d ■ h
3. 14,827 min = ■ d ■ h ■ min
4. 52,568 s = ■ h ■ min ■ s
5. Find the mass of the water that fills a pool 105 dm long, 82 dm wide, and 2.5 m deep.
6. Find the weight of the water that fills a pool 30 ft long, 30 ft wide, and 12 ft deep.

# Problem Solving Strategy

READ • PLAN • DO • ANSWER • CHECK

## Guess and Check

There are two small apartment buildings on Grayrock Road. The Bristol has 22 more apartments than the Northgate. If the number of apartments in the Northgate were doubled and then 10 were subtracted, the result would equal the number of apartments in the Bristol. How many apartments does each building have?

One way to do this problem is to use a **guess and check** strategy.

| Guess the number of Bristol apartments. | Find the number of Northgate apartments. | Check to see if your Bristol guess was right. |
|---|---|---|
| 50 | $50 - 22 = 28$ | $2 \times 28 - 10 = 46$ Guess was too small. |

Guess a larger number.

| | | |
|---|---|---|
| 52 | $52 - 22 = 30$ | $2 \times 30 - 10 = 50$ still too small |

Guess again.

| | | |
|---|---|---|
| 54 | $54 - 22 = 32$ | $2 \times 32 - 10 = 54$ Just right! |

The Bristol has 54 apartments, the Northgate has 32.

---

*Solve.*

1. There are 11 more cars on the first level of the garage than on the second level. If the number of cars on the second level were doubled and 19 were subtracted, the result would equal the number of cars on the first level. How many cars are on each level?

2. The supermarket has 15 more employees than the hardware store. If the hardware store had 3 fewer than twice as many employees, the result would equal the supermarket employees. How many employees does each store have?

3. A set of golf lessons costs $75 more than a set of tennis lessons. It would cost $305 to take lessons in both sports. How much does each set of lessons cost?

4. The Nature Club has 13 more members than the Photo Club. If the Photo Club would triple its membership, it would have 15 more members than the Nature Club. How many members does each club have?

# Problem Solving Project

READ • PLAN • DO • ANSWER • CHECK

## Time Zones

The sun shines on different parts of the earth at different times because the earth is constantly turning. Earth has been divided into 24 **time zones**—one for each hour in a day. The time when the sun is directly over the middle of a time zone is called **noon.**

**A.** The map shows the time zones of the world. The "first" time zone is the one passing through Greenwich, England. It is known as Universal Coordinated Time (UTC). Other time zones are labeled to show whether the time is *earlier* or *later* than Universal Coordinated Time. For example, Chicago is in the zone labeled $^{-}6$ (it is 6 hours earlier than UTC); Oslo, Norway is in the zone labeled $^{+}1$ (it is 1 hour later than UTC).

The day changes at the International Date Line. It is one day later in the week on the west side of the International Date Line than it is on the east side. If it is noon Universal Coordinated Time, then it is **midnight** at the International Date Line.

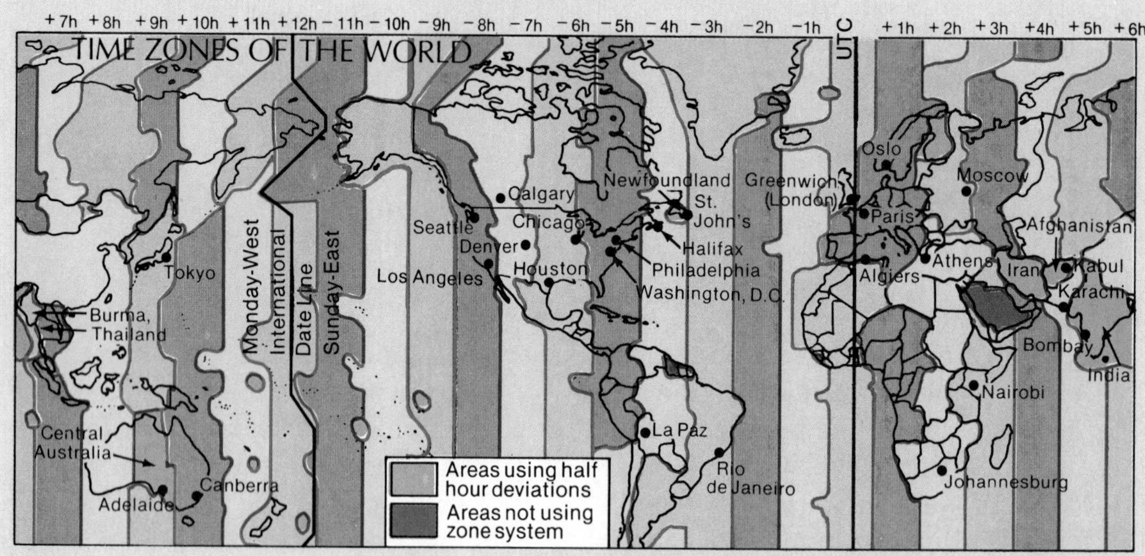


Note: Standard time zones in the U.S.S.R. are always advanced one hour.

*It is noon on Sunday in Houston. Find the time in each city.*

1. London
2. Calgary
3. Philadelphia
4. Denver
5. Rio de Jañeiro
6. Canberra
7. Johannesburg
8. Seattle
9. Karachi
10. La Paz
11. Paris
12. Athens
13. Nairobi
14. Algiers
15. Halifax
16. Tokyo

**B.** Most of North America changes from **standard time** (the sun is overhead at noon) to **daylight saving time** (the sun is overhead at 1:00 P.M.) from the end of April to the end of October every year. The Soviet Union uses daylight saving time all year.

*What time is it in Moscow, if it is:*

**17.** noon standard time in Washington, D.C.?

**18.** noon daylight saving time in Washington, D.C.?

**C.** Some places use times that differ by a **half hour** from the time zone.

| Place | Difference in Time from UTC |
|---|---|
| Newfoundland | $^-3\frac{1}{2}$ h (earlier) |
| Iran | $^+3\frac{1}{2}$ h (later) |
| Afghanistan | $^+4\frac{1}{2}$ h (later) |
| India | $^+5\frac{1}{2}$ h (later) |
| Burma, Thailand | $^+6\frac{1}{2}$ h (later) |
| Central Australia | $^+9\frac{1}{2}$ h (later) |

*It is 6:00 P.M. Wednesday in Los Angeles. Find the time in each city.*

**19.** St. John's

**20.** Adelaide

**21.** Bombay

**22.** Kabul

## ON YOUR OWN

**1.** Get an international airline schedule from a travel agent. The schedule will show departure and arrival times in the time for each city. (Times in North America are usually standard times.) Plan a vacation. Determine how long each flight actually takes.

**2.** Select seven different places around the world (cities, island groups, deserts, and so on). Be sure to include areas other than North America and Europe. Construct a chart listing 6–10 of your daily activities, and the usual time at which you do each of them. Then fill in the time it would be in each of the other places.

# Unit Review

*Select the measure that seems reasonable.* *(pages 234–235)*

**1.** The mass of a slice of bread:
**a.** 20 mg **b.** 20 g **c.** 200 g

**2.** The length of the Ohio River:
**a.** 160 km **b.** 1,600 m **c.** 1,600 km

**3.** The capacity of a watering can:
**a.** 8 L **b.** 80 mL **c.** 800 mL

**4.** The height of a classroom:
**a.** 3.4 cm **b.** 3.4 m **c.** 3.4 dm

*Complete.* *(pages 236–241)*

**5.** 60 daL = ■ kL
**6.** 4 mg = ■ cg
**7.** 0.7 km = ■ m
**8.** 146 mm = ■ cm
**9.** 0.512 L = ■ dL
**10.** 308 cg = ■ g
**11.** 0.094 kL = ■ hL
**12.** 43 m = ■ km
**13.** 162 dag = ■ kg

*Complete.* *(pages 246–247)*

**14.** 4 min 29 s ■ s
**15.** 546 min = ■ h ■ min
**16.** 8 wk 3 d = ■ d
**17.** 890 min = ■ h
**18.** $5\frac{2}{3}$ d = ■ h
**19.** 429 s = ■ min ■ s

*Add, subtract, multiply, or divide.* *(pages 246–247)*

**20.** 8 wk 5 d − 4 wk 6 d
**21.** 5 min 48 s × 6
**22.** 13 h 42 min + 21 h 28 min
**23.** 9)13 d 18 h
**24.** 17)42 min 30 s
**25.** 9 wk 5 d + 6 wk 4 d
**26.** 11 d − 3 d 16 h
**27.** 8 h 35 min × 18

*Give the 12-hour clock times.* *(pages 248–249)*

**28.** 0829 **29.** 1946 **30.** 0035

*Give the 24-hour clock times.* *(pages 248–249)*

**31.** 8:13 P.M. **32.** 5:45 A.M. **33.** midnight

*Select the measure that seems reasonable.* *(pages 252–253)*

**34.** The height of Mount St. Helens:
**a.** 1,800 ft **b.** 180 yd **c.** 1.8 mi

**35.** The volume of baby food in a jar:
**a.** 4 fl oz **b.** 4 cups **c.** 4 pt

**36.** The weight of a brick:
**a.** $2\frac{1}{2}$ oz **b.** $2\frac{1}{2}$ lb **c.** 25 lb

**37.** The width of a dinner knife:
**a.** $1\frac{3}{4}$ in. **b.** $\frac{3}{4}$ ft **c.** $\frac{3}{4}$ in.

*Complete.* *(pages 254–255)*

**38.** 105 in. = ■ ft ■ in.

**39.** 8 lb 11 oz = ■ oz

**40.** 145 fl oz = ■ cups  fl oz

**41.** 215 ft = ■ yd

**42.** $8\frac{3}{4}$ gal = ■ qt
35

**43.** 6,400 lb = ■ tn ■ lb

**44.** $2\frac{5}{8}$ mi = ■ ft

**45.** 492 in. = ■ yd ■ in.

**46.** $12\frac{3}{4}$ tn = ■ lb

*Solve the problems.* *(pages 242–245, 250–251, 256–259)*

**47.** Janice runs 25 hm every morning and 145 dam every evening. How many kilometers does she run in 1 week?

**48.** A service station tank holds 6 kL of gasoline. One day, the station sold a total of 1,854 L of gasoline to 36 customers. At that rate, how many more customers can buy gasoline?

**49.** A wading pool is 20 dm long, 18 dm wide, and 3 dm deep. How many liters of water will it hold? What is the mass of that water?

**50.** A tank can hold 50 t of water. The tank is 3 m long and 3 m wide. The water in the tank is 4.5 m deep. How much more water can be put in the tank?

**51.** It takes Will 25 min to shower and dress, 10 min to eat breakfast, and 1 h 40 min to get to school. If he has to be at basketball practice at 8:00 A.M. at what time should he get up?

**52.** A flight leaves Collins at 9:35 A.M., stops at Devon for 45 min, then goes on to Eastwood, arriving at 1:10 P.M. How much time does the flight spend in the air?

**53.** Mount Ararat in Turkey is 3 mi 1,106 ft high. Mont Blanc in France is 2 mi 5,211 ft high. Which mountain is higher? How much higher?

**54.** Which is the best buy for pasta?
1 lb 2 oz for $.69
1 lb 8 oz for $.94
or 2 lb for $1.20

**55.** A hot water heater holds 150 gal of water. What is the weight of the water? What is its volume in cubic feet?

**56.** An ice-maker is 5 ft long, 2 ft wide, and 4 ft high. How many gallons of water are needed to fill it? How heavy is that water?

# Enrichment

## Topology

**Topology** is a part of geometry that is about those properties of figures that have nothing to do with size. Topology deals with networks.

**A.** The figure at the right is a **network.** A network is made up of points **(vertices)** and paths **(arcs)** joining the vertices. Each arc starts at a vertex and ends at the next vertex.

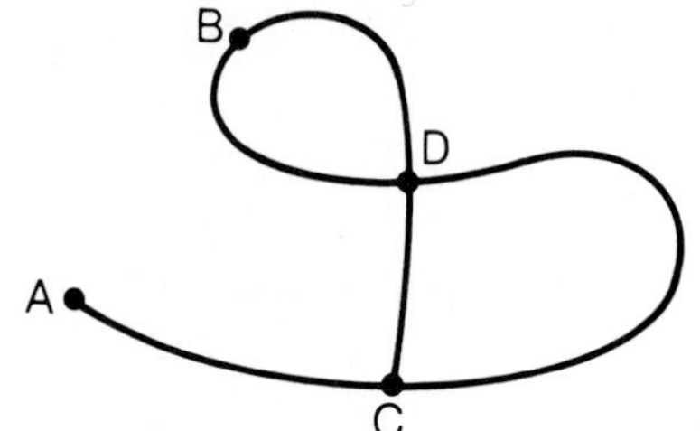


Vertex A is a 1-path point. It is an endpoint of 1 arc.
Vertex B is a 2-path point. It is an endpoint of 2 arcs.
Vertex C is a 3-path point. It is an endpoint of 3 arcs.
Vertex D is a 4-path point. It is an endpoint of 4 arcs.

You can think of the letters of the alphabet as networks if the vertices are shown.

ABCDEFGHIJKLMN

OPQRSTUVWXYZ

**1.** Copy and complete the table.

| Letter | Number of 1-path points | Number of 2-path points | Number of 3-path points | Number of 4-path points |
|---|---|---|---|---|
| A | 2 | 1 | 2 | 0 |

**2.** Which letters can you trace without lifting your pencil or retracing any arc? You must start and end at the same vertex. Look for a pattern.

**3.** Which letters can you trace without lifting your pencil or retracing any arc if you can start and end at different vertices? Look for a pattern.

**B.** Two-path points can be ignored when working with networks.

A can be treated in the same way as A — vertex ignored

Think of the letters as being made of rubber. You can stretch or shrink them as much as you want, but you cannot cut or tear. So points that do not touch when you begin stretching or shrinking will not touch when you are finished.

 can be stretched into 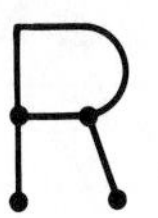. P cannot be stretched into 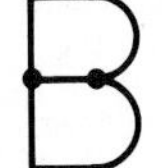.

**4.** Use your table from Exercise 1, but ignore the 2-path points. Separate the letters into classes. Put letters in the same class if all numbers in their rows of the table match.

**5.** Which letters can be stretched to form other letters? Put letters in the same class if each can be stretched to form each of the others.

**C.** A network separates a plane into **regions.** A network always has one outside region. The network at the right also has two inside regions (I and II).

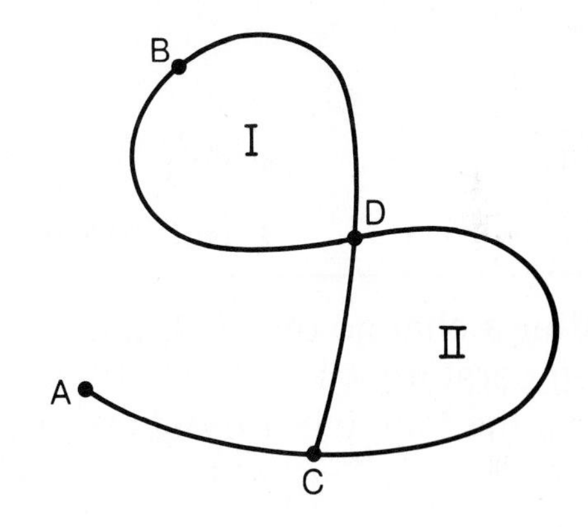

For the network at right:

Number of Vertices, V = 4
Number of Regions, R = 3
Number of Arcs, A = 5

$$V + R - A = \blacksquare$$
$$4 + 3 - 5 = 2$$

**6.** Find the values of V, R, and A for each letter of the alphabet on Page 246.

**7.** Does $V + R - A = 2$ for each letter? What do you conclude? Test your conclusion on other networks.

# Cumulative Review

1. $\frac{7}{8} \div \frac{5}{12} = \blacksquare$
   a. $\frac{35}{96}$
   b. $\frac{10}{21}$
   c. $2\frac{1}{10}$
   d. Not above

2. $^-8 \times {}^-9 = \blacksquare$
   a. $^-17$
   b. $^-72$
   c. $^-1$
   d. Not above

3. 3.9 kg = $\blacksquare$ g
   a. .0039 g
   b. 390 g
   c. 3,900 g
   d. Not above

4. 6.9 cm = $\blacksquare$ m
   a. .069 m
   b. 690 m
   c. .69 m
   d. Not above

5. $5\frac{1}{4} - 3\frac{5}{6}$
   a. $2\frac{7}{12}$
   b. $1\frac{5}{12}$
   c. $2\frac{5}{12}$
   d. Not above

6. Round to the nearest thousandth. $.75\overline{)2.6}$
   a. .035
   b. 3.467
   c. .347
   d. Not above

7. Compare $\frac{11}{12}$ and $\frac{13}{16}$.
   a. $\frac{11}{12} < \frac{13}{16}$
   b. $\frac{11}{12} > \frac{13}{16}$
   c. $\frac{11}{12} = \frac{13}{16}$
   d. Not above

8. Solve. $\frac{2}{3}x + \frac{1}{6} = \frac{5}{12}$
   a. $\frac{3}{8}$
   b. 2
   c. $\frac{1}{6}$
   d. Not above

9. $1\frac{5}{6} \times 2\frac{1}{2} = \blacksquare$
   a. $3\frac{2}{3}$
   b. $4\frac{7}{12}$
   c. $2\frac{5}{12}$
   d. Not above

10. What is the amount of time between 10:40 A.M. and 3:25 P.M.?
    a. 7 h 15 min
    b. 4 h 25 min
    c. 4 h 45 min
    d. Not above

11. After a change of $^-7$°C, the temperature was $^-12$°C. What was the temperature before this change?
    a. $^-5$°C
    b. 5°C
    c. $^-19$°C
    d. Not above

12. Janice mixed 4.65 L of white paint with 580 mL of red paint. How many liters of this mixture did she have?
    a. 584.65 L
    b. 10.45 L
    c. 5.23 L
    d. Not above

13. Each small plane can carry 126 people. Each large plane can carry 246 people. How many people in all can be carried by 5 small and 3 large planes?
    a. 2,976 people
    b. 1,368 people
    c. 380 people
    d. Not above

14. Kim had 15.6 m of ribbon. She used 3.4 m and gave 7.8 m to her father. How much ribbon did she have left?
    a. 11.2 m
    b. 26.8 m
    c. 20 m
    d. Not above

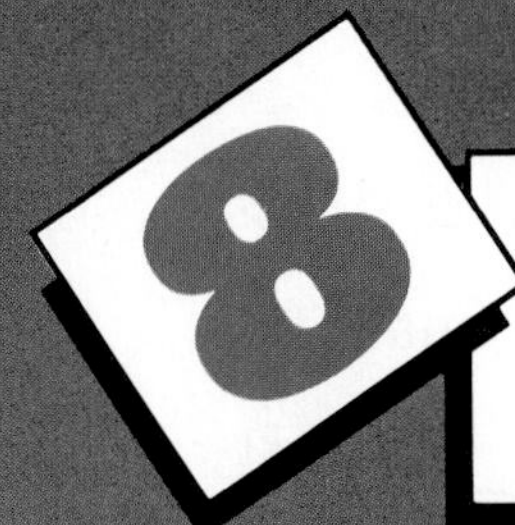

# Ratio, Proportion, and Percent

**GREAT DESERTS OF THE WORLD**

| **Name** | **Location** | **Area** □ = 300,000 square miles |
|---|---|---|
| Great Sandy | West Australia | ◺ |
| Gobi | Mongolia and China | □ ◺ |
| Libyan | North Africa | □ ◺ |
| Great Victoria | West Australia | ◺ |
| Rub al Khali | Arabian Peninsula | □ |
| Sahara | North Africa | □ □ □ □ □ □ □ □ □ □ □ ◺ |

# 8-1 Ratio and Proportion

**A.** You can use a **ratio** to compare two quantities.

| hours | 1 | 2 | 3 |
|---|---|---|---|
| minutes | 60 | 120 | 180 |

The ratio of hours to minutes is: 1 to 60 or 2 to 120 or 3 to 180.
Write 1 to 60, or 1:60, or $\frac{1}{60}$.

The ratio of minutes to hours is: 60 to 1 or 120 to 2 or 180 to 3.
Write 60 to 1, or 60:1, or $\frac{60}{1}$.

**B.** The ratios $\frac{1}{60}$, $\frac{2}{120}$, and $\frac{3}{180}$ are **equal ratios.**

You can write a **proportion** to show that two ratios are equal.

$\frac{1}{60} = \frac{2}{120}$ $\frac{1}{60} = \frac{3}{180}$ $\frac{2}{120} = \frac{3}{180}$

**C.** You can find any one of the numbers in a proportion if you know the other three numbers.

**Example 1**
Solve the proportion $\frac{x}{4} = \frac{3}{10}$.

Multiply by 4.

$\frac{x}{4} \cdot 4 = \frac{3}{10} \cdot 4$

$x = \frac{12}{10}$

$x = 1.2$

$\frac{12}{10} = 12 \div 10$

The value of x is 1.2.
The ratio $\frac{1.2}{4}$ equals the ratio $\frac{3}{10}$.

*Shortcut:*
Find the **crossproduct.**

$\frac{x}{4} = \frac{3}{10}$

x · 10 3 · 4

$10x = 12$

$10x \div 10 = 12 \div 10$

$x = 1.2$

**Example 2**

*Solve:* $\frac{1\frac{1}{3}}{5} = \frac{2}{y}$.

*Use the shortcut:* $\frac{1\frac{1}{3}}{5} = \frac{2}{y}$

$1\frac{1}{3}y = 10$

$10 \div 1\frac{1}{3} = 7\frac{1}{2}$

$y = 7\frac{1}{2}$ or 7.5

The value of y is $7\frac{1}{2}$ or 7.5.

**Example 3**

*Use a calculator to solve:*

$\frac{547}{635} = \frac{m}{229}$.

$635 \cdot m = 547 \times 229$

$635 \cdot m = 125{,}623$

$m = 197.26$

nearest hundredth

## CLASS EXERCISES

*Six crates of alarm clocks have a total mass of 135 kg and a total cost of $760.75. Find each ratio.*

**1.** kilograms to crates **2.** dollars to crates **3.** dollars to kilograms

*Solve.*

**4.** $\frac{x}{8} = \frac{9}{12}$ **5.** $\frac{8}{16} = \frac{7}{y}$ **6.** $\frac{5.2}{m} = \frac{13}{10}$ **7.** $\frac{w}{10} = \frac{3}{.4}$ **8.** $\frac{1\frac{2}{5}}{7} = \frac{4}{t}$

## EXERCISES

*Solve.*

**1.** $\frac{a}{3} = \frac{8}{12}$ **2.** $\frac{3}{2} = \frac{k}{18}$ **3.** $\frac{10}{t} = \frac{5}{6}$ **4.** $\frac{21}{14} = \frac{3}{w}$ **5.** $\frac{7}{10} = \frac{x}{12}$

**6.** $\frac{4}{y} = \frac{5}{3}$ **7.** $\frac{x}{12} = \frac{15}{20}$ **8.** $\frac{6}{m} = \frac{4}{10}$ **9.** $\frac{12}{9} = \frac{8}{t}$ **10.** $\frac{9}{4} = \frac{w}{16}$

**11.** $\frac{c}{12} = \frac{3}{5}$ **12.** $\frac{5}{4} = \frac{2}{n}$ **13.** $\frac{7}{12} = \frac{d}{9}$ **14.** $\frac{w}{15} = \frac{3}{20}$ **15.** $\frac{6}{14} = \frac{15}{y}$

**16.** $\frac{4}{t} = \frac{1\frac{1}{3}}{5}$ **17.** $\frac{5}{9} = \frac{s}{3.6}$ **18.** $\frac{4}{3.2} = \frac{.6}{x}$ **19.** $\frac{1.8}{t} = \frac{.2}{3}$ **20.** $\frac{9}{2} = \frac{e}{.5}$

**21.** $\frac{w}{\frac{3}{8}} = \frac{16}{3}$ **22.** $\frac{5}{\frac{1}{6}} = \frac{a}{\frac{2}{3}}$ **23.** $\frac{x}{1.6} = \frac{.3}{.2}$ **24.** $\frac{\frac{2}{3}}{5} = \frac{3}{c}$ **25.** $\frac{2.1}{u} = \frac{3}{.8}$

*Solve. Give decimals for answers. Round to the nearest hundredth.*

**26.** $\frac{x}{4} = \frac{3}{7}$ **27.** $\frac{5}{1.3} = \frac{w}{2}$ **28.** $\frac{3}{2} = \frac{5}{k}$ ★ **29.** $\frac{.6}{u} = \frac{.4}{1.7}$ ★ **30.** $\frac{m}{2\frac{2}{3}} = \frac{3}{1\frac{3}{5}}$

*Solve. Use a calculator if you wish.*

**31.** $\frac{4{,}250}{a} = \frac{1{,}250}{435}$ **32.** $\frac{2{,}715}{59{,}187} = \frac{b}{1{,}744}$

**33.** $\frac{c}{33.0119} = \frac{30}{42.78}$ **34.** $\frac{14.75}{1.888} = \frac{40.625}{d}$

### THINK!

**Related Ratios**

The ratio of red cars to blue cars is 4:1. The ratio of blue cars to brown cars is 1:3. What is the ratio of red cars to brown cars?

1\. 2 16. 15



Homework page 492

# Problem Solving

READ • PLAN **DO** ANSWER • CHECK

## 8-2 Using Proportions

Some ratios used to solve problems in everyday life are:

$\frac{\text{dollars spent}}{\text{amount bought}}$ $\frac{\text{dollars earned}}{\text{time worked}}$ $\frac{\text{kilometers traveled}}{\text{liters of fuel used}}$

You can use proportions and your calculator to solve problems with these and other ratios.

**A.** Ms. Ernesto is paid $900 for 4 weeks work. What is she paid for 30 weeks work?

$$\frac{\text{dollars}}{\text{weeks}} = \frac{900}{4} = \frac{x}{30}$$

$$900 \cdot 30 = x \cdot 4$$
$$27{,}000 = 4x$$
$$27{,}000 \div 4 = 4x \div 4$$
$$6{,}750 = x$$

You would get the same value of x using: $\frac{\text{weeks}}{\text{dollars}} = \frac{4}{900} = \frac{30}{x}$

She is paid $6,750 for 30 weeks.

**B.** A 1.5 L container of milk costs $1.25. Find the price *per 100 mL* of this milk. Round to the nearest cent.

$$\frac{\text{dollars}}{\text{milliliters}} = \frac{1.25}{1{,}500} = \frac{y}{100} \longrightarrow 125 = 1{,}500\,y$$

1.5 L = 1,500 mL

$$.08 \doteq y$$

The price is $0.08 per 100 mL. ($0.08/100 mL)

**C.** An airplane flew 1,900 km of a 2,964 km flight in 2.5 h. At this rate, how long will it take the airplane to complete the flight?

$$\frac{\text{kilometers}}{\text{hours}} = \frac{1{,}900}{2.5} = \frac{1{,}064}{x}$$

kilometers left = 2,964 − 1,900

$$1{,}900\,x = 2{,}660$$
$$x = 1.4$$

It will take the airplane 1.4 h to complete the flight.

## CLASS EXERCISES

1. Twelve cans of beans cost $4.48. How much will 15 cans cost?

2. A machine fills 30 cans in 20 min. How many will it fill in 5 h?

### PROBLEMS

1. A 1.5-L bottle of orange juice costs $1.35. What is the price per 100 mL of the orange juice?

2. Mrs. Kellog can drive 45.5 km in 35 min. At that rate, how far can she drive in 6 h?

3. A truck traveled 48 km in 40 min. At this rate, how long did it take the truck to go 252 km?

4. A car uses 6.5 L of gasoline to travel 78 km. At this rate, how much gas will it need to go 300 km?

5. Martin can type 240 words in 4 min. At that rate, how many words can he type in 10 min? How long will it take him to type 500 words?

6. Lee earns $26.10 for 6 h work. At this rate, how much does she earn for working 13 h? How many hours must she work to earn $108.75?

7. A fruit punch recipe serves 24 people. It calls for 2 L of orange juice and 1.5 L of grapefruit juice. How much of each is needed to make punch for 42 people?

8. In a survey of 75 students, 42 said red was their favorite color. If the 75 are a *representative sample* of all the students, how many of the 525 students should name red as their favorite?

### ON YOUR OWN

## Gear Ratios

Every time gear A makes 4 complete turns **(revolutions)**, gear B makes 3 revolutions.

$$\frac{\text{teeth on A}}{\text{teeth on B}} = \frac{12}{16} = \frac{3}{4} = \frac{\text{revolutions of B}}{\text{revolutions of A}}$$

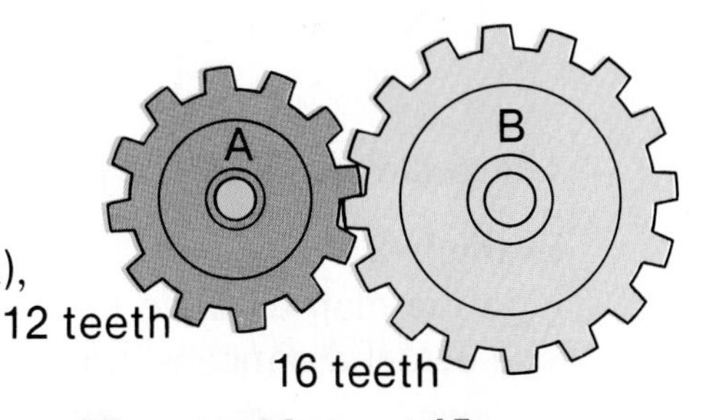


If gear A makes 48 revolutions per minute (48 rev/min), how many revolutions per minute does B make?

*Complete the table.*

| | 10. | 11. | 12. | 13. | 14. | ★15. |
|---|---|---|---|---|---|---|
| teeth on A | 12 | | 5 | 16 | 22 | n |
| teeth on B | 5 | 8 | 27 | | 12 | 6.5 n |
| rev/min for A | 36 | 6 | | 50 | 33 | |
| rev/min for B | | $6\frac{3}{4}$ | 4.5 | 40 | | 50 |

1. $0.09

Homework page 492

## 8-3 Scale Drawings

A map is a **scale drawing** of the region it represents.

**A.** The **scale** of this map is the ratio:

1 centimeter to 2.5 kilometers or 1 cm:2.5 km.

The ratio of the **map distance** to the **actual distance** is 1 cm:2.5 km.

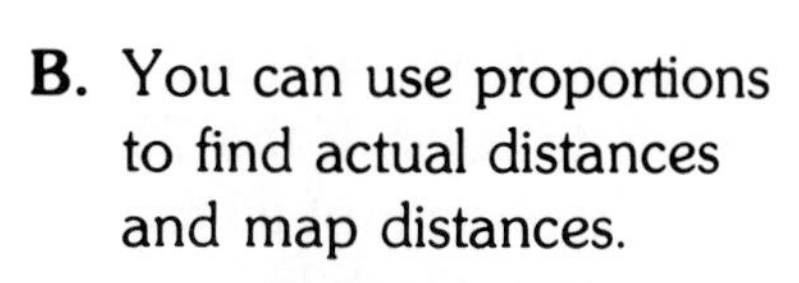


**B.** You can use proportions to find actual distances and map distances.

**Example 1**
Find the actual distance from Dover to Edgerton.

$$\frac{\text{actual distance (km)}}{\text{map distance (cm)}} = \frac{2.5}{1} = \frac{d}{8.7}$$ from the map

$$8.7 \cdot 2.5 = 1 \cdot d$$

$$21.75 = d$$

The actual distance is 21.75 km.

**Example 2**
Find the map distance from Abbottown to Centerville. The actual distance is 7.5 km.

$$\frac{\text{map distance (cm)}}{\text{actual distance (km)}} = \frac{1}{2.5} = \frac{m}{7.5}$$

$$1 \cdot 7.5 = m \cdot 2.5$$

$$7.5 \div 2.5 = m$$ $75 \div 25 = 3$

$$3 = m$$

The map distance is 3 cm.

## CLASS EXERCISES

*Use the map on the opposite page.*

1. Find the actual distance from Abbottown to Maple Hill.
2. Find the actual distance from Centerville to Dover.
3. The actual distance from Field Crest to Edgerton is 8.75 km. Find the map distance.
4. The actual distance from Maple Hill to Dover is 13.25 km. Find the map distance.

## PROBLEMS

*Use the diagram at the right.*
*Find the actual distance from:*

1. A to B
2. A to C
3. A to D
4. B to C
5. B to D
6. C to D

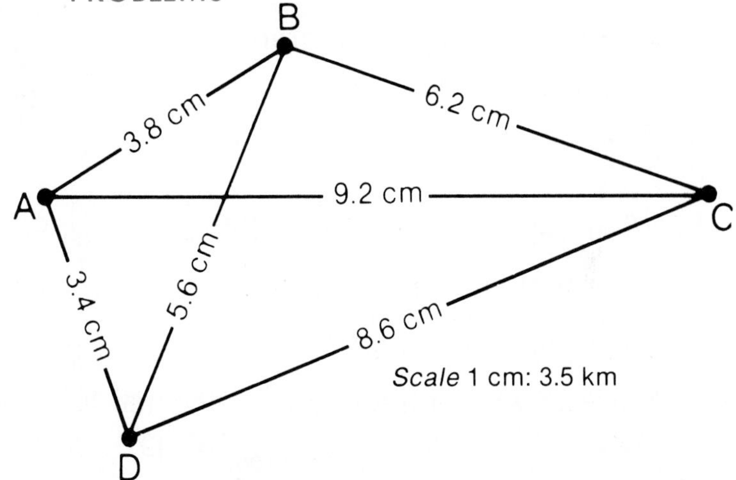


7. The actual distance of a point E from point A is 15.05 km. It is 18.2 km from point B. What would be the map distance from a point E to point A? to point B?
8. The actual distance of a point F from point C is 7.35 km. It is 18.55 km from point D. What would be the map distance from a point F to point C? to point D?

*The scale drawing at the right is of Mr. Ortega's apartment. Find the actual:*

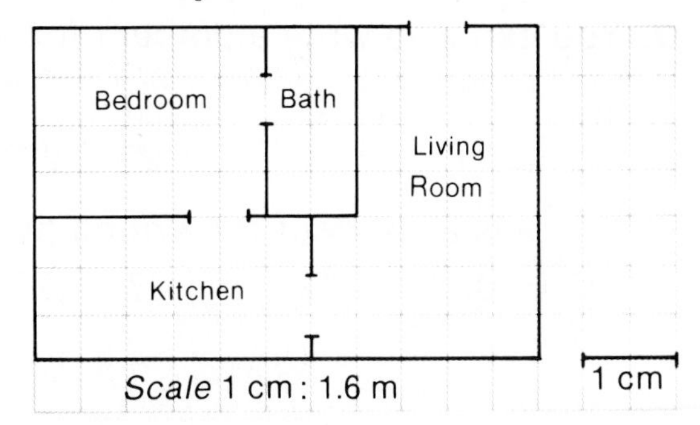


9. length and width of the apartment.
10. length and width of the bedroom.
11. length and width of the kitchen.
12. Mr. Ortega plans to use part of his living room as an office. The actual length and width of the office will be 2.4 m and 2 m. What would the length and width be on the scale drawing?

## ON YOUR OWN

Make a scale drawing of a room or rooms in your home or at your school. Give the scale.

1. 13.3 km

Homework page 493

## 8-4 Percent

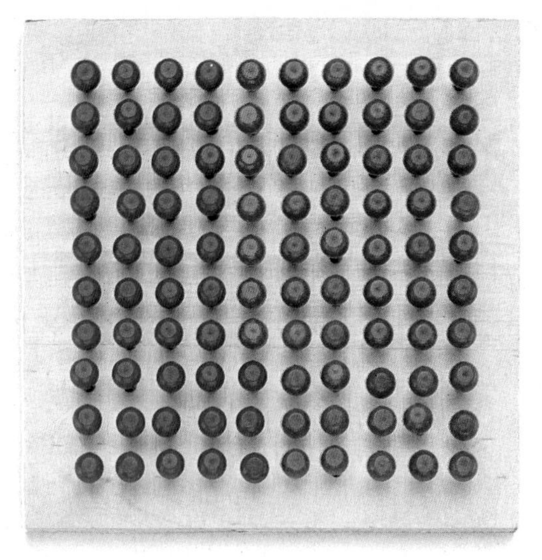

**A.** In the picture, the ratio of the blue pegs to all the pegs is:

43:100 or $\frac{43}{100}$ or .43.

Another name for that ratio is **43%.** ← Read % as percent.

**Percent** means per hundred.

$43\% = \frac{43}{100} = .43$

**B.** What part of the square is green? $\frac{50}{100}$ or .50 or 50%

What part is red? $\frac{7}{100}$ or .07 or 7%

What part is in color? $\frac{100}{100}$ or 1.00 or 100%

**C.** You can write a fraction or a decimal for a percent.

$29\% = \frac{29}{100} = .29$  $9\% = \frac{9}{100} = .09$  $241\% = \frac{241}{100} = 2.41$

There is a shortcut for writing decimals for percents.

29% = .29. = .29  8% = .08. = .08  376% = 3.76. = 3.76

Move the decimal point 2 places to the *left*. Do not write "%".

**D.** You can also write a percent for a fraction or decimal.

$\frac{7}{100} = 7\%$  $\frac{27}{100} = 27\%$  $1\frac{8}{100} = \frac{108}{100} = 108\%$

.07 = 7%  .27 = 27%  1.08 = 108%

There is a shortcut for writing percents for decimals.

.07 = .07.% = 7%  .27 = .27.% = 27%  1.08 = 1.08.% = 108%

Move the decimal point 2 places to the *right*. Write "%".

### CLASS EXERCISES

*Write a fraction and a decimal for each percent. Write a percent for each fraction or decimal.*

**1.** 3%  **2.** $\frac{37}{100}$  **3.** .04  **4.** 295%  **5.** 1.00  **6.** $1\frac{17}{100}$

*Write a fraction for each percent. Then write a decimal for each percent.*

**1.** 29% **2.** 6% **3.** 145% **4.** 79% **5.** 1% **6.** 137%

**7.** 8% **8.** 10% **9.** 100% **10.** 5% **11.** 50% **12.** 500%

*Write a percent for each fraction or decimal.*

**13.** $\frac{47}{100}$ **14.** .61 **15.** $\frac{42}{100}$ **16.** .03 **17.** $\frac{429}{100}$ **18.** 2.04

**19.** $\frac{98}{100}$ **20.** 1.99 **21.** .5 **22.** .05 **23.** 5.0 **24.** $\frac{2}{100}$

**25.** $\frac{1}{100}$ **26.** $\frac{10}{100}$ **27.** $\frac{100}{100}$ **28.** 1.0 **29.** .01 **30.** .1

## PROBLEMS

**31.** Sixty-eight of the 100 books the library bought were gardening books. What percent of the books purchased for the library were gardening books?

**32.** Jan planted 100 seeds. Of these 73% grew. How many seeds grew? How many seeds did not grow? What percent of the seeds did not grow?

**33.** Tara weeded .4 of the garden before lunch and .35 of it after lunch. What percent of the garden did she weed in all? What percent does she have left to weed?

**★34.** Karen got cucumbers from 83 of the 100 vines she planted. Tod got cucumbers from 87% of his vines. Who had fewer vines produce cucumbers? How many fewer?

## THINK!

### Math and Music

Middle C on a piano is produced by a string vibrating 256 times per second. To produce a C one octave *above* middle C, a string must vibrate twice as fast. To produce a C one octave *below* middle C, a string vibrates only half as fast. Find the number of vibrations for the Cs one octave above and below middle C.

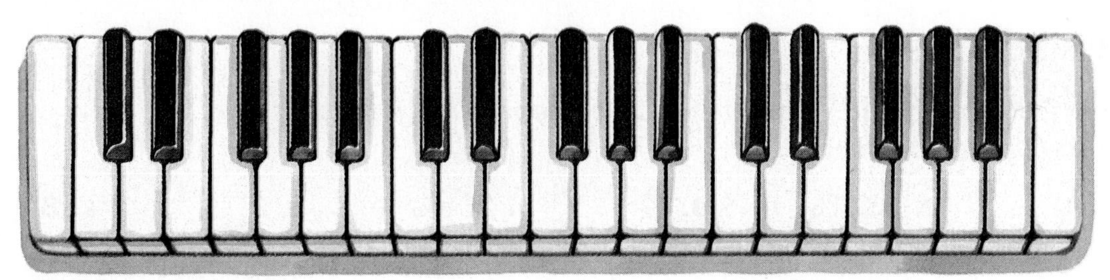

**1.** $\frac{29}{100}$; .29 **13.** 47%



Homework page 493

# 8-5 More About Percent

Some percents are not whole number percents.

**A.** Write a fraction and a decimal for 9.35%.

Since it is easy to use the shortcut to write decimals for percents, write the decimal first. Use the decimal to write the fraction.

*Decimal*

$$9.35\% = .09.35$$
$$= .0935$$

*Fraction*

$$9.35\% = .0935$$
$$= \frac{935}{10{,}000}$$

**B.** Write a fraction and a decimal for $648\frac{1}{2}\%$.

First use $\frac{1}{2} = 1 \div 2 = .5$ to write: $648\frac{1}{2}\% = 648.5\%$.

Now find a decimal and a fraction as you did in **A**.

*Decimal*

$$648\frac{1}{2}\% = 648.5\%$$
$$= 6.48.5$$
$$= 6.485$$

*Fraction*

$$648\frac{1}{2}\% = 6.485$$
$$= 6\frac{485}{1{,}000}$$
$$= \frac{6{,}485}{1{,}000}$$

**C.** Write a percent for .3625.

$$.3625 = .36.25\%$$
$$= 36.25\%$$

**D.** Write a percent for $4\frac{3}{20}$.

$$\frac{3}{20} = .15$$

$$4\frac{3}{20} = 4.15$$
$$= 4.15.\%$$
$$= 415\%$$

As in **C**

## CLASS EXERCISES

*Write a fraction and a decimal for each percent. Write a percent for each fraction or decimal.*

**1.** .812 **2.** 53.9% **3.** $\frac{9}{20}$ **4.** $26\frac{2}{5}\%$ **5.** 1.73 **6.** $8\frac{1}{2}$

## EXERCISES

*Write a fraction for each percent.*

**1.** 61% **2.** 6.9% **3.** $9\frac{3}{4}\%$ **4.** $\frac{1}{2}\%$ **5.** 207.9% **6.** 7.03%

*Write a decimal for each percent.*

**7.** 71.6% **8.** $43\frac{1}{4}\%$ **9.** 108.4% **10.** 3.5% **11.** $110\frac{3}{10}\%$ **12.** $2\frac{3}{4}\%$

**13.** 0.3% **14.** $7\frac{1}{5}\%$ **15.** $\frac{4}{25}\%$ **16.** $22\frac{1}{2}\%$ **17.** 106.9% **18.** 2.39%

$184\frac{3}{4}\%$ **20.** 100% **21.** .07% **22.** 33.33% **23.** $\frac{4}{5}\%$ **24.** .63%

*Write a percent for each decimal.*

**25.** .825 **26.** 1.608 **27.** .7 **28.** .092 **29.** .003 **30.** .016

**31.** .00125 **32.** 1.403 **33.** 1.000 **34.** .0009 **35.** 6.38 **36.** 2.05

*Write a percent for each fraction.*

**37.** $\frac{8}{25}$ **38.** $\frac{17}{10}$ **39.** $\frac{7}{16}$ **40.** $\frac{7}{8}$ **41.** $1\frac{3}{5}$ **42.** $\frac{27}{100}$

**43.** $\frac{37}{50}$ **44.** $\frac{24}{24}$ **45.** $\frac{2}{25}$ **46.** $3\frac{1}{2}$ **47.** $\frac{25}{20}$ **48.** $\frac{2}{1}$

## PROBLEMS

**49.** The Smiths have driven 196 km of their 4,000-km trip. What percent of their trip have they completed?

**50.** The Smiths spent $5\frac{1}{2}$ days of their 10-day vacation at Yellowstone National Park. What percent of their vacation did they spend at Yellowstone?

**51.** Roosevelt Smith collected 27 of the 200 rocks in the Smiths' collection. What percent of the rocks did Roosevelt collect?

**★ 52.** Toni Smith hiked $6\frac{1}{4}$ h on Monday. She hiked 20 h in all on her vacation. What percent of her hiking did Toni do on Monday?

## MIXED REVIEW

*Complete.*

**1.** 2.6 kg = ■ g **2.** 196 L = ■ daL **3.** 0.78 hm = ■ m **4.** 216 h = ■ d

*Simplify.*

**5.** $2^5 \cdot 2^{-2} \cdot 2^3$ **6.** $\frac{5^4 \cdot 5^{-3}}{5^{-2}}$ **7.** $\frac{3^3 \cdot 7^{-4} \cdot 3^{-2}}{7^2 \cdot 3^4}$ **8.** $2^6 \cdot 3^4 \cdot 2^{-1} \cdot 3^2$

**1.** $\frac{61}{100}$ **7.** .716 **25.** 82.5% **37.** 32%

## 8-6 The Basic Percent Formula: Finding the Part

**A.** There are 45 students in Mrs. Gilbert's third-period gym class. Of the students, 60% are on the gymnastics team. How many of the students are on the gymnastics team?

60% is a little more than half.

Use 60% = .60 and multiply to find how many.

60% of 45 is ■.

$.60 \times 45 = 27.00$

60% of 45 is 27. 27 of the students are on the team.

**B.** In the statement "60% of 45 is 27":

60% is the **rate.** 45 is the **base.** 27 is the **part.**

*Think:* rate of base is part

Write a decimal for the percent (rate) and multiply.

**rate × base = part** **r · b = p**

The equation r · b = p is the **basic percent formula.**

**Example 1**

Find $10\frac{3}{4}$% of \$560.

*Remember:* r · b = p

| $10\frac{3}{4}\% = .1075$ | \$560 |
|---|---|

$.1075 \cdot 560 = p$
$60.2000 = p$

$10\frac{3}{4}$% of \$560 is \$60.20.

**Example 2**

■ is 205% of 18.

r · b = p

| 205% = 2.05 | 18 |
|---|---|

$2.05 \cdot 18 = p$
$36.90 = p$

36.9 is 205% of 18.

## CLASS EXERCISES

**1.** 25% of 68 is ■. **2.** ■ is $12\frac{1}{2}$% of \$440. **3.** What is 145% of 60?

**4.** ■ is 9.5% of 40. **5.** What is $37\frac{5}{8}$% of 600? **6.** 275% of \$46 is ■.

## EXERCISES

**1.** What is 60% of 35? **2.** 8% of 600 is ■. **3.** ■ is 40% of 75.

**4.** ■ is 7% of 390. **5.** What is 80% of \$9.20? **6.** 4.7% of 500 is ■.

**7.** What is 52.6% of 95? **8.** ■ is 187% of 530. **9.** ■ is 50% of \$395.

**10.** $7\frac{1}{2}$% of 4,000 is ■. **11.** What is $40\frac{3}{8}$% of \$800? **12.** ■is 250% of 25.

**13.** What is $\frac{1}{2}$% of 560? **14.** $2\frac{3}{4}$% of 42 is ■. **15.** ■ is 26% of 39.

**16.** ■ is .03% of 975. **17.** is 10.5% of \$26. **18.** 350% of 29 is ■.

**19.** What is $12\frac{4}{5}$% of 85? **20.** ■ is 65% of 44. **21.** ■ is 8.5% of \$92.

## PROBLEMS

**22.** There are 950 students at Oakmoor High School. 52% of them take music. How many students take music?

**23.** Central High School's gym holds 3,500 people for basketball games. On Friday the gym was 93% full. How many people were in the gym?

**24.** Ellen attended 82% of the 50 band practices. How many band practices did Ellen attend?

**25.** 56% of the 350 tickets for the school play were adult tickets. How many adult tickets were there?

**26.** The school lunchroom was 46% full during the first lunch period. The lunchroom seats 550 people. How many people were in the lunchroom during the first lunch period?

**27.** 65% of the 5,620 fans at the Oakmoor-Central game were Oakmoor fans. What percent of the fans were Central fans? How many Oakmoor fans attended the game? How many Central fans?

## THINK!

### Mental Math

Can you multiply this expression mentally?

$1.9 \times 3.6 \times 4.8 \times 7.1 \times 6.9 \times 13.4 \times 8.5 \times 0 =$

**1.** 21 **10.** 300



Homework page 494

# 8-7 The Basic Percent Formula: Finding the Rate

**A.** Of the first 40 presidents of the United States, 8 were born in Virginia. What percent of those Presidents were born in Virginia?

*Find:* What percent of 40 is 8?

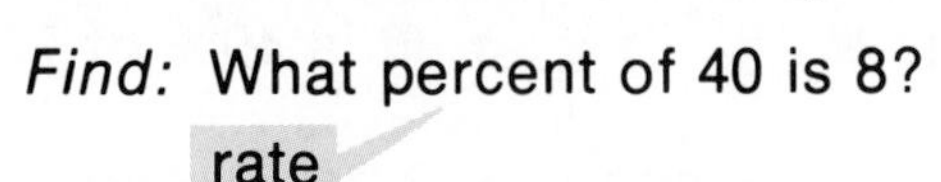


*Think:* $r \cdot b = p$

40 presidents — 8 from Virginia

*Do:*

$$r \cdot 40 = 8$$
$$r \cdot 40 \div 40 = 8 \div 40$$
$$r = .20 = 20\%$$

20% of the first 40 presidents were from Virginia.

**B.** There are other ways of telling you to find a rate.

**Example 1**

$84 is ▩% of $60.

$r \cdot b = p$

60 — 84

$$r \cdot 60 = 84$$
$$r \cdot 60 \div 60 = 84 \div 60$$
$$r = 1.40 = 140\%$$

$84 is 140% of $60.

**Example 2**

▩% of 44 is .11.

$r \cdot b = p$

44 — .11

$$r \cdot 44 = .11$$
$$r \cdot 44 \div 44 = .11 \div 44$$
$$r = .0025 = .25\%$$

.25% of 44 is .11.

**C.** Refer to the problem in **A.**
What percent of the first 40 presidents were not born in Virginia?

**Method 1**

Were not = Total − Were
= 40 − 8 = 32

32 is ▩% of 40.

$$r \cdot 40 = 32$$
$$r \cdot 40 \div 40 = 32 \div 40$$
$$r = .8 = 80\%$$

**Method 2**

Percent were not = 100% − Percent were
= 100% − 20% = 80%

From **A**

80% of those presidents were not born in Virginia.

## CLASS EXERCISES

**1.** What percent of 72 is 54?

**2.** 40 is ■% of 64.

**3.** ■% of $43.50 is $13.05.

**4.** ■ is $29\frac{1}{2}$% of 300.

## EXERCISES

**1.** What percent of 20 is 13?

**2.** $60 is ■% of $160.

**3.** ■ is 17% of 50.

**4.** 132 is ■% of 96.

**5.** ■% of $17.50 is $35.

**6.** What percent of $40 is $26?

**7.** 85 is ■% of 136.

**8.** What is 27% of 81?

**9.** 17 is what percent of 40?

**10.** What percent of 126 is 441?

**11.** ■% of 175 is 266.

**12.** 709.5 is ■% of 645.

**13.** $0.06 is what percent of $12?

**14.** ■ is $10\frac{1}{2}$% of 525.

**15.** .4% of $120 is ■.

**16.** ■% of 515 is 618.

**17.** 16.25 is ■% of 6,500. $\frac{1}{4}$%

**18.** What percent of 648 is 486?

## PROBLEMS

**19.** In the class election, 66 of the 75 students voted. What percent of the students voted? What percent of the students did not vote?

**20.** Of the 2,800 people attending the rally, 1,204 were students. What percent of the audience was students?

★ **21.** The Clarkson College library issued 5,975 library cards. 80% of the cards went to students. How many students got cards? The library had 9,560 cards printed. What percent of the cards printed went to students? What percent of the printed cards were issued?

**22.** Representative Klein received 1,358 of the 2,800 votes cast in her precinct. What percent of the votes did her opponent receive?

★ **23.** There are 888 students at Crane Junior High. Of these, $62\frac{1}{2}$% voted in the school election. How many students voted?

## THINK!

### Time Trick

It is exactly 2:30 P.M. What time will it be in 12,002 hours? in 9,598 hours?

1. 65% 5. 200%



Homework page 495

# 8-8 The Basic Percent Formula: Finding the Base

**A.** In each serving of Walton's Macaroni and Cheese Dinner, 27% of the calories comes from the cheese. The cheese in a serving contains 116.1 calories. How many calories in all does a serving contain?

*Must find:* number of calories in all

*Think:* $r \cdot b = p$    base
    27%      116.1

*Do:*
$$r \cdot b = p$$
$$.27 \cdot b = 116.1$$
$$b = 116.1 \div .27 = 430$$

One serving contains 430 calories.

**B.** There are other ways of telling you to find a base.

**Example 1**

$9\frac{1}{2}\%$ of ■ is \$38.

$$r \cdot b = p$$
$9\frac{1}{2}\% = .095$      38
$$.095 \cdot b = 38$$
$$b = 38 \div .095$$
$$= 400$$

$9\frac{1}{2}\%$ of \$400 is \$38.

**Example 2**

180% of what number is 142.2?

$$r \cdot b = p$$
$180\% = 1.80 = 1.8$      142.2
$$1.8 \cdot b = 142.2$$
$$b = 142.2 \div 1.8$$
$$= 79$$

180% of 79 is 142.2.

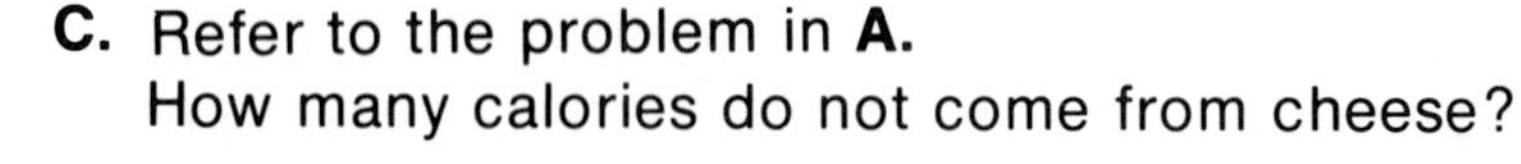

**C.** Refer to the problem in **A.**
How many calories do not come from cheese?

**Method 1**

Percent not cheese = 100% − Percent cheese
= 100% − 27%
= 73%

73% of 430 is ■.
$$.73 \cdot 430 = p$$
$$313.9 = p$$

**Method 2**

Not cheese = In all − Cheese
From **A** = 430 − 116.1
= 313.9

313.9 calories do not come from cheese.

## CLASS EXERCISES

1. $62\frac{1}{2}$% of what is 45?
2. 39 is 65% of ■.
3. ■% of 112 is 84.
4. 510 is 120% of what?
5. ■ is $1\frac{1}{2}$% of $310.
6. $9\frac{3}{4}$% of ■ is $40.95.

## EXERCISES

1. 50% of what is 12.5?
2. $18 is 5% of ■.
3. $58\frac{3}{4}$% of $1,576 is ■.
4. 6 is 15% of what?
5. 117 is ■% of 150.
6. 12% of ■ is 11.4.
7. What is $8\frac{3}{4}$% of 260?
8. ■% of 128 is 8.
9. $215 is 250% of ■.
10. 40% of ■ is 38.4.
11. 30% of ■ is 24.6.
12. ■ is $12\frac{1}{2}$% of $180.
13. .245 is .7% of ■.
14. 51.2 is ■% of 32.
15. 120% of ■ is 318.
16. ■ is 35% of 60.
17. 89.6 is 56% of ■.
18. 135% of ■ is $164.70.
19. $3\frac{1}{2}$% of $16 is ■.
20. 240% of ■ is 177.6.
21. $24 is ■% of $16?
22. 99 is ■% of 120.
23. 6 is ■% of 48.
24. 180% of 400 is ■.
25. $12\frac{1}{2}$% of ■ is 43.75.
26. 105 is 12.5% of ■.
27. 630 is 42% of ■.
28. ■% of 82.6 is 123.9.
29. .45 is .3% of ■.
30. 1,200 is ■% of 3,000.
31. ■ is $7\frac{1}{4}$% of 50.
32. 13.5 is $22\frac{1}{2}$% of ■.
33. 250% of ■ is $21.25.

## PROBLEMS

34. Gretchen paid $28.80 for a jacket that was on sale. She paid 75% of the regular price. What was the regular price of the jacket?

★ 36. Pulford College has 2,130 part-time students. This is $37\frac{1}{2}$% of the total number of students. How many students go to Pulford College? The college would be at full capacity with 2,320 more students. At what percent of capacity is the college now?

35. Alex missed 12 questions on a 150-question test. What percent of the questions did he miss? What percent of the questions did he answer correctly?

## THINK!

**Money Patterns**

How much is 10,000% of $1?

1. 25 13. 35



Homework page 495

## 8-9 More About Fractions and Percents

**A.** There are two ways to write percents for fractions. Find a percent for $\frac{2}{3}$. Use a calculator when helpful.

**Method 1**
Use division to find a decimal, then find a percent. Plan to round to the nearest thousandth.

$\frac{2}{3} \Rightarrow 3\overline{)2.0000}$ = .6666 → .667

$\frac{2}{3} \doteq .667 \doteq 66.7\%$

**Method 2**
Use a proportion.

$\frac{2}{3} = \frac{n}{100}$

$2 \cdot 100 = n \cdot 3$

$200 = 3n$

$66\frac{2}{3} = n$

$\frac{2}{3} = \frac{66\frac{2}{3}}{100} = 66\frac{2}{3}\% \doteq 66.7\%$

**B.** There are also two ways to write fractions or decimals for percents. Find a fraction and a decimal for $3\frac{5}{6}\%$.

**Method 1**
Use division to replace $\frac{5}{6}$ by a decimal. Plan to round to the nearest thousandth.

$\frac{5}{6} \Rightarrow 6\overline{)5.000}$ = .8333 → .833

$3\frac{5}{6}\% \doteq 3.833\%$

$\doteq .03833$ ← **decimal**

$\doteq \frac{3,833}{100,000}$ ← **fraction**

**Method 2**
Use fractions.

$3\frac{5}{6}\% = \frac{3\frac{5}{6}}{100}$

$= 3\frac{5}{6} \div 100$

$= \frac{23}{6} \times \frac{1}{100}$

$= \frac{23}{600}$ ← **fraction**

$\doteq .03833$ ← **decimal**

**C.** Find $76\frac{2}{3}\%$ of 90.

*Think:* $r \cdot b = p$ ($r = 76\frac{2}{3}\%$, $b = 90$)

**Method 1**

$r \cdot b = p$ ← $r = 76\frac{2}{3}\%$

$\doteq 76.667\%$

$\doteq .76667$

$.76667 \cdot 90 = p$

$69.00030 = p$

**Method 2**

$r \cdot b = p$ ← $r = 76\frac{2}{3}\%$

$= \frac{76\frac{2}{3}}{100}$

$= \frac{230}{3} \times \frac{1}{100}$

$= \frac{23}{30}$

$\frac{23}{30} \cdot 90 = p$

$69 = p$

$69.00030 \doteq 69$

## CLASS EXERCISES

1. Use division to find a percent for $\frac{5}{12}$. Plan to round to the nearest thousandth.
2. Use a proportion to find a percent for $\frac{5}{12}$. Give the percent name containing a lowest terms mixed numeral.
3. Use division to find a decimal for $9\frac{1}{3}\%$. Plan to round the decimal for $\frac{1}{3}$ to the nearest thousandth. .
4. Use fractions to find a lowest terms fraction for $9\frac{1}{3}\%$.

## EXERCISES

*Find a percent for each fraction. If you use division, plan to round to the nearest thousandth. If you use proportions, simplify your answer.*

**1.** $\frac{1}{3}$ **2.** $\frac{7}{12}$ **3.** $\frac{1}{6}$ **4.** $1\frac{3}{4}$ **5.** $1\frac{2}{3}$ **6.** $3\frac{5}{8}$

**7.** $\frac{7}{6}$ **8.** $\frac{3}{8}$ **9.** $4\frac{1}{4}$ **10.** $\frac{2}{5}$ **11.** $2\frac{5}{6}$ **12.** $1\frac{1}{7}$

*Use division to find a decimal for each percent. Plan to round to the nearest thousandth in all divisions.*

**13.** $16\frac{2}{3}\%$ **14.** $133\frac{1}{3}\%$ **15.** $66\frac{2}{3}\%$ **16.** $\frac{4}{15}\%$ **17.** $83\frac{1}{3}\%$ **18.** $9\frac{7}{8}\%$

**19-24.** Use fractions to find a lowest terms fraction or mixed numeral for each percent above. **19.** **20.** **21.** **22.** **23.** **24.**

*Solve. Give exact (not rounded) answers.*

**25.** $166\frac{2}{3}\%$ of ■ is 85. **26.** 11 is ■% of 80. **27.** $16\frac{2}{3}\%$ of \$150 is ■.

## PROBLEMS

**28.** In wood shop $23\frac{1}{3}\%$ of the 30 students got an "A" on their project. How many students got an "A"?

**29.** Mr. Dega's classes made 130 of the table decorations for the school dance. That was $86\frac{2}{3}\%$ of all the decorations. How many decorations were made in all?

## THINK!

### Visual Perception

How many triangles can you find in the figure below? **100**

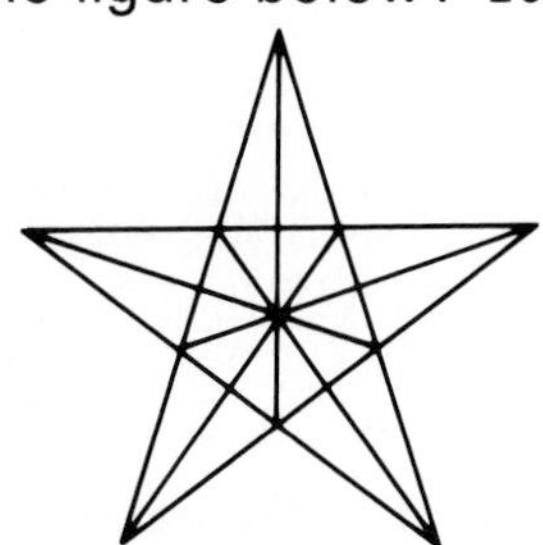

1. $33\frac{1}{3}\%$ 13. .16667



Homework page 496

## 8-10 Percent Increase or Decrease

The table shows the population of Westbank in four census years.

| Census Year | 1950 | 1960 | 1970 | 1980 |
|---|---|---|---|---|
| Population | 3,600 | 3,780 | 4,158 | 3,950 |

**A.** What was the increase in population from 1950 to 1970? What was the **percent increase** from 1950 to 1970?

r = % increase = ?
b = 3,600
p = increase = ?

Increase = 4,158 − 3,600
= 558

$r \cdot b = p$
$r \cdot 3{,}600 = 558$
$r = .155 = 15.5\%$

The increase in population was 558.

The percent increase was 15.5%.

**B.** What was the decrease in population from 1970 to 1980? What was the **percent decrease** from 1970 to 1980?

r = % decrease = ?
b = 4,158
p = decrease = ?

Decrease = 4,158 − 3,950
= 208

$r \cdot b = p$
$r \cdot 4{,}158 = 208$
$r \doteq .050 \doteq 5.0\%$

to the nearest tenth

The decrease in population was 208.

The percent decrease was 5.0%.

**C.** A clothing store increased its prices by 10% in September, then decreased its prices by 10% in January. A suit was $300 before the September increase. What was the price of the suit after the January decrease?

Price after decrease = Price after increase − 10% of price after increase

Price after increase = Price before increase + 10% price before increase
= $300 + 10% of $300
= $300 + $30
= $330

So, price after decrease = $330 − 10% of $330
= $330 − $33
= $297

The price after the January decrease was $297.

## CLASS EXERCISES

1. What was the increase in the population of Westbank from 1960 to 1980? What was the percent increase from 1960 to 1980?

2. A 5-kg sack of flour cost $1.60. The price decreased by 8% one month, then increased by 8% the next. What is the cost, to the nearest cent?

## PROBLEMS

1. From which countries did the U.S. import less oil in 1979 than in 1978? What was the percent decrease for each?

2. From which countries did the U.S. import more oil in 1979 than in 1978? What was the percent increase for each?

**U.S. OIL IMPORTS (millions of barrels)**

| Source | 1978 | 1979 |
|---|---|---|
| Algeria | 233.0 | 218.3 |
| Indonesia | 196.8 | 137.0 |
| Libya | 268.7 | 251.8 |
| Mexico | 112.1 | 162.7 |
| Nigeria | 322.0 | 401.7 |
| Saudi Arabia | 406.5 | 490.4 |

3. A garment worker received an $8\frac{1}{2}$% wage increase. The increase was $.68/h. What was the wage before the increase? After the increase?

4. An appliance dealer decreased the prices of old models by 18%. What is the new price of a dishwasher formerly priced at $439.50?

5. A moving company increased its rate by 15% in the summer, then decreased its rate by 15% in the winter. Before the summer increase, the company charged $25/h. What was its rate after the winter decrease?

★6. A department store plans to decrease its prices by 12% in January, then increase them by 12% in February. Will the final prices be higher or lower than before the changes? What percent higher or lower?

*The table shows a manufacturer's total annual sales for certain years. What should the sales be in the year 2000:*

★7. if sales increase at the same rate as from 1970 to 1980?

★8. if sales increase at the same rate as from 1960 to 1980?

| Year | Annual Sales |
|---|---|
| 1950 | $52.3 billion |
| 1960 | $80.5 billion |
| 1970 | $96.6 billion |
| 1980 | $140.1 billion |

## ON YOUR OWN

Use a newspaper to follow the stock of a company for 5 days. Give the percent increase or decrease for each day and for the entire 5-day period.

# Problem Solving Strategy

READ PLAN DO • ANSWER • CHECK

## 8-11 Buying and Selling

**A.** **Discount** is a decrease in the **regular price** of an item. An auto dealer advertises "5% off" auto prices. What is the discount for a van with a regular price of $12,500? What is the **sale price**?

| |
|---|
| r = 5% = .05 |
| b = $12,500 |
| p = discount = ? |

$$r \cdot b = p$$
$$.05 \cdot \$12{,}500 = p$$
$$\$625 = p$$

The discount is $625.

$$\text{Sale price} = \text{Regular price} - \text{Discount}$$
$$= \$12{,}500 - \$625$$
$$= \$11{,}875$$

The sale price of the van is $11,875.

**B.** **Sales tax** is charged on the price of items by many states and cities. If the **sales tax rate** is 7%, what is the sales tax on the van in **A**? What is the total cost of the van?

| |
|---|
| r = 7% = .07 |
| b = $11,875 |
| p = sales tax = ? |

$$r \cdot b = p$$
$$.07 \cdot \$11{,}875 = p$$
$$831.25 = p$$

The sales tax is $831.25.

$$\text{Total cost} = \text{Price} + \text{Sales tax}$$
$$= \$11{,}875 + \$831.25$$
$$= \$12{,}706.25$$

The total cost of the van is $12,706.25.

**C.** A salesperson receives a **salary** of $150 per week, plus a **commission** of $8\frac{1}{4}$% of the value of her sales for the week. What would be the salesperson's total earnings for a week in which her sales were $3,250?

| |
|---|
| r = $8\frac{1}{4}$% = .0825 |
| b = $3,250 |
| p = commission = ? |

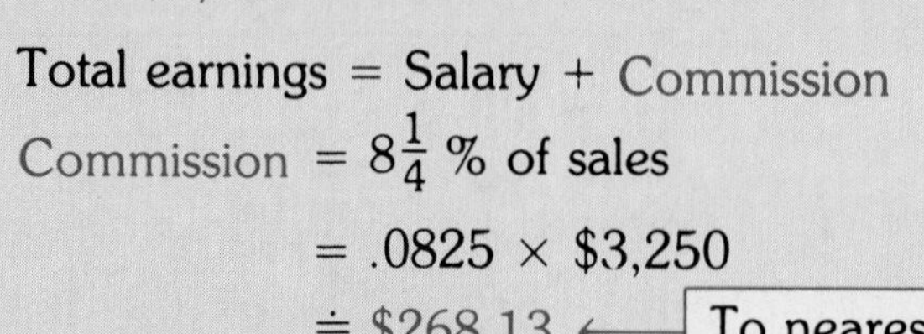

$$\text{Total earnings} = \text{Salary} + \text{Commission}$$
$$\text{Commission} = 8\tfrac{1}{4}\ \%\ \text{of sales}$$
$$= .0825 \times \$3{,}250$$
$$\doteq \$268.13 \leftarrow \text{To nearest cent}$$

$$\text{Total earnings} = \text{Salary} + \text{Commission}$$
$$= \$150 + \$268.13$$
$$= \$418.13$$

The salesperson's total earnings for the week were $418.13.

A calculator is helpful in many percent problems.

## CLASS EXERCISES

**1.** A salesperson is paid only a commission of 15% on the value of his sales for the month. What would the salesperson earn in a month in which his weekly sales were \$2,780; \$1,995; \$3,060; and \$2,975?

**2.** A furniture store is having a "40% off" sale. What is the sale price of a sofa whose regular price is \$990? The sales tax rate is 6%. What is the total cost of the sofa?

## PROBLEMS

**1.** A salesperson receives a salary of \$8,000 per year, plus a commission of 18% of the value of his sales for the year. His sales last year totaled \$264,300. What were the salesperson's earnings last year?

**2.** A department store held a "30% off" sale. The Carters bought a table with a regular price of \$415. The state sales tax rate is $7\frac{1}{2}$%. How much did the Carters pay in all?

**3.** A state charges a gasoline tax of 6% of the cost of the gasoline. After the tax has been added, the gasoline at one station is priced at 42.4¢/L. What is the cost of the gasoline before the tax is added?

★**4.** A salesperson is given a choice of pay schemes. She may take a salary of \$10,000 per year plus a commission of 15%, or she may take only a commission of 20%. What value of sales must she reach to make the second offer better?

Some wholesalers offer their best customers **multiple discounts** on large purchases. One wholesaler's discount schedule is shown.

| DISCOUNT RATES |
|---|
| 5% on all orders |
| + 10% on balance over \$10,000 |
| + 15% on balance over \$20,000 |
| + 20% on balance over \$50,000 |

How much would a customer pay for orders with these values?

★**5.** \$18,750 ★**6.** \$72,500

## THINK!

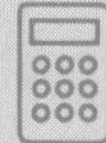

### Number Sense

If you had 1 billion dollars and gave away \$1 every second, about how long would it take to give away all the money? If you had 1 million dollars and gave away \$.01 every second, about how long would it take?

Homework page 497

## Kinds of Computer Languages

**A.** **Higher-order languages** are computer languages, like BASIC, that look very much like ordinary human language. Here is a simple program for evaluating an algebraic expression, as it would be written in different languages.

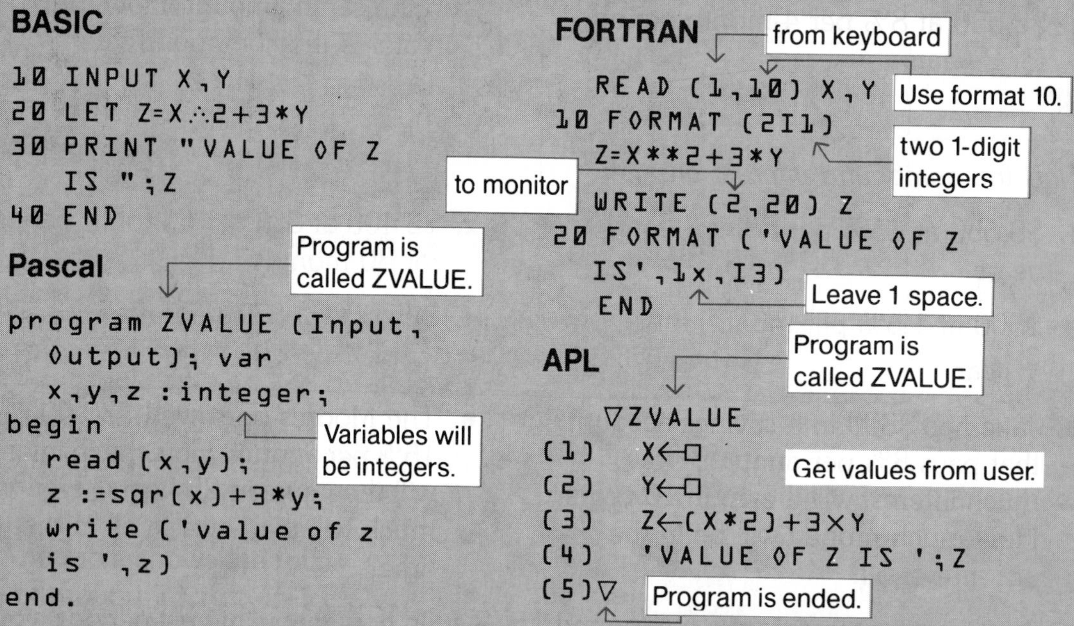


In a FORTRAN program, only lines referred to by other lines must be numbered. Lines in a Pascal program are not numbered. For an APL program, the computer supplies the line numbers.

**B.** **Assembly language** commands tell the computer exactly *what* steps to perform, *how* to do them, and *where* to store the results. This program tells the computer to subtract 1 from 60.

```
LDX 60 ------ Load 60 in the X-register (a storage
              location).
DEX    ------ Decrement the contents of the
              X-register: subtract 1.
STX 910------ Store the contents of the X-register in
              location 910.
```

1. What commands in FORTRAN, Pascal, and APL do the same thing as:
   **a.** `LET Z=X∴2+3*Y` **b.** `INPUT X,Y` **c.** `PRINT "VALUE OF Z IS";Z`

2. Write an assembly-language program that would tell a computer to find 38 − 1 and store the difference in location 915.

*Solve the problems. (pages 272–275, 288–297)*

**56.** A 2.4-kg pot roast costs $18.24 at Fresh-Food Mart. A 2.8-kg pot roast costs $21.14 at Shop-Smart Shoppe. Find the price per 100 g for each roast. Which is the better buy?

**57.** A blueprint is drawn to the scale 2 mm:10 cm. What are the actual dimensions of a room that is 140 mm long and 110 mm wide on the drawing?

**58.** A theater that seats 650 people was 84% full for the afternoon performance and 92% full for the evening performance. How many people in all attended these performances?

**59.** In a survey, 1,200 people were asked whether they supported candidate Miller or Smith for mayor. 570 said Miller, 485 said Smith, and the rest were undecided. What percent did not support Miller?

**60.** The number of people using buses increased by 2% in December, then decreased by 3% in June. If 2.5 million people used buses before the increase, how many used them after the decrease?

**61.** In 1978, the U.S. produced 601 million bushels of oats. In 1979, 534 million bushels were produced. By how much did oats production decrease? What was the percent of decrease?

**62.** During a 30% off sale, the Lunds paid $94.08 for an area rug. If the sales tax rate is 5%, what was the regular price of the rug? How much did the Lunds save?

**63.** Ms. Creighton earns $800 per month, plus commission. During March her sales had a value of $4,875, and she was paid $1,141.25 in all. What is Ms. Creighton's rate of commission?

**64.** Use the table on page 292. Mr. Zachary's taxable income is $1,354 per month. How much income tax should he pay in 1 year?

**65.** Miss Krang's gross earnings are $310 per week. Her net earnings are $271.25 per week. What percent of her earnings are deducted from her pay?

**66.** Mr. Torrance bought a $2,000 savings bond that pays $3\frac{1}{2}$% simple interest per 3-month period. How much will his money earn in 2 years?

**67.** Use the table on page 296. The Barrows have $1,850 in a savings account that pays 1.5% compound interest per month. What will be the total amount in the savings account at the end of 9 months?

# Enrichment

## Working with Money

### A. Compound Interest

You have used a table to find amounts of compound interest. You can also use a formula to find these amounts.

Let $P_0$ = original principal invested.
Let $r$ = interest rate per interest period.

After 1 interest period, the new principal is $P_1$.

$$P_1 = P_0 + P_0 \times r$$
$$= P_0(1 + r)$$

$P_1 = P_0(1 + r)$

Interest earned in 1 period $= P_1 - P_0$

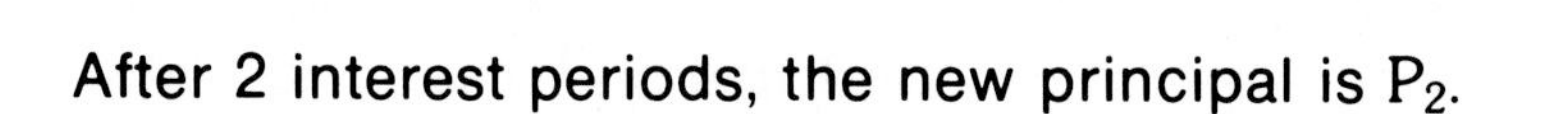

After 2 interest periods, the new principal is $P_2$.

$$P_2 = P_1 + P_1 \times r$$
$$= P_1(1 + r)$$
$$= [P_0(1 + r)](1 + r)$$
$$= P_0(1 + r)^2$$

$P_1 = P_0(1 + r)$

$P_2 = P_0(1 + r)^2$

Interest earned in 2 periods $= P_2 - P_0$

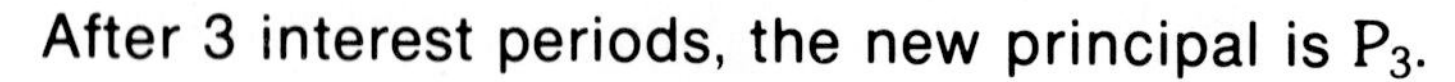

After 3 interest periods, the new principal is $P_3$.

$$P_3 = P_2 + P_2 \times r$$
$$= P_2(1 + r)$$
$$= [P_0(1 + r)^2](1 + r)$$
$$= P_0(1 + r)^3$$

$P_2 = P_0(1 + r)^2$

$P_3 = P_0(1 + r)^3$

Interest earned in 3 periods $= P_3 - P_0$

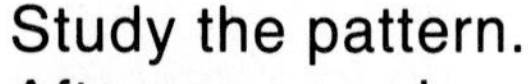

Study the pattern.
After any number, $n$, of interest periods:

$P_n = P_0(1 + r)^n$

Interest earned in $n$ periods $= P_n - P_0$

1. Use $r = 1.5\%$. Find $P_1$, $P_2$, and $P_3$ if $P_0 = \$100$. Then find $P_1 - P_0$, $P_2 - P_0$, and $P_3 - P_0$.

2. Repeat Exercise 1 for $r = 8\%$ and for $r = 15\%$. Compare with the table on Page 296.

3. If you have a calculator, repeat Exercises 1 and 2 for $n = 4$, $n = 5$, $n = 10$, $n = 15$, $n = 20$, $n = 25$, and $n = 30$.

4. Find the least amount to be invested now to yield at least $1,000 in 5 years at a rate of 10% per year compounded annually.

## B. Total Value of Equal Deposits

Ms. Keller deposits $100 in her savings account on the first day of each month. The bank pays interest at a rate of .5% per month compounded monthly. How much will Ms. Keller have in her account after she makes twelve deposits if she does not withdraw any money during this time?

The formula for the total value (T) of n equal deposits (D) made on a regular basis with the deposits earning r% interest per deposit period is:

$$T = D \times \frac{(1 + r)^n - 1}{r}$$

For Ms. Keller,

$$T = 100 \times \frac{(1.005)^{12} - 1}{.005}$$

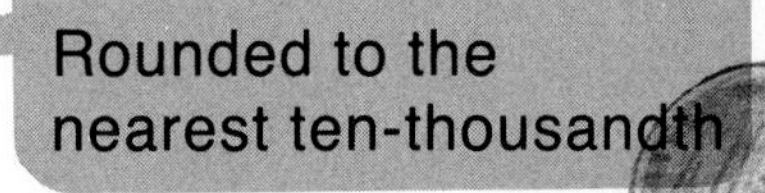


$$= 100 \times \frac{1.0617 - 1}{.005}$$

$$= 100 \times 12.34$$

$$= \$1,234.00$$

*Find the total value of:*

5. Three yearly deposits of $1,000 at $r = 15\%$ per year, compounded annually.

6. Five monthly deposits of $200 each at $r = .5\%$ per month, compounded monthly.

7. Twenty-five yearly deposits of $1,200 each at $r = 18\%$ per year, compounded annually.

8. Forty yearly deposits of $10,000 each at $r = 15\%$ per year, compounded annually.

# Cumulative Review

1. $^-14 + 26 = \blacksquare$
   - a. $^-40$
   - b. 40
   - c. $^-12$
   - d. NG

2. Give a percent for $\frac{4}{5}$.
   - a. 45%
   - b. 125%
   - c. 80%
   - d. NG

3. $.026 \times .03$
   - a. .00078
   - b. .78
   - c. .000078
   - d. NG

4. $\frac{7}{8} \div \frac{9}{12} = \blacksquare$
   - a. $\frac{21}{32}$
   - b. $1\frac{11}{21}$
   - c. $1\frac{1}{6}$
   - d. NG

5. Give a decimal for 3%.
   - a. .3
   - b. .03
   - c. 3.0
   - d. NG

6. $\frac{5}{6} - \frac{3}{5} = \blacksquare$
   - a. $\frac{2}{1}$
   - b. $\frac{1}{15}$
   - c. $\frac{7}{30}$
   - d. NG

7. 20% of 30 = $\blacksquare$
   - a. 6
   - b. 600
   - c. 60
   - d. NG

8. Give a decimal for $\frac{5}{12}$.
   - a. 2.4
   - b. .42
   - c. $.41\overline{6}$
   - d. NG

9. $39{,}796 + 5{,}879 + 693 = \blacksquare$
   - a. 46,368
   - b. 167,886
   - c. 45,268
   - d. NG

10. 50 is what percent of 20?
    - a. 40%
    - b. 250%
    - c. 10%
    - d. NG

11. Mr. Kain borrowed $1,000 for one year at $12\frac{1}{2}$% per year simple interest. How much did he pay back at the end of the year?
    - a. $125.00
    - b. $1,012.50
    - c. $1,125.00
    - d. NG

12. Ms. Janice spends $240 each month for food. This is 20% of her monthly income. How much does Ms. Janice earn each month?
    - a. $480
    - b. $240.20
    - c. $120.00
    - d. NG

13. The regular price of a suit is $260.80. During a sale the suit is priced at a discount of 15%. What is the sale price of this suit?
    - a. $221.68
    - b. $39.12
    - c. $299.92
    - d. NG

14. The map distance from City A to City B is 6.2 cm. The map scale is 1 cm: 50 km. What is the actual distance from City A to City B?
    - a. 56.2 km
    - b. 310 km
    - c. 0.124 km
    - d. NG

9
Geometry

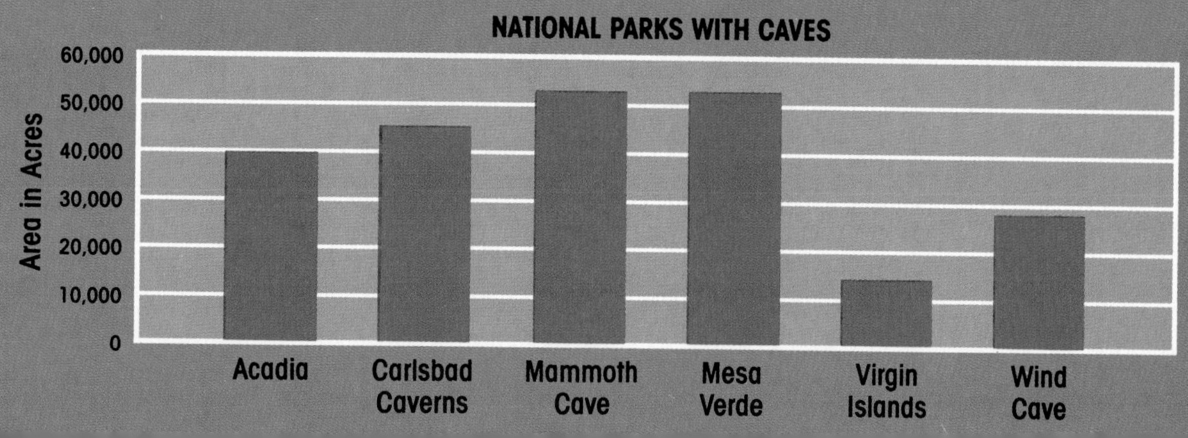
NATIONAL PARKS WITH CAVES
Area in Acres
60,000
50,000
40,000
30,000
20,000
10,000
0
Acadia
Carlsbad Caverns
Mammoth Cave
Mesa Verde
Virgin Islands
Wind Cave

# 9-1 Figures, Terms, and Symbols

**A.** A **plane** is a flat surface that goes on forever in all directions.

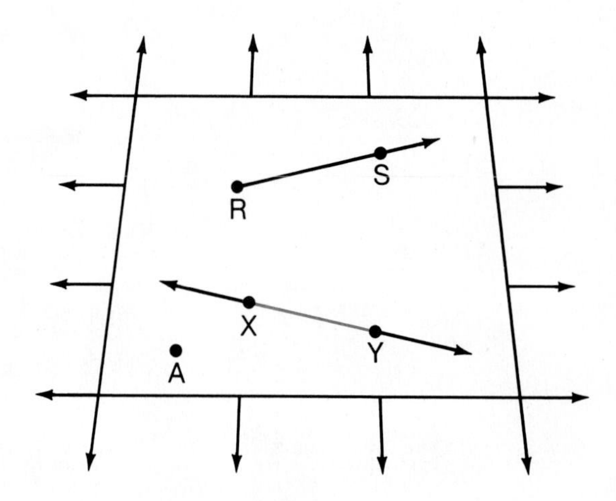


A **point** is a position in a plane.
points A, Y, and R: A, Y, R

A **line** is a straight path of points that goes on forever in two directions.
line XY: $\overleftrightarrow{XY}$ or $\overleftrightarrow{YX}$

A **ray** is part of a line. It has one endpoint and goes on forever in one direction. ray RS: $\overrightarrow{RS}$

A **line segment** is part of a line with two endpoints.
line segment XY: $\overline{XY}$ or $\overline{YX}$

**B.** Two rays with the same endpoint form an **angle.**

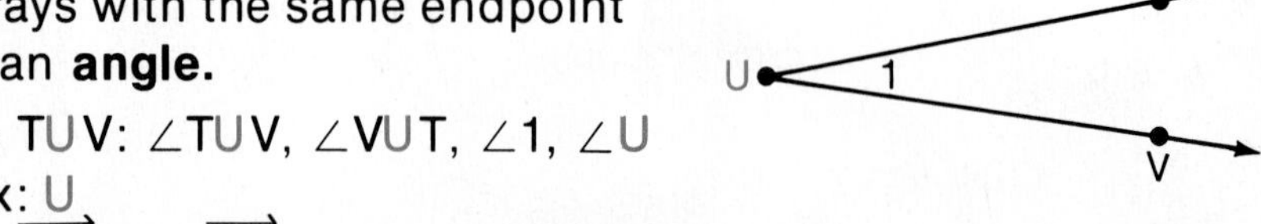


angle TUV: ∠TUV, ∠VUT, ∠1, ∠U
vertex: U
sides: $\overrightarrow{UT}$ and $\overrightarrow{UV}$

**C.** **Intersecting lines** $\overleftrightarrow{MN}$ and $\overleftrightarrow{PQ}$ meet or **intersect** at R.

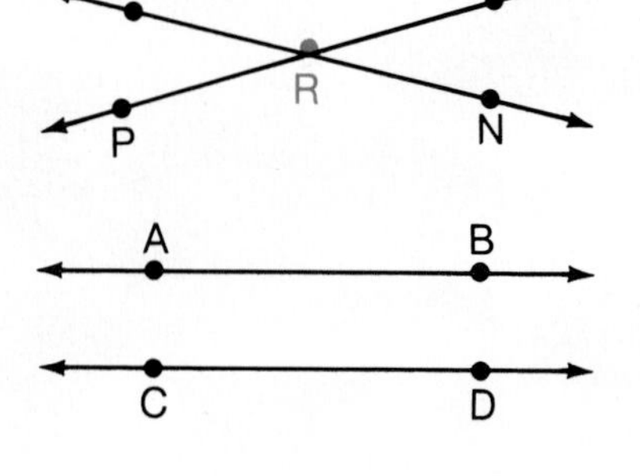


**Parallel lines** are lines in a plane that never intersect.
$\overleftrightarrow{AB}$ is parallel to $\overleftrightarrow{CD}$: $\overleftrightarrow{AB} \parallel \overleftrightarrow{CD}$

**D.** **Congruent line segments** are line segments with equal lengths. They will fit exactly on each other.
$\overline{XY}$ is congruent to $\overline{ZW}$: $\overline{XY} \cong \overline{ZW}$

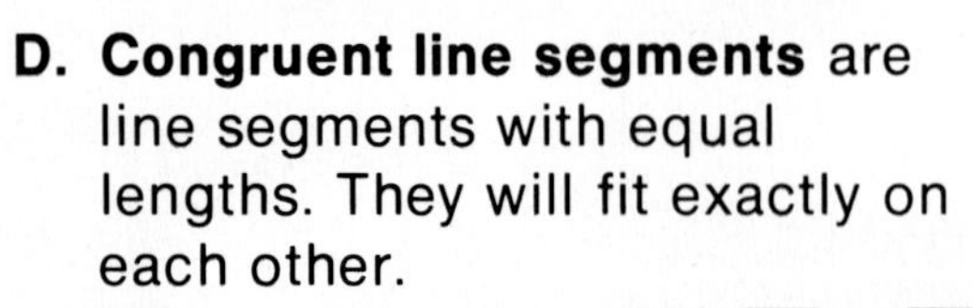

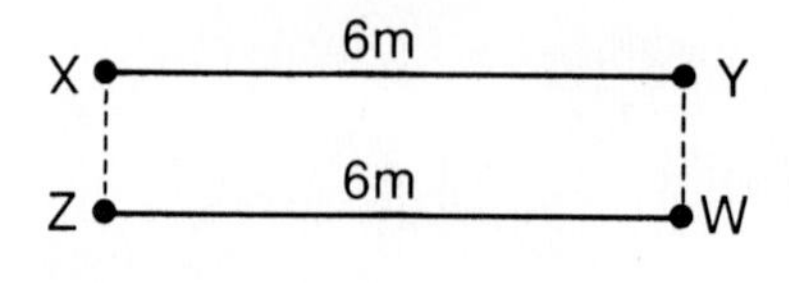


$\overleftrightarrow{AB}$ **bisects** $\overline{XY}$. The **midpoint** of $\overline{XY}$ is M. $\overline{XM} \cong \overline{MY}$

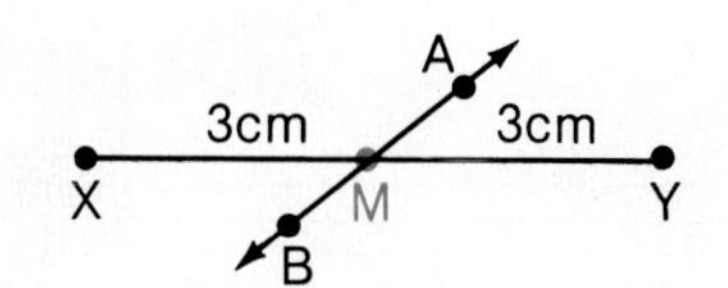

## CLASS EXERCISES

*Match the names and the figures.*

1. $\overrightarrow{MN}$  2. $\overrightarrow{NM}$  3. $\overline{NM}$  4. $\overleftrightarrow{MN}$

a. M N  b. M N  c. M N  d. M N

## EXERCISES

*For each exercise, copy points R, S, T, and U on grid paper. Draw the figures.*

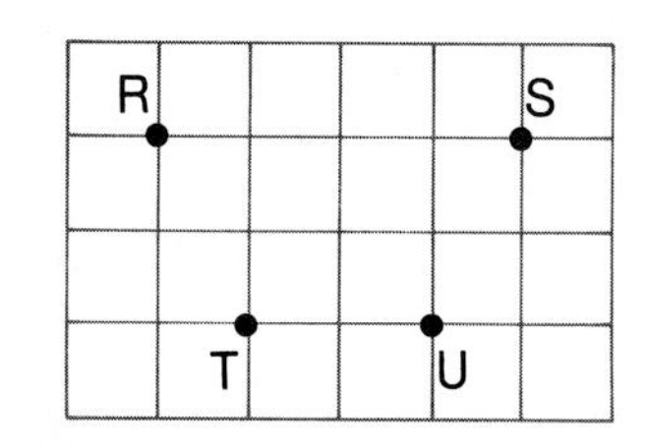


1. A pair of intersecting lines.
2. A pair of parallel lines.
3. $\overrightarrow{RU}$
4. $\overrightarrow{UR}$
5. $\overleftrightarrow{ST}$
6. $\overline{TU}$
7. $\angle RTU$
8. $\angle TRU$
9. $\angle TUR$
10. $\angle RTS$
11. Draw $\overleftrightarrow{RU}$ and $\overleftrightarrow{ST}$. Label their intersection V. Name the 6 line segments in your figure. Name the 4 rays in your figure that have V as their endpoint.
12. Mark points D and E so that $\overline{DE} \cong \overline{TU}$. If the length of $\overline{TU}$ is 13 mm, what is the length of $\overline{DE}$?

★13. Draw $\overline{RS}$ with midpoint M and bisector $\overleftrightarrow{GH}$. If the length of $\overline{MS}$ is 13 mm, what is the length of $\overline{RS}$?

### Visual Perception

**Skew lines** are lines that are not in a plane and do not intersect. This is a picture of a corner of a room. Which lines are intersecting lines? parallel lines? skew lines?

# 9-2 Angles and Angle Measures

**A.** You can use a **protractor** to measure angles. The unit for measuring angles is the degree (°).

measure of ∠APB

m ∠APB = 60°
m ∠APQ = 90°
m ∠HPB = 120°
m ∠HPQ = 90°
m ∠APH = 180°
m ∠BPQ = 30°

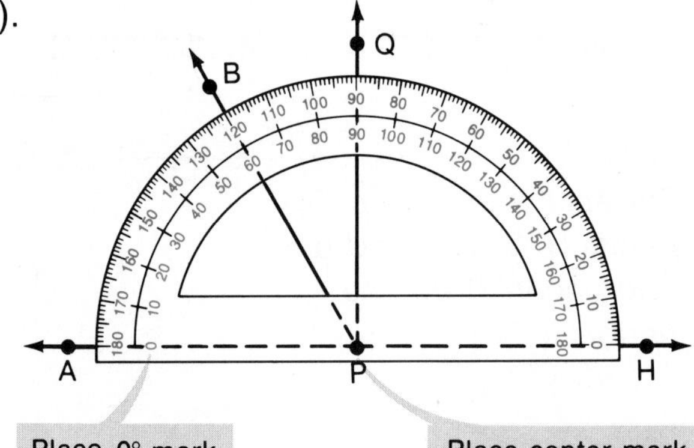


Place 0° mark on one side.

Place center mark on vertex.

A **right angle** is an angle with measure 90°.

An **acute angle** is an angle with measure less than 90°.

An **obtuse angle** is an angle with measure greater than 90° but less than 180°.

A **straight angle** is an angle with measure 180°. A straight angle forms a line.

| **right angle** | **acute angle** | **obtuse angle** | **straight angle** |
|---|---|---|---|
| ∠APQ or ∠HPQ | ∠APB or ∠BPQ | ∠HPB | ∠APH |

**B.** $\overrightarrow{ON}$ **bisects** ∠BOC.

m ∠BON = m ∠NOC

∠BON is congruent to ∠NOC

∠BON ≅ ∠NOC

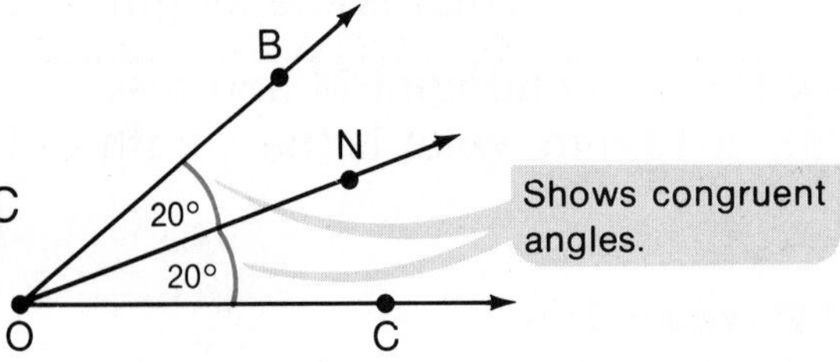


**C.** Two angles are **supplementary** if the sum of their measures is 180°. Each angle is a **supplement** of the other.

**supplementary angles**
∠ABC and ∠CBF
∠ABE and ∠EBF
∠ABD and ∠DBF

Two angles are **complementary** if the sum of their measures is 90°. Each angle is a **complement** of the other.

**complementary angles**
∠ABC and ∠CBD
∠DBE and ∠EBF

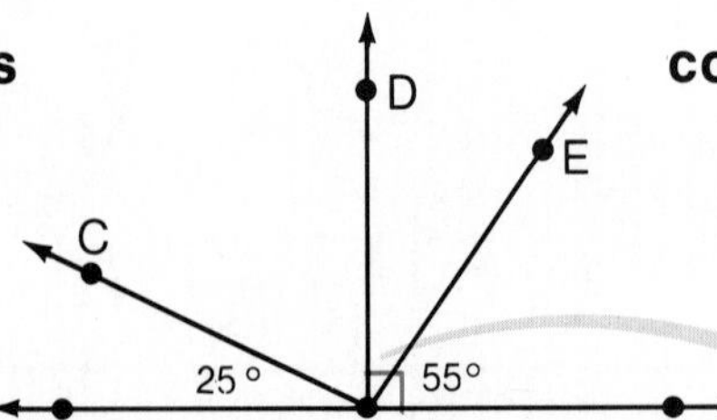


⌉ means right angle

## CLASS EXERCISES

*Measure each angle. Label each as right, acute, or obtuse.*

**1.** 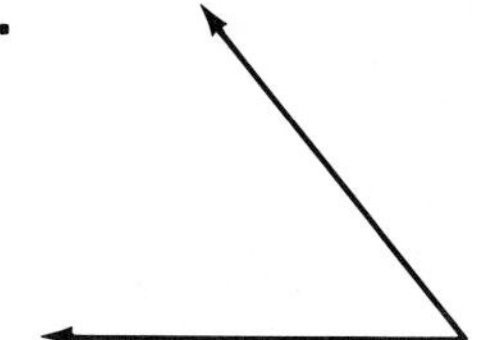

**2.** 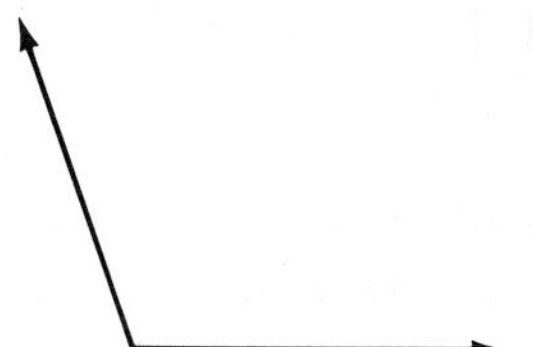

**3.** 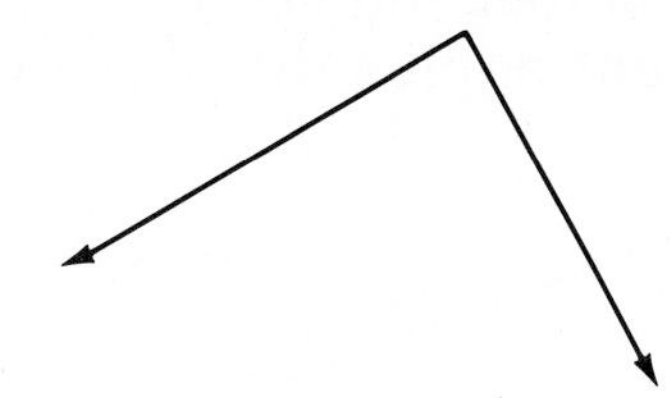

**4.** What is the measure of a complement of the angle in **1**?

**5.** What is the measure of a supplement of the angle in **2**?

## EXERCISES

*Find the measure of each angle. Label each as right, acute, obtuse, or straight.*

**1.** ∠SPT
**2.** ∠SPX
**3.** ∠SPQ
**4.** ∠MPN
**5.** ∠MPX
**6.** ∠MPT
**7.** ∠MPS
**8.** ∠TPX
**9.** ∠QPX
**10.** ∠NPB
**11.** ∠XPN
**12.** ∠BPQ
**13.** ∠NPT
**14.** ∠BPX
**15.** ∠MPQ
**16.** ∠NPS
**17.** ∠MPB
**18.** ∠TPQ

**19.** Name the bisector of ∠MPX.

**20.** Name two pairs of supplementary angles.

**21.** Name two pairs of complementary angles.

**22.** Can two acute angles be complementary? supplementary?

**23.** Can two right angles be complementary? supplementary?

**24.** Can two obtuse angles be supplements of each other?

### Logical Reasoning

It takes 3 workers 20 minutes to pack 6 cartons. At the same rate, how long would it take 12 workers to pack 30 cartons?

1. 35°, acute

Homework page 499

# 9-3 Lines and Angles

**A.** Two intersecting lines form several pairs of **adjacent angles** that are supplementary.

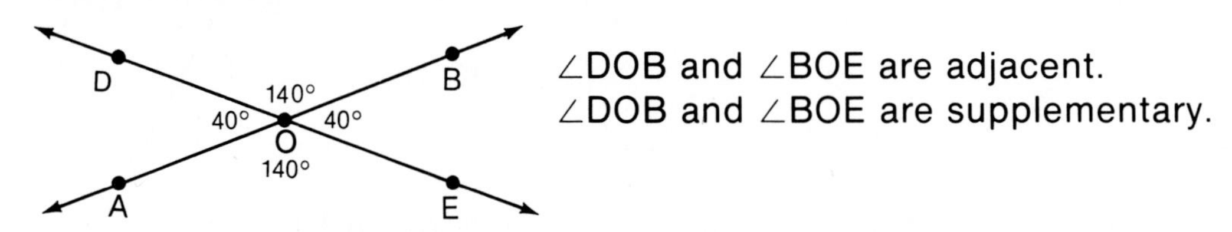


∠DOB and ∠BOE are adjacent.
∠DOB and ∠BOE are supplementary.

**B.** Two intersecting lines also form two pairs of **vertical angles.** Vertical angles are congruent.

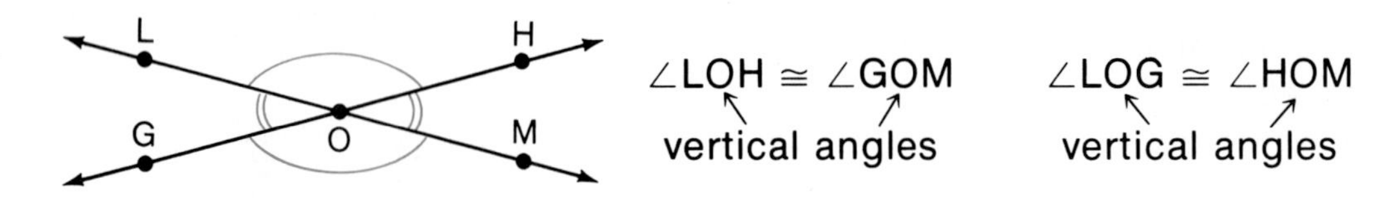


**C.** If one of the angles formed by two intersecting lines is a right angle, all four angles are right angles. The two intersecting lines are **perpendicular lines.**

$\overleftrightarrow{MN}$ is perpendicular to $\overleftrightarrow{RS}$

$\overleftrightarrow{MN} \perp \overleftrightarrow{RS}$

M
90°
S
R
N

**D.** When two parallel lines are cut by a third line, many angles have equal measures. Many pairs of angles are supplementary.

**Example 1**

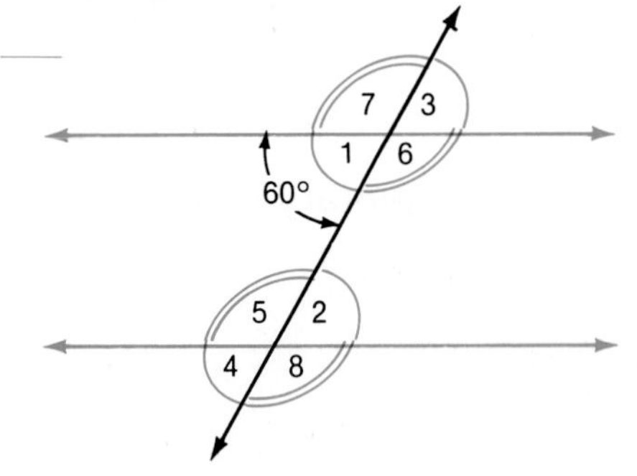


m ∠1 = m ∠2 = m ∠3 = m ∠4 = 60°
m ∠5 = m ∠6 = m ∠7 = m ∠8 = 120°

**Example 2**

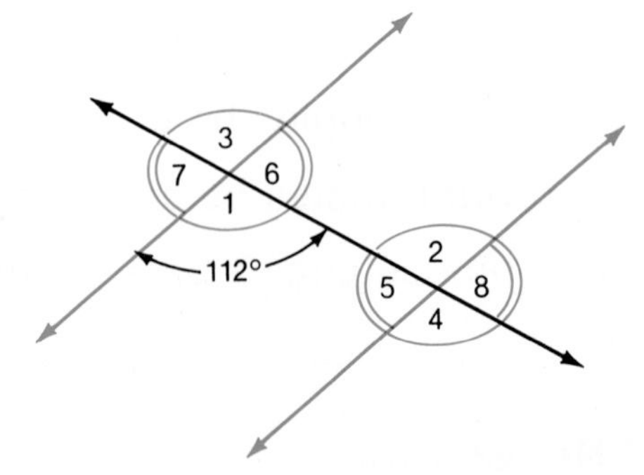


m ∠1 = m ∠2 = m ∠3 = m ∠4 = 112°
m ∠5 = m ∠6 = m ∠7 = m ∠8 = 68°

## CLASS EXERCISES

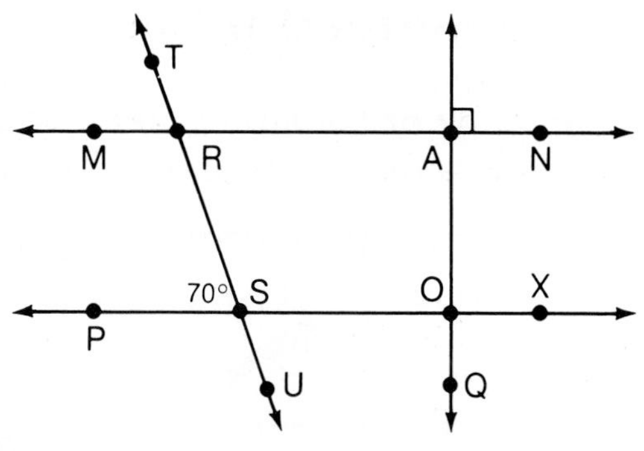


*$\overleftrightarrow{MN} \parallel \overleftrightarrow{PX}$. Find the measure of each angle.*

1. ∠OSU  2. ∠SRA  3. ∠MRT
4. ∠XOQ  5. ∠RSO  6. ∠AOQ
7. Name an angle adjacent to ∠PSR.
8. Name 3 pairs of vertical angles.

## EXERCISES

*Use **Figure 1** to find the measures.*

**Figure 1**

1. ∠VWY  2. ∠YWX  3. ∠VWX
4. ∠XWZ  5. ∠XWV  6. ∠YWZ
7. Name an angle adjacent to ∠XWZ.
8. Name an angle adjacent to ∠YWV.

*Use **Figure 2** to find the measures.*

**Figure 2**

9. ∠DEG  10. ∠GEF  11. ∠IEF
12. ∠DEI  13. ∠IEH  14. ∠FEH
15. Name the bisector of ∠GEF
16. Name two perpendicular lines.

*Use **Figure 3** to find the measures. $\overleftrightarrow{MN} \parallel \overleftrightarrow{PQ}$.*

**Figure 3**

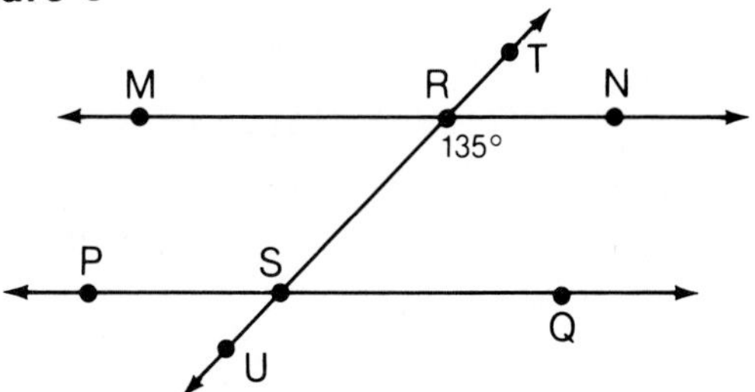


17. ∠NRT  18. ∠MRT  19. ∠RSQ
20. ∠SRM  21. ∠QSU  22. ∠TRU
23. What is the measure of a supplement of ∠PSU?

★ 24. When will a pair of adjacent angles be right angles?

## THINK!

### Angle Patterns

Find all the pairs of supplementary, complementary, and adjacent angles in the figure. How many of each are there?

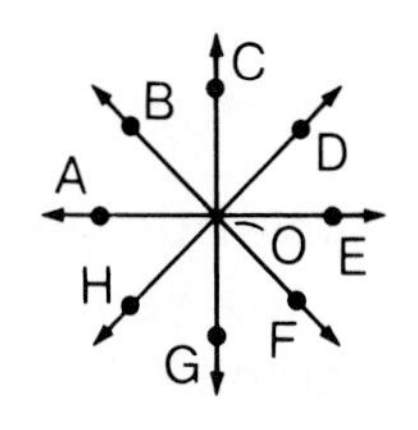


1. 65° 9. 90° 17. 45°

Homework page 500

# 9-4 Constructions

You can copy or construct many figures using only a **compass** and an unmarked ruler, or **straightedge.**

**A.** Construct a line segment congruent to $\overline{XY}$.

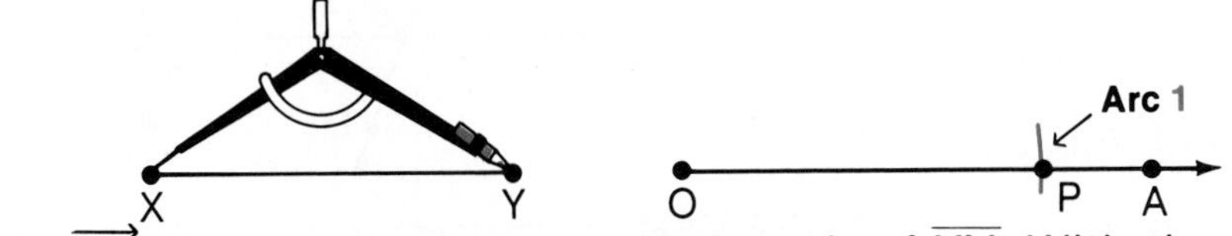


Draw $\overrightarrow{OA}$. Set the compass to the length of $\overline{XY}$. With the compass point on O, draw Arc 1. $\overline{OP} \cong \overline{XY}$

**B.** Construct a bisector perpendicular to $\overline{AB}$.

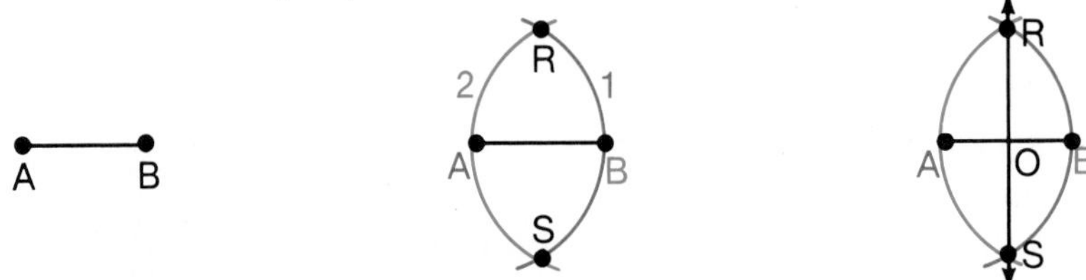


With the compass point on A, draw Arc 1. With the compass point on B and the same compass setting, draw Arc 2. Draw $\overleftrightarrow{RS}$. $\overleftrightarrow{RS}$ is the **perpendicular bisector** of $\overline{AB}$. O is the midpoint of $\overline{AB}$.

**C.** Construct an angle congruent to $\angle C$.

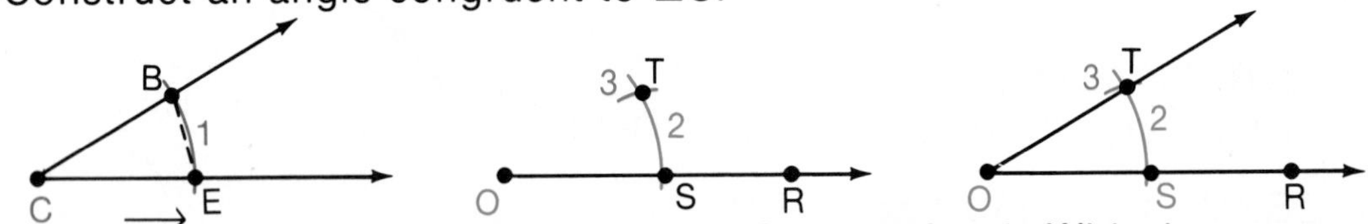


Draw $\overrightarrow{OR}$. With the compass point on C, draw Arc 1. With the compass point on O and the same setting, draw Arc 2. Set the compass to the length of $\overline{BE}$. With the compass point on S, draw Arc 3. Draw $\overrightarrow{OT}$. $\angle O \cong \angle C$.

**D.** Construct the bisector of $\angle R$.

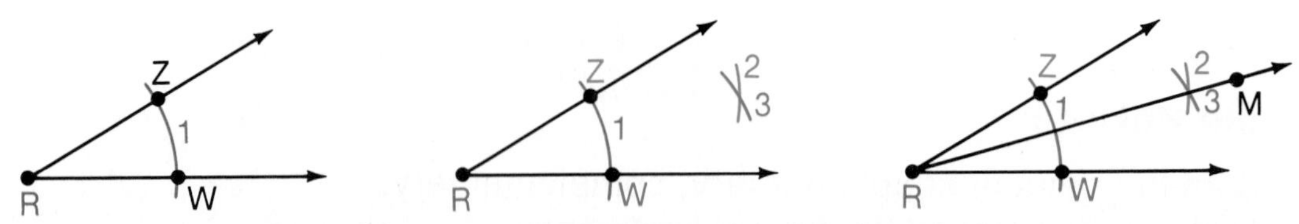


With the compass point on R, draw Arc 1. With the compass point on Z and the same setting, draw Arc 2. With the compass point on W and the same setting, draw Arc 3. Draw $\overrightarrow{RM}$. $\overrightarrow{RM}$ bisects $\angle R$.

## CLASS EXERCISES

1. The diagram shows the construction of $\overleftrightarrow{AB}$ perpendicular to $\overleftrightarrow{CD}$ at O on $\overleftrightarrow{CD}$. Explain how constructing the bisector of an angle was used to construct $\overleftrightarrow{AB}$.

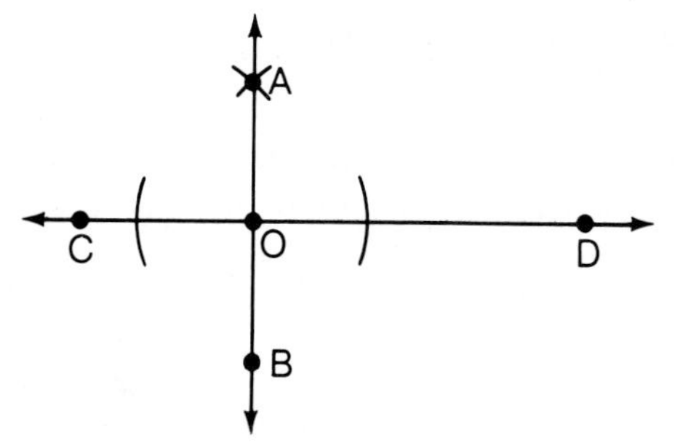


2. The diagram below shows the construction of $\overleftrightarrow{XY}$ parallel to $\overleftrightarrow{MN}$ that passes through O. Explain how copying an angle was used to construct $\overleftrightarrow{XY}$.

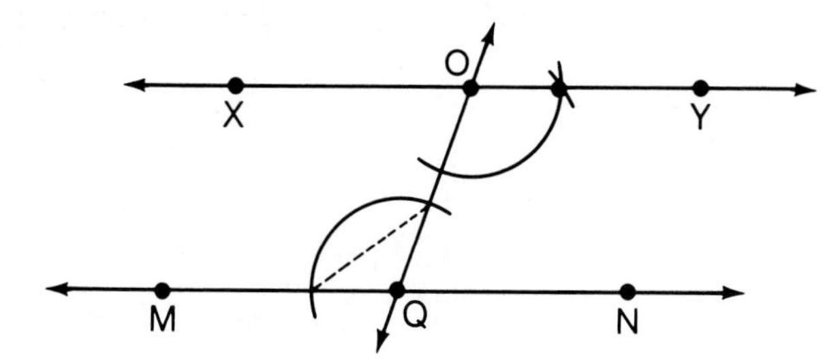


## EXERCISES

1. Draw a line segment. Copy it.
2. Draw an obtuse angle. Copy it.
3. Draw an obtuse angle. Construct its bisector.
4. Draw a line segment. Construct its perpendicular bisector.
5. Draw $\overline{XY}$. By construction, divide $\overline{XY}$ into four congruent line segments.
6. Draw acute $\angle B$. Construct an angle with measure three times that of $\angle B$.

★7. Copy the figure at the right. Bisect $\overline{AB}$, $\overline{BC}$, and $\overline{CA}$. Label the point of intersection of the bisectors O

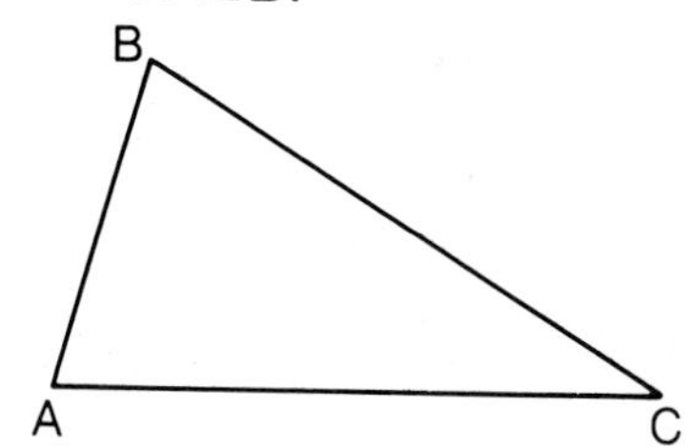


## THINK!

### Logical Reasoning

A farmer goes to the well with a 5-liter jar and a 3-L jar. The farmer wants to bring back exactly 7 liters of water. How can this be done using only the jars above and no measuring cups? (Water can be poured from one jar to the other or back into the well.)

Homework page 500

# 9-5 Triangles

**A.** A **triangle** is a **closed plane figure** with three line segments for **sides.** To name a triangle use $\triangle$ and name its **vertices** in any order.

sides: $\overline{AB}$, $\overline{BC}$, $\overline{CA}$
vertices: A, B, C
triangle ABC: $\triangle ABC$

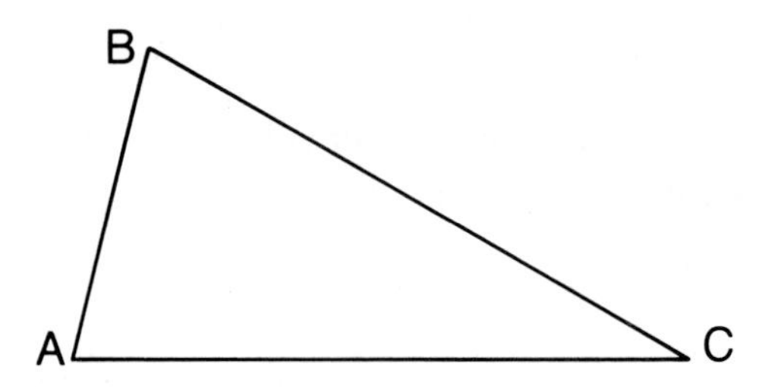


**B.** You can classify triangles according to the lengths of their sides.

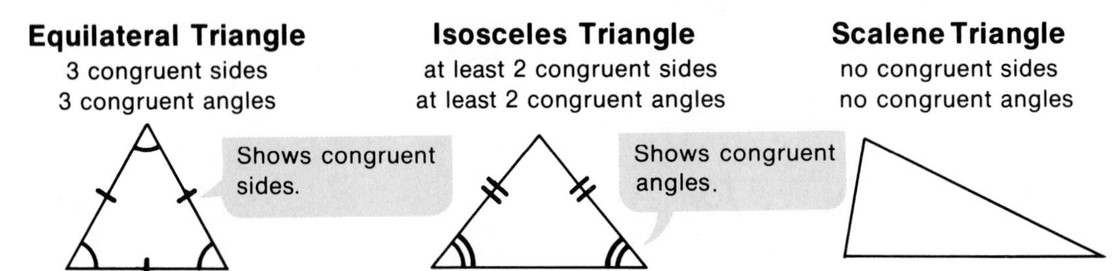


**C.** You can also classify triangles according to the types of angles they contain.

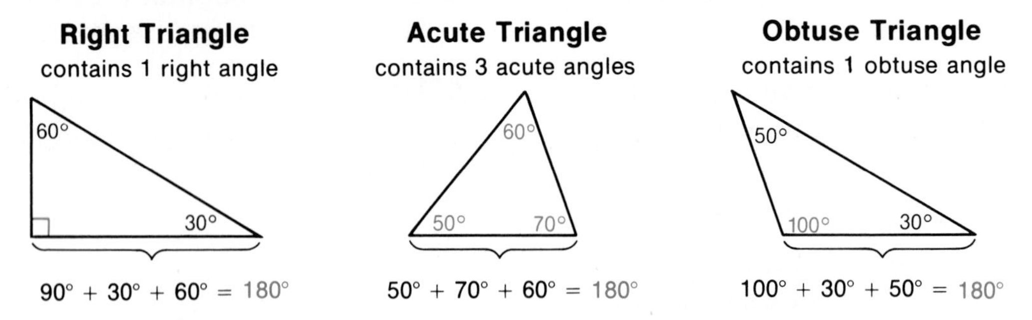


Notice that the sum of the measures of the angles of a triangle is 180°.

**D.** In an isosceles triangle, the angles **opposite** congruent sides are congruent angles.

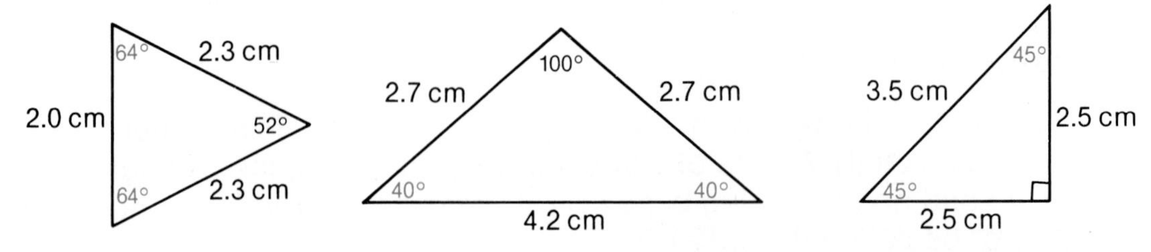

## CLASS EXERCISES

*Name each triangle and classify it two ways.*

**1.**

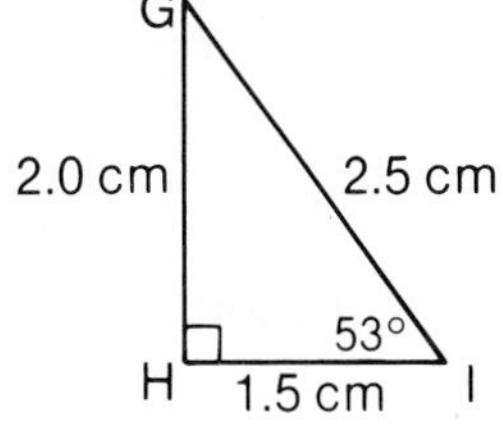


**2.**

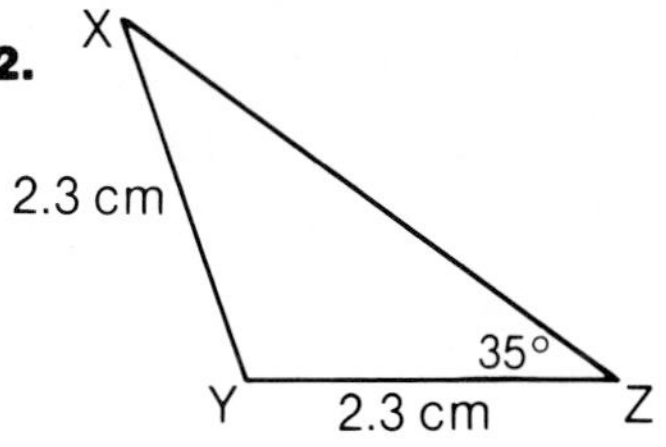


**3.**

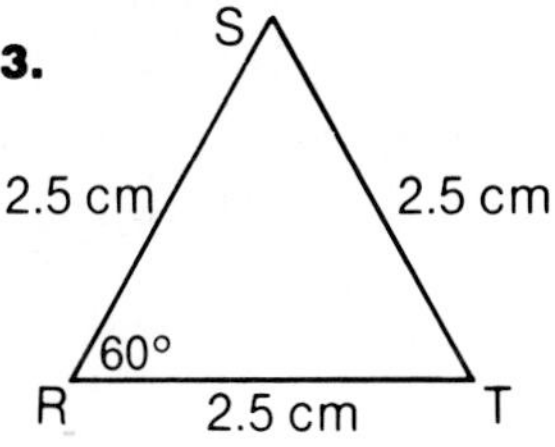


**4.** Find the measures of the other angles in Exercises **1–3.**

**5.** What is the measure of each angle of an equilateral triangle?

## EXERCISES

*The measures of two angles of a triangle are given. Find the measure of the third angle.*

**1.** 30°, 80° **2.** 110°, 48° **3.** 130°, 25° **4.** 63°, 27°

**5.** 65°, 50° **6.** 25°, 45° **7.** 60°, 60° **8.** 45°, 90°

*Give the exercise numbers* ***1–8*** *of the triangles that are:*

**9.** obtuse **10.** right **11.** acute **12.** scalene

**13.** isosceles **14.** equilateral **15.** acute, scalene **16.** obtuse, isosceles

**17.** right, scalene **18.** acute, isosceles **19.** right, isosceles

★ **20.** One angle of an isosceles triangle has a measure of 116°. Find the measures of the other two angles.

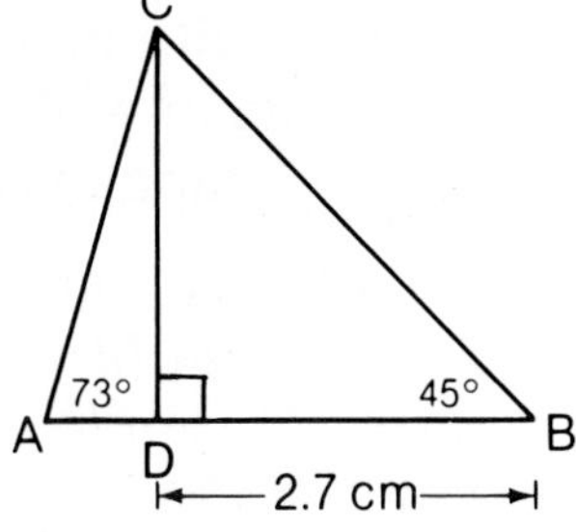


*Use $\triangle ABC$ shown at the right. $m\angle A = 73°$, $m\angle B = 45°$ Find the following:*

**21.** m $\angle$BCA **22.** m $\angle$BCD

**23.** m $\angle$ACD **24.** length of $\overline{CD}$

## THINK!

### Write an Equation

If one pumpkin balances a $\frac{2}{3}$ pound weight plus $\frac{2}{3}$ pumpkin, what is the exact weight, in pounds, of one pumpkin?

**1.** 70° **9.** 2, 3, 6



Homework page 501

# 9-6 Polygons and Circles

A polygon is a closed plane figure with **sides** that are line segments. The sides meet at the **vertices** of the polygon. The name of each type of polygon tells how many sides and how many angles it has. In **regular polygons,** all sides are congruent and all angles are congruent.

**Quadrilateral**

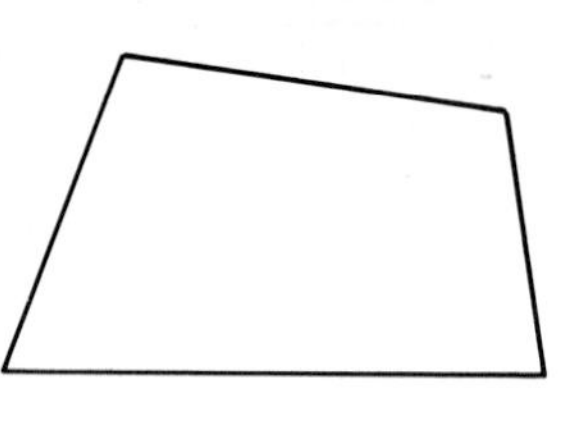

4 sides

**Regular Hexagon**

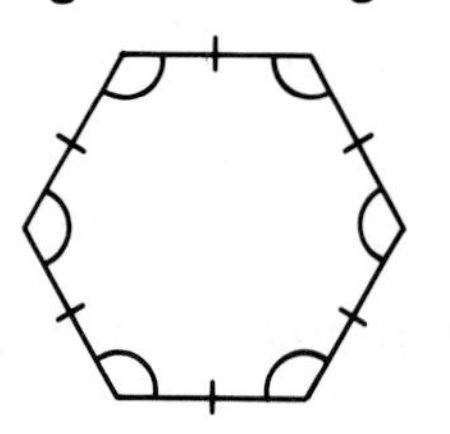

6 congruent sides
6 congruent angles

**Octagon**

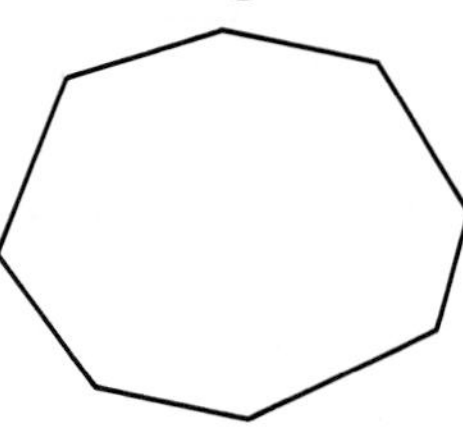

8 sides

B. **Diagonals** drawn from one vertex of a polygon form triangles. You can use the sum of the measures of the angles of the triangles to find the sum of the measures of the angles of the polygon.

**Pentagon OPQRS**

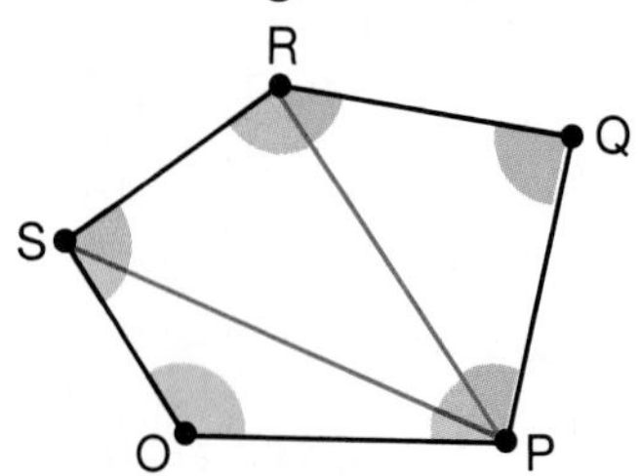


Sum for OPQRS = Sum for $\triangle PQR$ + Sum for $\triangle PRS$ + Sum for $\triangle PSO$
$= 180^\circ + 180^\circ + 180^\circ = 540^\circ$

The sum of the measures of the angles of a pentagon is 540°.

C. A **circle with center P** is the set of all points in a plane that are the same distance from point P.

A **radius** is a line segment with the center and a point of the circle as endpoints.

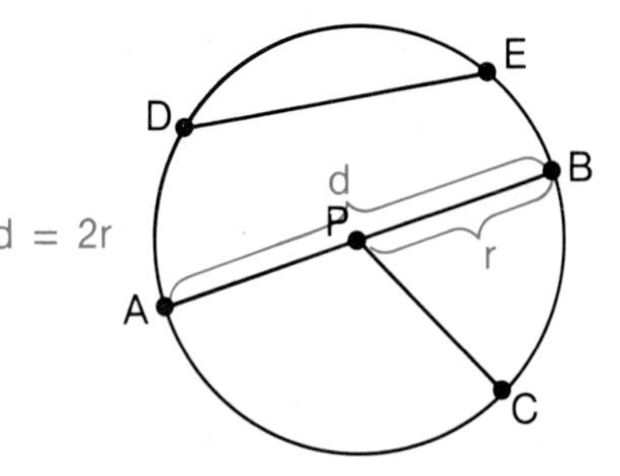


A **chord** is a line segment that has two points of the circle as endpoints. A **diameter** is a chord that contains the center. The length of a diameter (d) is twice the length of a radius (r).

Radii: $\overline{PA}$, $\overline{PB}$, $\overline{PC}$
Chords: $\overline{AB}$, $\overline{DE}$
Diameter: $\overline{AB}$
Central Angles: ∠BPC, ∠APC

A **central angle** has the center as its vertex.

## CLASS EXERCISES

*Tell what type of polygon each figure is and whether it is regular.*

**1.**

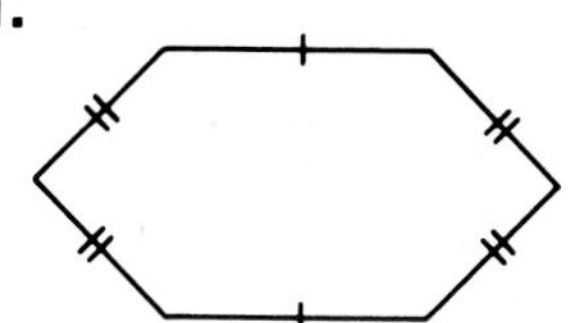

**2.**

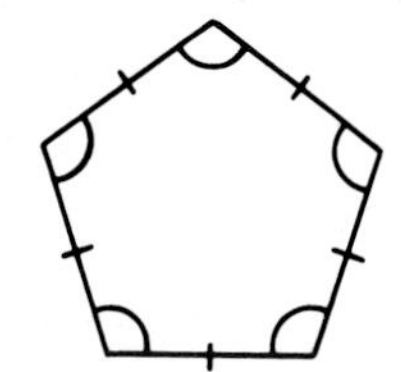

**3.**

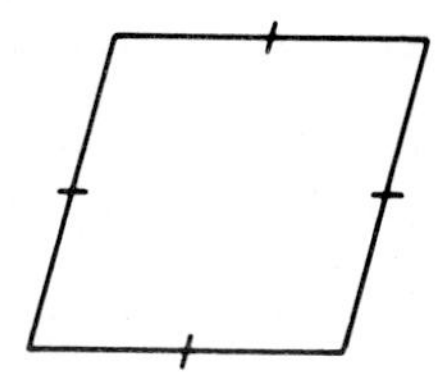

**4.** Copy the polygon in Exercise **1.** Draw all of the diagonals from one vertex. How many triangles are formed?

## EXERCISES

*Copy and complete.*

| Type of polygon | Number of sides | Sum of angle measures | Measure of each angle if the polygon is regular |
|---|---|---|---|
| triangle | 3 | 180° | 60° |
| quadrilateral | 4 | **1.** | **2.** |
| pentagon | 5 | 540° | **3.** |
| hexagon | 6 | **4.** | **5.** |
| octagon | 8 | **6.** | **7.** |

*M is the center of this circle. The length of a diameter is 3.0 cm. Name all the following:*

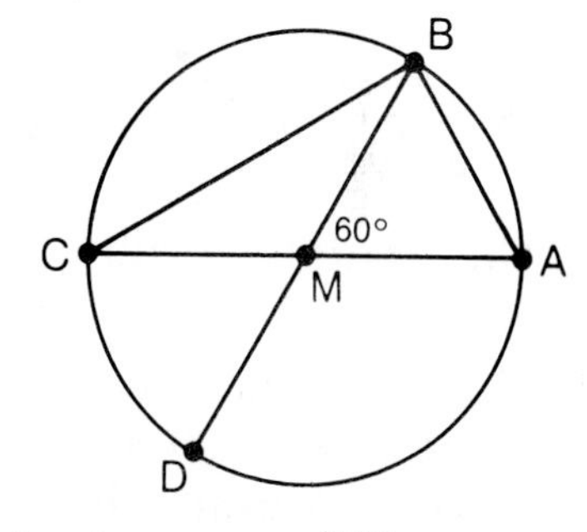


**8.** radii **9.** chords

**10.** diameters **11.** central angles

**12.** Find the measures of all central angles.

**13.** Find the length of $\overline{MA}$, $\overline{MC}$, $\overline{BD}$. ★**14.** Find the length of $\overline{AB}$.

### Use Equations

Cheryl's father gives her 8¢ for every homework problem she gets right and he deducts 5¢ for each problem she misses. There were 26 problems on one night's assignment. When her father asked how much he owed her, Cheryl said, "Nothing, we're even." How many problems did Cheryl get right and how many did she miss?

1. 360° 2. 90°

# 9-7 Special Quadrilaterals

**A.** A **trapezoid** is a quadrilateral with one pair of **opposite sides** parallel.

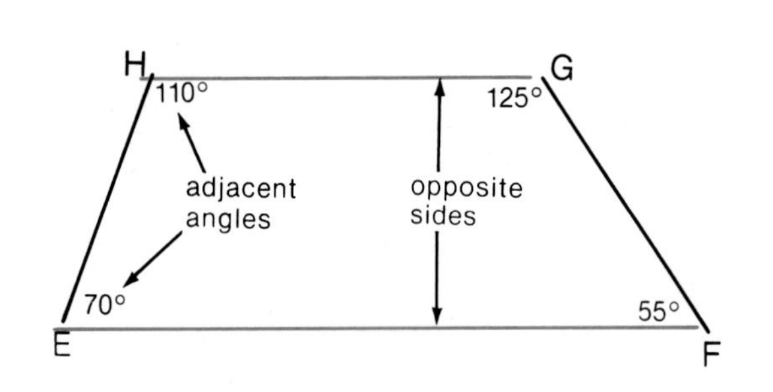


$\overline{HG}$ **is parallel to** $\overline{EF}$
$\overline{HG} \parallel \overline{EF}$

Note that m ∠H + m ∠E = 180°
and m ∠F + m ∠G = 180°
In a trapezoid, two pairs of **adjacent angles** are supplementary.

**B.** A **parallelogram** is a quadrilateral with two pairs of parallel sides.

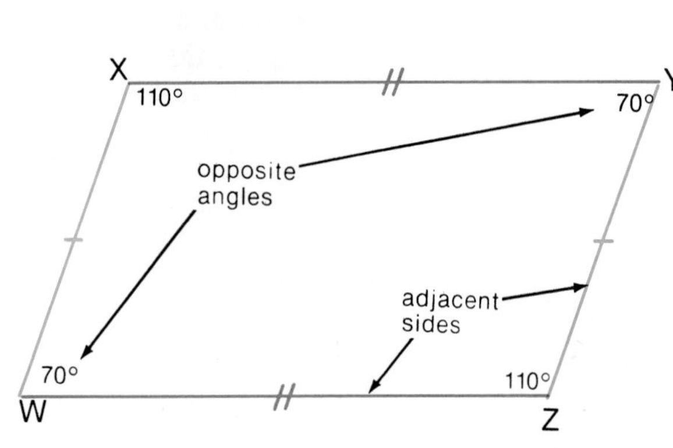


$\overline{XY}$ is parallel to $\overline{WZ}$
$\overline{XY} \parallel \overline{WZ}$

and $\overline{XW}$ is parallel to $\overline{YZ}$
$\overline{XW} \parallel \overline{YZ}$

You can see that opposite sides are congruent and **opposite angles** are congruent.
$\overline{XY} \cong \overline{WZ}$ and $\overline{XW} \cong \overline{YZ}$
∠X ≅ ∠Z and ∠W ≅ ∠Y

In a parallelogram, all pairs of adjacent angles are supplementary.

**C.** A **rectangle** is a parallelogram with 4 right angles.

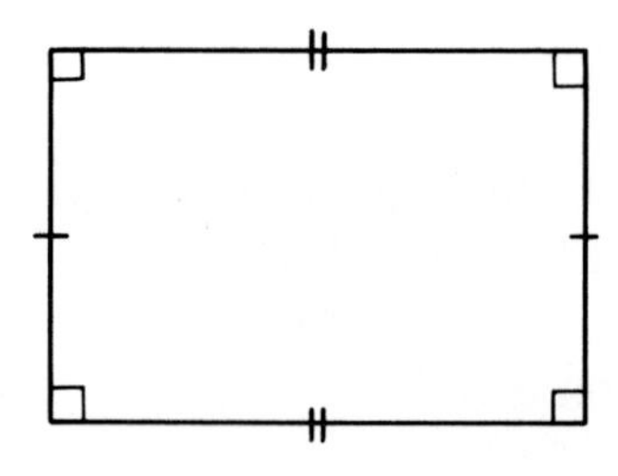

**D.** A **rhombus** is a parallelogram with 4 congruent sides.

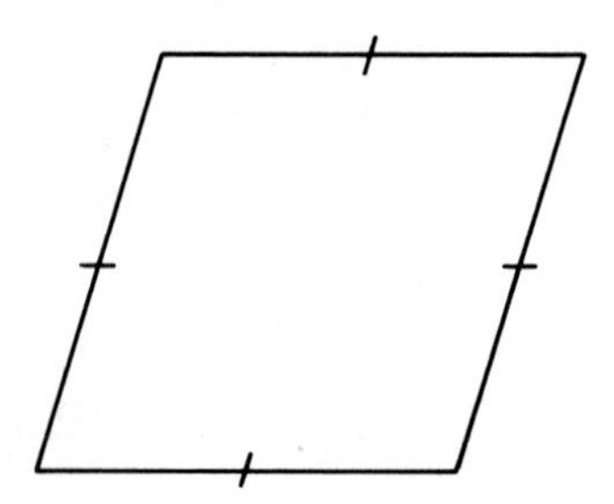

**E.** A **square** is a parallelogram with 4 congruent sides and 4 right angles.

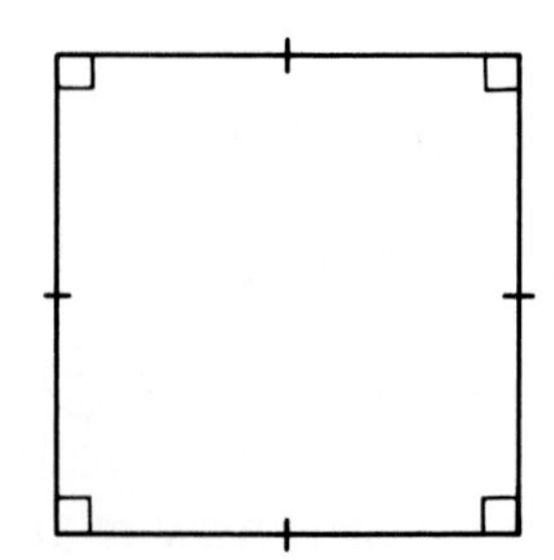

## CLASS EXERCISES

*Identify each quadrilateral as a trapezoid, parallelogram, rhombus, rectangle, or square.*

**1.**

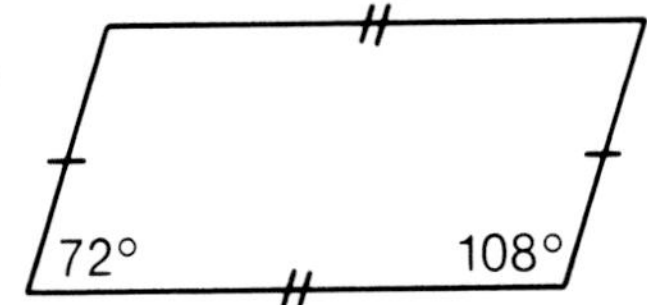


**2.**

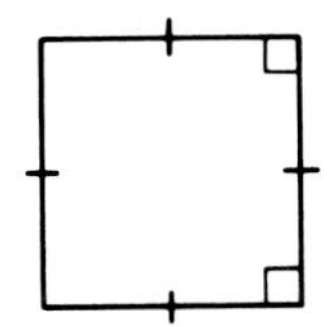

**3.**

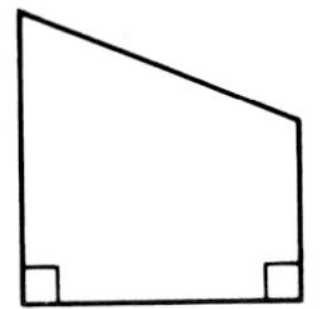

**4.**

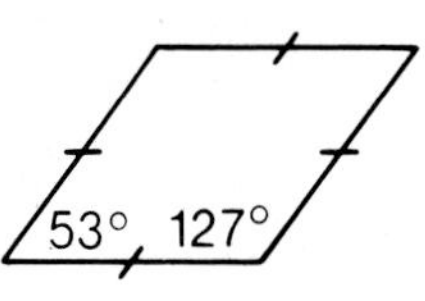


## EXERCISES

*In parallelogram MNPQ the length of $\overline{MN}$ is 5.2 m, the length of $\overline{NP}$ is 3.9 m, m ∠N = 70°. Find the following:*

Q P M N

**1.** length of $\overline{QM}$ **2.** length of $\overline{PQ}$

**3.** m ∠P **4.** m ∠M

*Use parallelogram RSTU. Find the following:*

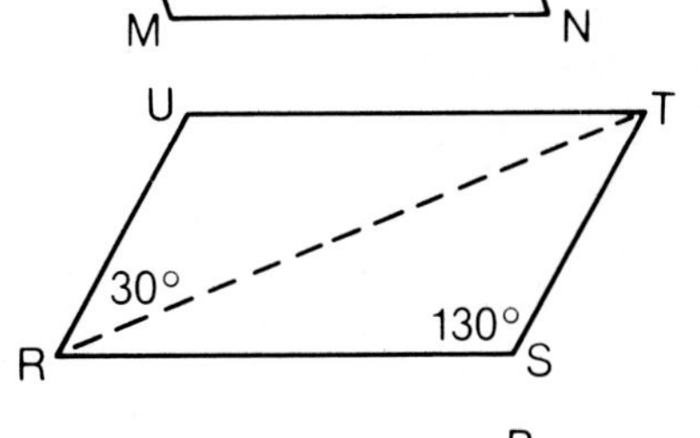


**5.** m ∠SRU **6.** m ∠SRT **7.** m ∠TUR

**8.** m ∠STU **9.** m ∠STR **10.** m ∠RTU

*In square ABCD the length of $\overline{AB}$ is 4 cm, m ∠BCA = m ∠BDA = 45°. Find the following:*

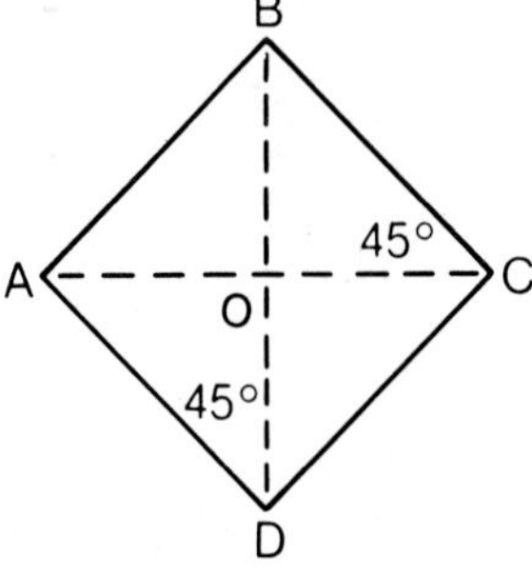


**11.** m ∠ABD **12.** m ∠ACD **13.** m ∠BAC

**14.** m ∠AOD **15.** m ∠BOC **16.** length of $\overline{BC}$

★**17.** How many right triangles are in the figure?

★**18.** How many isosceles triangles are in the figure?

## MIXED REVIEW

*Write the standard numeral or decimal for each.*

**1.** $2.3 \times 10^{-4}$ **2.** $1.65 \times 10^{3}$ **3.** $5.04 \times 10^{-7}$ **4.** $8.9 \times 10^{8}$

*Solve.*

**5.** 15% of 130 is ■. **6.** 42 is ■ % of 35. **7.** 8.5% of ■ is $20.40.

1. 3.9 m 5. 50° 11. 45°

Homework page 502

## 9-8 Similar Triangles

**A.** You can match the angles of $\triangle ABC$ and $\triangle XYZ$ so that the angles that are paired are congruent angles. Angles that are paired are called **corresponding angles.**

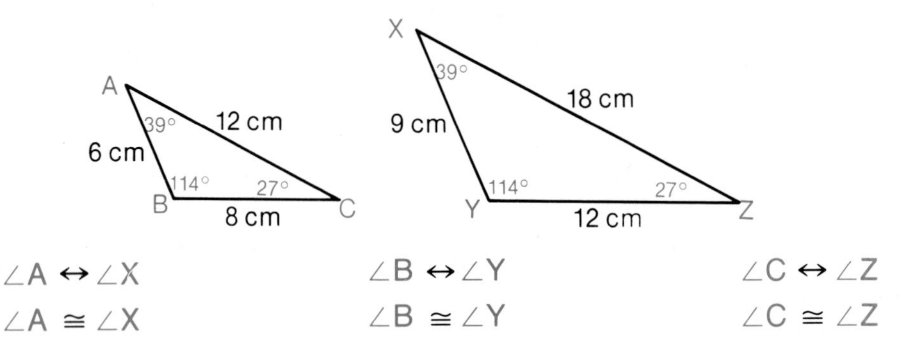


$\angle A \leftrightarrow \angle X$ $\quad$ $\angle B \leftrightarrow \angle Y$ $\quad$ $\angle C \leftrightarrow \angle Z$

$\angle A \cong \angle X$ $\quad$ $\angle B \cong \angle Y$ $\quad$ $\angle C \cong \angle Z$

$\triangle ABC$ and $\triangle XYZ$ have the same shape. They are **similar triangles.** The corresponding angles of similar triangles are congruent.

**B.** Two sides are **corresponding sides** if their endpoints are vertices of corresponding angles. Matching the congruent angles of $\triangle ABC$ and $\triangle XYZ$ gives pairs of corresponding sides.

$\overline{AB} \leftrightarrow \overline{XY}$ $\quad$ $\overline{BC} \leftrightarrow \overline{YZ}$ $\quad$ $\overline{CA} \leftrightarrow \overline{ZX}$

Compare the ratios of the lengths of these corresponding sides.

$$\frac{\text{length of } \overline{AB}}{\text{length of } \overline{XY}} = \frac{6}{9} = \frac{2}{3} \qquad \frac{\text{length of } \overline{BC}}{\text{length of } \overline{YZ}} = \frac{8}{12} = \frac{2}{3} \qquad \frac{\text{length of } \overline{CA}}{\text{length of } \overline{ZX}} = \frac{12}{18} = \frac{2}{3}$$

The ratios of the lengths of corresponding sides of similar triangles are equal.

**C.** $\triangle PQR$ and $\triangle HIJ$ are similar triangles with $\angle P \leftrightarrow \angle H$, $\angle Q \leftrightarrow \angle I$, and $\angle R \leftrightarrow \angle J$. Find the length of $\overline{JH}$.

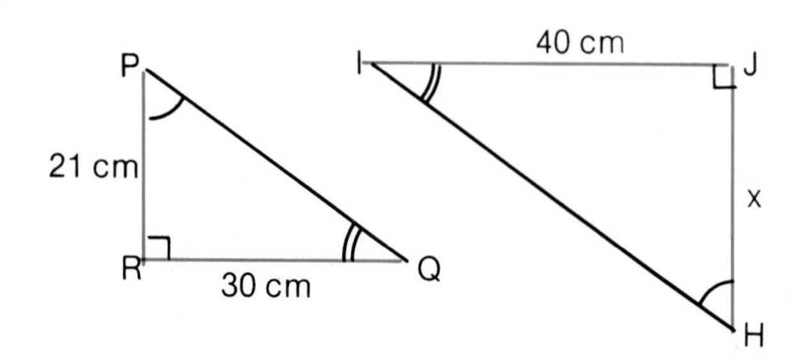


$\overline{PQ} \leftrightarrow \overline{HI}$, $\overline{QR} \leftrightarrow \overline{IJ}$, and $\overline{RP} \leftrightarrow \overline{JH}$

so $\dfrac{\text{length of } \overline{QR}}{\text{length of } \overline{IJ}} = \dfrac{\text{length of } \overline{RP}}{\text{length of } \overline{JH}}$

$$\frac{30}{40} = \frac{21}{x}$$

$$30x = 840$$

$$x = 28$$

The length of $\overline{JH}$ is 28 cm.

## CLASS EXERCISES

△ABC and △DEF are similar.

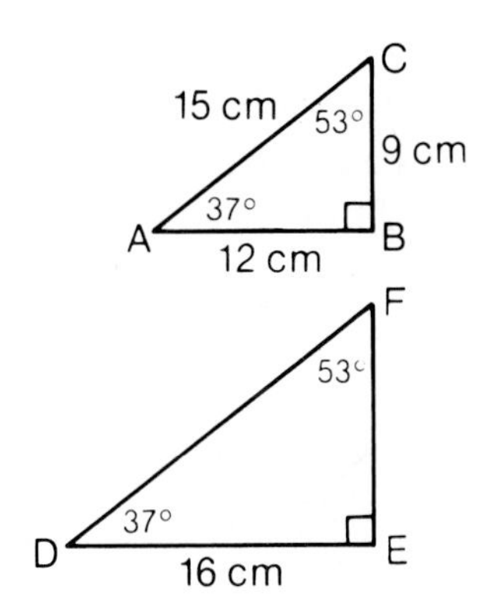


1. List the congruent corresponding angles.
2. List the corresponding sides.
3. Find the lengths of $\overline{EF}$ and $\overline{DF}$.

## EXERCISES

Any two of the triangles △GHI, △JKL, and △NKM are similar to each other.

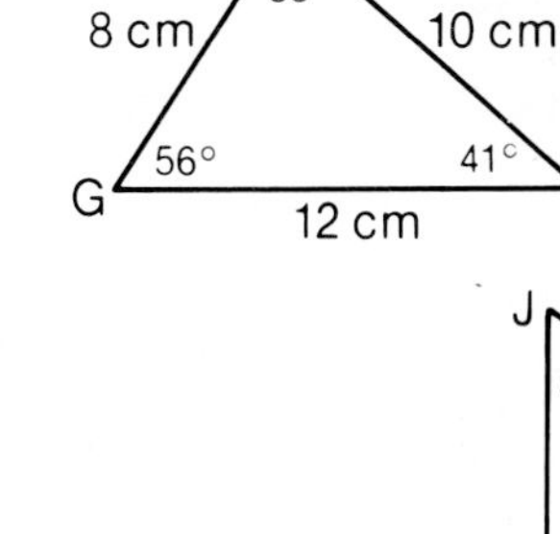


*Copy and complete the table.*

| Similar triangles | Pairs of corresponding angles | Pairs of corresponding sides |
|---|---|---|
| △GHI and △JKL | 1. **∠G ↔ ∠J, ∠I ↔ ∠L, ∠H ↔ ∠K** | 2. **$\overline{GI} \leftrightarrow \overline{JL}$, $\overline{IH} \leftrightarrow \overline{LK}$, $\overline{HG} \leftrightarrow \overline{KJ}$** |
| △GHI and △MKN | 3. **∠G ↔ ∠N, ∠I ↔ ∠M, ∠H ↔ ∠K** | 4. **$\overline{GI} \leftrightarrow \overline{NM}$, $\overline{IH} \leftrightarrow \overline{MK}$, $\overline{HG} \leftrightarrow \overline{KN}$** |
| △JKL and △MKN | 5. **∠J ↔ ∠N, ∠L ↔ ∠M, ∠K ↔ ∠K** | 6. **$\overline{JL} \leftrightarrow \overline{NM}$, $\overline{LK} \leftrightarrow \overline{MK}$, $\overline{KJ} \leftrightarrow \overline{KN}$** |

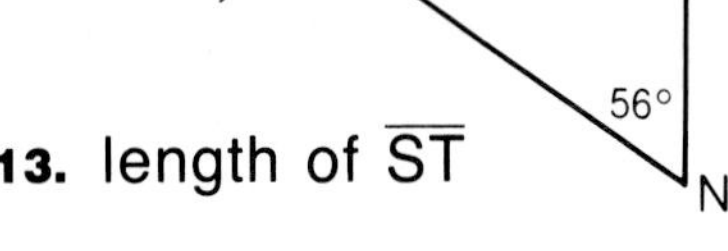


*Find the length of:*

7. $\overline{JK}$ 8. $\overline{KL}$ 9. $\overline{MN}$ 10. $\overline{KN}$

*Draw △RST similar to △GHI. m ∠R = 56°, m ∠S = 41°, and the length of $\overline{RT}$ is 1,000 cm. Find:*

★11. m ∠T ★12. length of $\overline{RS}$ ★13. length of $\overline{ST}$

### THINK!

**Odd Integers**

Find three consecutive odd integers who sum is ⁻81. **⁻29, ⁻27, ⁻25**

1. ∠G ↔ ∠J, ∠I ↔ ∠L, ∠H ↔ ∠K 7. 9 cm



Homework page 502

# 9-9 Congruent Triangles

**A.** Two triangles that have the same size and shape are **congruent triangles.** Triangle XYZ is congruent to triangle RST. Their six pairs of corresponding parts are congruent.

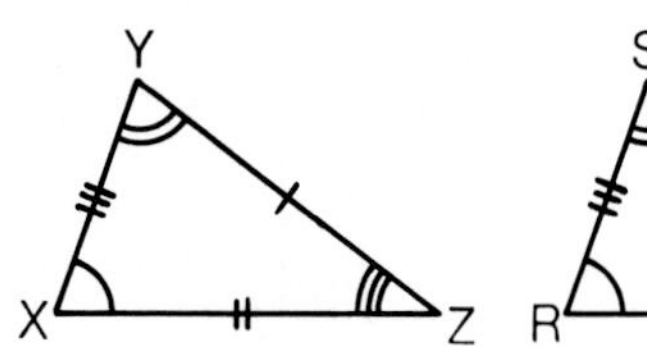

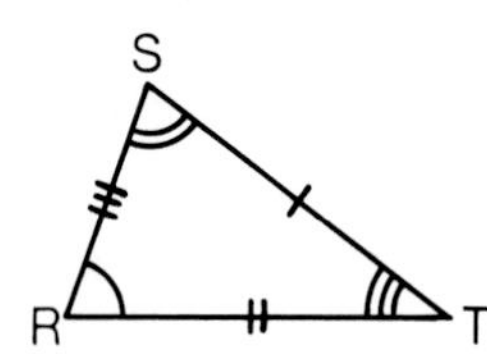


$\angle X \cong \angle R$ $\quad \overline{XY} \cong \overline{RS}$

$\angle Y \cong \angle S$ $\quad \overline{YZ} \cong \overline{ST}$

$\angle Z \cong \angle T$ $\quad \overline{ZX} \cong \overline{TR}$

$\triangle XYZ \cong \triangle RST$

List corresponding vertices in the same order.

**B.** Sometimes when you know that three pairs of corresponding parts are congruent, you can show that the triangles are congruent.

**Example 1** Two sides and the angle between them (SAS).

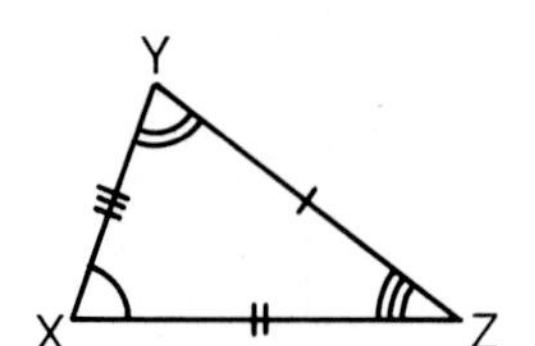

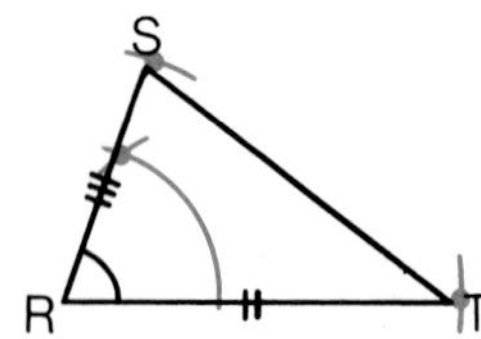


Construct $\overline{RT} \cong \overline{XZ}$.
Construct an angle congruent to $\angle X$ at R.
Construct $\overline{RS} \cong \overline{XY}$.
Draw $\overline{ST}$.

$\triangle RST \cong \triangle XYZ$

**Example 2** Two angles and the sides between them (ASA).

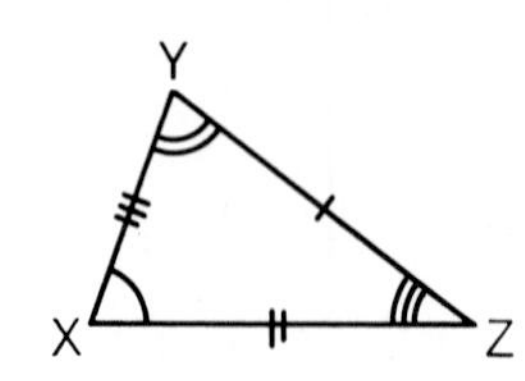

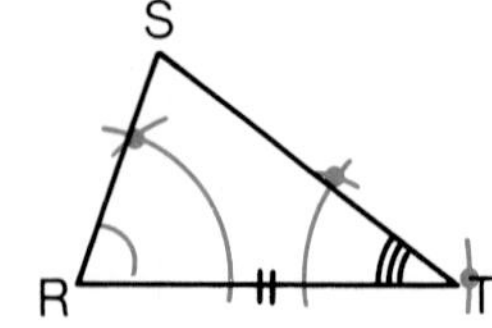


Construct $\overline{RT} \cong \overline{XZ}$.
Construct an angle congruent to $\angle X$ at R.
Construct an angle congruent to $\angle Z$ at T.

$\triangle RST \cong \triangle XYZ$

**Example 3** Three sides (SSS).

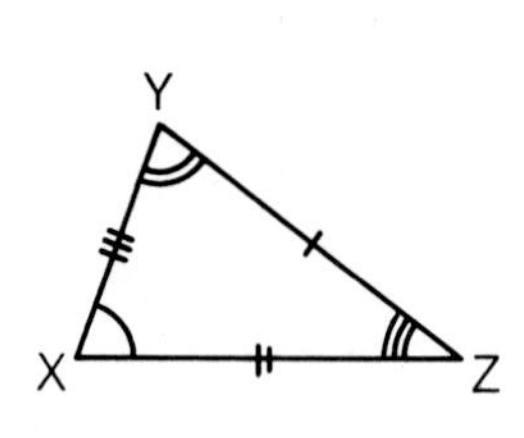

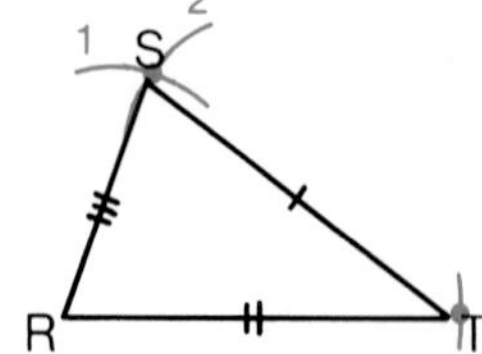


Construct $\overline{RT} \cong \overline{XZ}$.
With compass set to the length of $\overline{XY}$, draw arc 1 from R.
With compass set to the length of $\overline{ZY}$, draw arc 2 from T.
Draw $\overline{RS}$ and $\overline{TS}$.
$\overline{RS} \cong \overline{XY}$ and $\overline{TS} \cong \overline{ZY}$.

$\triangle RST \cong \triangle XYZ$

## CLASS EXERCISES

*Each triangle in Exercises **1** and **2** is congruent to △GHI. Name the 6 pairs of congruent corresponding parts for these congruent triangles. Write a congruence statement for the triangles.*

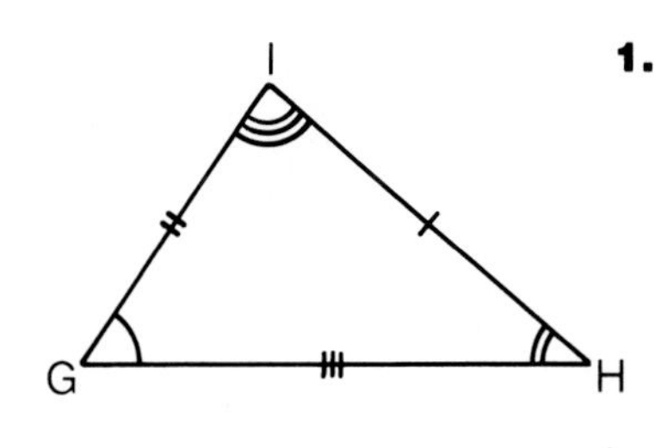


**1.**

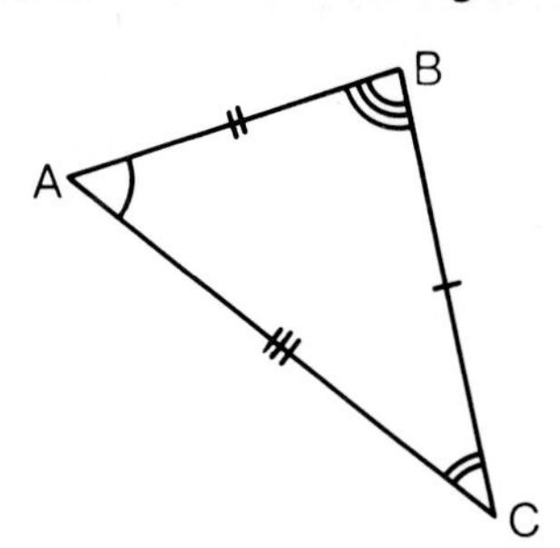


**2.**

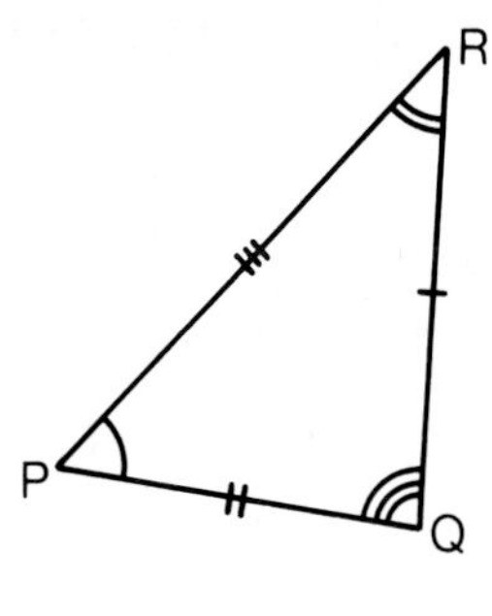


## EXERCISES

**1.** Which triangles are congruent to △XYZ? Write SAS, ASA, or SSS to show how you decided that the triangles are congruent.

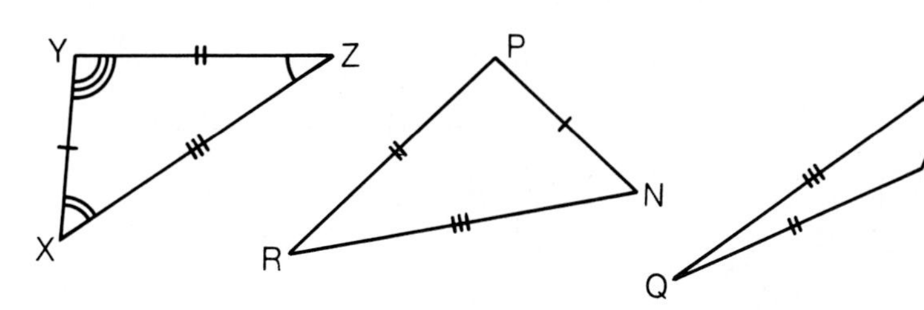


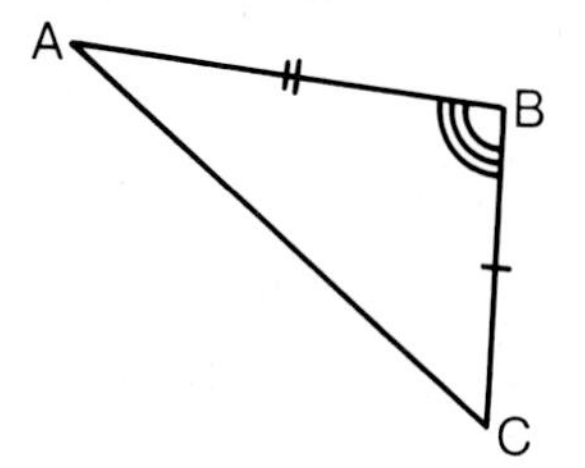


**2.** Which triangles are congruent to △MNO? Write SAS, ASA, or SSS to show how you decided that the triangles are congruent.

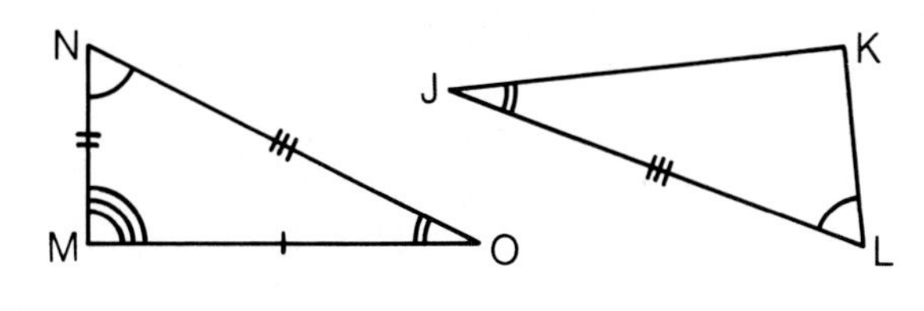


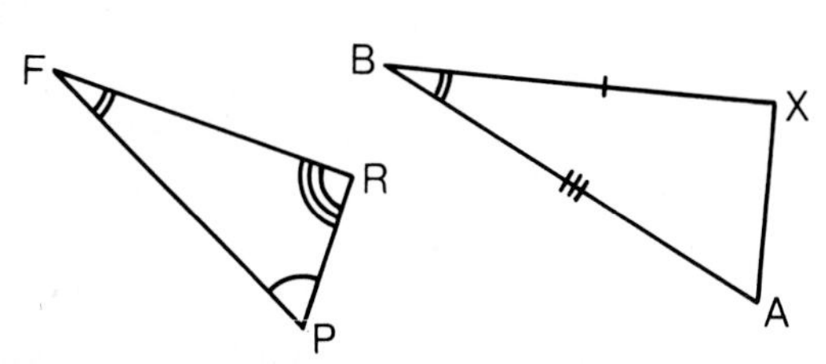


**3.** Draw △DEF. Construct △JKL with ∠J ≅ ∠D, ∠K ≅ ∠E, and ∠L ≅ ∠F. Will △JKL necessarily be congruent to △DEF?

**4.** Draw a parallelogram and draw one diagonal. Why are the two triangles formed by the diagonal congruent?

**★5.** Draw △DEF with ∠D ≅ ∠E. Construct $\overline{FG}$ so that ∠DFG ≅ ∠EFG. Why is △DFG ≅ △EFG?

**★6.** When are two similar triangles congruent triangles?

Homework page 503

# Problem Solving

READ **PLAN** DO • ANSWER • CHECK

## 9-10 Using Perimeter Formulas

**A.** The **perimeter** of a polygon is the distance around the polygon. Add the lengths of the sides to find the perimeter.

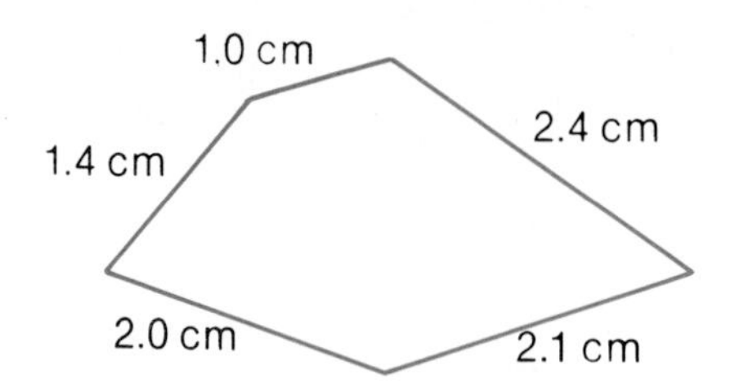


Perimeter = 2.0 + 2.1 + 2.4 + 1.0 + 1.4

**P** = 8.9 cm

**B.** You can use formulas to find the perimeters of some polygons.

**Parallelogram**

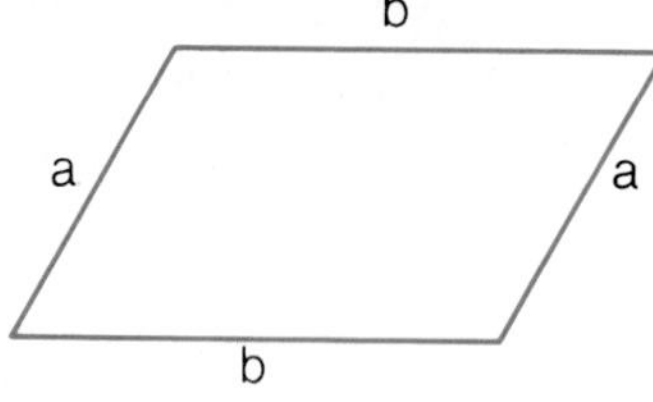


$$\begin{aligned} P &= a + b + a + b \\ &= (a + a) + (b + b) \\ &= 2a + 2b \end{aligned}$$

**Rectangle**

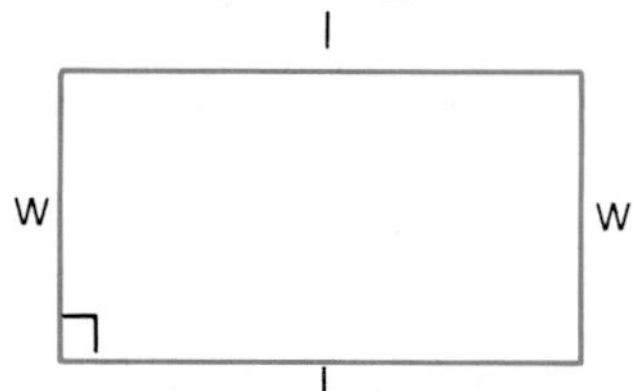


$$\begin{aligned} P &= l + w + l + w \\ &= (l + l) + (w + w) \\ &= 2l + 2w \end{aligned}$$

**Regular Polygons**

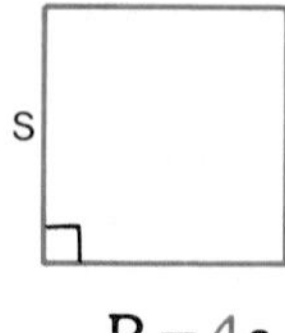


$P = 4s$

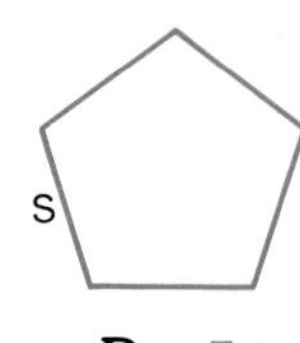


$P = 5s$

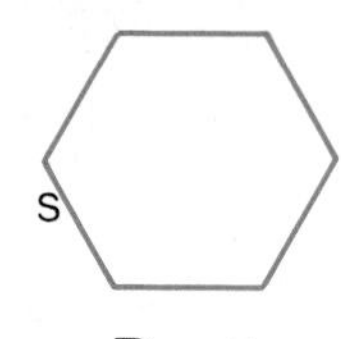


$P = 6s$

For regular polygons with n sides use $P = ns$.

**C.** Find the perimeter of a garden shaped like a parallelogram with sides of lengths 7.9 m and 14.3 m.

$$\begin{aligned} P &= 2a + 2b \\ &= (2 \times 7.9) + (2 \times 14.3) \\ &= 15.8 + 28.6 \\ &= 44.4 \end{aligned}$$

The perimeter is 44.4 m.

**D.** Find the length of each side of a design shaped like a regular octagon with perimeter 20.8 cm.

$$\begin{aligned} P &= 8s \\ 20.8 &= 8s \\ 20.8 \div 8 &= s \\ 2.6 &= s \end{aligned}$$

8 sides

The length of each side is 2.6 cm.

## CLASS EXERCISES

*Find the perimeter.*

**1.** 2.4 cm, 1.3 cm, 0.7 cm, 1.6 cm, 2.1 cm, 1.9 cm

**2.** Parallelogram

Side lengths of 6.2 cm and 8.1 cm.

**3.** Regular pentagon

Length of one side: 5.3 m.

**4.** A rectangular lot has perimeter 133 m. Its width is 16.3 m. Find its length.

## PROBLEMS

**1.** A rectangular rug is 4.2 m wide. It is 2.5 m longer than it is wide. Find its perimeter.

**2.** The perimeter of a rectangular tile is 130 cm. Its length is 40 cm. What is the width of the tile?

**3.** A square garden has each side of length 42 m. Fencing comes in 25 m rolls. How many rolls are needed to fence the garden?

**4.** The Pentagon in Washington, D.C., is a regular pentagon with perimeter 1,403.60 m. What length is each side of the Pentagon?

★ **5.** Fencing costs \$0.90/m. Find the cost of building two fences 10 m apart around this field, as shown.

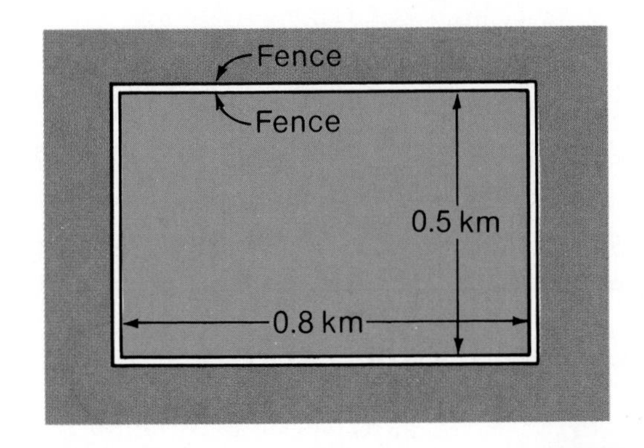


★ **6.** Ribbon costs \$0.15/m. Find the cost of the ribbon on this package. Allow 80 cm for overlap and the bow.

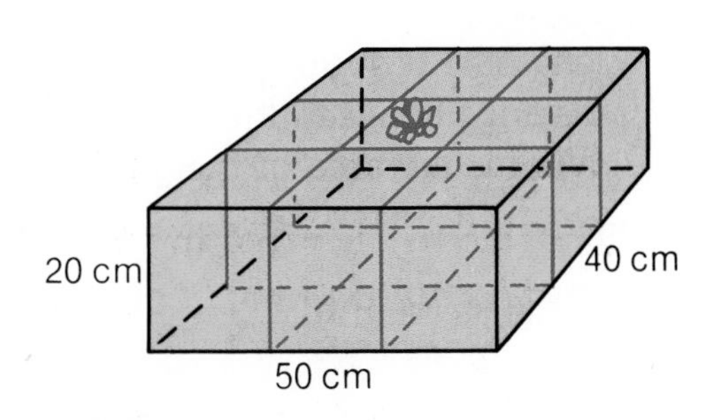


## ON YOUR OWN

### Visual Perception

How many different shaped boxes can you find in the diagram?

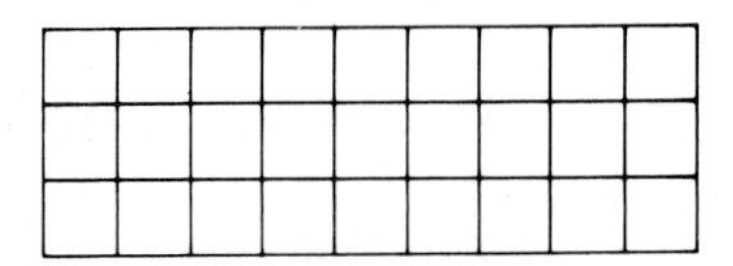

Homework page 503

# Problem Solving READ PLAN DO • ANSWER • CHECK

## 9-11 Using Area Formulas

**A.** The **area** of a plane figure is the number of unit squares that will fit in its interior. Common metric units of area are the **square centimeter** ($cm^2$), the **square meter** ($m^2$), and the **square kilometer** ($km^2$). You can use formulas to find the area of some polygons.

**Rectangle**

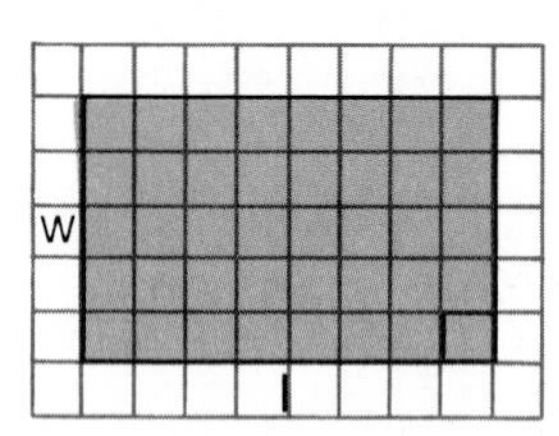


Area = **l**ength × **w**idth

$A = lw$

**Square**

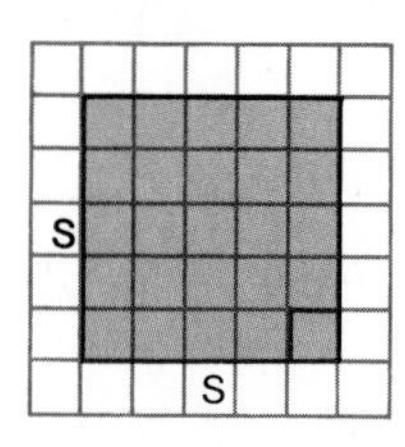


Area = (**s**ide length)$^2$

$A = s^2$

**Parallelogram**

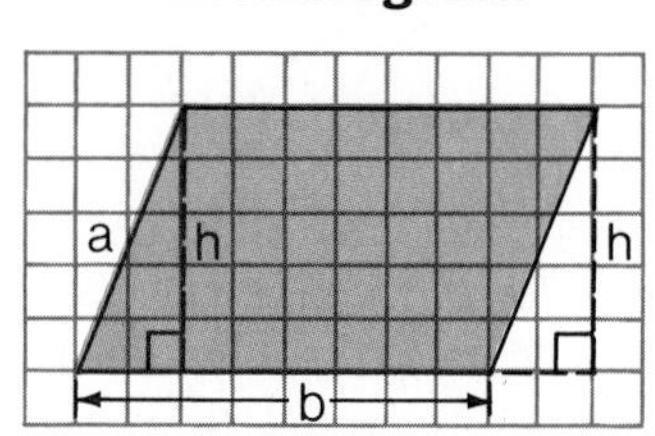


Area = length of **b**ase × **h**eight

$A = bh$

**Triangle**

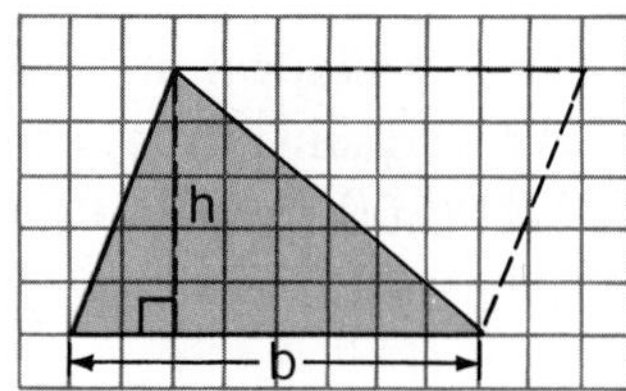


Area $= \frac{1}{2} \times$ area of parallelogram

$= \frac{1}{2} \times$ length of base × height

$A = \frac{1}{2}\, bh$

**Trapezoid**

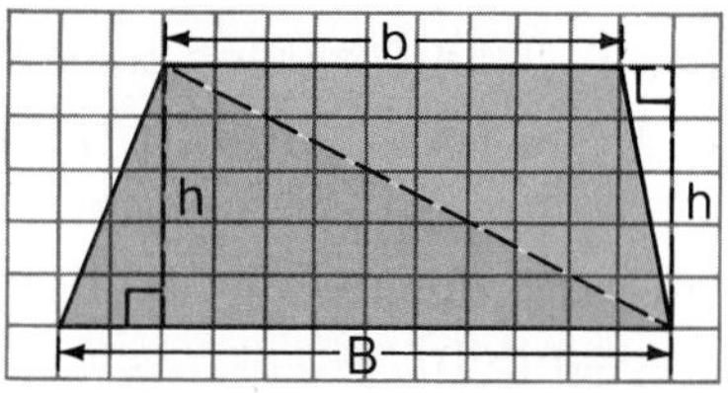

Area = Sum of areas of triangles

$= \frac{1}{2}\, Bh + \frac{1}{2}\, bh$

$A = \frac{1}{2} \cdot (B + b) \cdot h$

**C.** A garden has the shape of a trapezoid with parallel sides of lengths 8.6 m and 6.4 m. The distance between the sides is 7.8 m. What is the area of the garden?

$B = 8.6$ m   $b = 6.4$ m   $h = 7.8$ m

$A = \frac{1}{2} \cdot (B + b) \cdot h$

$= \frac{1}{2} \times (8.6 + 6.4) \times 7.8$

$= 58.5$

The area of the garden is 58.5 $m^2$.

**D.** A design made of 8 congruent triangles has a total area of 150 $cm^2$. The base of each triangle has length 7.5 cm. What is the height of each triangle?

Total area = 8 × area of each $\triangle$

$150 = 8 \times \left(\frac{1}{2} \times 7.5\, h\right)$

$150 = 30\, h$

$5 = h$

The height of each triangle is 5 cm.

## CLASS EXERCISES

*Find the area of each figure.*

**1.** 25 m; 18 m; 16 m; 18 m; 25 m

**2.** 17.1 cm; 25.0 cm; 15.2 cm; 23.1 cm

**3.** Trapezoid

Parallel sides:
6.4 m, 4.6 m
Height: 3.8 m

## PROBLEMS

**1.** The cloth on a roll is 0.8 m wide. Find the length of a piece that must be cut to fill an order for a rectangular piece with area 6 $m^2$.

**2.** Find the cost of a rectangular piece of carpet that is 4.6 m long and 3.5 m wide. The cost of the carpet is $\$12/m^2$.

**3.** Find the perimeter of a square tile with area 400 $cm^2$.

**4.** Find the area of a square tile with perimeter 104 cm.

**5.** This parallelogram-shaped piece of glass is cut to make three pieces as shown. Find the area of each piece.

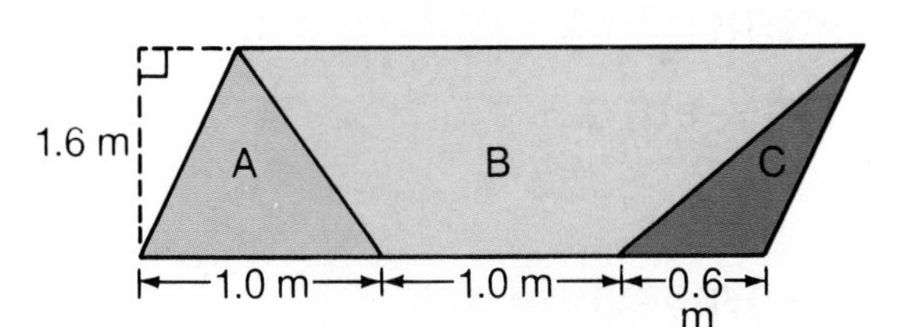


**6.** Ms. Clarke has plowed the shaded portion of the field. What is the area of the part left to be plowed?

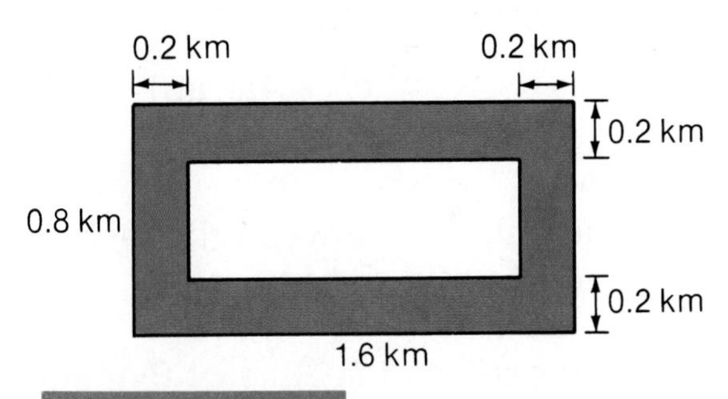


★ **7.** Mr. Lee has mowed the shaded part of this trapezoid-shaped yard. What percent of the entire yard has he mowed?

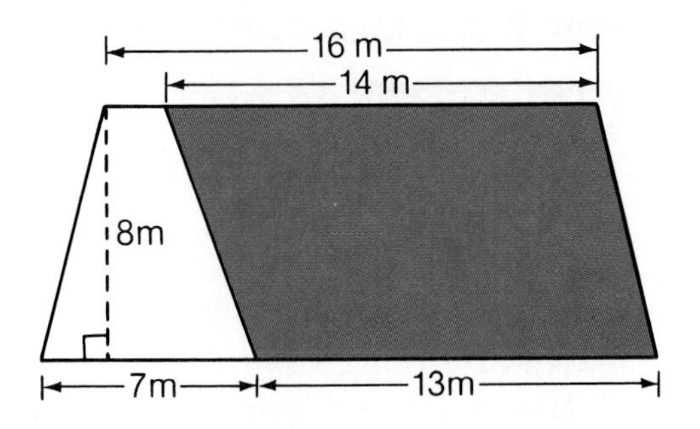


### ON YOUR OWN

**Geometric Perception**

How would you divide the figure below into four congruent parts?

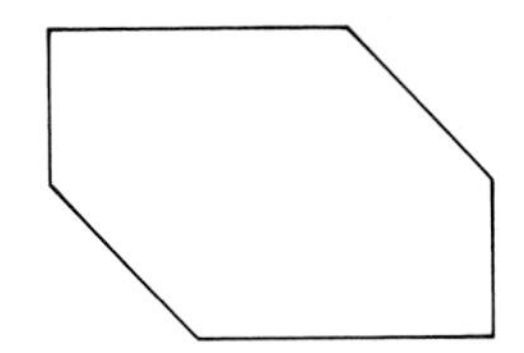

## 9-12 The Rule of Pythagoras

**A.** In a right triangle, the side opposite the right angle is the **hypotenuse.** The sides forming the right angle are the **legs** of the right triangle.

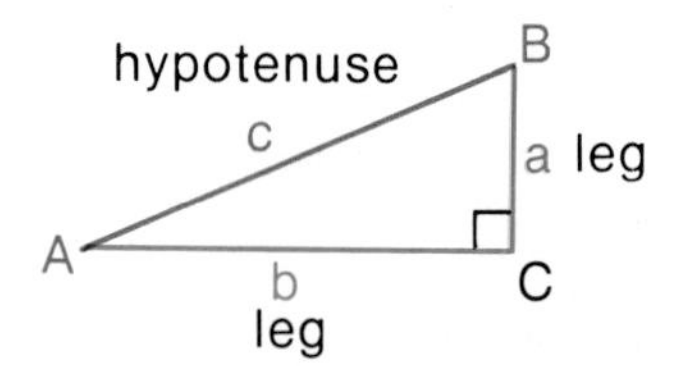


In $\triangle ABC$, the hypotenuse is $\overline{AB}$ with length c units. $\overline{AC}$ is a leg with length b units. $\overline{BC}$ is a leg with length a units.

**B.** Squares KLMN and PQRS are congruent. Each right triangle is congruent to $\triangle ABC$ above.

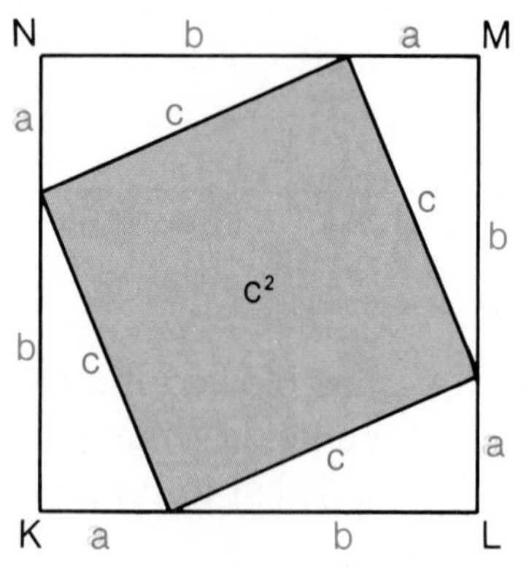


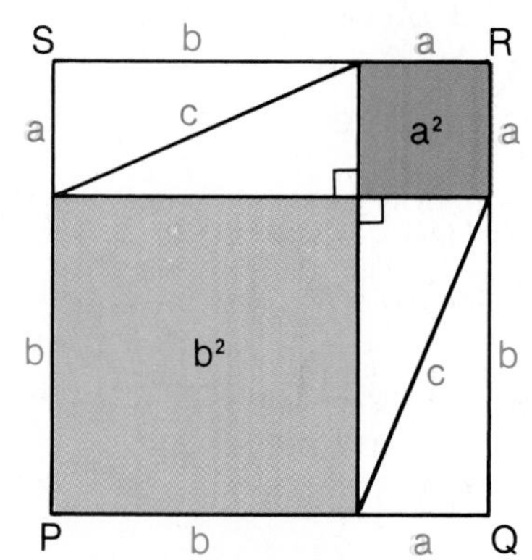


$$\text{Area of KLMN} = \text{Area of PQRS}$$

$$c^2 + 4\left(\frac{1}{2}ab\right) = a^2 + b^2 + 4\left(\frac{1}{2}ab\right)$$

$$c^2 = a^2 + b^2$$

This relation between the lengths of the hypotenuse and the legs of a right triangle is called the **Rule of Pythagoras.**

**C.** You can use the Rule of Pythagoras to find the length of the third side of a right triangle when you know the lengths of the other two sides.

**Example 1**

c = ?  
a = 15 cm  
b = 20 cm

$c^2 = a^2 + b^2$  
$c^2 = 15^2 + 20^2$  
$c^2 = 225 + 400$  
$c^2 = 625$  
$c = \sqrt{625} = 25$ cm

**Example 2**

a = 12 cm  
b = ?  
c = 13 cm

$c^2 = a^2 + b^2$  
$13^2 = 12^2 + b^2$  
$169 = 144 + b^2$  
$25 = b^2$  
$b = \sqrt{25} = 5$ cm

## CLASS EXERCISES

*Find the length of the third side of each right triangle. Use the table on page 218, if necessary.*

**1.**

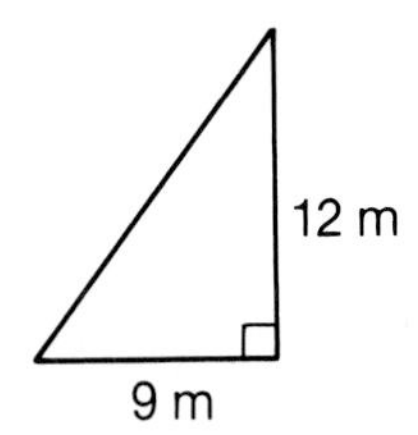


**2.**

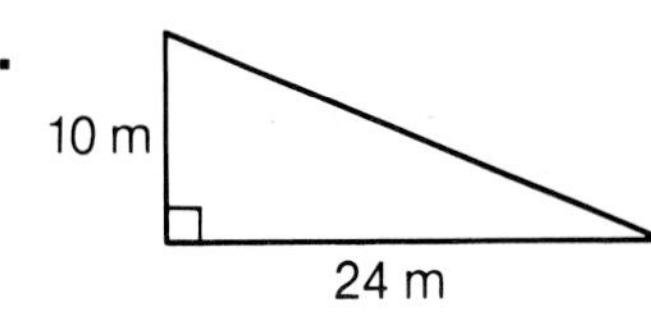


**3.**

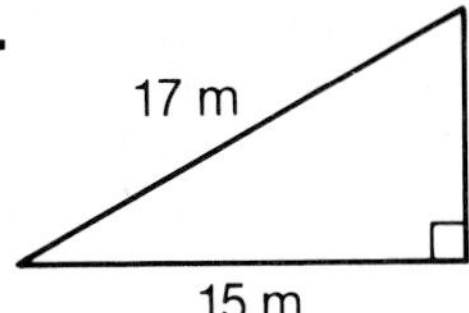


**4.** Find h. Then find the area of parallelogram XYZW.

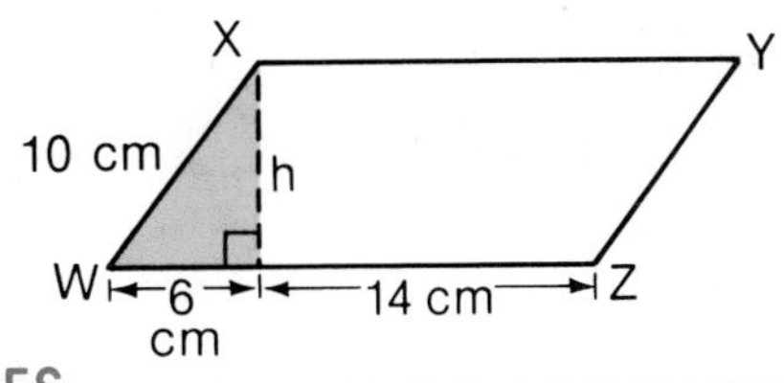


## EXERCISES

*Use the table on page 218, if necessary.*

| **Leg** | 3 cm | 2 m | 16 km | **4.** | 2 m | 30 cm | 5 m |
|---|---|---|---|---|---|---|---|
| **Leg** | 4 cm | 3 m | **3.** | 24 cm | 4 m | **6.** | 10 m |
| **Hypotenuse** | **1.** | **2.** | 20 km | 25 cm | **5.** | 50 cm | **7.** |

**8.** Find the total length of the sides and the two diagonals of a square with one side of length 2 cm.

**9.** Find the total length of the sides and the two diagonals of a rectangle with length 4.5 m and the length of one diagonal 7.5 m.

**10.** Find the perimeter of an isosceles right triangle with congruent sides of lengths 2 m.

## PROBLEMS

**11.** The bottom of a 5-m ladder leaning against a house is 2 m from the house. How far up is the top?

**12.** The diagonal of a rectangular gate is 2 m long. The length of the gate is 1 m. What is its height?

**★13.** The area of this trapezoid-shaped field is 276 m². Find its perimeter.

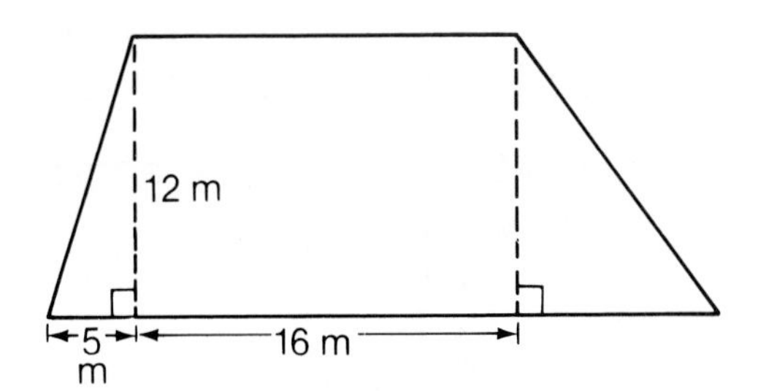


1. 5 cm

Homework page 504

## 9-13 Circles

**A.** The **circumference** of a circle is another name for its perimeter.

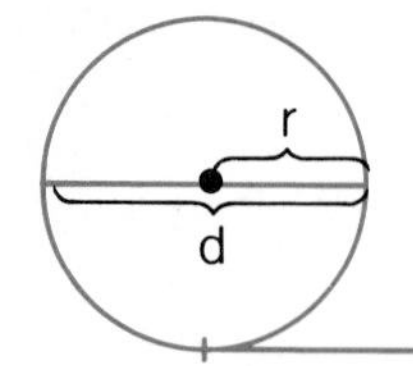


Circumference C

$C = \pi \times$ length of a diameter

$C = \pi d$

$C \doteq 3.14d$

> $\pi$ names an irrational number.
> $\pi \doteq 3.14$

For radius length r, $d = 2r$ and $C = \pi \cdot (2r) = 2\pi r$

**B.** For any circle:

Area $= \pi \times (\text{length of a radius})^2$

$A = \pi r^2$

$A \doteq 3.14r^2$

**C.** Find the circumference and the area of a circular flower bed with diameter of length 6 m.

$C = \pi d \doteq 3.14d$

$\doteq 3.14 \times 6 \doteq 18.84$

The circumference is 18.84 m.

$A = \pi r^2 \doteq 3.14r^2$

$\doteq 3.14 \times (3)^2 \doteq 28.26$

The area is 28.26 $m^2$.

**D.** A central angle determines an **arc** and a **sector** of a circle.

Arc
Sector
Central angle
$n°$
P

For a central angle with measure $n°$:

The arc is $\frac{n}{360}$ of the entire circle.

Arc length $= \frac{n}{360} \times C$

The sector is $\frac{n}{360}$ of the interior of the circle.

Sector area $= \frac{n}{360} \times A$

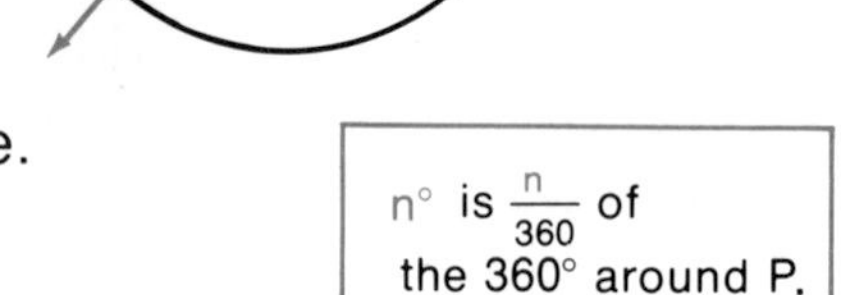

> $n°$ is $\frac{n}{360}$ of the $360°$ around P.

**E.** For the flower bed in **C,** find the arc length and sector area determined by a $90°$ central angle.

Arc length $\doteq \frac{90}{360} \times 18.84$

$\doteq 4.71$ m

Sector area $\doteq \frac{90}{360} \times 28.26$

$\doteq 7.065\ m^2$

## CLASS EXERCISES

*Find the circumference and area of each circle. Use 3.14 for $\pi$.*

**1.**

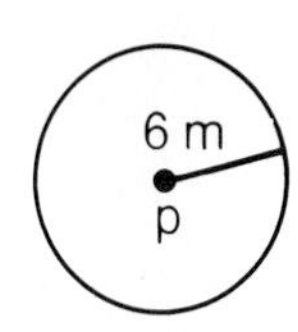


**2.**

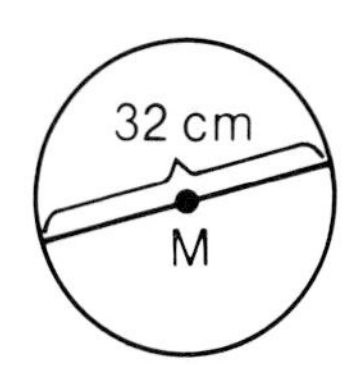


**3.** r = 3 cm

**4.** d = 12 m

**5.** Find the arc length and the sector area determined by a central angle of 36° in the circle in Exercise **1.**

## EXERCISES

*Find the circumference and area of each circle. Use 3.14 for $\pi$.*

**1.**

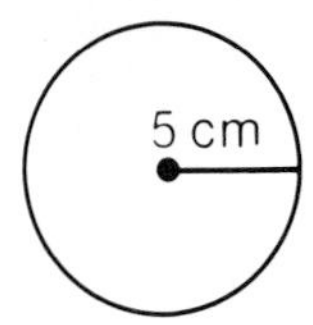


**2.**

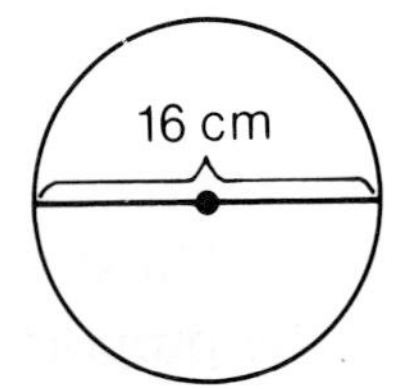


**3.**

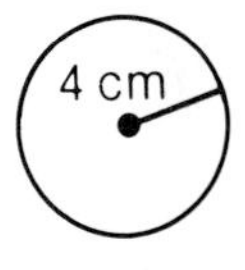


*Find the arc length and the area of the shaded portion determined by each central angle. Use 3.14 for $\pi$. Round your answers to the nearest hundredth.*

**4.**

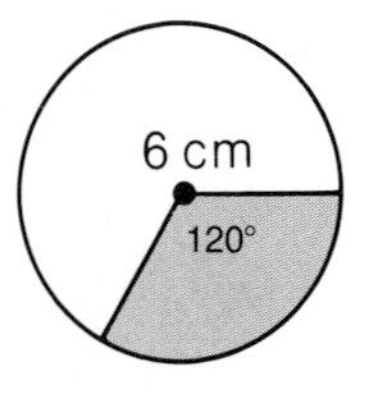


**5.**

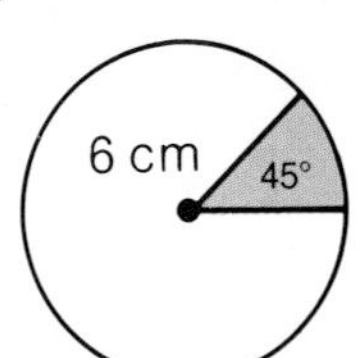


**★6.**

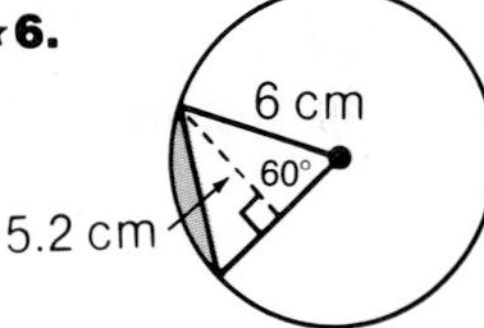


## PROBLEMS

*Solve. Use 3.14 for $\pi$. Round answers to the nearest hundredth.*

**7.** A circular pond has a radius of length 2.4 m. Find the area of the surface of the water. Find the circumference of the pond.

**★8.** The arc length of a semi-circular arch is 40.82 m. What is the diameter of the arch? What is the area of the semi-circle?

### Geometric Perception

Copy the circle below with points A, B, C, D, E. Draw all chords joining these points. How many regions are formed?

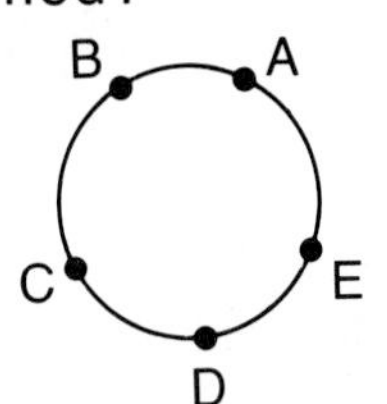


**1.** C = 31.4 cm; A = 78.5 cm²

Homework page 505

## 9-14 Circle Graphs

**A.** A **circle graph** can be used to show the parts into which a total amount is divided. This circle graph shows Ms. Varley's **budget.** This is her plan for allocating the $1,300 she earns each month.



**B.** This table shows the number of students in each class at State University.

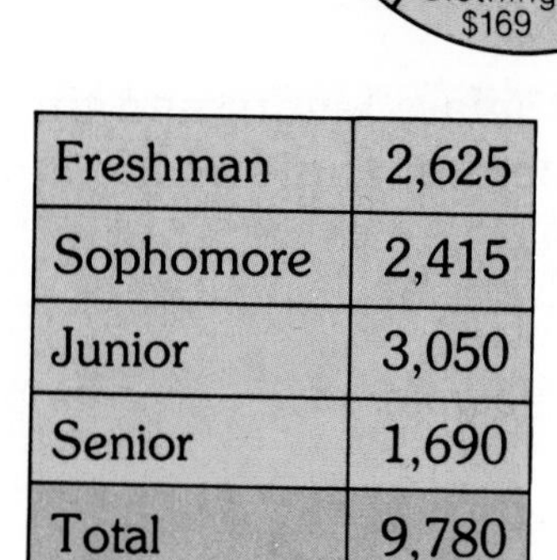

| Freshman | 2,625 |
|---|---|
| Sophomore | 2,415 |
| Junior | 3,050 |
| Senior | 1,690 |
| Total | 9,780 |

To make a circle graph to show the part of the total in each class, use these steps:

**Step 1.** Find the part of the circle that shows each class. For "Freshman" write the proportion:

$$\frac{\text{Number in freshman class}}{\text{Total}} = \frac{\text{Part of circle for "Freshman"}}{\text{Entire circle}}$$

To find the part of the circle find the measure of the central angle for the part. Round the measure to the nearest degree.

$$\frac{2{,}625}{9{,}780} = \frac{x^\circ}{360^\circ}$$

$$2{,}625 \cdot 360^\circ = 9{,}780 \cdot x^\circ$$

$$97^\circ \doteq x^\circ$$

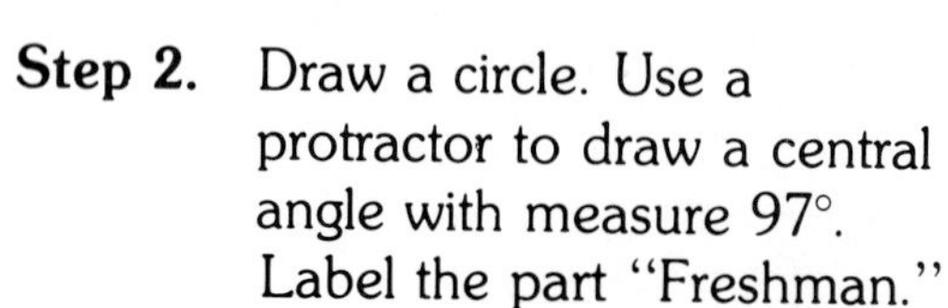

**Step 2.** Draw a circle. Use a protractor to draw a central angle with measure 97°. Label the part "Freshman."

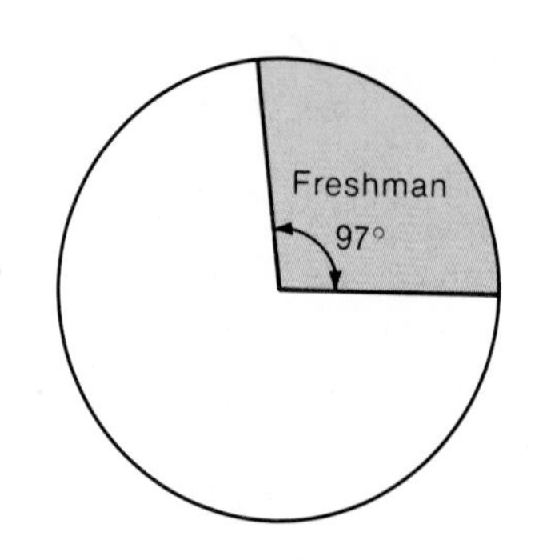



Draw parts for other classes the same way.

**C.** Parts are sometimes given as percents. Use the basic percent formula to find parts for a circle graph.

| Income Source | Part of Mr. Tim's Income |
|---|---|
| Salary | 60% |
| Commission | 25% |
| Investments | 15% |

For "Salary," $r = 60\%$, $b = 360^\circ$

$$r \cdot b = p$$

$$.60 \cdot 360^\circ = p$$

$$216^\circ = p$$

Draw a 216° central angle for "Salary."

## CLASS EXERCISES

1. Complete the circle graph for the part of the students in each class at State University.

2. Draw a circle graph to show the parts of Mr. Tim's income that came from each of the three sources.

## PROBLEMS

1. Ms. Fifer's monthly budget is shown at the right. How much does she earn each month? Draw a circle graph. Round angle measures to the nearest degree.

| | |
|---|---|
| Rent | $360 |
| Food | $405 |
| Clothing | $150 |
| Transportation | $240 |
| Entertainment | $75 |
| Savings | $150 |
| Other | $120 |

2. This table shows the percents of the total amount of corn sold in the United States that are sold in the four major markets and in other markets. Draw a circle graph. Round angle measures to the nearest degree.

| Market | Percent of total |
|---|---|
| Chicago | 41% |
| Omaha | 19% |
| Milwaukee | 17% |
| Kansas City | 13% |
| Other | 10% |

3. This table shows the reactions of 240 people to the statement, "I expect to be happier next year," included in an opinion poll. Draw a circle graph showing what part gave each reaction. Round angle measures to the nearest degree.

| | |
|---|---|
| Strongly Agree | 14 |
| Agree | 60 |
| Disagree | 40 |
| Strongly Disagree | 52 |
| Don't Know | 74 |

4. A state university gets $\frac{1}{5}$ of its total income from students' fees, $\frac{2}{3}$ from the state government, $\frac{1}{10}$ from the federal government, and $\frac{1}{30}$ from gifts. Draw a circle graph.

## ON YOUR OWN

Make a circle graph to show how you spend the 24 hours of your day. Round angle measures to the nearest degree, if necessary.

Homework page 505

## 9-15 Prisms and Pyramids

The **surface area** of a three-dimensional figure is the total area of its faces.

The **volume** of a three-dimensional figure is the number of unit cubes that will fill its interior. Commonly used metric units of volume are the **cubic centimeter** ($cm^3$) and the **cubic meter** ($m^3$).

**A.** **Prisms** and **pyramids** are types of three-dimensional figures.

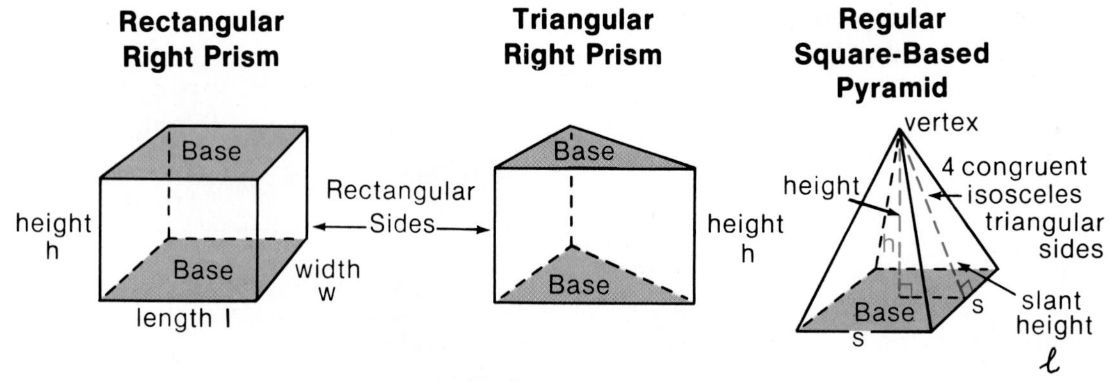


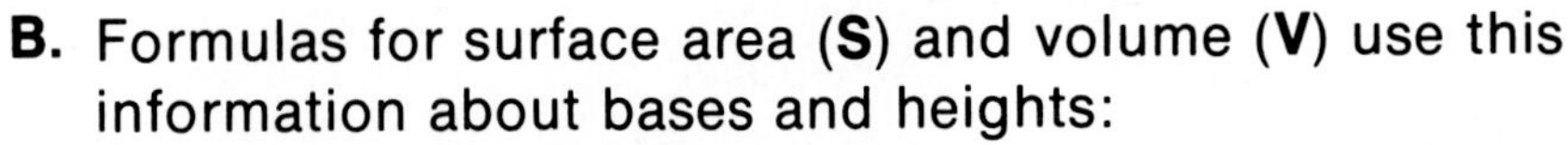

**B.** Formulas for surface area (**S**) and volume (**V**) use this information about bases and heights:

B = Area of base
P = Perimeter of base

h = Height
$\ell$ = Slant height

For prisms:

$S = 2B + Ph$
$V = Bh$

For pyramids:

$S = B + \frac{1}{2}P\ell$
$V = \frac{1}{3}Bh$

**C.** 103 $m^2$ of sheet metal was used to build a rectangular storage bin 5 m long and 4 m wide. Find the height of the bin.

$B = lw = 20 \text{ m}^2$
$P = 2l + 2w = 10 + 8 = 18$
$S = 2B + Ph$
$103 = (2 \times 20) + 18h$
$63 = 18h$
$3.5 = h$

The height is 3.5 m.

**D.** Find the volume of a square-based pyramid with base sides of length 16 cm, height 6 cm, and slant height 10 cm.

$V = \frac{1}{3}Bh = \frac{1}{3} \times 16^2 \times 6$
$= \frac{1}{3} \times 256 \times 6$
$= 512$

The volume is 512 $cm^3$.

## CLASS EXERCISES

*Find the surface area and volume.*

**1.** Triangular prism

Base:

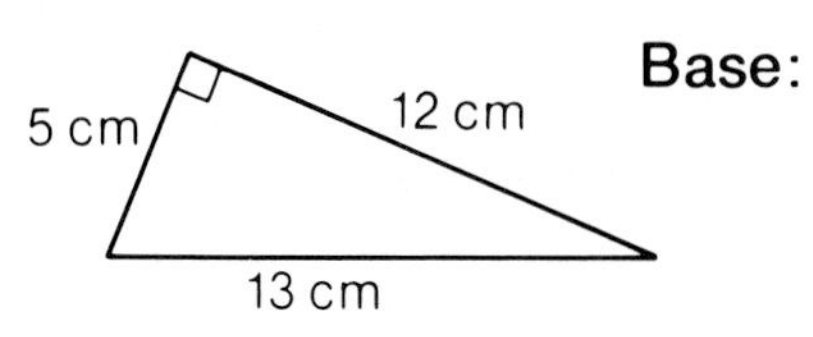


Height: 12 cm

**2.** Pyramid

Base:

24 m

24 m

Height: 16 m; slant height: 20 m

**3.** Cube

Length of each edge: 2 m

## EXERCISES

*Find the surface area and volume.*

**1.**

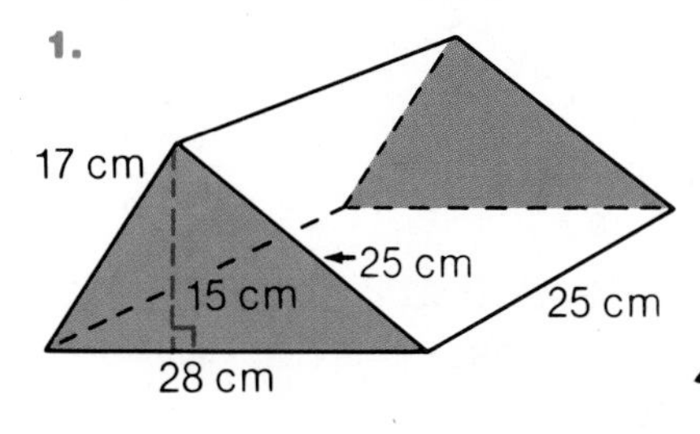


**2.**

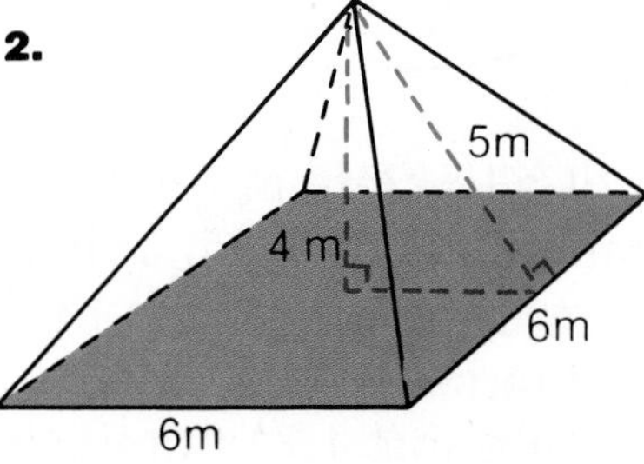


**3.**

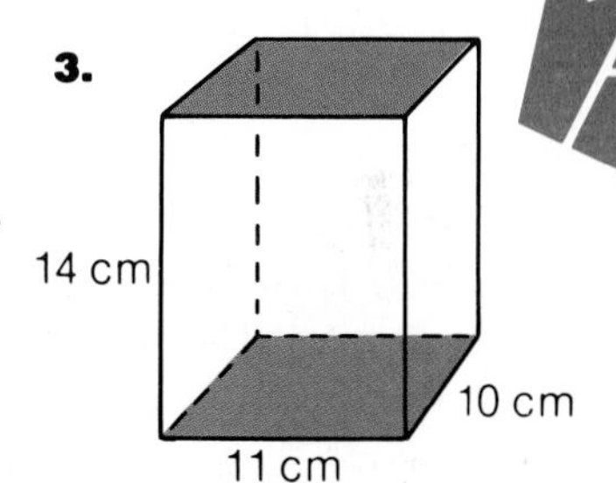


**4.**

3 m

4 m

3 m

**5.**

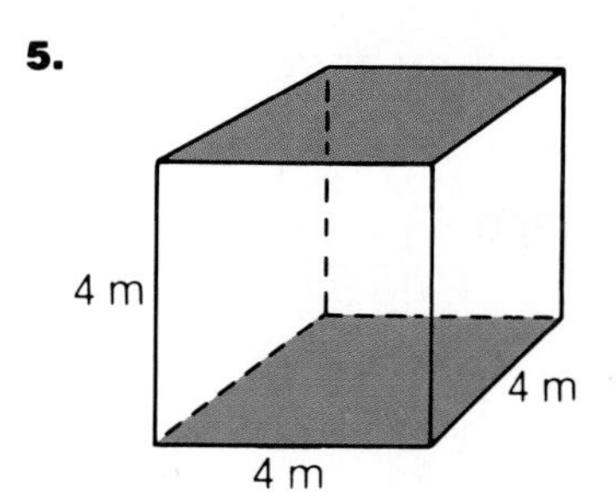


**★6.**

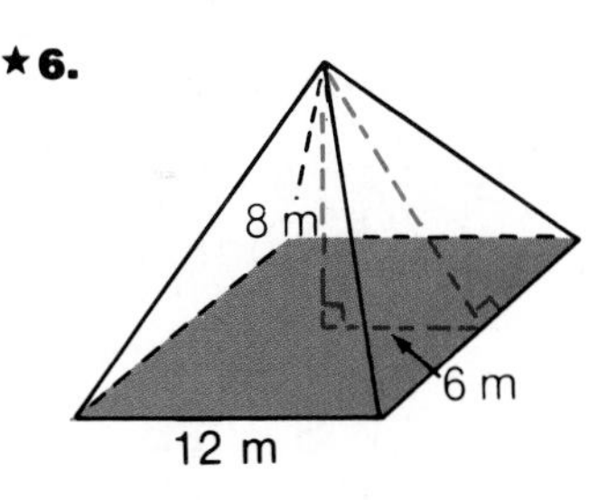


## PROBLEMS

**7.** A box shaped like a rectangular prism has a square base and a height of 30 cm. The box has a volume of 4,320 cm. What is the length of each side of the base?

**★8.** A paper drinking cup has the shape of a regular square-based pyramid. Each side of the top has length 8 cm and the cup is 6 cm deep. How much water will it hold?

## THINK!

### Visual Perception

In how many ways can a 3 × 3 × 3 cube be positioned in a 4 × 4 × 4 cube?

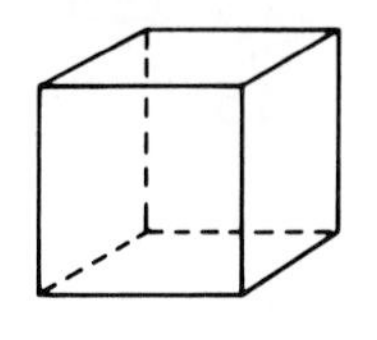

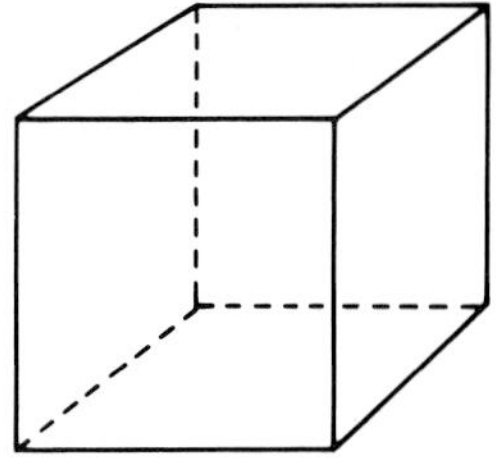

# 9-16 Cylinders, Cones, and Spheres

**A.** **Cylinders, cones,** and **spheres** are other important three-dimensional figures.

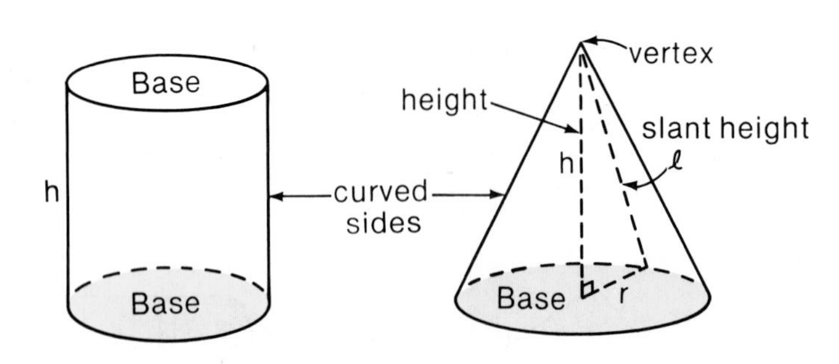


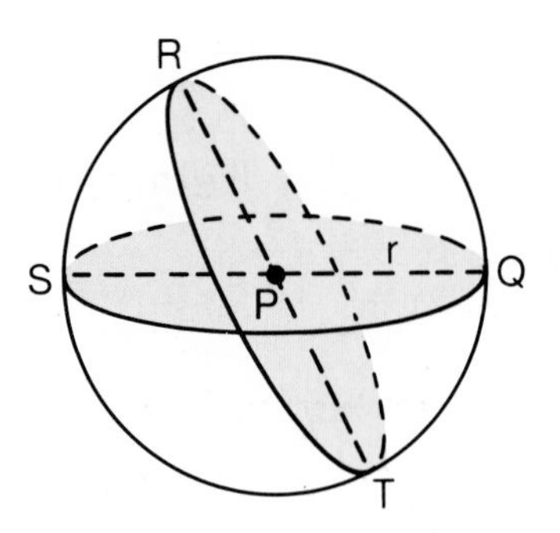


The sphere is the set of all points in three-dimensional space that are the same distance from **center** P. Any circle with P as center and radius length the same as that of the sphere is a **great circle** of the sphere. Each great circle separates the sphere into two **hemispheres.**

**B.** Use this information to find surface area and volume.

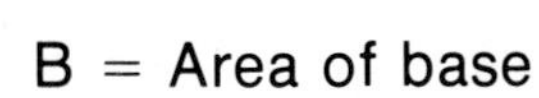

B = Area of base
C = Circumference of base

h = height
$\ell$ = slant height

r = length of radius

| Cylinders | Cones | Sphere |
|---|---|---|
| $S = 2B + Ch$ | $S = B + \frac{1}{2}C\ell$ | $S = 4\pi r^2$ |
| $V = Bh$ | $V = \frac{1}{3}Bh$ | $V = \frac{4}{3}\pi r^3$ |

**C.** The height of a cone is 15 m. The length of a radius of the base is 4 m. Find the volume of the cone.

$V = \frac{1}{3}Bh$

$\doteq \frac{1}{3} \times (3.14 \times 4^2) \times 15$

$\doteq 251.2$

The volume is 251.2 $m^3$

**D.** Find the surface area of a sphere that has a radius of length 9 m.

$S = 4\pi r^2$

$\doteq 4 \times 3.14 \times 9^2$

$\doteq 1{,}017.36$

The surface area is 1,017. 36 $m^2$.

## CLASS EXERCISES

*Find the surface area and volume. Use 3.14 for π. Round your answers to the nearest hundredth.*

1. Sphere. Great circle: diameter = 10 cm
2. Cylinder. Base: r = 4 cm Height: 12 cm
3. Cone. Base: r = 7 m Height: 8 m Slant Height: 15 m
4. The circumference of a great circle of a sphere is 3.14 cm. Find the volume of the sphere.

## EXERCISES

*Find the surface area and volume. Use 3.14 for π. Round your answers to the nearest hundredth.*

**1.**

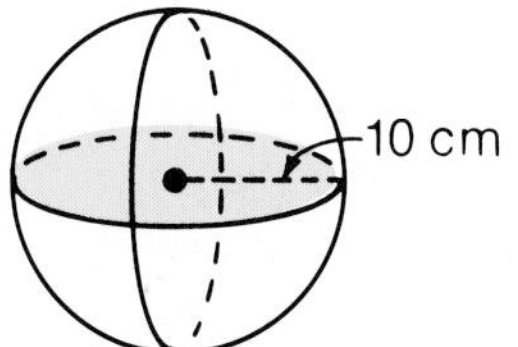


**2.**

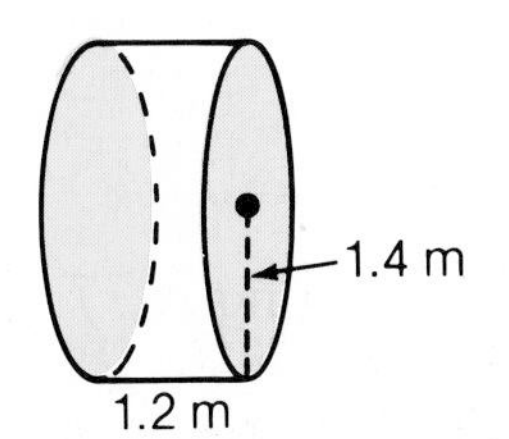


**3.**

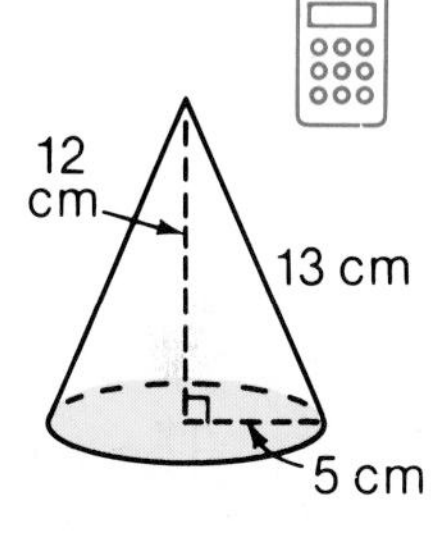


**4.**

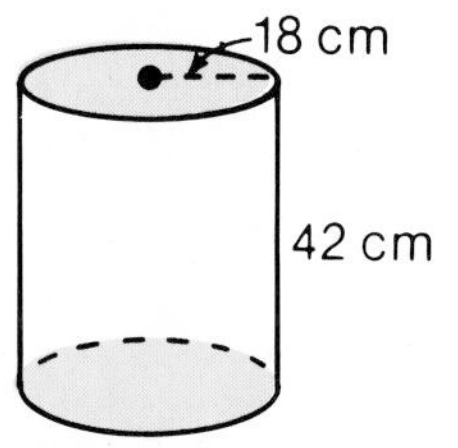


**5.**

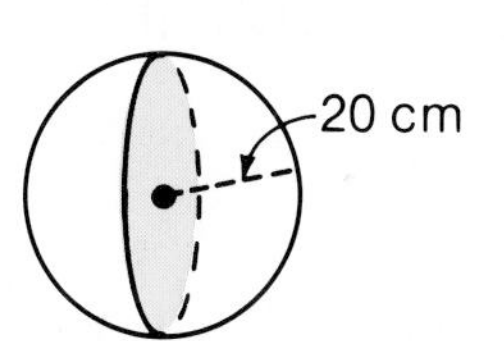


**★ 6.**

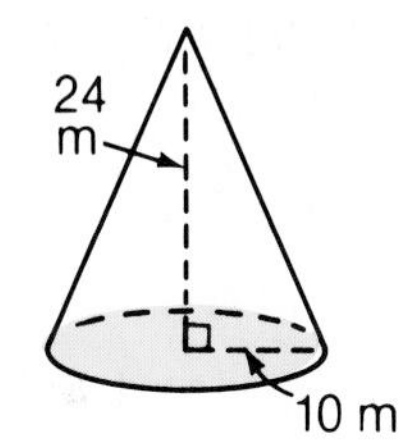


## PROBLEMS

*Solve. Use 3.14 for π. Round to the nearest hundredth.*

7. A cylindrical tank has a radius of length 3 m and a height of 10 m. How much can the tank hold?
8. The length of a radius and height of a conical funnel are 6 cm. Find its volume.
9. ★ The surface area of a sphere is 113.04 $m^2$. Find the length of a radius and the volume.

### Cube Percent

What percent of the cubes are touching the floor?

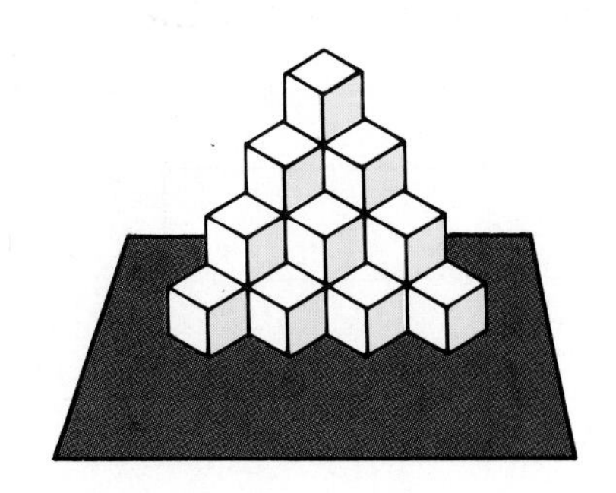

# Problem Solving READ **PLAN** DO • ANSWER • CHECK

## 9-17 Using Formulas (Metric)

**A.** A cylindrical can is packed in a box. The remainder of the box is filled with packing. Find the volume of the packing.

Volume of packing = Volume of box − Volume of can

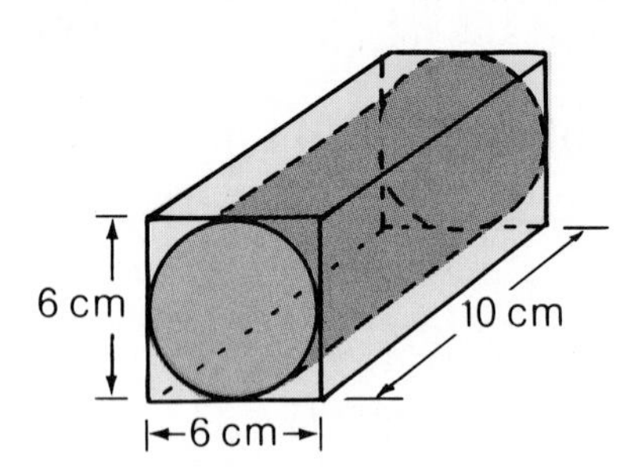


Volume of box: $V = Bh$

$= (6 \times 10) \times 6$

$= 360$

Volume of can: $V = Bh$

$\doteq (3.14 \times 3^2) \times 10$

$\doteq 282.6$

So, volume of packing = 360 − 282.6

= 77.4

The volume of the packing is 77.4 $cm^3$.

**B.** The length of a radius of a baseball is about 3.6 cm. Find its surface area. Round your answer to the nearest 0.1 cm.

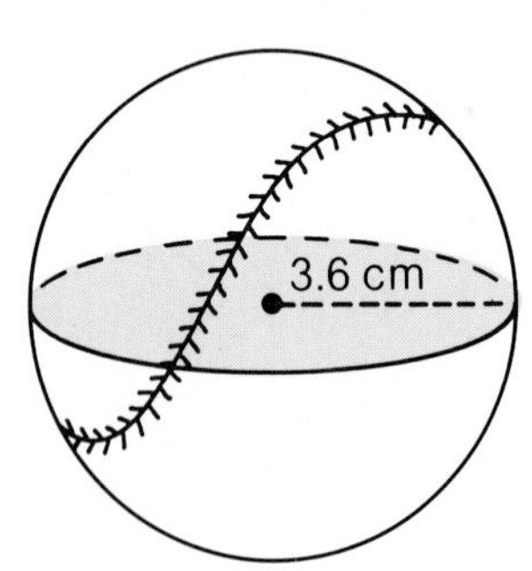


$S = 4\pi r^2$

$\doteq 4 \times 3.14 \times (3.6)^2$

$\doteq 162.8$

The surface area of a baseball is about 162.8 $cm^2$.

### CLASS EXERCISES

*Find the surface area and volume. Use 3.14 for $\pi$, when necessary.*

**1.** Rectangular prism.
Base:

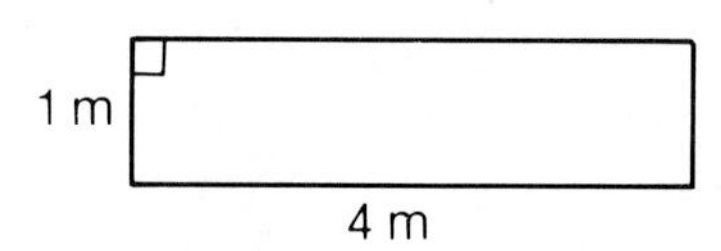


Height: 2 m

**2.** Regular square-based pyramid.
Base:

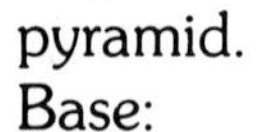

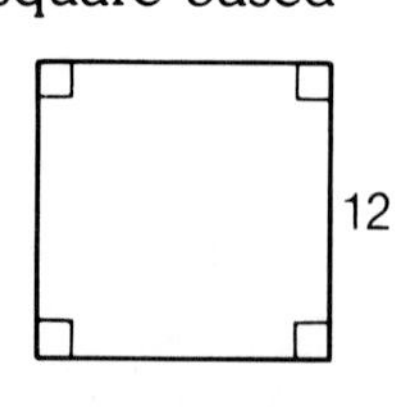


Height: 8 cm
Slant height: 10 cm

**3.** Cone.
Base:

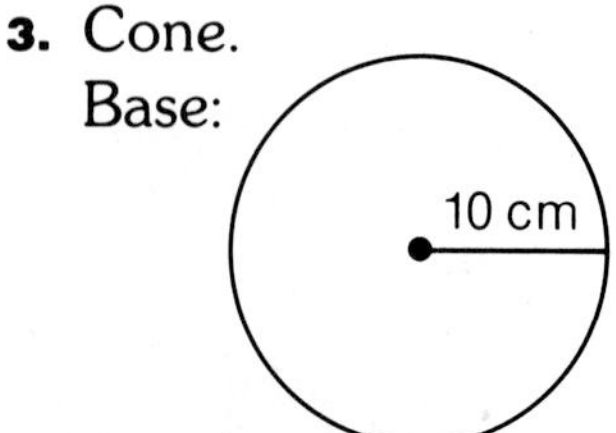


Height: 12 cm
Slant height: 13 cm

1. A box shaped like a rectangular prism has a square base and height of 30 cm. Its volume is 6,750 $cm^3$. What is the length of each side of the base of the box?

2. The length of a radius of the inside of a spherical tank is 6 m. The side of the tank is 0.3 m thick. Find the volume of the metal used to make the tank. Round to the nearest 0.1 $cm^3$.

3. Find the surface area (including the floor) of this building. Find the volume of the building.

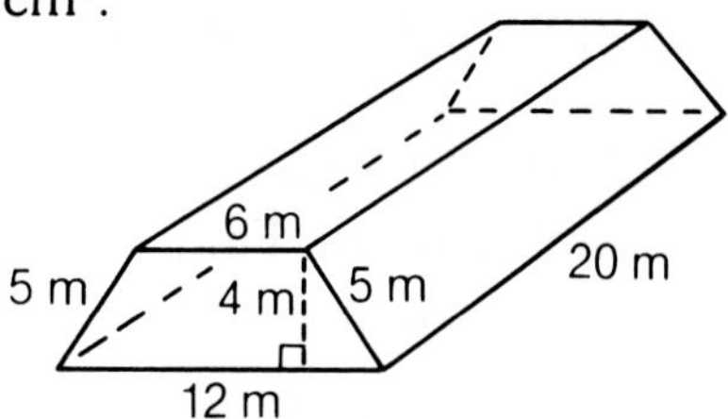


4. The radius of a basketball is 12.1 cm in length. Find its surface area. Round the answer to the nearest 0.1 $cm^2$.

5. Find the surface area of a hemisphere with radius of length 6 m.

★6. Find the volume of each container below. What relation do you see among the three volumes? Replace r = h = 1 cm by r = h = 2 cm for these containers. Does the relation still hold?

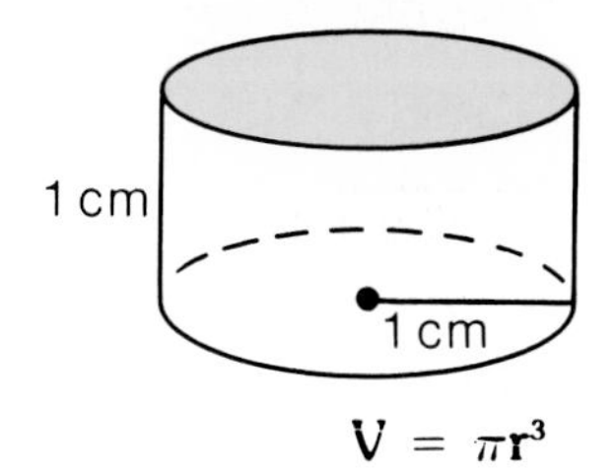


$V = \pi r^3$

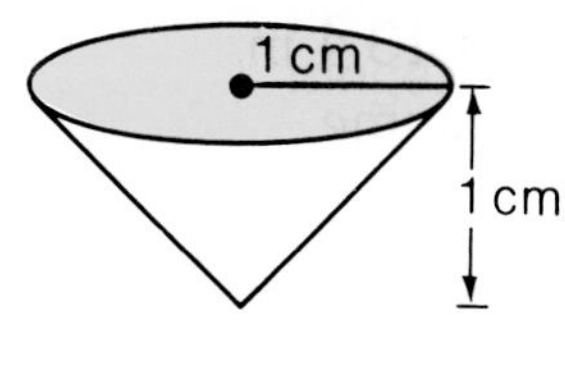


$V = \frac{1}{3}\pi r^3$

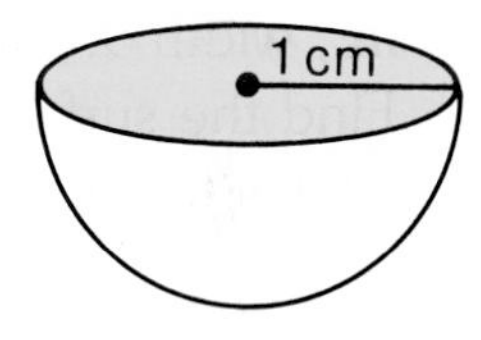


$V = \frac{2}{3}\pi r^3$

## ON YOUR OWN

### Geometric Perception

Which line segments can you draw joining two named points so that the area of one part of the square will be seven times the area of the other part?

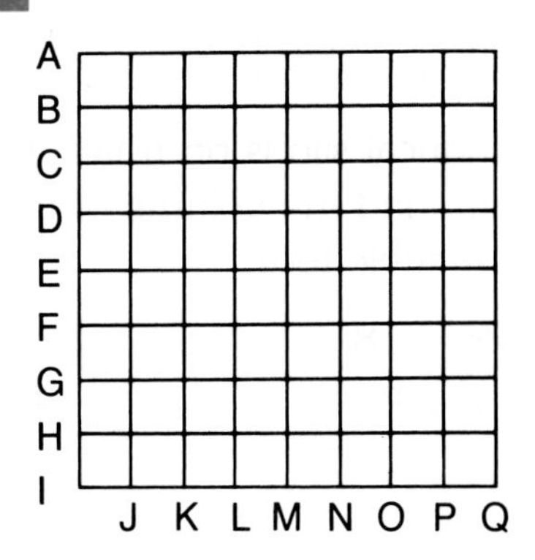

**TECHNOLOGY**

## Geometric Formulas with a Calculator

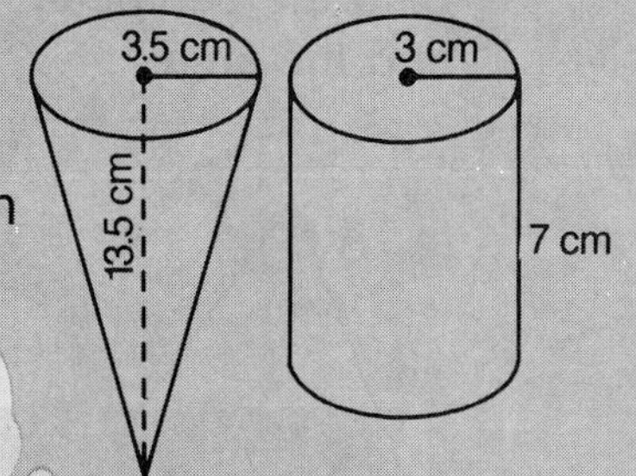


You can often use geometric formulas with a calculator.

**A.** A vendor sells orange juice in either of these cups. If both cost the same, which is the better buy? Use 3.14 for $\pi$.

$V = \frac{1}{3}Bh$
$B = \pi r^2$

$V = Bh$
$B = \pi r^2$

**Conical cup**

[3] [.] [1] [4] [×] [3] [.] [5] [×]
[3] [.] [5] [×] [1] [3] [.] [5] [÷] [3] [=]

173.0925

**Cylindrical cup**

[3] [.] [1] [4] [×] [3] [×] [3] [×] [7] [=]

197.82

The volumes are 173.0925 cm³ and 197.82 cm³. Since 197.82 > 173.0925, the cylindrical cup is the better buy.

**B.** A company manufactures spherical rubber balls. It plans to increase the radius of the Hi Bouncer from 4 cm to 5 cm. By how much will the ball's surface area increase? Find each surface area with a calculator. Use 3.14 for $\pi$.

$S = 4\pi r^2$

**Old surface area**

[4] [×] [3] [.] [1] [4] [×] [4] [×] [4] [=] [M+]

200.96

store in memory

**New surface area**

[4] [×] [3] [.] [1] [4] [×] [5] [×] [5] [=]

314.

Be careful *not* to clear the calculator yet. To find the increase in surface area, press:

[−] [MR] [=] 113.04 The increase in surface area is 113.04 cm².

*Find the surface area and volume of the following figures with your calculator. Use 3.14 for $\pi$.*

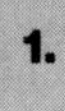

**1.**

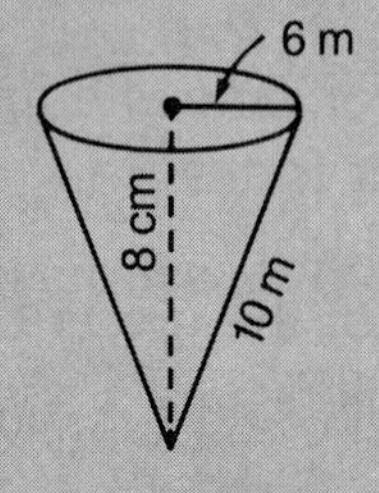


**2.** 7.2 cm

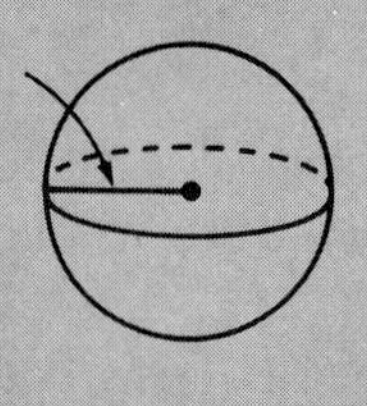

**3.**

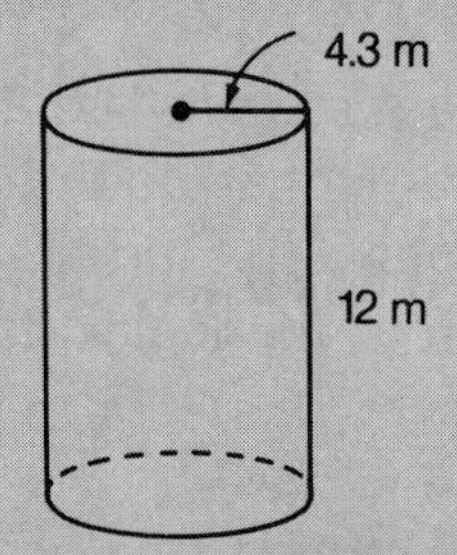


*Solve using your calculator. Use 3.14 for $\pi$.*

**4.** By how much will the volume of the Hi Bouncer in paragraph B increase? Round to the nearest hundredth.

**5.** Which has the greater surface area: a spherical tank with radius 13 m or a cylindrical tank with radius 10 m and height 7 m?

# Problem Solving Strategy

READ • PLAN • DO • ANSWER • CHECK

## Make a Model

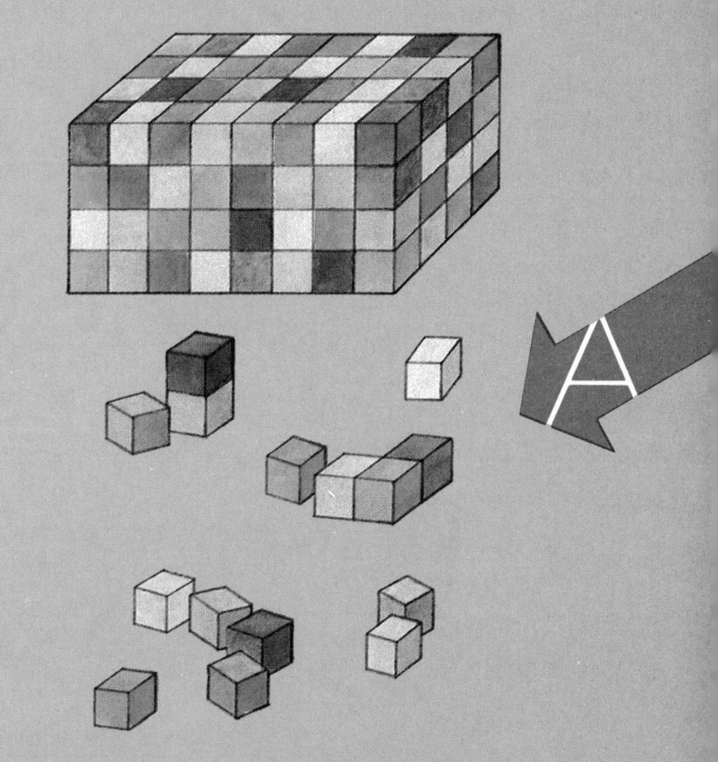


The rectangular solid shown at the right is made up of 1-cm cubes. The solid has dimensions 4 cm by 8 cm by 4 cm.

The surface area of this rectangular solid can be found using the formula:
(B represents the area of the base.
P represents the perimeter of the base.)

$$S = 2B + Ph$$
$$B = l \times w = 4 \times 8 = 32$$
$$P = 2(l + w) = 2(12) = 24$$

so

$$S = 2(32) + 24(4)$$
$$= 64 + 96 = 160$$
$$S = 160 \text{ cm}^2$$

The volume may be found using the formula:

$$V = Bh$$
$$V = 32(4) = 128 \text{ cm}^3$$

Suppose a new solid was constructed with dimensions 8 cm by 16 cm by 8 cm.

1. What is the surface area of the new solid?
2. What is the volume of the new solid?
3. What is the ratio of the length of the sides of the $4 \times 8 \times 4$ solid and the $8 \times 16 \times 8$ solid?
4. What is the ratio of the surface areas of the $4 \times 8 \times 4$ solid and the $8 \times 16 \times 8$ solid?
5. What is the ratio of the volumes of the $4 \times 8 \times 4$ solid and the $8 \times 16 \times 8$ solid?
6. Suppose the dimensions of the original $4 \times 8 \times 4$ solid were tripled. What would the ratios of the surface areas and volumes of the two solids be?

## Trigonometry

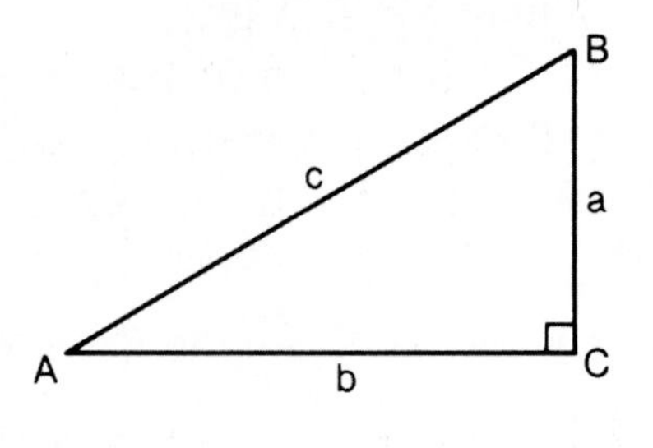


**A.** The lengths of the sides of a right triangle can be used to define **trigonometric ratios.** In right $\triangle$ ABC the lengths of the sides *opposite* angles A, B, and C are a, b, and c, respectively. Then:

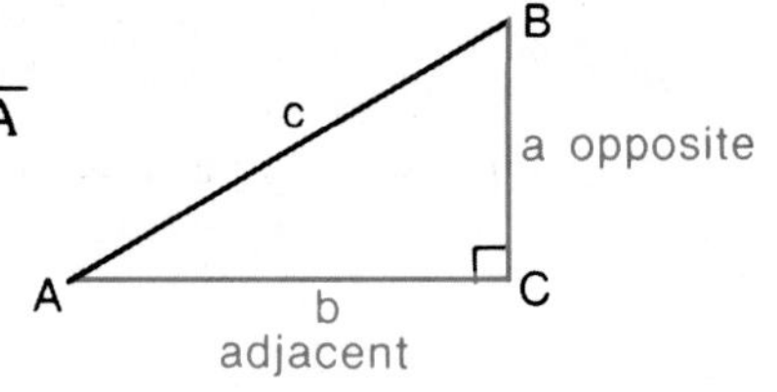


$$\text{Tangent of } \angle A = \frac{\text{length of side opposite } \angle A}{\text{length of side adjacent to } \angle A}$$

or

$$\tan A = \frac{a}{b}$$

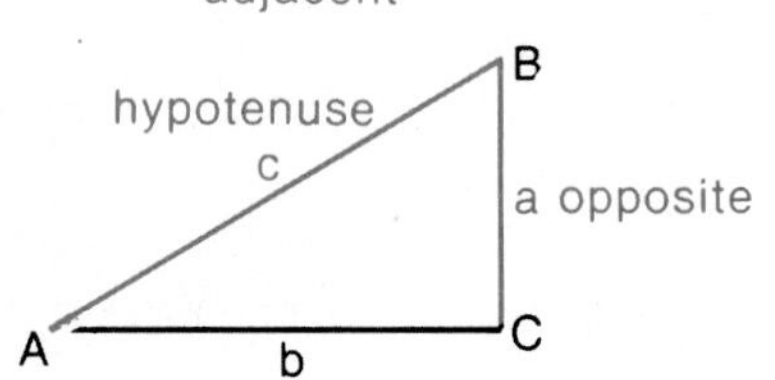


$$\text{Sine of } \angle A = \frac{\text{length of side opposite } \angle A}{\text{length of hypotenuse}}$$

or

$$\sin A = \frac{a}{c}$$

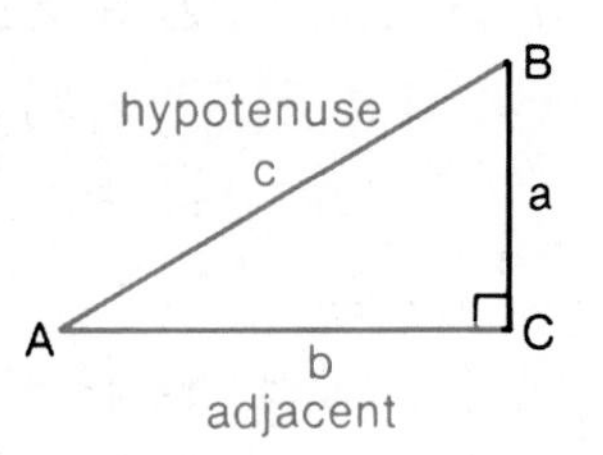


$$\text{Cosine of } \angle A = \frac{\text{length of side adjacent } \angle A}{\text{length of hypotenuse}}$$

or

$$\cos A = \frac{b}{c}$$

Trigonometric ratios can also be written for $\angle$B.

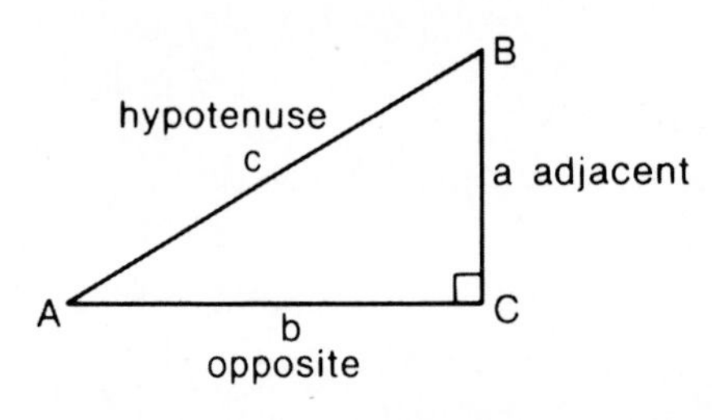


$$\tan B = \frac{\text{length of side opposite } \angle B}{\text{length of side adjacent to } \angle B} = \frac{b}{a}$$

$$\sin B = \frac{\text{length of side opposite } \angle B}{\text{length of hypotenuse}} = \frac{b}{c}$$

$$\cos B = \frac{\text{length of side adjacent to } \angle B}{\text{length of hypotenuse}} = \frac{a}{c}$$

**B.** Fractions or decimals can be written for the values of trigonometric ratios.

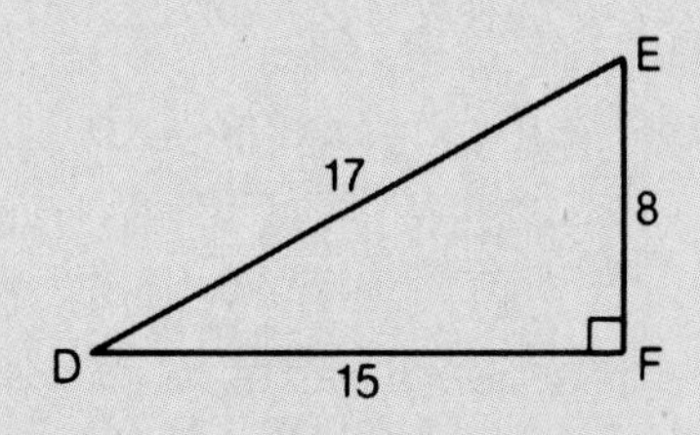


$$\tan D = \frac{\text{opposite}}{\text{adjacent}} = \frac{8}{15} \doteq .533$$

$$\sin D = \frac{\text{opposite}}{\text{hypotenuse}} = \frac{8}{17} \doteq .471$$

$$\cos D = \frac{\text{adjacent}}{\text{hypotenuse}} = \frac{15}{17} \doteq .882$$

*Find a decimal for the value of each trigonometric ratio.*

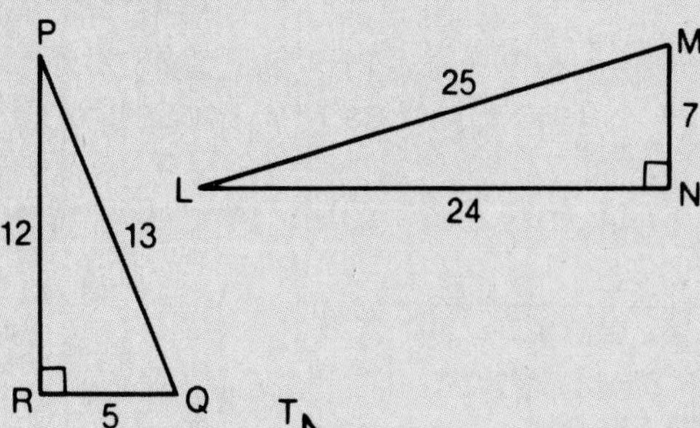


**1.** tan P **2.** sin P **3.** cos P **4.** tan Q

**5.** sin Q **6.** cos Q **7.** tan L **8.** sin L

**9.** cos L **10.** tan M **11.** sin M **12.** cos M

*△TUV and △XYZ are similar triangles. Find the value of each trigonometric ratio.*

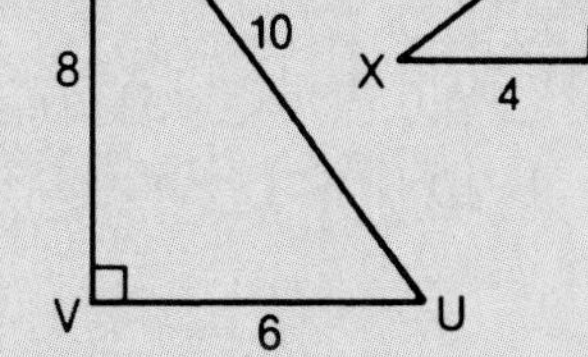


**13.** tan T **14.** tan X **15.** sin U **16.** sin Y **17.** cos T

**18.** cos X **19.** sin T **20.** sin X **21.** tan U **22.** cos Y

**C.** You can use a trigonometric ratio and the length of one side of a right triangle to find the length of another side.

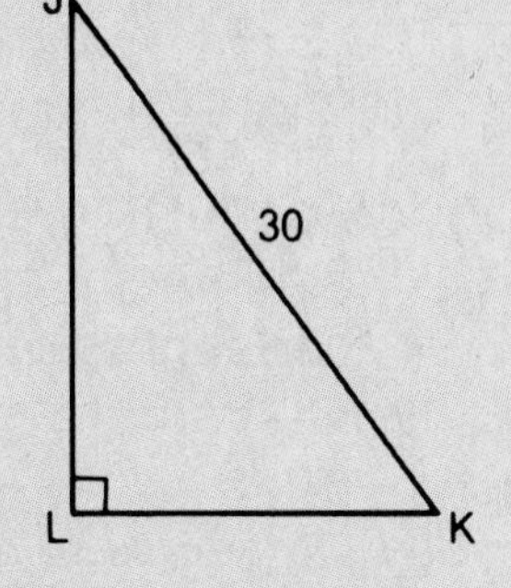


In △JKL, the length of $\overline{JK}$ is 30 and sin J = .6. Find the length of $\overline{KL}$.

$$\sin J = \frac{\text{length of } \overline{KL}}{30} = .6$$

So, length of $\overline{KL} = 30(.6) = 18$

**23.** In △JKL, sin K = .8. Find the length of $\overline{JL}$.

## ON YOUR OWN

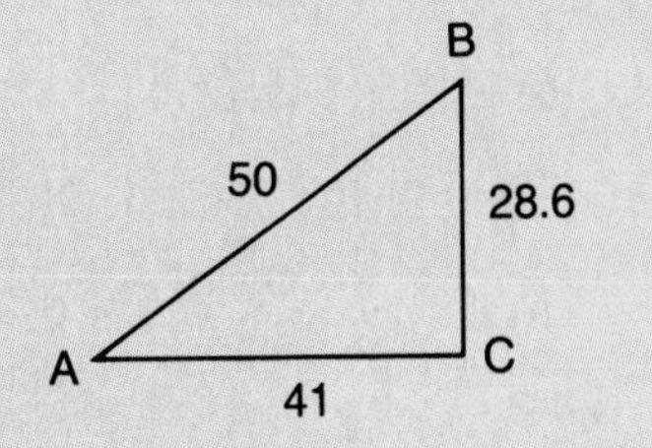


Make up three trigonometry problems about triangle ABC. Ask a classmate to solve the problems. Check the answers.

# Unit Review

*Use the picture. (pages 308–313, 316–317)*

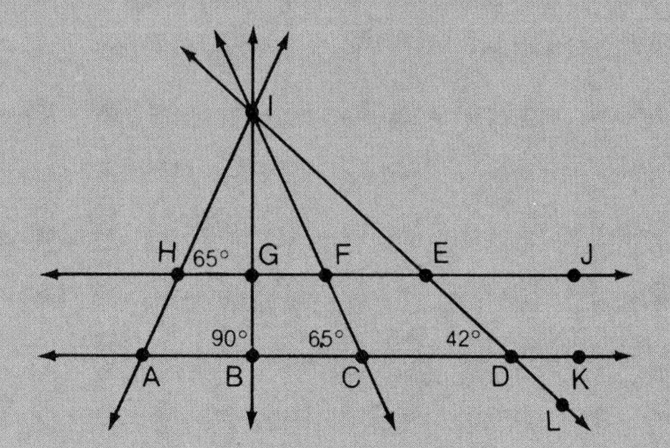


1. Name 2 parallel lines.
2. Name 3 line segments with endpoint A.
3. Name 2 angles with vertex F.
4. Name 4 angles with measure 138°.
5. Name 2 complements of $\angle$GHI.
6. Name 2 right angles.
7. Name 2 obtuse angles.
8. Name 2 isosceles triangles.
9. Name 2 scalene triangles.

*Use a compass and straightedge. (pages 314–315)*

10. Draw a line $\overleftrightarrow{AB}$. Mark a point P not on $\overleftrightarrow{AB}$. Construct $\overleftrightarrow{PQ} \parallel \overleftrightarrow{AB}$.

*Complete. (pages 318–321)*

11. One side of a regular decagon (10 sides) has length 6.2 cm. What is the length of each of its sides? What is the measure of each of its angles?
12. A parallelogram has two adjacent sides of lengths 5.7 cm and 7.6 cm, and one angle with measure 43°. What are the lengths of its other two sides? What are the measures of its other angles?

*Use the figures to find the measure. (pages 322–325, 330–331)*

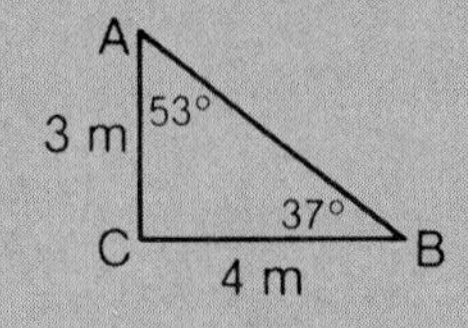


13. m $\angle$ACB
14. length of $\overline{AB}$
15. length of $\overline{DE}$
16. Construct $\triangle$GHI with m $\angle$I = 90°, $\overline{GI} \cong \overline{AC}$, $\overline{HI} \cong \overline{BC}$. Is $\triangle$GHI congruent to $\triangle$ABC? Tell how you decided.

*Use the pictures. (pages 326–327, 332–333, 336–339)*

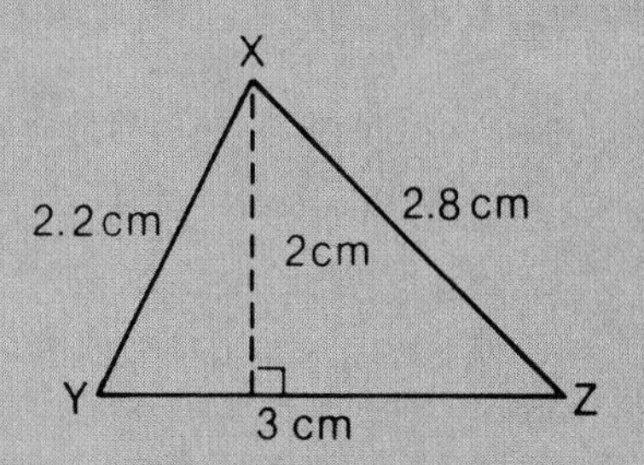


**17.** Find the perimeter and area of $\triangle XYZ$.

**18.** Find the surface area and volume of a right prism with height 8 cm, and with $\triangle XYZ$ as base.

**19.** Find the circumference and area of this circle.

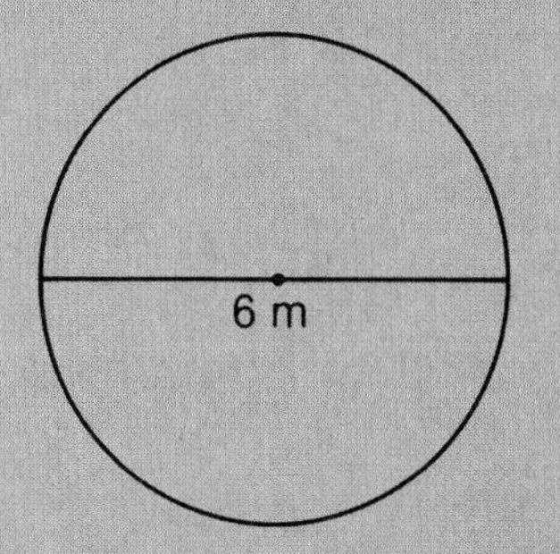


**20.** Find the length of the arc and the area of the sector determined by a 30° central angle.

**21.** Find the surface area and volume of a cylinder with height 5 m and this circle as base.

**22.** Find the surface area and volume of a cone with height 4 m, slant height 5 m and this circle as base.

*Solve. (pages 326–329, 334–335, 340–343)*

**23.** A patio is shaped like a trapezoid with parallel sides of lengths 6.4 m and 4.2 m. The perpendicular distance between these sides is 5.6 m. What is the area of the surface of the patio?

**24.** A propane gas storage tank is shaped like a sphere with a radius of length 6 m. What is the surface area of this tank? What is its volume?

**25.** The base of a pyramid-shaped tent is a square with sides of length 3.6 m. The height of the tent is 2.4 m and its slant height is 3 m. What is the surface area of this tent, not including the floor?

**26.** A grain bin has the shape of a rectangular right prism with length 5.8 m, width 4.5 m, and height 10 m. The bin is 70% filled with grain. How many cubic meters of grain are in the bin?

**27.** Nora saves 30% of her weekly allowance. What is the measure of the central angle that she should use to represent this part of her allowance in a circle graph?

**28.** In a circular garden with diameter of length 36 ft, the sector planted in tulips has a central angle of 40°. What is the area of the part planted in tulips?

# Enrichment

## Symmetry and Transformations

**A.** If you fold the grid along $\overleftrightarrow{AB}$, Point P will match with Point P′.

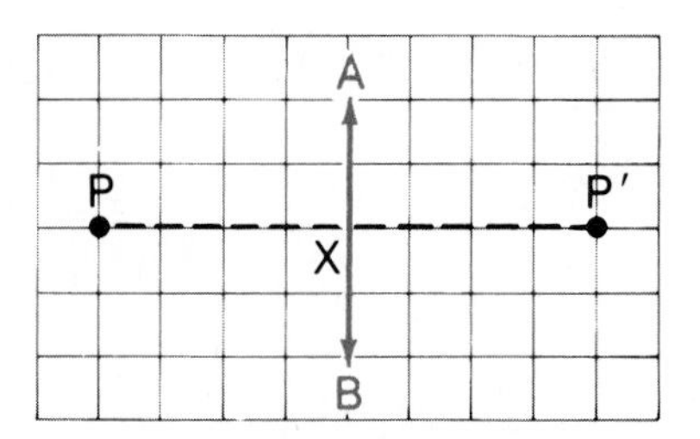


P′ is the **reflection image** of P, with $\overleftrightarrow{AB}$ as the **axis of reflection.**

In the reflection, $\overline{PX} \cong \overline{XP'}$ and $\overleftrightarrow{PP'} \perp \overleftrightarrow{AB}$.

With $\overleftrightarrow{MN}$ as the axis of reflection, every point of △DEF has a point of △DEF as its reflection image.

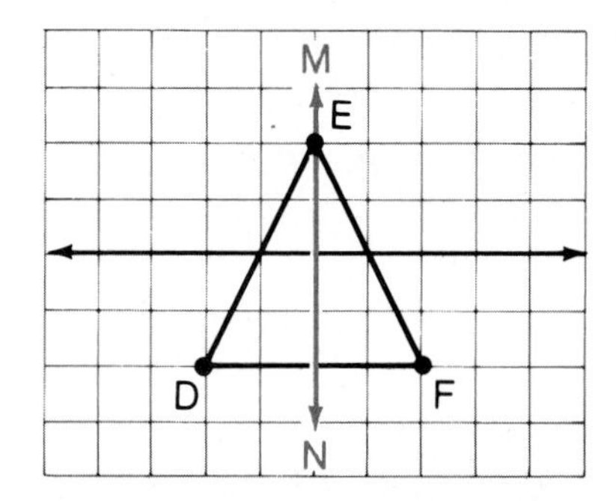


$\overleftrightarrow{MN}$ is a **line of symmetry** of △DEF.

△DEF is **symmetric** about $\overleftrightarrow{MN}$.

*Draw the reflection image of each figure. The red line is the axis of reflection.*

**1.**

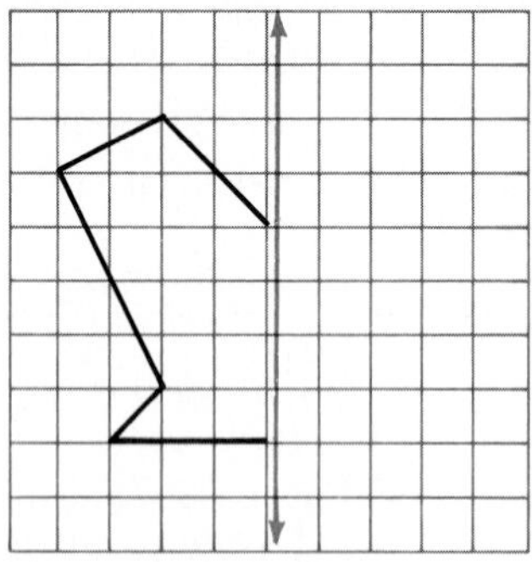

**2.**

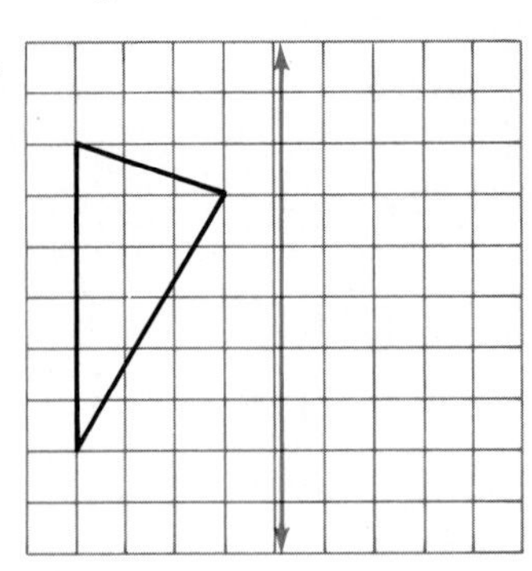

**3.**

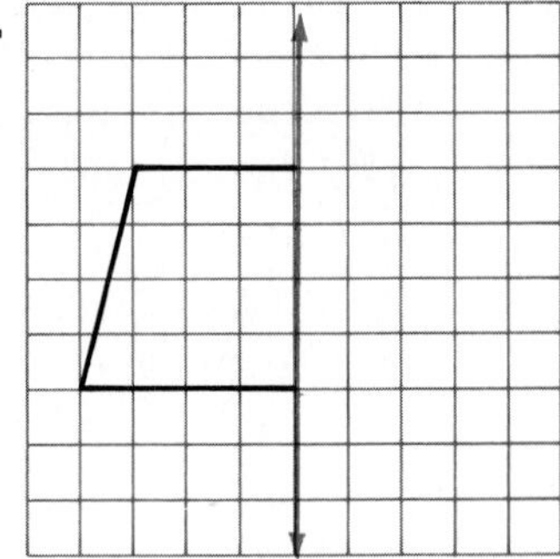

*Copy the figures and draw all lines of symmetry.*

**4.**

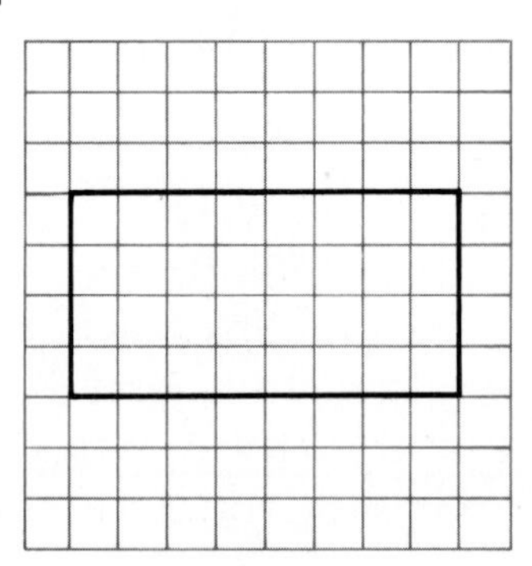

**5.**

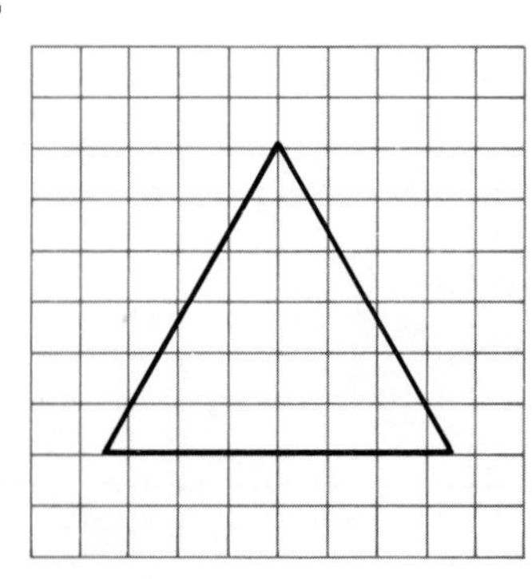

**6.**

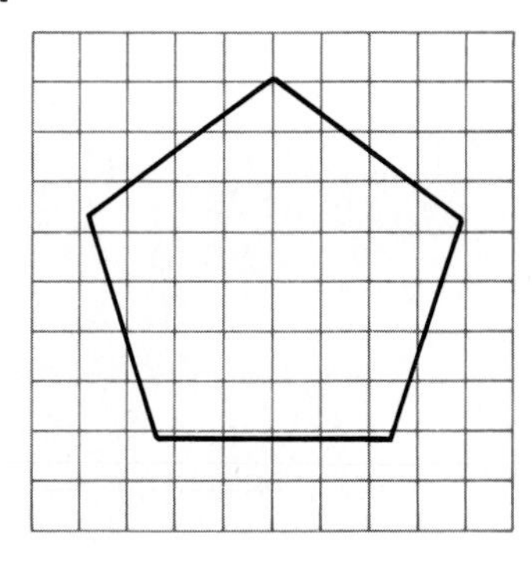

**B.** If you spin the grid 180° around Point Y, Point R will match with Point R′.

R′ is the **half-turn rotation image** of R with Y as the **center of rotation.**

In the rotation, $\overline{RY} \cong \overline{YR'}$ and $\angle RYR'$ is a straight angle.

With T as center of rotation, every point of parallelogram GHG′H′ has a point of GHG′H′ as its half-turn rotation image.

T is a **center of symmetry** of GHG′H′.

GHG′H′ is **symmetric** about T.

*Draw the half-turn rotation image of each figure with the given point as the center of symmetry.*

**7.**

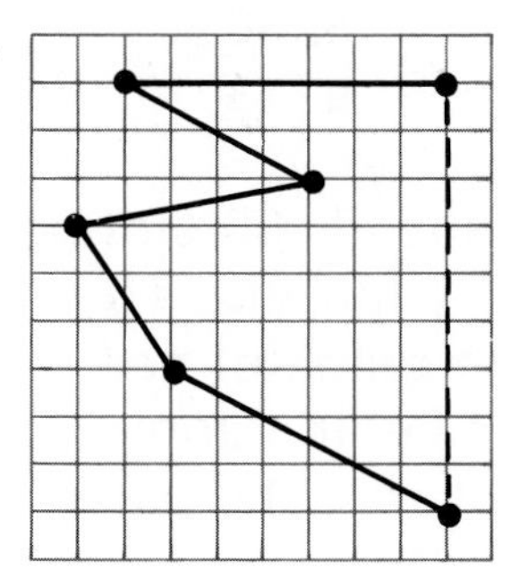

**8.**

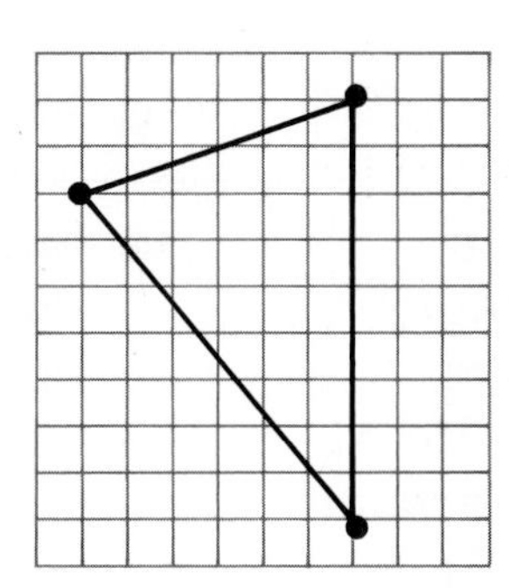

**9.**

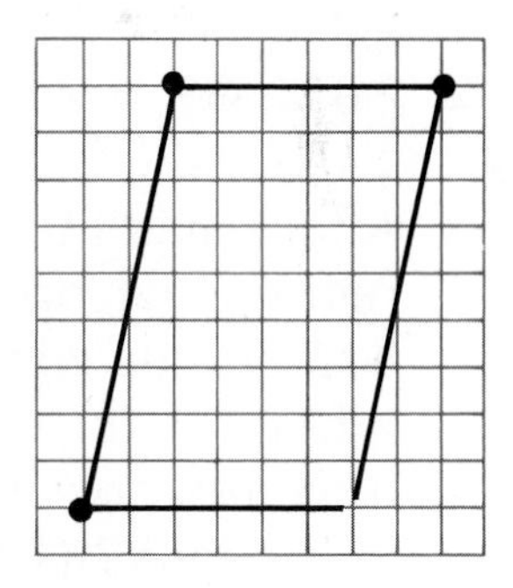

*Copy the figures and mark the center of symmetry of each.*

**10.**

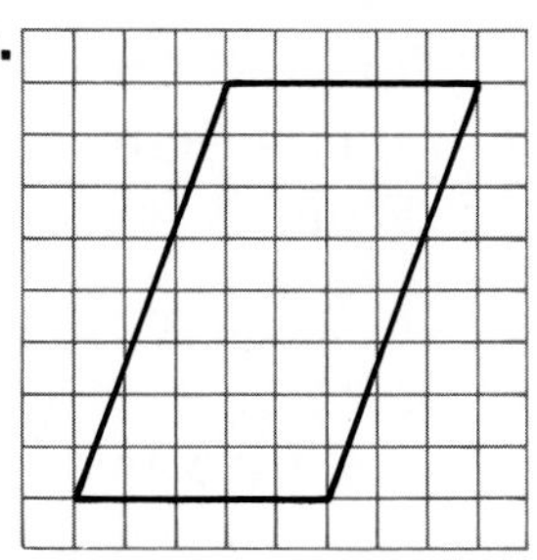

**11.**

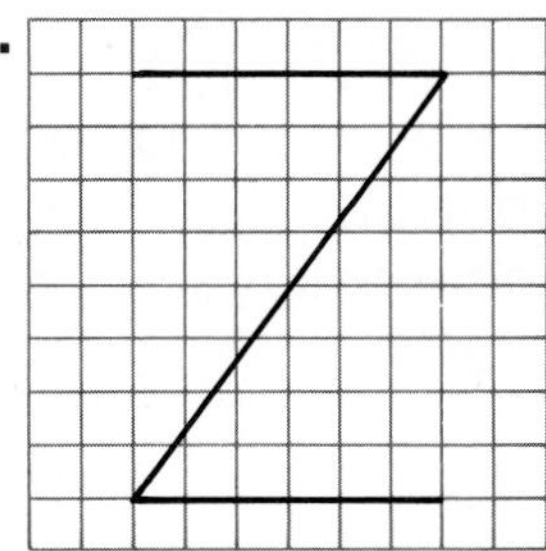

**12.**

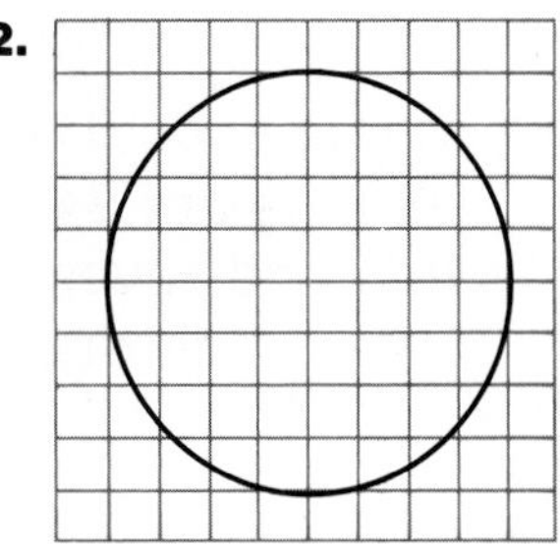

# Cumulative Review

**1.** Round to the nearest thousandth.
$.035\overline{)2.7}$

**a.** .771
**b.** .007
**c.** 61.611
**d.** 77.143

**2.** Give the symbol for

**a.** $\overleftrightarrow{MN}$
**b.** $\overrightarrow{NM}$
**c.** $\overrightarrow{MN}$
**d.** $\overline{MN}$

**3.** $$\begin{array}{r} 3\frac{5}{8} \\ +1\frac{7}{12} \\ \hline \end{array}$$

**a.** $4\frac{5}{24}$
**b.** $4\frac{3}{5}$
**c.** $4\frac{1}{2}$
**d.** $5\frac{5}{24}$

**4.** 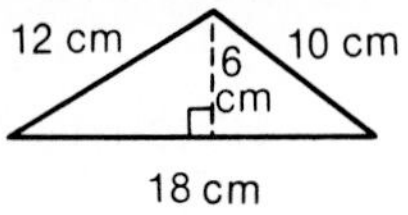


Find the area.

**a.** 40 $cm^2$
**b.** 108 $cm^2$
**c.** 54 $cm^2$
**d.** 24 $cm^2$

**5.** $\frac{4}{25} \times \frac{5}{16} = \square$

**a.** $\frac{9}{41}$
**b.** $\frac{1}{20}$
**c.** $\frac{9}{400}$
**d.** $\frac{4}{5}$

**6.** $^-35 - {}^-25 = \square$

**a.** $^-10$
**b.** $^-60$
**c.** 10
**d.** 60

**7.** $$\begin{array}{r} 52{,}607 \\ \times \quad 903 \\ \hline \end{array}$$

**a.** 4,892,451
**b.** 47,504,121
**c.** 631,282
**d.** 615,284

**8.** Which is $6\frac{1}{2}\%$ of 40?

**a.** 26
**b.** 46.5
**c.** 16.25
**d.** 2.6

**9.** Compare 2,694,413 and 2,694,314.

**a.** 2,694,413 > 2,694,314
**b.** 2,694,413 < 2,694,314
**c.** 2,694,413 = 2,694,314

**10.** Find the measure of a supplement of $\angle B$ with m $\angle B = 50°$.

**a.** 40°
**b.** 90°
**c.** 130°
**d.** 180°

**11.** A tank has the shape of a rectangular prism. Its length is 8 m and its width is 6.5 m. When the tank contains 364 kL of water, how deep is the water in the tank? (1 kL = 1 $m^3$)

**a.** 7 m
**b.** 18,928 m
**c.** about 25 m
**d.** 378.5 m

**12.** Mrs. Clarey spends 30% of her monthly salary for rent. To make a circle graph of her budget, what central angle should she use for the part representing rent?

**a.** 30°
**b.** 108°
**c.** 54°
**d.** 60°

**13.** Jim spends 9% of his weekly earnings of $40 for transportation and saves $12.50 each week. How much does he have left?

**a.** $18.50
**b.** $27.41
**c.** $23.90
**d.** $8.50

**14.** A circular patio has a diameter of length 10 m. What is the area of this patio?

**a.** 31.4 $m^2$
**b.** 62.8 $m^2$
**c.** 314 $m^2$
**d.** 78.5 $m^2$

# 10 Probability and Statistics

**NATURAL BRIDGES IN THE UNITED STATES**

| Name | Height | Span |
|---|---|---|
| Sipapu | 220 feet | 268 feet |
| Kachina | 205 feet | 186 feet |
| Owachomo | 108 feet | 194 feet |
| Rainbow Bridge | 309 feet | 278 feet |

## 10-1 Probability

Ray's favorite tapes are shown below. There are 6 tapes, so there are 6 possible outcomes of selecting a tape.

If Ray selects a tape without looking each tape is **equally likely** to be selected. The tape is selected at **random.**

**A.** Ray's favorite singer is Hippo. What is the probability Ray will select a tape by Hippo at random?

A **probability** is a number that tells how likely it is that a statement about an outcome will be true.

Probability that "A tape by Hippo will be selected" will be true = P(Hippo)

$\frac{3}{6}$ of the set of tapes is by Hippo. $= \frac{3}{6} = \frac{1}{2}$

The probability that a tape by Hippo is selected is $\frac{3}{6}$, or $\frac{1}{2}$.

**B.** Find P(Mel-O **or** green).

$\frac{4}{6}$ of the tapes are by Mel-O or have a green label.

P(Mel-O or green) $= \frac{4}{6} = \frac{2}{3}$

**C.** Find P(Mel-O **and** green).

$\frac{1}{6}$ of the tapes are by Mel-O and have a green label.

P(Mel-O and green) $= \frac{1}{6}$

**D.** Find P(Hippo **and** blue).

$\frac{0}{6}$ of the tapes are by Hippo and have a blue label.

P(Hippo and blue) $= \frac{0}{6} = 0$

A statement that cannot be true has probability 0.

**E.** Find P(red **or** blue **or** green).

$\frac{6}{6}$ of the tapes have a red or a blue or a green label.

P(red or blue or green) $= \frac{6}{6} = 1$

A statement that must be true has probability 1.

## CLASS EXERCISES

*Use the tapes on page 354. Find the probabilities.*

1. P(The Noise)
2. P(The Noise or red)
3. P(The Noise and red)
4. P(Hippo and green)
5. P(Mel-O or red)
6. P(Mel-O or Hippo)

## EXERCISES

*Each student who wants a pen pal selects a tag at random from this set.*

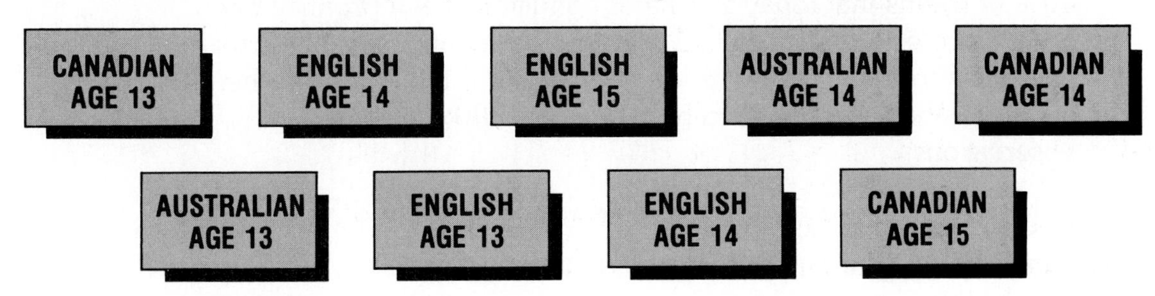


*Find the probabilities.*

1. P(13)
2. P(English and 14)
3. P(English or 14)
4. P(Spanish)
5. P(Canadian)
6. P(Australian and 14)
7. P(Canadian or 15)
8. P(13 or 14)
9. P(English or Canadian)
10. P(not 13)
11. P(not English)
12. P(not English and not 13)
13. P(13 or 14 or 15)
14. P(13 and 15)
15. P(Canadian and not 15)
16. P(Canadian or not 15)
17. P(not French)
18. P(13 and not Australian)

## PROBLEMS

19. The first two students who selected tags from the set above got the tags "English, Age 14" and "Canadian, Age 15." What is the probability that the third student who selects a tag will get an Australian pen pal?

20. The first three students who selected tags got "English, Age 14," "Canadian, Age 15," and "English, Age 13." What is the probability that the fourth student gets a pen pal who is not 15?

## THINK!

### Even and Odd

Find the least two positive numbers whose sum is an even integer and whose difference is an odd integer.

1. $\frac{1}{3}$ 10. $\frac{2}{3}$

Homework page 508

# Problem Solving

READ PLAN • DO • ANSWER • CHECK

## 10-2 Empirical Probability

When you find a **mathematical probability,** you use a part of the set of possible outcomes. To find an **empirical probability,** you must use a large number of outcomes that have already occurred.

**A.** When a weather announcer says that the chance of rain today is 40%, it means that today's weather conditions have produced rain an average of 40 times in 100 previous observations. What is the probability of rain for the 4th of July parade if the day's weather conditions have produced rain in 125 of 1,000 previous observations?

$$\text{P(rain)} = \frac{125}{1{,}000} = .125 = 12\tfrac{1}{2}\%$$

The probability of rain for the parade is $12\frac{1}{2}\%$.

**B.** In a survey, 5,000 adult males were selected at random and their heights (h) were measured. There were 260 heights of 189 cm or greater. What is the probability that the next adult male to be selected at random will have a height of 189 cm or greater?

$$\text{P(h} \geq 189 \text{ cm)} = \frac{260}{5{,}000} = .052$$

The probability that the next male will have a height of 189 cm or greater is .052.

## CLASS EXERCISES

June has scored on 63 of her last 100 serves in tennis games with Sarah. What is the probability that she will score on her next serve?

**2.** In the last 200 chess games they have played, Clem has won 106 and Karl has won 94. What is the probability that Karl will lose the next game?

## PROBLEMS

**1.** What is the probability of snow if current conditions have produced snow in 65 of 130 previous observations?

**2.** What is the probability of Ann's getting an A on her English quiz if she got an A on 4 of the last 5 English quizzes?

**3.** There are 37 students in a speech class. What is the probability that the teacher will ask Jerry to give the first speech if the selection is random?

**4.** In 150 times at bat, Lynn has had 30 home runs. What is the probability that she will get a home run the next time she goes to bat?

*In 50 games they have played, Ginnie has won 22 times, Martha has won 12 times, and Rick has won 16 times. Find these probabilities for the next game they play:*

**5.** P(Ginnie wins)

**6.** P(Martha wins)

**7.** P(Martha and Ginnie lose)

*An accident insurance company found that an average of 103 of every 1,000 construction workers it insures have an accident in each 1-year period. The company's average payment is $892 per accident.*

**8.** What is the probability that a construction worker selected at random from this insurance company's customers will have an accident in a 1-year period.

★ **9.** The company's **expected loss** per worker is the product of the probability that a worker has an accident and the average cost of the accident if one occurs. What is the company's expected loss per worker in a 1-year period?

## ON YOUR OWN

### Pascal's Triangle

Follow the arrows. Write the number of paths leading to each box inside the box. This pattern is known as **Pascal's Triangle**, named for the French mathematician Blaise Pascal (1632–62). Use the pattern to write the next 5 lines of Pascal's Triangle.

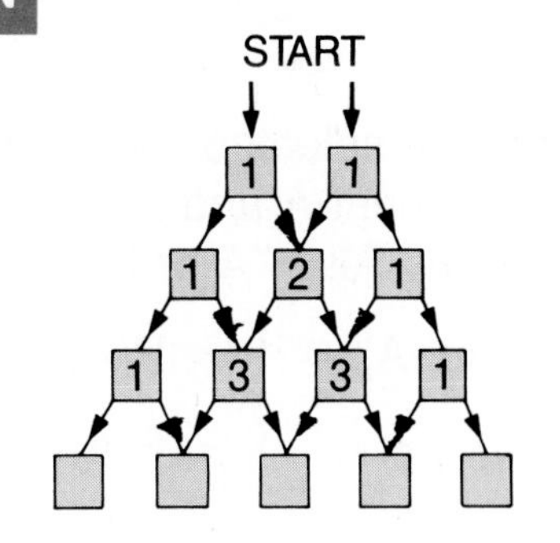


1. .50



Homework page 508

# 10-3 Using "Or" in Compound Statements

One hundred people selected red, yellow, or white as their favorite flower color. Any who could not decide selected two colors. The results are shown in the **Venn diagram.**

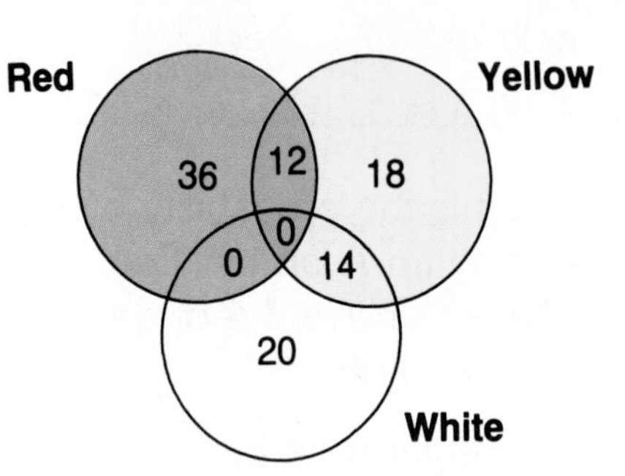


Red: 48
Yellow: 44
White: 34
Red and yellow: 12
Red and white: 0
Yellow and white: 14
All three: 0

**A.** If one of these 100 people were selected at random, from the diagram:

$$\text{P(red or yellow)} = \frac{36 + 12 + 18 + 14}{100} = \frac{80}{100}$$

Note that: $\text{P(red)} = \frac{48}{100}$ $\text{P(yellow)} = \frac{44}{100}$ $\text{P(red and yellow)} = \frac{12}{100}$

$$\frac{80}{100} = \frac{48}{100} + \frac{44}{100} - \frac{12}{100}$$

P(red or yellow) = P(red) + P(yellow) − P(red and yellow)

**If A and B are any two statements,**
**P(A or B) = P(A) + P(B) − P(A and B).**

**B.** "Red is selected" and "White is selected" cannot both be true of a single selection. They are **exclusive statements.** P(red and white) = 0, so P(red or white) = P(red) + P(white).

**If A and B are exclusive statements, P(A and B) = 0**
**so, P(A or B) = P(A) + P(B).**

**C.** "Red is not selected" is the **negation** of "Red is selected." Any statement A and its negation not-A are exclusive statements. Also "A or not-A" must be true, so

P(A or not-A) = 1 = P(A) + P(not-A)

and 1 − P(A) = P(not-A)

## CLASS EXERCISES

*Use the Venn diagram on page 358. Find the probabilities.*

1. P(selected *only* red)
2. P(selected *only* yellow)
3. P(selected *only* red and *only* yellow)
4. P(selected *only* red or *only* yellow)
5. P(did not select white)
6. P(yellow or not-white)

## EXERCISES

*This Venn diagram shows the favorite subject selected by 36 students. Some selected two subjects.*

English
Science
8
0
8
0
4
10
6
Mathematics

1. Which two of these statements are exclusive?

   **a)** Selected science **b)** Selected mathematics **c)** Selected English

*Find these probabilities.*

2. P(sci.)
3. P(math.)
4. P(Eng.)
5. P(not-sci.)
6. P(Eng. or sci.)
7. P(Eng. or math.)
8. P(sci. or math.)
9. P(not-math.)

★ 10. P(not-sci. or not-math.)

★ 11. P(not-Eng. or not-sci.)

## PROBLEMS

12. The probability that Jamie will get an A in math is .6, in science .4, and in both .3. What is her chance of getting an A in at least 1 of these?

13. Jamie's probability of getting an A in science is .4, and of getting a B is .5. What is her probability of getting an A or a B in science?

## THINK!

### More about Pascal's Triangle

Copy the rows of Pascal's Triangle on page 357. On the left side, write the number of each row. On the right side, write the sum of the numbers in each row. Do this for rows 0–8. What pattern do you see in the sum column?

| Row Number | | Sum of Numbers in Row |
|---|---|---|
| 0 | 1 | 1 |
| 1 | 1 1 | 2 |
| 2 | 1 2 1 | 4 |
| 3 | 1 3 3 1 | 8 |

**2.** $\frac{1}{2}$ **6.** $\frac{5}{6}$ **12.** .7



Homework page 509

## 10-4 Multiple Selections: Independent Statements

**A.** These 6 red cards are put into a red bowl.

These 3 green cards are put into a green bowl.

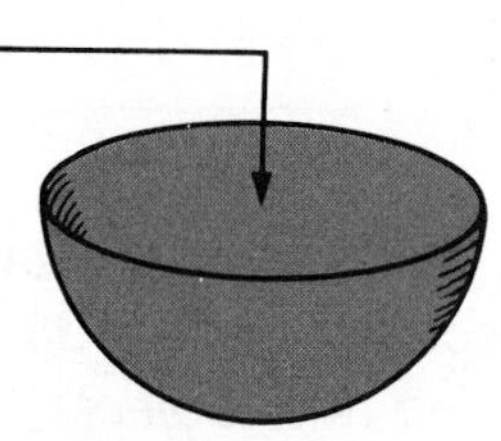

Joy selects one card at random from the red bowl, then one from the green bowl. What is the probability that she selects a red 3-card and a green 1-card?

The statements "selects a red 3-card" and "selects a green 1-card" are **independent** statements because the card Joy selects from the red bowl has no effect on the card she selects from the green bowl.

$$P(\text{red 3 and green 1}) = P(\text{red 3}) \times P(\text{green 1})$$
$$= \frac{2}{6} \times \frac{2}{3}$$
$$= \frac{4}{18}, \text{ or } \frac{2}{9}$$

**If A and B are independent statements, P(A and B) = P(A) x P(B).**

**B.** Find P(red 1 and green 3).

P(red 1 and green 3)
= P(red 1) and P(green 3)
$= \frac{1}{6} \times \frac{0}{3}$
$= \frac{0}{18} = 0$

**C.** Find P(both 5's).

P(both 5's) = P(red 5 and green 5)
= P(red 5 x P(green 5)
$= \frac{3}{6} \times \frac{1}{3}$
$= \frac{3}{18} = \frac{1}{6}$

### CLASS EXERCISES

*Use the cards above. Find the probabilities.*

1. P(red 3 and green 5)
2. P(both 1's)
3. P(both 3's)
4. P(red 5 and green 1)

## EXERCISES

*Sal made this table to show the probabilities of his getting certain grades in mathematics and English. The statements are independent. Find the probabilities.*

| Grade | Math | English |
|---|---|---|
| A | .5 | .2 |
| B | .2 | .4 |
| Below B | .3 | .4 |

**1.** P(A in math and B in English)

**2.** P(B in math and A in English)

**3.** P(both B's)

**4.** P(both A's)

**5.** P(both below B)

**6.** P(B in math and below B in English)

★ **7.** P(A or B in math and B in English)

★ **8.** P(B in math and A or B in English)

*A bowl contains these cards. One is selected at random, replaced, and a second is selected at random. (This is the same as selecting from two identical bowls of cards.) Find the probabilities.*

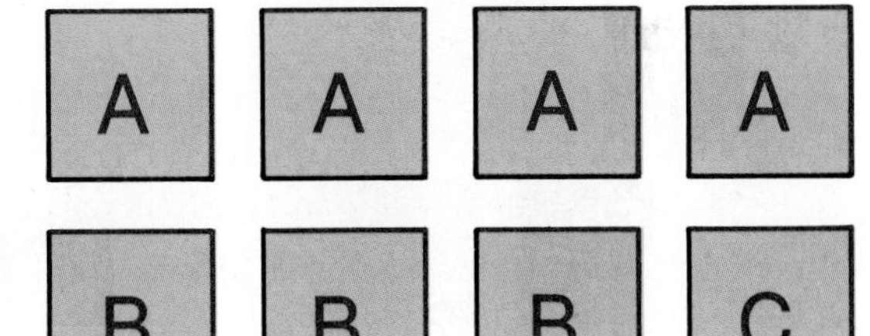


**9.** P(A on the first and B on the second)

**10.** P(both A)

**11.** P(B on the first and A on the second)

**12.** P(both B)

★ **13.** Use the results for the exclusive statements in Exercises **9** and **11.** Find P(one A, one B).

## THINK!

### Coin Tossing

If you toss two coins, how many ways can you get 2 heads? ■ 1 head? ■ 0 heads? ■

Look back at the second row of Pascal's Triangle on page 357. What do you see?

The numbers in row 2 match those for the outcomes above.

Use the third row of the triangle to find the results for tossing 3 coins.

In how many ways can you get 3 heads? ■ 2 heads? ■ 1 head? ■ 0 heads? ■

What is the probability of tossing 3 heads? Of tossing exactly 2 tails?

**1.** .2 **9.** $\frac{3}{16}$



Homework page 509

# 10-5 Multiple Selections: Dependent Statements

**A.** Helen must select one card at random from this set of cards. Then, *without replacing* that card she must select a second card. What is the probability that she gets a blue card and then a red card?

Without replacement, Helen's chance of getting a red card on her second selection is **dependent** upon what happened on the first selection.

**First selection** **Second selection given blue on the first**

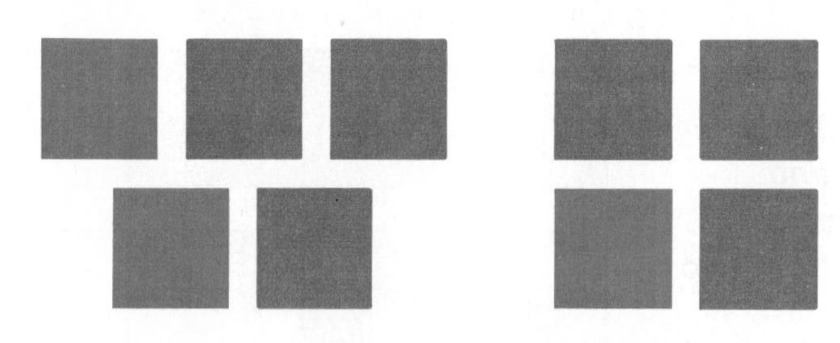

$P(\text{blue}) = \frac{2}{5}$ $P(\text{red } \textbf{given} \text{ blue}) = \frac{3}{4}$

$$P(\text{blue } \textbf{then} \text{ red}) = P(\text{blue}) \times P(\text{red } \textbf{given} \text{ blue}) = \frac{2}{5} \times \frac{3}{4}$$

$$= \frac{6}{20} = \frac{3}{10}$$

**If A and B are any statements,**
**P(A then B) = P(A) × P(B given A).**

**B.** What is P(red then blue)?

2 blue, 2 red remain, given red

$$P(\text{red then blue}) = P(\text{red}) \times P(\text{blue } \textbf{given} \text{ red}) = \frac{3}{5} \times \frac{2}{4}$$

$$= \frac{6}{20} = \frac{3}{10}$$

**C.** Three cards are drawn without replacement. Find P(red then blue then red).

$$P(\text{red then blue then red}) = P(\text{red}) \cdot P(\text{blue } \textbf{given} \text{ red}) \cdot P(\text{red } \textbf{given} \text{ red then blue})$$

$$= \frac{3}{5} \qquad \frac{2}{4} \qquad \frac{2}{3}$$

$$= \frac{12}{60} = \frac{1}{5}$$

## CLASS EXERCISES

*Add one red card to the set on page 362 to have 2 blue and 4 red cards. Draw one card at random, then draw a second without replacement. Find the probabilities.*

1. P(red then red)
2. P(both blue)
3. P(red then blue)
4. P(blue then red)
5. P(blue then blue then red)
6. P(red then green)

## EXERCISES

*Use the set of cards shown here. Select one card at random. Then, without replacement, select a second card. Find the probabilities.*

1. P(brown then orange)
2. P(orange then brown)
3. P(both green)
4. P(both brown)
5. P(green then orange)
6. P(orange then green)
7. Use the results from exercises **5.** and **6.** Find P(one orange, one green).

**8.–14.** Repeat exercises **1–7**, this time replacing the first card before the second is selected.

*Use the set of cards above. Select three cards in succession, without replacement. Find the probabilities.*

15. P(brown then brown then orange)
16. P(3 orange)
17. P(orange then brown then brown)
18. P(3 brown)
19. P(brown then orange then brown)
20. P(3 green)

★**21.** Use the results in exercises **15, 17,** and **19.** Find P(2 brown, 1 orange).

**22.–27.** Repeat exercises **15–20**, replacing each card before selecting the next.

## THINK!

### Making Logical Choices

How many people would you have to ask to be sure of finding at least 2 with birthdays in the same month? At least 3? At least 10? At least how many are sure to have birthdays in the same month in a school with 500 students?

1. $\frac{3}{14}$ 8. $\frac{3}{16}$ 15. $\frac{1}{14}$

Homework page 510

## 10-6 Listing Outcomes

**A.** Alice, Betty, and Charles are running in the class elections. How many possible outcomes of the election are there?

You can list the possible outcomes as **ordered sets** of (President, Vice President).

A **tree diagram** can help you find the ordered sets. List the choices for President, and then the choices for Vice President for each choice for President.

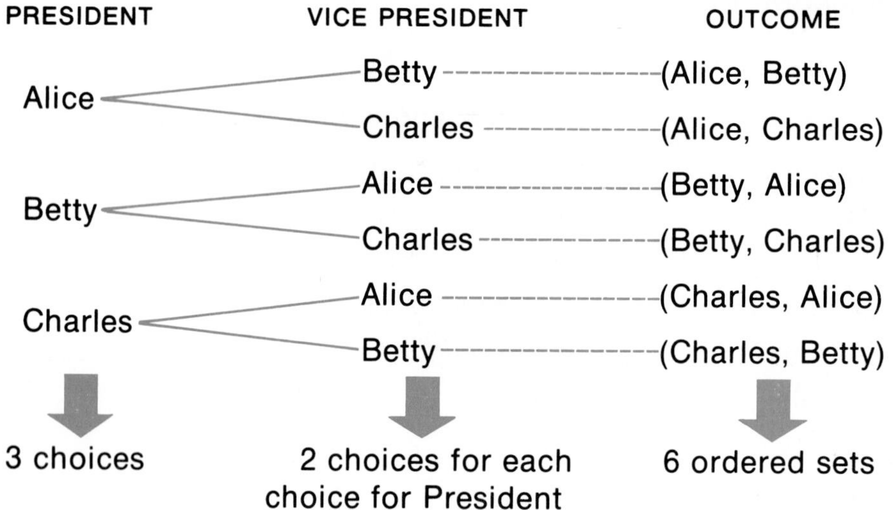


There are 6 possible outcomes of the election.

**B.** How many possible outcomes are there if two of Alice, Betty, and Charles are to be co-chairpersons of the dance committee?

The possible outcomes are **unordered sets** because the order of listing the members doesn't matter.

{Alice, Betty} and {Betty, Alice} are the same unordered sets.

{Alice, Charles} and {Charles, Alice} are the same unordered sets.

{Betty, Charles} and {Charles, Betty} are the same unordered sets.

There are 3 possible outcomes for co-chairpersons.

## CLASS EXERCISES

1. Four race horses, Flash, Midnight, Spearmint, and Lucky, are in a race. Copy and complete the tree diagram to show the possible outcomes for 1st and 2nd place.

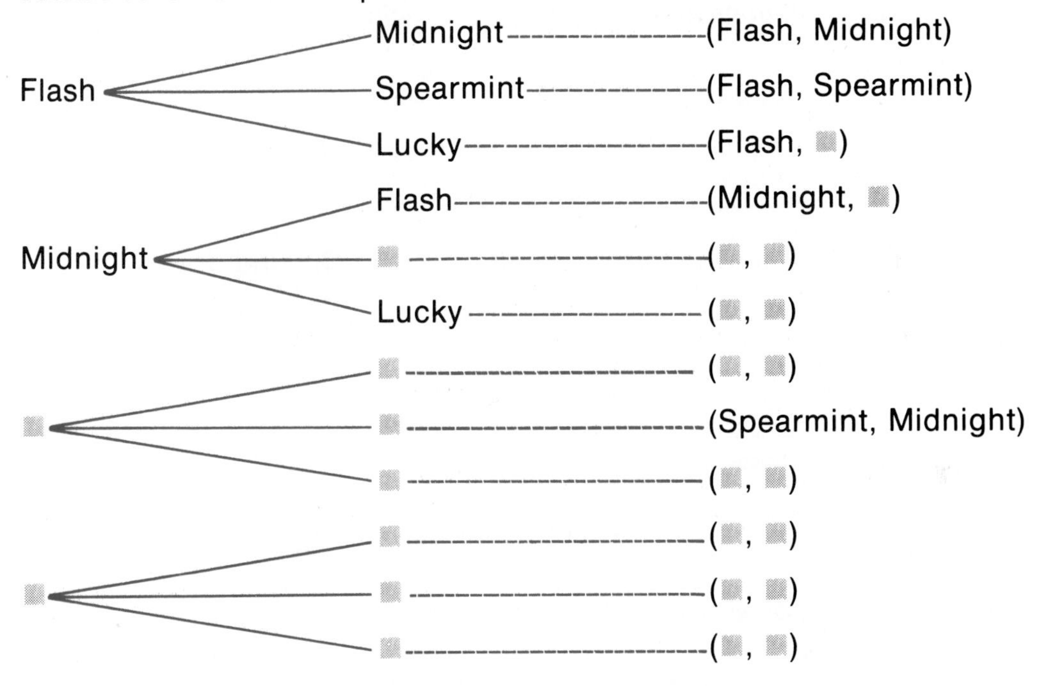


2. What are the possible outcomes if 2 of the horses are to be shown at an exhibit?

## EXERCISES

*Use tree diagrams.*

1. In how many different orders can you do your math, science, history, and English homework?

2. If order doesn't matter, in how many ways can you do your homework in the 4 subjects?

3. Evan, Frank, Rita, and Barbara are in a public speaking competition. Give the possible outcomes for winner and runner-up.

4. In how many ways can 2 of the 4 speakers give speeches at a meeting of the Math and Science Club if the speaking order doesn't matter?

★5. A penny, a nickel, and a dime are tossed. Give the possible heads/tails outcomes as ordered sets with 3 members in each.

**Using Sevens**

Can you make 100, using only four 7's, decimal points, and two operations?

1. 24

Homework page 510

# 10-7 Permutations

**A.** An ordered set is called a **permutation.** The number of ordered sets of 2 things each that can be formed from 5 things is *the number of permutations of 5 things taken 2 at a time.*

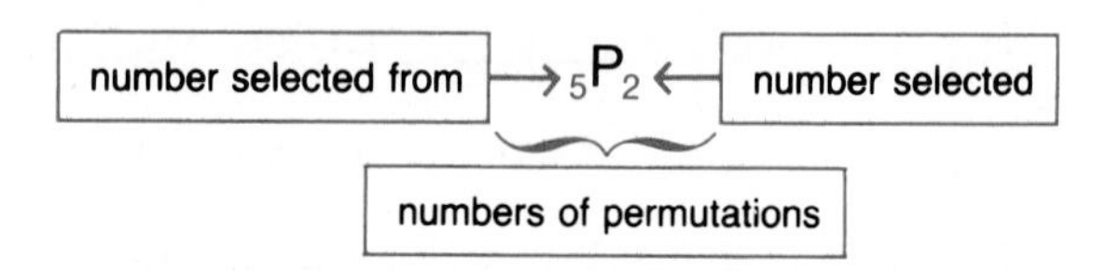


**B.** Find $_5P_2$ without drawing a tree diagram.

*Think:*

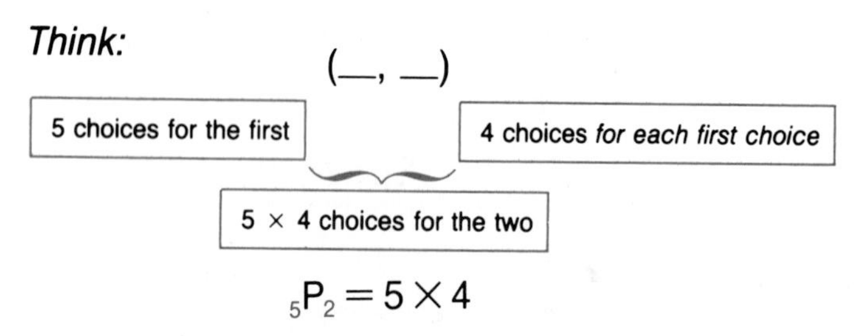


**C.** Find $_7P_3$.

| 1st | 2nd | 3rd |
|---|---|---|

$$_7P_3 = 7 \times 6 \times 5$$
$$= 210$$

**D.** You can use **factorial notation** as a shortcut.

$5! = 5 \times 4 \times 3 \times 2 \times 1$ ← five factorial

$3! = 3 \times 2 \times 1$ ← three factorial

**Example 1** $\dfrac{5!}{(5-2)!} = \dfrac{5!}{3!} = \dfrac{5 \times 4 \times \overset{1}{\cancel{3}} \times \overset{1}{\cancel{2}} \times 1}{\underset{1}{\cancel{3}} \times \underset{1}{\cancel{2}} \times 1} = 5 \times 4 = {_5P_2}$

**Example 2** $_5P_5 = \dfrac{5!}{(5-5)!} = \dfrac{5!}{0!} = \dfrac{5 \times 4 \times 3 \times 2 \times 1}{1} = 120$

$0! = 1$ and $1! = 1$

## CLASS EXERCISES

*Write a standard numeral for each.*

**1.** $2!$ **2.** $6!$ **3.** $\dfrac{8!}{3!}$ **4.** $\dfrac{2!}{0!}$ **5.** $\dfrac{4!}{1!}$ **6.** $\dfrac{10!}{2!}$

*Give factorial notation and a standard numeral for each.*

**7.** $_5P_2$ **8.** $_8P_3$ **9.** $_{10}P_4$ **10.** $_4P_4$ **11.** $_{12}P_1$ **12.** $_7P_5$

## EXERCISES

*Give factorial notation and a standard numeral for each.*

1. $_6P_2$ 2. $_9P_4$ 3. $_5P_5$ 4. $_7P_3$ 5. $_{10}P_5$ 6. $_5P_3$
7. $_8P_1$ 8. $_6P_4$ 9. $_{20}P_2$ 10. $_{100}P_3$ 11. $_6P_6$ 12. $_9P_7$

## PROBLEMS

**13.** In how many ways can the offices of president and vice president be filled if 8 students are candidates for the offices and each can fill either position?

**14.** In how many ways can the coach list a starting line-up for the basketball game if there are 9 players from which to choose and each can play any position?

**15.** In how many different ways can the coach make a batting order using 9 players of the baseball team?

**16.** Two students enter a classroom with 26 seats. In how many ways can they seat themselves?

**17.** In how many different ways can you list the names of the members of your family?

★ **18.** How many different seating arrangements are possible for your mathematics class?

## MIXED REVIEW

*Find the surface area and volume of each figure. Use 3.14 for $\pi$.*

**1.** Prism with base:

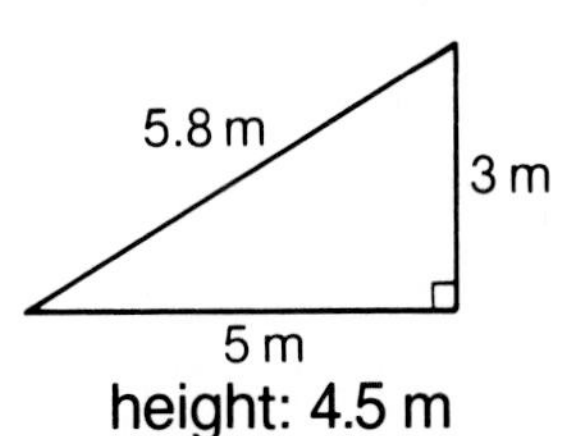


height: 4.5 m

**2.**

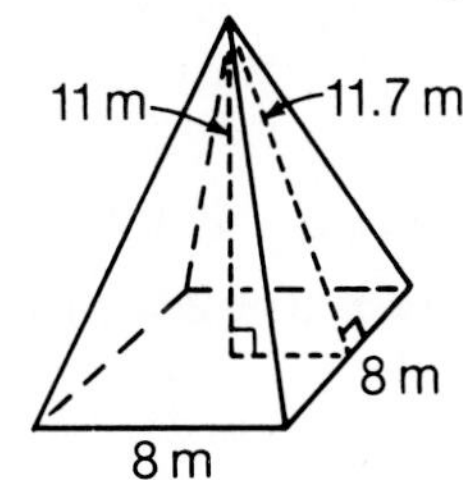


**3.** Rectangular prism with length: 16 cm width: 8.2 cm height: 3.9 cm

**4.** Sphere with length of radius: 12 cm

*Write >, <, or = for ●.*

**5.** $^-8$ ● 4
<

**6.** $|^-7|$ ● $|^-10|$
<

**7.** $|.5|$ ● $^-.50$
=

1. $\frac{6!}{(6-2)!}$; 30

Homework page 511

# 10-8 Combinations

**A.** A senior citizens' club must select a committee of 3 of its 5 officers to study the club's constitution. In how many ways can this committee be selected?

Each committee is an unordered set, or **combination,** of 5 people taken 3 at a time. The number of combinations is written:

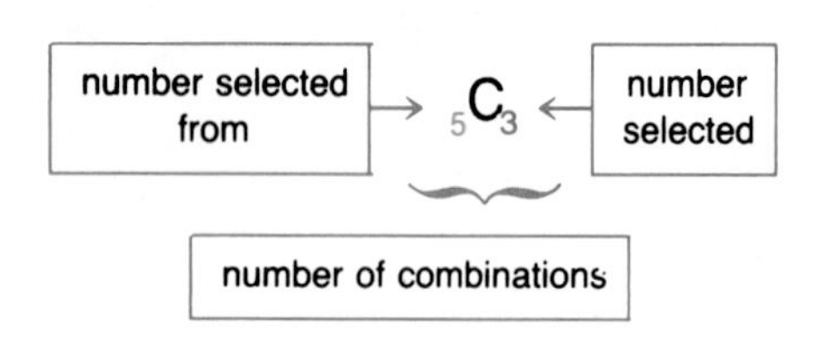


To find $_5C_3$, think of finding $_5P_3$ in two steps:

$$_5C_3 \times {}_3P_3 = {}_5P_3$$

| $_5C_3$ | $_3P_3$ | $_5P_3$ |
|---|---|---|
| unordered sets of 3 from 5 | ordered sets of 3 from each ordered set of 3 | ordered sets of 3 from 5 |

$$_5C_3 = {}_5P_3 \div {}_3P_3$$

$$_5C_3 = \frac{5!}{(5-3)!} \div \frac{3!}{(3-3)!} = \frac{5!}{(5-3)!} \times \frac{0!}{3!} = \frac{5!}{(5-3)! \times 3!}$$

$$_5C_3 = \frac{5 \times 4 \times 3 \times 2 \times 1}{(2 \times 1) \times (3 \times 2 \times 1)} = 10$$

There are 10 ways to select the committee.

**B.** Find $_9C_4$.

$$_9C_4 = \frac{9!}{(9-4)! \times 4!} = \frac{9 \times 8 \times 7 \times 6 \times 5 \times 4 \times 3 \times 2 \times 1}{(5 \times 4 \times 3 \times 2 \times 1) \times (4 \times 3 \times 2 \times 1)} = 126$$

## CLASS EXERCISES

*Give factorial notation and a standard numeral for each.*

**1.** $_6C_2$ ______ **2.** $_7C_2$ ______ **3.** $_7P_2$ ______ **4.** $_3C_3$ ______ **5.** $_3P_3$ ______ **6.** $_{10}C_1$ ______

## EXERCISES

*Give factorial notation and a standard numeral for each.*

| | | | | | |
|---|---|---|---|---|---|
| 1. ${}_5C_2$ | 2. ${}_8C_4$ | 3. ${}_5C_5$ | 4. ${}_7C_3$ | 5. ${}_9P_1$ | 6. ${}_9C_1$ |
| 7. ${}_{10}C_4$ | 8. ${}_6P_4$ | 9. ${}_{20}C_2$ | 10. ${}_{90}P_2$ | 11. ${}_8C_3$ | 12. ${}_{11}C_9$ |
| 13. ${}_6P_6$ | 14. ${}_4C_4$ | 15. ${}_{15}C_2$ | 16. ${}_7P_7$ | 17. ${}_{11}C_4$ | 18. ${}_5C_1$ |

## PROBLEMS

**19.** How many committees of 5 students can be formed from the 20 students in Mr. Lyons' class?

**20.** In how many ways can (Chairperson, Recorder) selections be made for a committee of 5?

**21.** If you are to answer 5 out of 7 questions on an examination, in how many ways can you make the selection?

**22.** Mrs. Tyler said George could watch 2 of the 6 television shows that are on at different times on Saturday morning. In how many ways can George make his selection?

★**23.** A teacher wants to choose 5 out of 25 words on a vocabulary list for an examination. In how many ways can she make the selection? How many lists of 5 words can she make?

★**24.** Irene has these choices of classes: 9:00–9:40 math, science, or English; 9:40–10:30 math, science, or English; 10:30–11:20 math or English. How many different schedules of her classes can she make if she must take math, science, and English?

## THINK!

### Logical Reasoning

Matt and Pat each had a large sack of peanuts. For every 6 peanuts in Matt's sack, there were 7 peanuts in Pat's sack. If they had 1,391 peanuts altogether, how many were in each sack?

1. $\frac{5!}{(5-2)!2!} = 10$



Homework page 511

# 10-9 Mean, Median, Mode, and Range

A zookeeper kept a record of the amount of hay nine elephants ate each day for a two-week period. The *amounts in tons,* rounded to the nearest hundredth, are given below.

| | | | | | | |
|---|---|---|---|---|---|---|
| 2.24 | 2.30 | 2.07 | 2.32 | 2.46 | 2.38 | 2.09 |
| 2.14 | 2.28 | 2.12 | 2.43 | 2.24 | 2.13 | 2.30 |

**A.** Statisticians use several statistics to describe the center of a set of information, or **data.**

The **mean,** or average, of these data are given by

$$\begin{aligned} \text{Mean} &= \text{Sum of amounts} \div \text{Number of amounts} \\ &= 31.50 \div 14 \\ &= 2.25 \end{aligned}$$

The mean is 2.25 tn.

The **median** is the middle number, or mean of the two middle numbers, when the data are listed in order from least to greatest. For these amounts of hay:

2.07 2.09 . . . (6 numbers) 2.24 2.28 (2 middle numbers) . . . 2.43 2.46 (6 numbers)

$$\begin{aligned} \text{Median} &= (2.24 + 2.28) \div 2 \\ &= 2.26 \end{aligned}$$

The median is 2.26 tn.

The **mode** of a set of data is the number that occurs most often. A set of data can have more than one mode. For these amounts of hay there are two modes because there are two amounts that occur twice.

2.24 tn and 2.30 tn

**B.** The **range** of a set of data tells whether the data is tightly grouped or is widely spread out.

Range = Greatest number − Least number

For these amounts of hay:

$$\begin{aligned} \text{Range} &= 2.46 - 2.07 \\ &= 0.39 \text{ tn} \end{aligned}$$

## CLASS EXERCISES

1. Find the mean weight of the rare animals given in the table.
2. What is the median weight of these animals?
3. Find the mode of these weights.
4. What is the range of the animals' weights?

| Rare Animals | Length (ft) | Weight (lb) | Life Span (yr) |
|---|---|---|---|
| European Bison | 11.5 | 2,500 | 28 |
| Asiatic Lion | 5.5 | 420 | 30 |
| Giant Tortoise | 3.5 | 400 | 190 |
| Bengal Tiger | 10.0 | 400 | 25 |
| Giant Panda | 6.0 | 300 | 15 |
| Wolf | 5.5 | 176 | 10 |
| Cheetah | 7.0 | 130 | 17 |

## EXERCISES

1. Find the mean, median, mode, and range of the life spans of the rare animals given in the table.
2. Find the mean, median, mode, and range of the lengths of the rare animals given in the table.
3. Replace the giant tortoise in the table by the leatherback turtle whose length is 6.3 ft. Find the mean, median, mode, and range of this new set of lengths. Which statistical measures are changed by changing this one number?

★4. Which life span has the greatest effect on the range? Replace this number with another number to give the smallest possible range.

★5. Which weight most effects the mean weight? Eliminate this number. Find the new mean. Replace the number with one that gives a mean weight of 301 lb.

## THINK!

**Use Algebra**

- Pick any two-digit number except 99.
- Double the number.
- Add 4.
- Multiply by 5.
- Add 12.
- Multiply by 10.
- Subtract 320.
- Cross out the 0's in your answer

What is the result?
Try to explain why this trick works.

# 10-10 Grouped Data and Histograms

**A.** It is often useful to group large sets of data into **classes.**

**DATA**

| Ages of Members of the Island Manor Health Club | | | | |
|---|---|---|---|---|
| 17 | 40 | 37 | 41 | 33 |
| 33 | 45 | 20 | 47 | 51 |
| 52 | 41 | 27 | 31 | 59 |
| 57 | 50 | 25 | 39 | 41 |
| 30 | 46 | 35 | 23 | 53 |

**GROUPED DATA**

| Class Limits | Class Mark | Class Frequency |
|---|---|---|
| 15.5–24.5 | 20 | 3 |
| 24.5–33.5 | 29 | 6 |
| 33.5–42.5 | 38 | 7 |
| 42.5–51.5 | 47 | 5 |
| 51.5–60.5 | 56 | 4 |

The **class limits** of the grouped data are selected so that each age is in one class. The **class marks** of the grouped data are the middle numbers of each class.

**B.** You can work with grouped data as if all items in a class were equal to the class mark. You can use the data above as if there were:

3 of age 20    6 of age 29    7 of age 38    5 of age 47    4 of age 56

For the grouped data:

Mean $= [(3 \times 20) + (6 \times 29) + (7 \times 38) + (5 \times 47) + (4 \times 56)] \div 25$

$= 38.36$

**C.** A **histogram** is a bar graph that shows class limits, class marks, and class frequencies for grouped data.

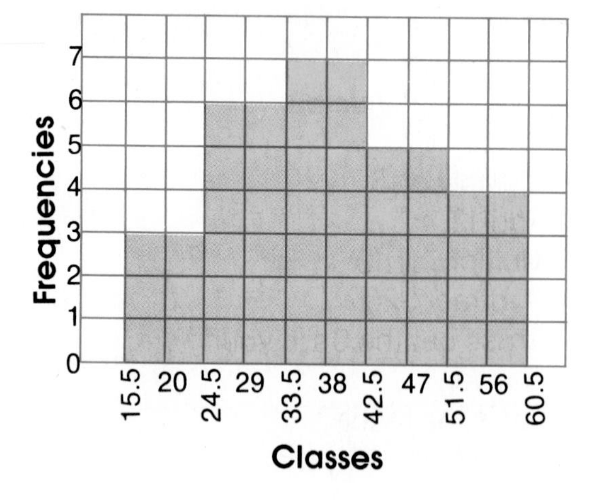


**D.** A **frequency polygon** is a line graph through the midpoints of the tops of the bars of a histogram.

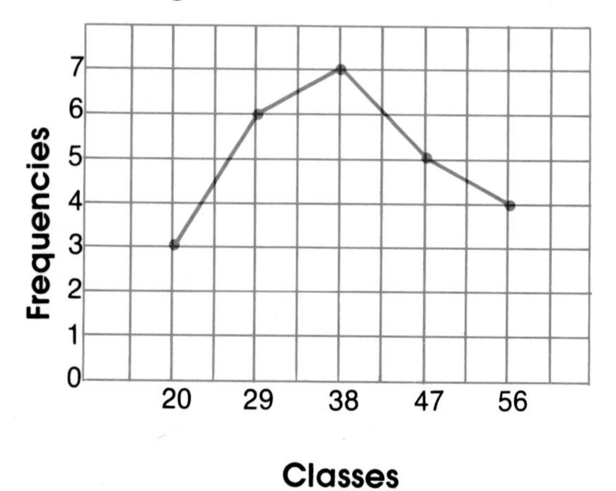

## CLASS EXERCISES

1. Find the median, mode, and range of the grouped data on page 372.

*Use this histogram of grouped test scores.*

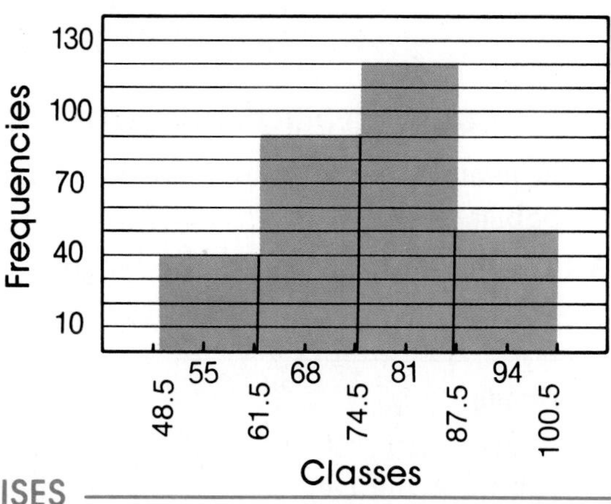


2. What is the total number of scores?
3. Find the mean, median, mode, and range.

## EXERCISES

*Use the table.*

1. Group the data on budgets. Use these class limits (millions): 5.5–14.5, 14.5–23.5, 23.5–32.5, 32.5–41.5, 41.5–50.5. How many libraries are in each class? What is the class mark for each class?
2. Use your group data from exercise **1.** Find the mean, median, mode, and range.
3. Draw a histogram for the budgets.
4. Group the data on books. Use these class limits (millions): 1.05–3.95, 3.95–6.85, 6.85–9.75. Give the class mark for each class.
5. Use your grouped data from exercise **4.** Find the mean, median, mode, and range.
6. Draw a frequency polygon for the numbers of books.

| Library | Budget (Millions) | Books (Millions) |
|---|---|---|
| Baltimore | $ 9 | 2.2 |
| Chicago | $24 | 6.2 |
| Cleveland | $16 | 2.7 |
| Dallas | $ 8 | 1.8 |
| Denver | $ 8 | 1.7 |
| Detroit | $13 | 2.5 |
| Houston | $10 | 2.1 |
| Los Angeles | $20 | 4.1 |
| Miami | $11 | 1.4 |
| Minneapolis | $ 8 | 1.5 |
| NY-Manhattan | $47 | 9.3 |
| NY-Brooklyn | $17 | 3.8 |
| Philadelphia | $19 | 3.1 |
| San Francisco | $ 7 | 1.6 |
| Seattle | $ 7 | 1.5 |
| Washington, D.C. | $10 | 1.9 |

### Logical Reasoning

If you buy scarves at 4 for $5 and sell them at 3 for $5, how many scarves will you have to sell to make $100 profit?

## 10-11 Using Probability and Statistics

Data given in graphs can be used to find statistical measures and probabilities.

**A.** The **pictograph** shows the lengths of the world's longest bridges. All lengths are rounded to the nearest 1,000 m.

| Bridge | Length Each ● represents 4,000 m |
|---|---|
| Chesapeake Bay | ● ● ● ● ● ● ● |
| Lake Maracaibo | ● ● ◔ |
| Lake Pontchartrain I | ● ● ● ● ● ● ● ● ● ◖ |
| Lake Pontchartrain II | ● ● ● ● ● ● ● ● ● ◖ |
| Marathon Key | ● ● ● |
| Presidente Costa e Silva | ● ● ● ◖ |
| San Mateo-Hayward I | ● ● ◕ |
| San Mateo-Hayward II | ● ● ◕ |

Find the mean length of these bridges.

$$\begin{aligned} \text{Mean} &= (\text{Number of } \bullet \times 4{,}000) \div 8 \\ &= \left(40\tfrac{1}{4} \times 4{,}000\right) \div 8 \\ &= 161{,}000 \div 8 \\ &= 20{,}125 \end{aligned}$$

The mean length of the bridges is 20,125 m.

**B.** The 8 members of the geography club decided to write reports about the world's longest bridges. They wrote the name of each bridge on a card and put the cards in a bag. Each member will select a card at random. (The cards are not replaced.) Find the probability that each of the first 2 members selects one of the 3 longest bridges.

P(1st and 2nd members get one of 3 longest bridges)

$$\begin{aligned} &= \text{P(a longest bridge)} \times \text{P(a longest bridge, given a longest bridge)} \\ &= \frac{3}{8} \times \frac{2}{7} \\ &= \frac{6}{56} = \frac{3}{28} \end{aligned}$$

## CLASS EXERCISES

*Use the pictograph on page 374*

**1.** Find the median, mode, and range of this set of data.

*Find these probabilities for the bridges selected by the members of the geography club.*

**2.** P(1st gets a San Mateo-Hayward bridge)

**3.** P(1st does *not* get a bridge with length = mode)

**4.** P(1st gets Marathon Key and 2nd gets Chesapeake Bay)

## PROBLEMS

*The pictograph shows the areas of the first 13 states to enter the Union. All areas are rounded to the nearest 5,000 km².*

| State | Area ■ represents 20,000 km² |
|---|---|
| Delaware | ▸ |
| Pennsylvania | ■■■■■▙ |
| New Jersey | ■ |
| Georgia | ■■■■■■■◣ |
| Connecticut | ▙ |
| Massachusetts | ■ |
| Maryland | ■▸ |
| S. Carolina | ■■■■ |
| New Hampshire | ■▸ |
| Virginia | ■■■■■▸ |
| New York | ■■■■■■◣ |
| N. Carolina | ■■■■■■■▙ |
| Rhode Island | ▸ |

**1.** Find the mean area of these states.

**2.** Find the median, mode, and range.

*Each member of the history club selected one of these 13 states at random, without replacement. Find:*

**3.** P(1st member gets a state with first letter N)

**4.** P(1st member gets a state with area $<$ mean)

**5.** P(1st member gets one of the Carolinas)

**6.** P(1st and 2nd members get one of the 5 smallest states)

**7.** P(1st member gets Virginia and 2nd member gets Georgia)

★ **8.** P(1st, 2nd, and 3rd members get one of the 3 largest states)

### THINK!

**A Long Way?**

Two volumes of Shakespeare's plays are standing side by side on a shelf. A bookworm starts at page 1 of Volume I and eats its way to the last page of Volume II. If each cover is 4 mm thick, and each book, (without its cover) is 50 mm thick, how far does the bookworm travel?

**3.** $\frac{4}{13}$

Homework page 512

# Problem Solving READ • PLAN DO ANSWER • CHECK

## 10-13 Interpreting Information

Sometimes the same information is presented in different ways to support different points of view.

**A.** This graph was presented to the stockholders of Company A to show how successful the company had been compared to its major competitor, Company B.

This graph was presented to the stockholders of Company B to prove their success compared to Company A.

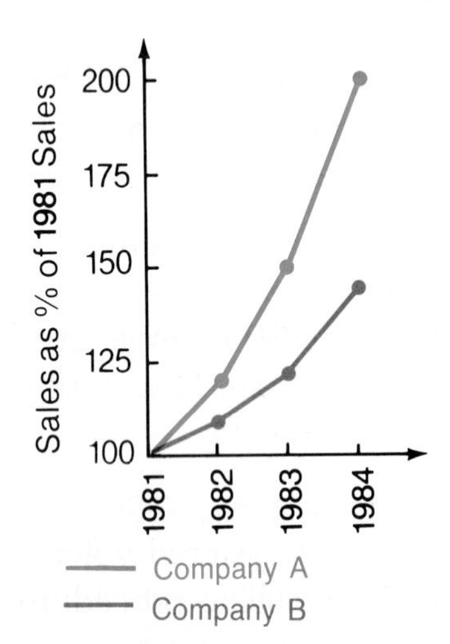


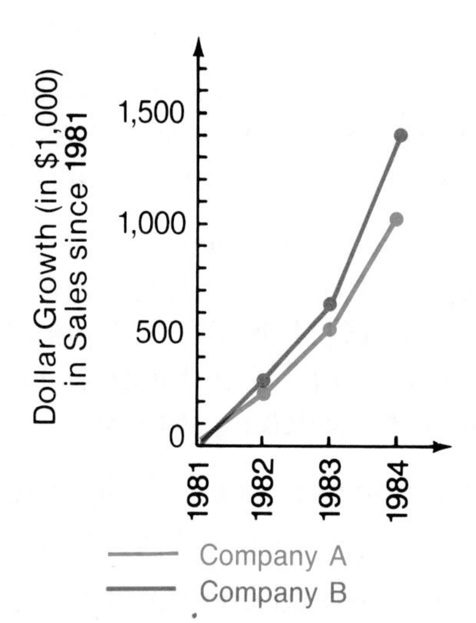


Both graphs give the *same* information from a different viewpoint. The total sales for these companies were:

| Total Sales (in $1,000) | 1981 | 1982 | 1983 | 1984 |
|---|---|---|---|---|
| Company A | 1,000 | 1,200 | 1,500 | 2,025 |
| Company B | 3,000 | 3,300 | 3,630 | 4,362 |

Because of smaller total sales in 1981 Company A shows a larger rate (%) of growth, although Company B has a greater dollar-growth per year in each of the years.

**B.** Jan's batting average improved 25% over her last year's average. Micki's average improved 20%. Which showed greater improvement?

Jan had the greater *rate* of improvement. However, Micki may have had a greater *total* improvement. For example, if Jan's average last year was .220, she improved $.25 \times .220 = .055$ to .275. If Micki's average was .300, she improved $.20 \times .300 = .060$ to .360.

## CLASS EXERCISES

1. The information in the table on page 378 could also be presented as rate (%) of increase each year, compared to the previous year. Which company would appear more successful using this presentation? Why does the one they used better express their point of view?

2. Use the information in **B** on page 378. What could you conclude from the last year's averages that are given if Jan had improved her average by 30% for this year? What could you conclude from the given rates of improvement if Micki's average last year had been .275?

## PROBLEMS

1. A company's total costs were $1,000,000; its total sales were $1,250,000, leaving a profit of $250,000. Its rate of profit was 25%. Its rate of profit *as a part of sales* was 20%. Which is the company more likely to report to its stockholders? To the public who think its prices are too high?

2. An advertiser claims "Our new, improved product is 20% better." What does the advertiser hope you will think this means? What could it mean that is not as strong a statement about the product?

3. Each of the graphs below shows the total sales of Company A (table, page 378). Which makes the company appear more successful? What differences in graphs cause this?

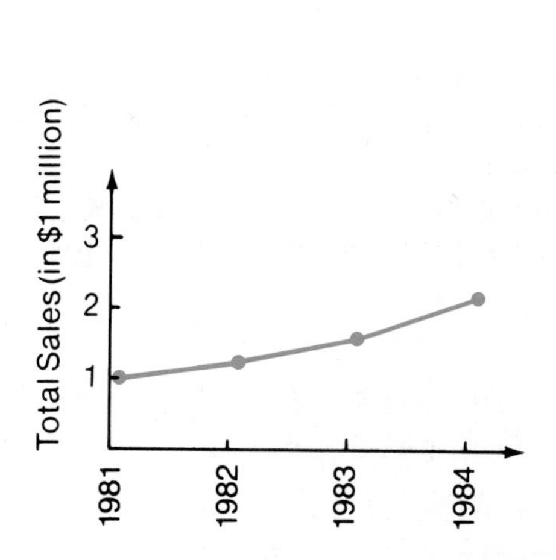


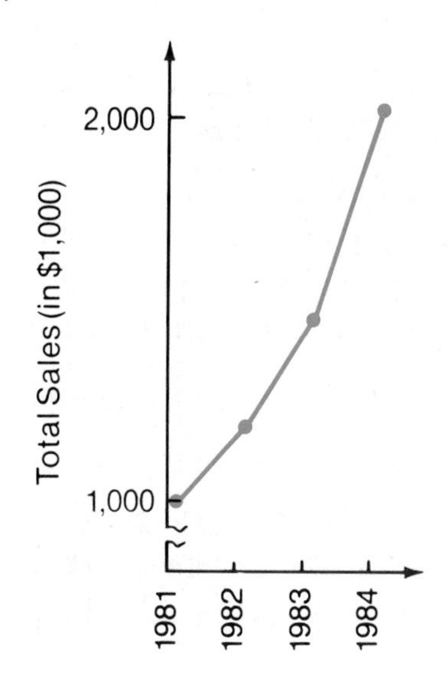


## ON YOUR OWN

Find two line graphs in the newspaper. Redraw the graphs to create a different impression.

## Computers and Data Bases

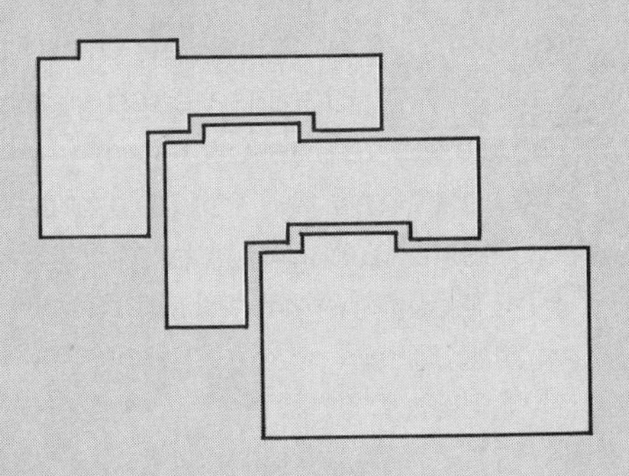

A **data base** is a place where data, or information, is stored for computer use. Data bases are designed so that users can work easily with the data. For example, an insurance company might store the birth dates of all its policy holders. The data might be arranged alphabetically by the policy holders' last names.

The data base itself is only one part of a **data base management system** (DBMS). The other important part is the **data base manager.** The data base manager is a program that controls the input, processing, and output of data. In using a DBMS, you want to be able to organize, enter, store, retrieve, and change data. A good data base manager makes efficient data retrieval possible while preventing unauthorized changes or searches of the data.

The largest organizational unit of a data base is a **file.** A file holds all the data on a specific topic. For example, a file might consist of insurance policy statistics for the largest city in each state. Another file might hold data on accidents and fires in various cities.

Each file is made up of **records.** A record holds all the facts about one of the file items. For example, there would be one record for each person listed in the file of policy holders. The record might contain the following **fields**: the number of policies held, the type of policies (fire, life, accident, etc.), the value of each policy, and the annual premiums to be paid by the customer. Data bases are helpful for calculating the empirical probability of an event. An insurance underwriter could examine many records and then make a prediction about the probability that there will be more than 100 fires in a city in a given month.

1. What is a data base management system? What are its two main parts?
2. What is the largest organizational unit of a data base?
3. An insurance company might need to calculate the mean of all amounts it paid on accident policies in Chicago during 1986. Explain how records in a data base might be used.
4. Make a list of some data bases you have used. How could these data bases be used to calculate empirical probabilities?
5. How would you create a data base for something that would be useful to you, such as a record or book collection, recipes, or sports scores?

# Problem Solving Strategy

READ **PLAN** DO • ANSWER • CHECK

## Make an Organized List

Neil wants to buy three different souvenirs. He has $10 to spend. How many different combinations can he choose?

> To solve this problem, you must do more than just find how many different combinations of three items can be selected from five items. You need to find the total cost of each combination to see if it is greater than $10. For this type of problem, a good approach is to **make an organized list.**

Use the first letter of each item.

List all the combinations of three with a mug as an item.

Then list all remaining combinations with a poster as an item.

Finally, list the remaining combination with a T-shirt as an item.

If you cross off all combinations that cost over $10, the list will show 7 choices remain.

| BOARDWALK SOUVENIRS | |
|---|---|
| Mug | $3.50 |
| Poster | $2.45 |
| T-shirt | $4.50 |
| Key ring | $1.25 |
| Conch shell | $3.75 |
| (prices include tax.) | |

| Choice | Cost | Total |
|---|---|---|
| MPT | 3.50+2.45+4.50 | $10.45 |
| MPK | 3.50+2.45+1.25 | $ 7.20 |
| MPC | 3.50+2.45+3.75 | $ 9.70 |
| MTK | 3.50+4.50+1.25 | $ 9.25 |
| MTC | 3.50+4.50+3.75 | $11.75 |
| MKC | 3.50+1.25+3.75 | $ 8.50 |
| PTK | 2.45+4.50+1.25 | $ 8.20 |
| PTC | 2.45+4.50+3.75 | $10.70 |
| PKC | 2.45+1.25+3.75 | $ 7.45 |
| TKC | 4.50+1.25+3.75 | $ 9.50 |

---

**1.** Rachel wants to buy 4 different souvenirs from the list above. How many different combinations can she choose? List them.

**2.** If Rachel only has $11 to spend, which combinations of items can she choose?

**3.** Amy, Bob, Cora, and Dave want to sit in four seats on the roller coaster, one behind the other. Amy and Cora are not to sit directly in front of or behind one another. How many different ways can the four friends be seated?

**4.** At the Yogurt Hut you can order vanilla or strawberry yogurt. There is also a choice of toppings: chopped nuts, granola, or sliced bananas, in any combination. How many different choices are possible if your order has only one flavor of yogurt?

Challenge Problems page 521

## Using Probability to Approximate Pi

It has already been shown that the ratio of the circumference to the length of the diameter of any circle is equal to the number **pi** ($\pi$). However, there are many other surprising relationships in mathematics involving $\pi$. Two probability experiments follow.

**A.** A prime number has exactly two whole number factors, itself and 1. A pair of numbers are **relatively prime**, when their greatest common factor is 1. For example, 31 and 15 are relatively prime but 35 and 20 are not (5 is a common factor).

For this experiment, find random pairs of two-digit numbers. Such pairs can be found using a telephone book; simply copy the last two digits of a group of telephone numbers. Why wouldn't the first two digits be a good choice?

**Choose 30 number pairs (n=30). Then complete a table like this one:**

| Number of Pairs (N) | Pair | Relatively Prime? | Number of Relatively Prime Pairs (P) |
|---|---|---|---|
| 1 | 16,38 | No | 0 |
| 2 | 41,19 | Yes | 1 |
| 3 | 35,96 | Yes | 2 |
| 4 | 72,50 | No | 2 |

You will need a table of square roots or a calculator with a square-root key. Use the formula:

$\sqrt{\frac{6 \times N}{P}}$ to find an approximate value of $\pi$.

In this case $6 \times N = 6(30) = 180$. If 17 of the 30 pairs tested were relatively prime, $P = 17$ and:

$$\pi \doteq \sqrt{\frac{180}{17}} \doteq \sqrt{10.588} \doteq 3.254$$

1. Repeat the experiment several times, increasing the number of pairs tested to 50. Compare your results with $\pi = 3.14159\ldots$. Do the approximations get closer as the number of pairs increases?

**B.** To perform this experiment, you will need a nickel and a large grid of squares drawn on paper or cardboard. The sides of each square of the grid should be drawn the same length as the nickel's diameter (2 cm).

Toss the nickel onto the grid. If the nickel covers a point of intersection on the grid, then the outcome is a "hit." If the nickel does not cover an intersection point, then the outcome is a "miss."

Toss the nickel 100 times. Record the number of hits and misses using tally marks. The total number of tosses (T) equals hits (H) + misses (M). Use the formula

$\frac{4 \times H}{T}$ to find an approximate value of $\pi$.

In this case T = 100. If there were 67 hits, the approximation would be

$\frac{4 \times 67}{100} = 2.68.$

Keep in mind that results will vary widely from the true value of $\pi$.

**2.** Do the experiment several times. Compare your results with $\pi = 3.14159 \ldots$.

## ON YOUR OWN

**1.** Compare results for the experiment in B with some classmates. Try combining your hits and misses with theirs, then use the formula again with the combined totals. Is the result a better approximation for $\pi$? Do you think the results would be even closer to $\pi$ if the coin were tossed 1,000 times? 10,000 times?

**2.** Try to find a book or computer printout that gives the value of $\pi$ to 200 decimal places. Separate the first group of 100 places from the second group of 100 places. Record the frequency of each digit from 0 to 9 in the first group, then the second group. Compute the total frequency of each digit. Does any digit stand out as being much more frequent? Does any digit appear to be falling behind the rest in the second grouping?

# Unit Review

*One card is selected at random from this set of cards.*
*Find the probabilities. (pages 354–355)*

**1.** P (green) **2.** P (1)

**3.** P (orange or red) **4.** P (2 or 3)

**5.** P (green or 1) **6.** P (green and 1)

**7.** P (orange and 3) **8.** P (1 or 2 or 3)

1 2 3 1 2 1 1 2

*Find the probabilities. (pages 358–359)*

**9.** For one student selected at random from Mr. Bell's class, P (student likes music) = .8
P (student collects stamps) = .3
P (student likes music and collects stamps) =
Find P (student likes music or collects stamps). **.85**

**10.** P (Carla gets an A in math.) = .6
P (Carla gets a B in math.) = .3
Find P (Carla gets a grade below B in math.)

*One card is selected at random from the set of cards above. Then, a second card is selected. Find the probabilities:*
*a) with the first card replaced.*
*b) without the first card replaced. (pages 360–363)*

**11.** P (green then red) **12.** P (blue then green) **13.** P (both green)

**14.** P (both red) **15.** P (both blue) **16.** P (both 1)

*Draw a tree diagram. (pages 364–365)*

**17.** List all possible orders of finish for a race in which Hugh, Clark, and Frank compete.

*Give factorial notation and a standard numeral for each. (pages 366–369)*

**18.** $_5P_2$ **19.** $_5C_2$ **20.** $_7C_4$ **21.** $_6P_6$ **22.** $_8C_1$

*Find the mean, median, mode, and range for these sets of data. (pages 370–371)*

**23.** 37, 56, 47, 68, 37

**24.** 95, 80, 110, 101, 80, 110

*Use the grouped data in this table. (pages 372–373)*

**25.** Find the class marks.

**26.** Find the total number in the set of data.

**27.** Find the mean, median, mode, and range.

**28.** Draw a histogram and a frequency polygon.

| Class limits | Class mark | Class frequency |
|---|---|---|
| 9.5–16.5 | | 10 |
| 16.5–23.5 | | 11 |
| 23.5–30.5 | | 13 |
| 30.5–37.5 | | 6 |

*Solve the problems. (pages 356–357, 374–379)*

**29.** On 27 of the last 300 days, Flight 524 has been late in arriving at Los Angeles. What is the probability it will be late on a day selected at random in the future?

**30.** Of 100 homes surveyed 94 had at least one radio. Based on this sample, how many of the 28,500 homes from which this sample was selected have at least one radio?

**31.** When a store advertises "Our prices are 20% less," what does the advertiser hope you will think this means? What could it mean that would be a weaker statement?

**32.** The salaries of five salespersons for a company are $86,000, $50,000, $12,000, $10,000 and $10,000. In an advertisement for a new salesperson, which of the mean, median, or mode is the company most likely to use?

**33.** In how many ways can an auto dealer select 2 of 8 cars to be put on sale?

**34.** In how many ways can first and second place in a race be awarded if there are 8 runners in the race?

**35.** Use the pictograph on page 374. The name of one bridge is selected at random, then the name of a second is selected without replacement. Find P(length of each $<$ 14,000 m)

**36.** Use the pictograph on page 375. The names of two states are selected in succession, without replacement. Find P(both names have N as first letter).

# Enrichment

## Standard Deviation

The mean, median, and mode give information about the "middle" or "center" of a set of data.

The range gives information about the "spread" of the data.

Other statistics give information about how a set of data groups about the mean.

**A.** Average Difference

**Example**
Find the **average difference** from the mean for:

*Data:* 20, 36, 54, 90
*Mean:* $(20 + 36 + 54 + 90) \div 4 = 50$

**Step 1** Subtract each number from the mean.

$50 - 20 = 30$ $\quad$ $50 - 54 = {}^{-}4$
$50 - 36 = 14$ $\quad$ $50 - 90 = {}^{-}40$

**Step 2** Add the absolute values of the differences.

$$|30| + |14| + |{}^{-}4| + |{}^{-}40| = 88$$

**Step 3** Divide by the number of entries in the data set.

$$88 \div 4 = 22$$

The average difference from the mean is 22.

*Find the average difference from the mean for each set of data. The mean in each case is 50.*

**1.** 0, 0, 100, 100
**2.** 48, 49, 51, 52
**3.** 50, 50, 50, 50
**4.** 38, 44, 56, 62
**5.** 35, 45, 55, 65
**6.** 20, 40, 60, 80

*Compare the average differences from the mean in Exercises 1–6. Decide without computing which set of data in Exercises 7–9 has the greatest average difference from the mean, and which set of data has the least average difference from the mean.*

**7.** *Mean:* 50
- **a.** 34, 42, 58, 66
- **b.** 10, 25, 75, 90
- **c.** 46, 50, 50, 54

**8.** *Mean:* 60
- **a.** 30, 45, 75, 90
- **b.** 37, 46, 72, 85
- **c.** 5, 45, 78, 112

**9.** *Mean:* 72
- **a.** 70, 71, 73, 74
- **b.** 64, 64, 78, 82
- **c.** 31, 43, 100, 114

**B.** Standard Deviation

Statisticians have found that with samples from large populations, the standard deviation gives a better picture of the whole population than the average difference from the mean.

**Example**

Find the **standard deviation** from the mean for:

*Data:* 20, 36, 54, 90
*Mean:* 50

**Step 1** Subtract each number from the mean.

$50 - 20 = 30$ $\quad$ $50 - 54 = {}^-4$
$50 - 36 = 14$ $\quad$ $50 - 90 = {}^-40$

**Step 2** Square each difference.

$30^2 = 900$ $\quad$ $({}^-4)^2 = 16$
$14^2 = 196$ $\quad$ $({}^-40)^2 = 1{,}600$

**Step 3** Add the squares of the differences.

$$900 + 196 + 16 + 1{,}600 = 2{,}712$$

**Step 4** Divide the sum of the squares of the differences by the number of entries in the data set. This gives the variance.

$$\text{Variance} = 2{,}712 \div 4 = 678$$

**Step 5** Find the positive square root of the variance.

$$\sqrt{678} = 26.0 \text{ to the nearest tenth}$$

The standard deviation from the mean is 26.0.

*Use the method on page 220 or a calculator to find each square root to the nearest tenth.*

**10.** $\sqrt{10{,}000}$ **11.** $\sqrt{10}$ **12.** $\sqrt{0}$ **13.** $\sqrt{360}$ **14.** $\sqrt{500}$ **15.** $\sqrt{2{,}000}$

*Find the variance and standard deviation for each set of data. The mean in each case is 50.*

**16.** 0, 0, 100, 100 **17.** 48, 49, 51, 52 **18.** 50, 50, 50, 50

**19.** 38, 44, 56, 62 **20.** 35, 45, 55, 65 **21.** 20, 40, 60, 80

# Cumulative Review

**1.** ${}_6P_4 = $ ▒
- **a.** 30
- **b.** 360
- **c.** 180
- **d.** Not given

**2.** 698 m = ▒ km
- **a.** 698,000 km
- **b.** 69.8 km
- **c.** 0.698 km
- **d.** Not given

**3.** $352\overline{)14,100}$
- **a.** 40 R20
- **b.** 4 R12
- **c.** 4 R20
- **d.** Not given

**4.** 40 is 16% of ▒.
- **a.** 6.4
- **b.** 250
- **c.** .004
- **d.** Not given

**5.** Find the mean of this set of data: 4, 10, 10, 3, 8
- **a.** 8
- **b.** 35
- **c.** 10
- **d.** Not given

**6.** Solve. $3x - 14 = 40$
- **a.** $8\frac{2}{3}$
- **b.** 18
- **c.** 162
- **d.** Not given

**7.** $2.347 \times 3.8$
- **a.** 8.9186
- **b.** 89.186
- **c.** 6.147
- **d.** Not given

**8.** D C A 20 cm B

Perimeter = 64 cm
Length of $\overline{BC}$ = ▒
- **a.** 44 cm
- **b.** 22 cm
- **c.** 12 cm
- **d.** Not given

**9.** P(A in English) = .6
P(A in math) = .7
P(A in Eng. and not in math.) = ▒
- **a.** .42
- **b.** .18
- **c.** .88
- **d.** Not given

**10.** Round 3,699,763 to the nearest thousand.
- **a.** 3,700,000
- **b.** 3,690,000
- **c.** 3,699,000
- **d.** Not given

**11.** Mrs. Chander's monthly salary before her pay raise was $1,250. After her raise her salary was $1,400. What was the percent of increase of her salary?
- **a.** 150%
- **b.** about 10.7%
- **c.** 12%
- **d.** Not given

**12.** When the stock exchange closed, the price of one share of a stock was $42.90. During that day the stock's change in value per share was ⁻$8.65. What was this stock's opening value per share that day?
- **a.** $51.55
- **b.** $34.25
- **c.** ⁻$34.25
- **d.** Not given

**13.** A machine can fill 198 cartons in $4\frac{1}{2}$ h. How many cartons can it fill in 1 h?
- **a.** 891 cartons
- **b.** 44 cartons
- **c.** $202\frac{1}{2}$ cartons
- **d.** Not given

**14.** Light travels at the speed of $3 \times 10^5$ km/s. How far does light travel in $8 \times 10^{-3}$ s?
- **a.** $24 \times 10^8$ km
- **b.** $24 \times 10^{-15}$ km
- **c.** 2,400 km
- **d.** Not given

# 11 Coordinate Graphing

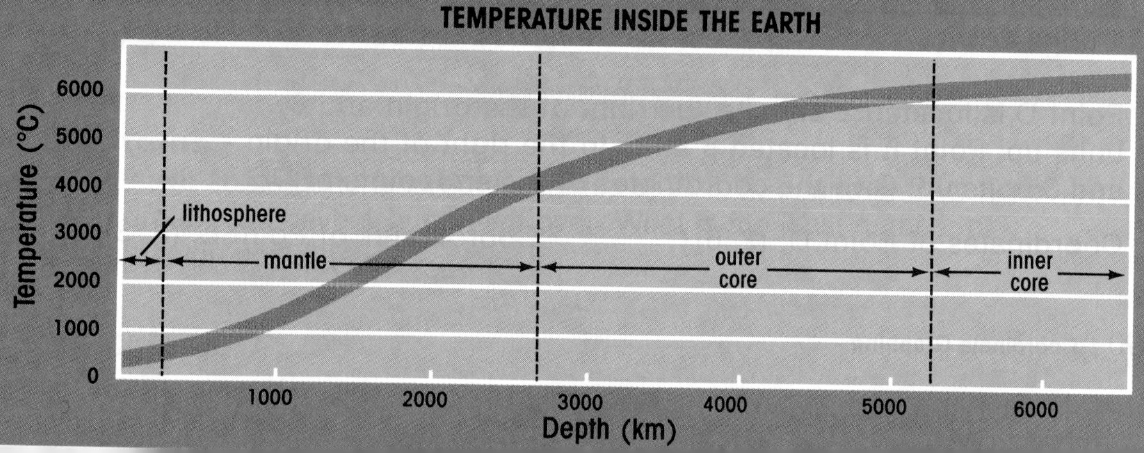

## TECHNOLOGY

### Graphics and Communications with Computers

**A.** Computers frequently can display **graphics** on a video screen. The screen is like a grid. Every location—or cell—on it is identified by a row coordinate and a column coordinate. A cell is called a **pixel** (picture element). By lighting up the various pixels, the program creates a graphic display.

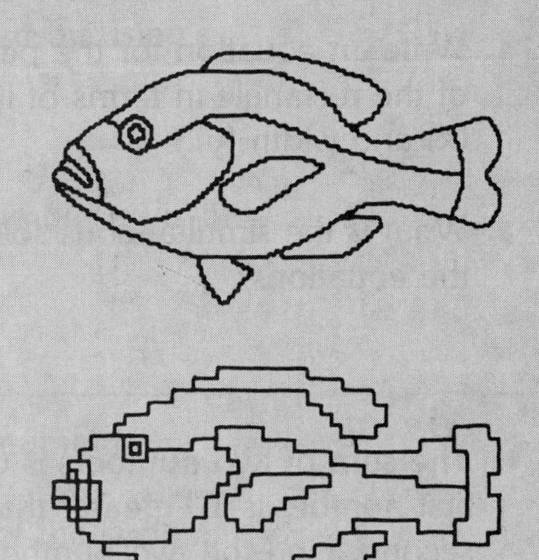

**High-resolution graphics** use a grid of 60,000 pixels or more. **Low resolution graphics** use about 2,000 groups of pixels. A display made with high-resolution graphics can show much more detail.

**B.** Today, computer data are constantly being sent, or **transmitted,** from one machine to another. This is possible because computer data are made up of electronic signals, which can be carried by electrical wire. Both computer cables and telephone lines can carry data.

Although cable is expensive to install, it can transmit data faster than telephone wires. Telephone wire transmission, although slower, can make use of the telephone wires that already exist in most of the world. A **modem** (modulator-demodulator) converts computer data for transmission over phone wires and converts it back to computer data at the other end of the line.

If you have a home computer, modem, and access to telephone lines, you may be able to use services such as shopping at home (from a catalog your video screen displays), banking at home, or electronic mail. Electronic mail sends messages to another person's computer and returns the person's answer to you.

1. Which gives a more detailed graphic display, high-resolution or low-resolution graphics? Which type do you think is simpler to use?
2. Why can computer data be transmitted over wires?
3. Which method of transmitting computer data, over cables or over telephone lines, is faster?
4. Which method of transmitting data uses a modem?
5. What advantages and disadvantages do you think a shop-at-home service would have?

# Problem Solving Strategy

READ · PLAN · **DO** · ANSWER · CHECK

## Mixed Strategies

| Use Logical Reasoning | Guess and Check | Make an Organized List |
| --- | --- | --- |
| Draw a Diagram | Make a Model | Make a Table |
| | Work a Simpler Problem | |

*Solve the problems.*

1. Frank has twice as many stamps in his collection as Joe. Paula has twice as many stamps as Frank. All together, they have 651 stamps. How many stamps does each person have?

2. Lisa is taking a picture of her friends Sue, Richard, Jaime, and Karla. She wants two people to sit in front and two people to stand between them. How many different ways can she arrange her friends for the photograph?

3. Marta, Ned, Olga, and Paul each like different sports. One swims, one skates, one is a runner, and one is a skier. Each sat on a different side of a square table during lunch. The swimmer sat on Marta's right. The runner sat opposite Ned. Olga sat next to Paul, on his right. A male sat on the skater's left. What is each person's sport?

4. Five families live along the same road. The Greens live 12 km south of the Browns. The Greens live 16 km north of the Drews. The Smiths live midway between the Browns and the Drews. The Lobels live midway between the Smiths and the Browns. List the families in order from north to south and tell how far each is from the family just to its north.

5. On Day 1 of an experiment, plant A was 8 cm tall and plant B was 5 cm tall. Plant A was not given sunlight and grew 0.3 cm a day. Plant B got plenty of sunlight and grew .6 cm a day. On what day were both plants the same height?

6. Find the total number of angles in the figure below.

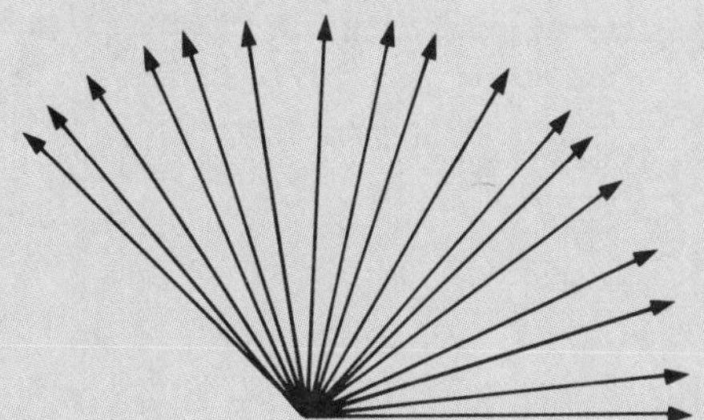

Challenge Problems page 522

# Problem Solving Project

READ PLAN DO • ANSWER • CHECK

## Trigonometry

**A.** If two right triangles have a pair of acute angles of equal measure, then the triangles are similar.

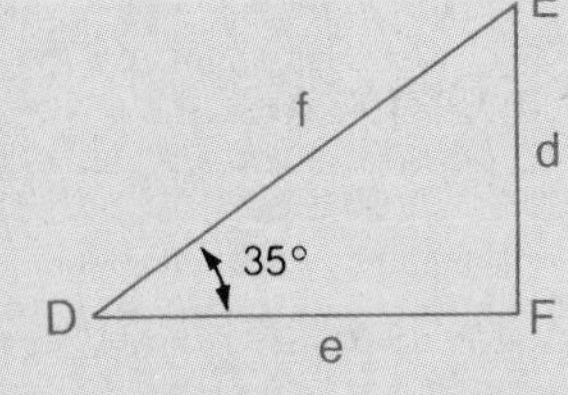


$m\angle C = m\angle F = 90°$
$m\angle A = m\angle D = 35°$

Then,
$m\angle B = m\angle E = 180° - (90° + 35°)$
$= 55°$

The lengths of corresponding sides of similar triangles are in proportion.

So, $\frac{a}{d} = \frac{b}{e}$

$$\frac{d}{b} \cdot \frac{a}{d} = \frac{d}{b} \cdot \frac{b}{e} \Rightarrow \frac{\cancel{d}^{1} \cdot a}{b \cdot \cancel{d}_{1}} = \frac{d \cdot \cancel{b}^{1}}{\cancel{b}_{1} \cdot e}$$

$\frac{a}{b} = \frac{d}{e}$, or $\tan A = \tan D$

The trigonometric ratios for $\angle A$, $\angle D$ and any angle of measure 35° are equal. You can write:

$\tan A = \tan D = \tan 35°$
$\sin A = \sin D = \sin 35°$
$\cos A = \cos D = \cos 35°$

**If two angles have equal measures, then the trigonometric ratios for the angles have the same values.**

**B.** Values of the tangent, sine, and cosine ratios for various angle measures are given in this table (to the nearest thousandth).

**Example** The length of the side of a right triangle adjacent to its 50° angle is 6.8 cm. Find the length of the side opposite this angle.

$\frac{y}{6.8} = \tan 50°$

$\frac{y}{6.8} = 1.192$

So, $y = (1.192) \cdot (6.8) \doteq 8.1$

The length of the side is 8.1 cm, to the nearest tenth.

| x° | tan x° | sin x° | cos x° |
|---|---|---|---|
| 10° | .176 | .174 | .985 |
| 20° | .364 | .342 | .940 |
| 30° | .577 | .500 | .866 |
| 40° | .839 | .643 | .766 |
| 45° | 1.000 | .707 | .707 |
| 50° | 1.192 | .766 | .643 |
| 60° | 1.732 | .866 | .500 |
| 70° | 2.747 | .940 | .342 |
| 80° | 5.671 | .985 | .174 |

Use the tangent ratio to complete the table below. △ABC is a right triangle, with right angle C.

| Measure of ∠A | 30° | 70° | 20° | 80° | 45° |
|---|---|---|---|---|---|
| Length of $\overline{AC}$ (b) | 10 m | 8 cm | 3.1 km | 40 mm | **5.** |
| Length of $\overline{BC}$ (a) | **1.** | **2.** | **3.** | **4.** | 12 m |

**Example**

The length of the hypotenuse of a right triangle is 7 m. Find the length of the side opposite its 30° angle and the length of the side adjacent to its 30° angle.

$\frac{y}{7} = \sin 30°$

$\frac{y}{7} = .500$

$y = (7) \cdot (.500) = 3.5$

The length of the opposite side is 3.5 m.

$\frac{x}{7} = \cos 30°$

$\frac{x}{7} = .866$

$x = (7) \cdot (.866) \doteq 6.1$

The length of the adjacent side is about 6.1 m.

Use the sine and cosine ratios to complete the table below. △ABC is a right triangle, with right angle C.

| Measure of ∠A | 20° | 50° | 60° | 10° | 30° |
|---|---|---|---|---|---|
| Length of $\overline{AB}$ (c) | 8 m | 10 m | 3.4 km | 50 mm | **10.** |
| Length of $\overline{BC}$ (a) | **6.** | **7.** | **8.** | **9.** | 20 km |
| Length of $\overline{AC}$ (b) | **11.** | **12.** | **13.** | **14.** | 35 km |

**15.** A 17-meter guy wire makes an angle of 50° with the ground. It is fastened 2 meters from the top of a pole. How tall is the pole, to the nearest meter?

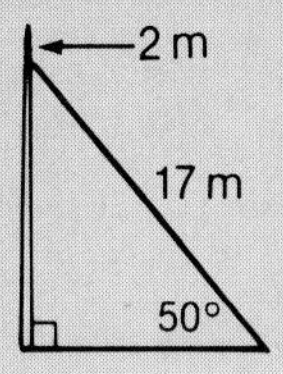


## ON YOUR OWN

Use the drawing at the right. Make up your own trigonometry problem. Ask a classmate to solve it, then check the answer.

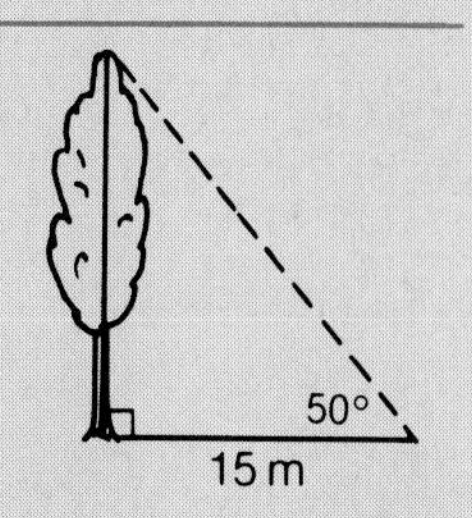

# Unit Review

*Use grid paper to draw a coordinate system. Graph and label each point.* *(pages 390–391)*

**1.** A (4,0) **2.** B $({}^-1, {}^-3)$ **3.** C $({}^-1, 1)$ **4.** D $({}^-3, 3)$ **5.** E (2, 3)

**6.** Use the answers to Exercises 1–5. Draw: $\overline{AB}$, $\overline{BC}$, $\overline{CD}$, $\overline{DE}$, $\overline{EA}$.

**7.** Which line segment is parallel to the x axis; to the y axis?

*Copy and complete.* *(pages 392–393)*

| x | 0 | 2 | $^-2$ | 4 | $^-4$ |
|---|---|---|---|---|---|
| $y = {}^-2x + {}^-2$ | **8.** | **9.** | **10.** | **11.** | **12.** |

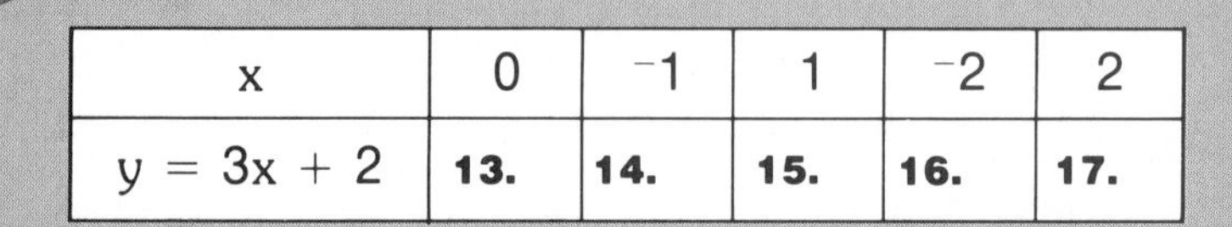

| x | 0 | $^-1$ | 1 | $^-2$ | 2 |
|---|---|---|---|---|---|
| $y = 3x + 2$ | **13.** | **14.** | **15.** | **16.** | **17.** |

*Graph each equation on a coordinate system. Use these values of x: $^-4$, $^-2$, 0, 2, 4.* *(pages 392–395)*

**18.** $y = {}^-2x + {}^-2$

**19.** $y = 3x + 2$

**20.** $y = {}^-4x$

**21.** $y = x - 3$

**22.** $y = 2x + {}^-1$

**23.** $y = {}^-3x + 4$

**24.** $x + y = 0$

**25.** $2x - y = {}^-8$

**26.** $4y - x = 4$

**27.** ${}^-2x + 2y = 2$

**28.** $4x + y = 6$

**29.** $x + {}^-2y = {}^-4$

*Find three solutions of each equation. Then graph each pair of equations on a coordinate grid and find the solution of the system.* *(pages 398–399)*

**30.** $y = x + 5$
$y = {}^-2x - 1$

**31.** $y = 2x + {}^-6$
$y = {}^-3 - x$

**32.** $y = x + {}^-2$
$x + 3y = {}^-6$

**33.** $y = 2x + 1$
${}^-2x + 3y = 11$

**34.** $2y - x = {}^-3$
$2x + 4y = 6$

**35.** $2x - y = {}^-5$
$3x - 2y = {}^-7$

*The graph shows the amount of energy (e) in kilowatt-hours used by a 40-watt light bulb that burns for given times (t) in hours. (pages 396–397)*

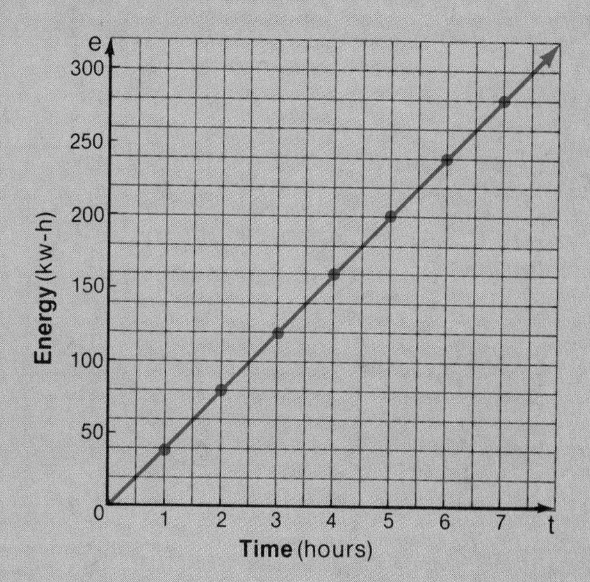


*Find the amount of energy used by the light bulb when:*

**36.** it burns for 4 hours.

**37.** it burns for $\frac{1}{2}$ hours.

**38.** it burns for $6\frac{1}{2}$ hours.

*Find how long the light bulb burned if:*

**39.** it used 80 kw-h of energy.

**40.** it used 140 kw-h of energy.

**41.** it used 200 kw-h of energy.

*Use a system of equations to solve each problem. (pages 400–401)*

**42.** The sum of two numbers is 31. The first number is 15 less than the second. Find the two numbers.

**43.** The perimeter of a rectangle is 56 m. It is 6 m longer than it is wide. Find the length and width of the rectangle.

**44.** Gina has 7 coins, all dimes and nickels. The coins have a total value of 55¢. How many dimes and how many nickels does she have?

**45.** Bobby is twice as old as Sean. The sum of their ages is 39. How old is each?

**46.** A total of $746 was paid by the 218 people who attended the game. Adult tickets cost $5 each and student tickets cost $3 each. How many of each kind of ticket was sold?

**47.** A school supply store received 192 pens, some red and some blue. There are 6 red pens per box and 10 blue pens per box. The store received 22 boxes in all. How many boxes of each color pen did it receive?

# Enrichment

## Variation

**A.** The table and the graph show ordered pairs (d, W) for amounts of work, W, done by a constant force pushing an object distances, d.

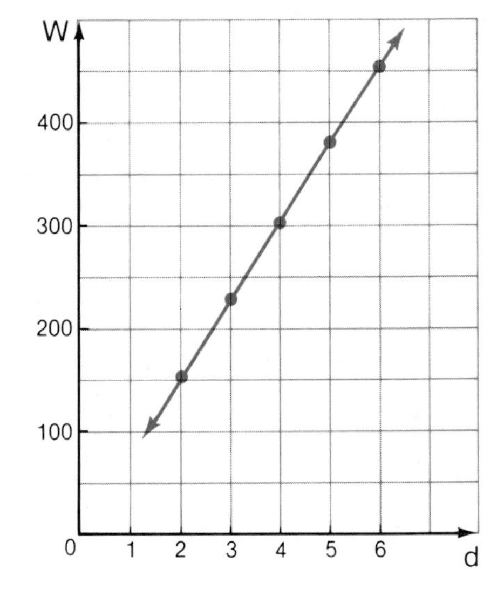


| d | 2 | 3 | 4 | 5 | 6 |
|---|---|---|---|---|---|
| W | 150 | 225 | 300 | 375 | 450 |

For every pair of values in the table,

$\frac{W}{d} = \frac{75}{1}$ so $W = 75 \times d$

W is **directly proportional** to d, or W **varies directly** as d, with **constant of proportionality** 75.

**B.** If you know that one quantity is directly proportional to another, you can write a **proportionality equation.**

**Example**

For a constant voltage, the current, c, flowing in an electrical circuit is directly proportional to the power, p, used in the circuit.

*Write:* $\frac{c}{p} = k$ or $c = k \times p$, where k is the constant of proportionality

If you know one pair of values for p and c, you can find the value of k and write an **exact equation.**

If $c = 10$ when $p = 1{,}200$, $\quad 10 = k \times 1{,}200$

$$k = \frac{1}{120}$$

The exact equation is $c = \frac{1}{120} \times p$

*Write a proportionality equation and an exact equation. Find other values of the variables and draw the graph.*

**1.** The distance, $d$, that a spring is stretched is directly proportional to the force, $F$, applied to it. When $F$ is 40, $d$ is 2.

**2.** The volume, $V$, of water in a tank varies directly with the height, $h$, of the water. The value 4 of $h$ gives the value 200 of $V$.

**3.** $y$ is directly proportional to $x$. The $x$-value 40 gives the $y$-value $^-8$.

**4.** $t$ varies directly as $m$. The value 6 of $m$ gives the value 3 of $t$.

**C.** This table and graph show ordered pairs $(t, P)$ for the amount of power, $P$, used and the amount of time, $t$, used for a constant amount of work.

| t | 1 | 2 | 4 | 10 | 16 |
|---|---|---|---|---|---|
| P | 20 | 10 | 5 | 2 | 1.25 |

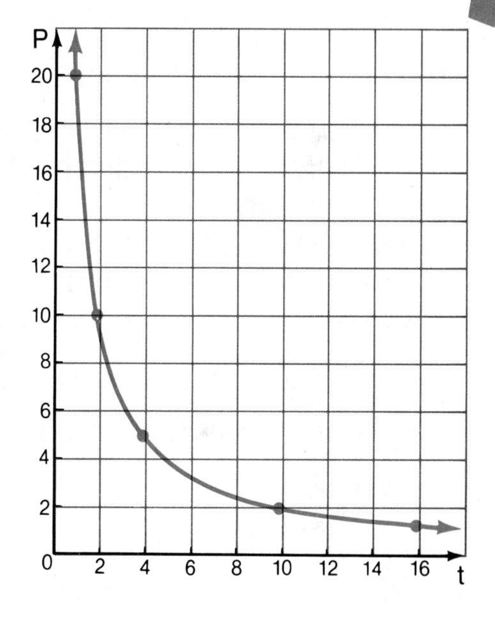


For every pair of values in the table,

$$P \times t = 20$$

$P$ is **inversely proportional** to $t$, or $P$ **varies inversely** as $t$, with constant of proportionality 20.

If you know that one quantity is inversely proportional to another, you can write a proportionality equation.

$$P \times t = k$$

Since you know that $k = 20$, you can write an exact equation.

$$P \times t = 20$$

*Write a proportionality equation and an exact equation. Find other values of the variables and draw the graph.*

**5.** $y$ varies inversely as $x$. When $x$ has the value 2, $y$ has the value 3.

**6.** $r$ is inversely proportional to $w$. When $w$ has the value 5, $r$ has the value $^-2$.

# Cumulative Review

**1.** Find the value of $5x - \frac{y}{2}$ when $x$ is .9 and $y$ is 7.2.

**a.** 8.1
**b.** $-.9$
**c.** .9
**d.** Not given

**2.** Solve.

$\frac{3}{4}d - \frac{7}{8} = 1\frac{1}{2}$

**a.** $3\frac{1}{6}$
**b.** $\frac{5}{6}$
**c.** $2\frac{3}{8}$
**d.** Not given

**3.** Compute.

$$\begin{array}{r} 4 \text{ d } 18 \text{ h} \\ +17 \text{ d } 16 \text{ h} \\ \hline \end{array}$$

**a.** 11 d 10 h
**b.** 12 d 12 h
**c.** 12 d 10 h
**d.** Not given

**4.** What is 65% of 180?

**a.** 115
**b.** 160
**c.** 117
**d.** Not given

**5.** ∠ABC and ∠CBD are supplementary. Find ∠ABC.

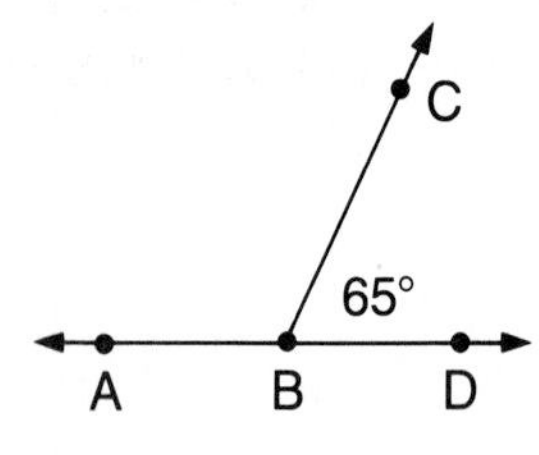


**a.** 115°
**b.** 25°
**c.** 105°
**d.** Not given

**6.** Find the volume.

4 cm
5 cm
12 cm

**a.** 120 $cm^2$
**b.** 240 $cm^3$
**c.** 120 $cm^3$
**d.** Not given

**7.** Write in exponent form.

$4 \times 4 \times 4 \times 4 \times 4$

**a.** $4 \times 5$
**b.** $4^5$
**c.** $5^4$
**d.** Not given

**8.** Find the surface area. Use $\pi = 3.14$.

8 cm
8 cm

**a.** 301.44 $cm^2$
**b.** 251.20 $cm^2$
**c.** 200.96 $cm^2$
**d.** Not given

**9.** Graph the system of equations on a coordinate grid. Find the solution of the system.

$y = 3x - 6$
$y = 2x + {}^{-}4$

**a.** (2, 0)
**b.** (1, 1)
**c.** (0, 2)
**d.** (1, 0)

**10.** A bowl contains 8 red cards, 6 blue cards, and 1 green card. One card is selected at random. Find P (red or green).

**a.** $\frac{8}{15}$
**b.** $\frac{3}{5}$
**c.** $\frac{1}{15}$
**d.** Not given

# Problem Solving Situations

## Fair Pricing

You and your three friends decide to order a pizza pie. You have a choice of three sizes: small, regular, or large. You think the price of the pie should be in proportion to the size of the pie. You don't want to be overcharged. Which size pie will you choose?

**Your Notes**

**Small Pizza Pie**
diameter = 14 in.
price = $3.60

**Regular Pizza Pie**
diameter = 18 in.
price = $7.25

**Large Pizza Pie**
diameter = 21 in.
price = $9.00

**Other Conditions**

- Each slice is $\frac{1}{8}$ of the pie.
- 8% tax on each order.
- Extra cheese is an additional $.75 for a small pie.
- The cost of extra cheese is in proportion to the radius of the pie.

*Work in small groups to find answers and make decisions.*

1. If you order a regular pizza pie with extra cheese, how much change will you receive from a $20 bill?
2. Find the area of each pie. Assuming that $3.60 is a fair price for a small pizza pie and that the price of a pie should be in proportion to its area, what are the "fair" prices of a regular and large pizza pie?
3. About how much larger is the circumference of a large pizza than a small pizza?
4. If you order a regular pie and leave 25% of it over, how much of the area of the pie was eaten?
5. What other things should you think about?
6. What size pie will you choose?

## Carpeting a Room

Your room measures 10 ft by 12 ft. You want to purchase a rug for your room. You have a choice of two different rug sizes. Which size will you choose?

**Your Notes**

**Size of Rugs**
Rug 1: 8 ft by 10 ft
Rug 2: 12 ft by 15 ft

**Cost of Rugs**
Rug 1: \$12.33 per yd²
Rug 2: \$9.75 per yd²

**Other Conditions**
- Installation fee for wall-to-wall carpeting is \$15 per hour.
- The installer can lay 9 yd² of carpet in 28 minutes.
- Your floor is polished oak.

*Work in small groups to find answers and make decisions.*

1. If you choose Rug 1, what percent of the floor area will not be covered?

2. What is the cost of Rug 1? Rug 2?

3. If you choose Rug 2, what percent of the material is excess?

4. About how much time will it take to install a wall-to-wall carpet in your room? About how much will installation cost?

5. What other things should you think about?

6. Which rug will you choose? Explain.

## Maximize Profit

You are working on part of a class economics project to plan the operation of a restaurant. The maximum seating capacity is 152 people. You must order tables for the restaurant. Some tables seat 4 people and some tables seat 6 people. How many tables of each type must you order to maximize your profit?

### Your Notes

**Conditions**

- You must choose at least 15 tables that seat four people.
- You must choose between 10 and 17 tables for six.
- The maximum number of tables that fit in the restaurant is 32.
- Most people who come to your restaurant need a table for four.
- The cost of a complete dinner averages between $16 and $24.
- Most diners prefer to eat when the restaurant is about $\frac{3}{4}$ full.

*Work in small groups to find answers and make decisions.*

1. You choose the same number of tables for four as tables for six. How many of each did you choose? Explain how you made your decision.

2. If you choose 20 tables for four, how many tables for six will you order to maximize the seating capacity? (Hint: Let x represent the number of tables for six.)

3. Using your decision for problem 2, suppose $\frac{3}{5}$ of the tables for four are completely filled and $\frac{2}{3}$ of the tables for six are completely filled with diners. How much money can you expect to make?

4. What other things should you think about?

5. How will you order the tables to maximize your profit?

## Buying a Car

Your family is interested in buying a new car. They have narrowed their choice to three makes of car. Each make has a different mpg (miles per gallon) rating for city and highway driving. What make of car will your family choose?

**Your Notes**

| Make of Car | City mpg | Highway mpg | Quarterly Insurance |
|---|---|---|---|
| Stallion | 26 | 38 | $175 |
| Cheetah | 24 | 32 | $225 |
| Thunderbolt | 18 | 24 | $350 |

**Other Conditions**

- gasoline: unleaded super—$1.29/gallon
  unleaded regular—$1.09/gallon
- Full-size cars use only unleaded super gasoline.
- Steel-belted radial tires are used on all cars.

*Work in small groups to find answers and make decisions.*

1. How much would car insurance cost for one year if your family bought a Thunderbolt?
2. If your family bought a Cheetah and traveled 72 miles in the city and 48 miles on the highway, how many gallons of gasoline would your family use?
3. If your family had a Thunderbolt and paid $19.35 for gasoline, how many gallons would your family buy?
4. Your family bought $5.45 of unleaded regular gasoline for your Stallion. How many miles of highway driving could your family travel?
5. What other things should your family think about?
6. What type of car will your family buy? Explain.

## Buy or Rent a Computer?

Your family wants a computer for word processing and data base management. Computers are expensive, so your family is considering the alternatives to paying cash. You have a choice of three plans: an installment plan, a rent-to-buy plan, or a regular rental plan. Which plan will you recommend?

**Your Notes**

| 24-Month Installment Plan | Rent-to-Buy Plan | Rental Plan |
|---|---|---|
| $57.50 per month | $115 per month for the first 6 months<br>$37 per month for the remaining 18 months | $65 per month for the the first 6 months<br>$55 per month for each additional month |

**Other Conditions**

- A computer store has the computer your family wants on sale for $1,259, cash only.
- There is no charge for service calls on either rental plan.
- There is a $25 charge per service call on the installment plan.
- You can resell a computer for $\frac{5}{8}$ of its original value.

*Work in small groups to find answers and make decisions.*

1. If you choose the 24-month installment plan, how much will the computer cost? How much more is this than renting a computer for 2 years?
2. How much money will you save if you buy the computer for cash instead of using the rent-to-buy plan?
3. Suppose that you bought the computer on the installment plan. During the first 6 months, your computer had to be serviced twice. Over the next year, your computer had to be serviced three times more often than during the first 6 months. During the last 6 months, your computer had to be serviced 3 fewer times than the total number of service calls during the first 18 months. How much did you spend in service charges for the 2 years?
4. What other things should you think about?
5. Which plan will you choose? Explain.

## Choosing Land

There are 3 plots of land suitable for gardening: plot I, plot II, and plot III. You have to decide whether to plant plots I and III together or only plot II. Which choice will you make?

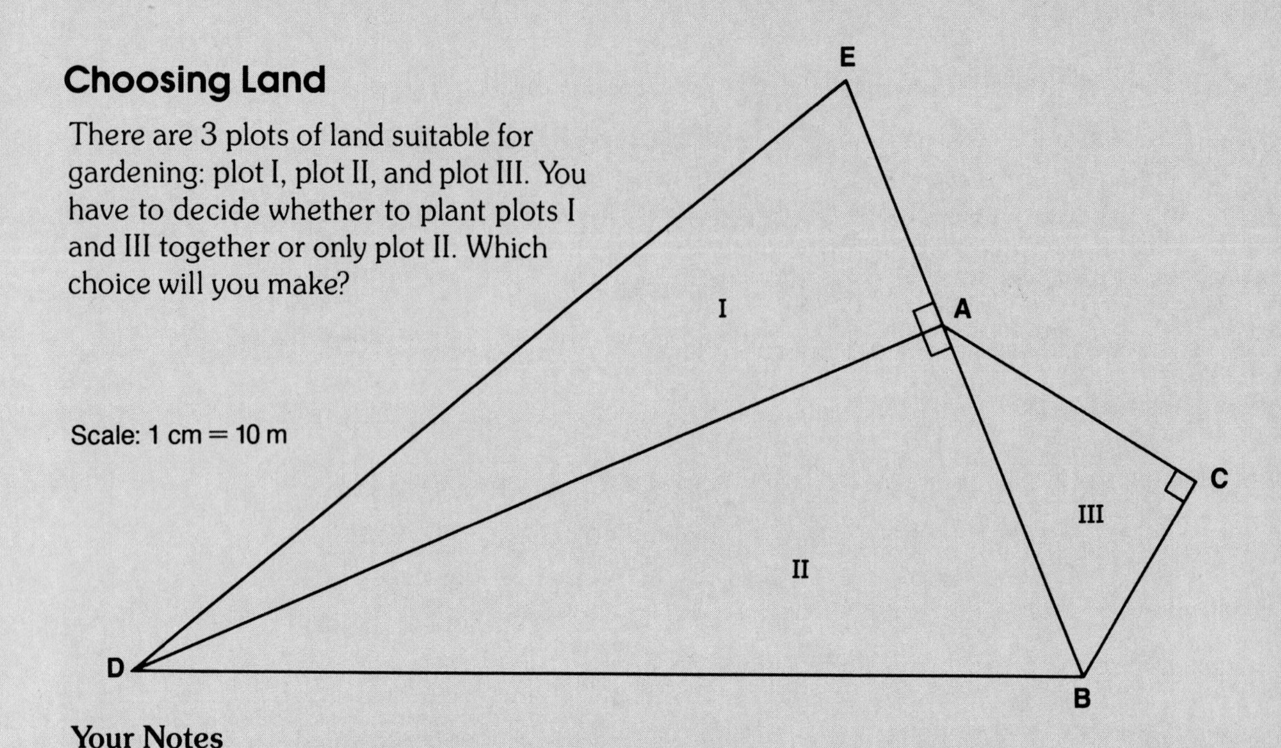


### Your Notes

**Dimensions**

$\overline{BC} = 30$ meters
$\overline{AC} = 40$ meters
$\overline{AD} = 120$ meters
$\overline{BE} = 85$ meters

**Geometric Conditions**

$\overline{BC} \perp \overline{AC}$
$\overline{AD} \perp \overline{BE}$

**Other Conditions**

- 4 meters of metal fencing cost $35.
- 5 meters of wood fencing cost $18.
- Plot II must be completely fenced on all 3 sides with metal fencing.
- Plots I and III must be fenced on only their 2 outer sides with wooden fencing.
- You must not cross plot II to travel between plots I and III.

*Work in small groups to find answers and make decisions.*

1. What are the lengths of $\overline{AB}$, $\overline{BD}$, and $\overline{DE}$?
2. What is the area of plot II? The combined area of plots I and III?
3. What percent of the area of plot II is the combined area of plots I and III?
4. What is the cost of fencing plot II? Plots I and III combined?
5. What percent of the cost of fencing plot II is the cost of fencing both plots I and III?
6. What other things should you think about?
7. What choice will you make? Explain.

**Whole Number Review**
Place Value ........ 418
Comparing Whole Numbers ........ 419
Adding Whole Numbers ........ 420
Subtracting Whole Numbers ........ 422
Multiplying by Ones, Tens, Hundreds, and Thousands ........ 424
More Multiplying ........ 426
Dividing by Ones, Tens, Hundreds, and Thousands ........ 428
More Dividing ........ 432
**Computer Programming** ........ 433
**Homework**
Unit 1 ........ 449
Unit 2 ........ 456
Unit 3 ........ 461
Unit 4 ........ 467
Unit 5 ........ 473
Unit 6 ........ 480
Unit 7 ........ 486
Unit 8 ........ 492
Unit 9 ........ 499
Unit 10 ........ 508
Unit 11 ........ 514
**Challenge Problems**
Units 1–2 ........ 517
Units 3–4 ........ 518
Units 5–6 ........ 519
Units 7–8 ........ 520
Units 9–10 ........ 521
Units 11–12 ........ 522
**Tables of Measure** ........ 523
**Estimation Strategies** ........ 524
**Mental Math Strategies** ........ 525
**Glossary** ........ 526
**Index** ........ 532

## Place Value

**A.** You can use the ten **digits** 0, 1, 2, 3, 4, 5, 6, 7, 8, and 9 to write **standard numerals** for whole numbers. A place value table shows the meaning of the digits in a numeral.

| Trillions | | | | Billions | | | | Millions | | | | Thousands | | | | Ones | | |
|---|---|---|---|---|---|---|---|---|---|---|---|---|---|---|---|---|---|---|
| H | T | O | | H | T | O | | H | T | O | | H | T | O | | H | T | O |
| | 4 | 8 | , | 3 | 2 | 0 | , | 5 | 7 | 0 | , | 7 | 1 | 6 | , | 9 | 1 | 5 |
| | | | | | 8 | 6 | , | 1 | 2 | 4 | , | 5 | 7 | 6 | , | 0 | 3 | 9 |
| | | | | | | | | 5 | 6 | 8 | , | 7 | 9 | 0 | , | 1 | 2 | 3 |

In 48,320,570,716,915 the digit 8 means 8 trillions.
In 86,124,576,039 the digit 8 means 8 ten-billions.
In 568,790,123 the digit 8 means 8 millions.

**B.** Commas separate numerals into groups of three digits called **periods.** To read a numeral, read the digits in each period as a 3-digit numeral, followed by the name of the period.

*Write:* 48,320,570,716,915
*Read:* forty-eight trillion, three hundred twenty billion, five hundred seventy million, seven hundred sixteen thousand, nine hundred fifteen

### EXERCISES

*What does the digit 2 mean in each numeral?*

1. 720
2. 2,307
3. 7,082
4. 28,706
5. 4,329
6. 47,200
7. 612,647
8. 275,009
9. 427,593
10. 56,132
11. 742,819,356
12. 407,216,000
13. 217,348,569
14. 427,613,857
15. 28,617,338
16. 32,364,558
17. 48,291,065
18. 124,475,667
19. 429,136,701,335,101
20. 12,400,365,911,716
21. 238,496,388,609

*Write the standard numeral.*

22. nine thousand, two hundred fourteen
23. seven hundred fifty-four thousand, eighty
24. eighty-four thousand, seven hundred fifty
25. sixty-four million, one hundred thirty-two thousand, one
26. three million, two thousand, seven hundred eighty-six
27. two hundred fifty-six billion, five million, four
28. seven billion, eight hundred fifty thousand, one hundred nine
29. seven trillion, five hundred twenty-one billion, twenty-four million, four hundred twenty-three thousand, one hundred eighty-nine

## Comparing Whole Numbers

**A.** To compare two whole numbers, compare the digits from left to right until you find two that are different. If all digits are the same, the whole numbers are equal.

Compare 46,371 and 2,850.

More digits

46,371 is **greater than** 2,850.

$46,371 > 2,850$

Compare 5,694 and 5,712.

$6 < 7$

5,694 is **less than** 5,712.

$5,694 < 5,712$

**B.** Order 463,419; 463,275; and 463,280 from least to greatest.

Find the greatest.

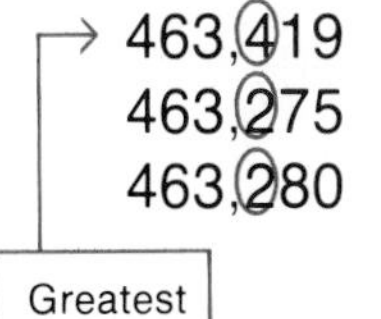


Find the next greatest.

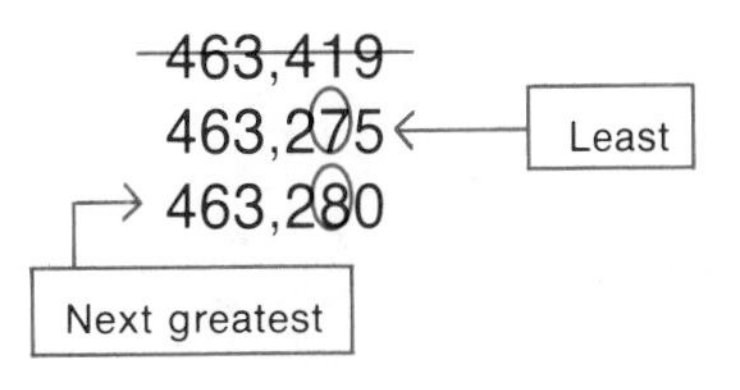


Least to greatest: 463,275; 463,280; 463,419

### EXERCISES

*Write >, <, or = for ●.*

**1.** 13,000 ● 9,849 **2.** 3,893 ● 3,897 **3.** 62,375 ● 62,465

**4.** 23,047 ● 23,047 **5.** 569,438 ● 568,843 **6.** 78,060 ● 78,606

**7.** 939,716 ● 939,716 **8.** 294,651 ● 284,651 **9.** 811,231 ● 812,311

**10.** 645,358 ● 645,358 **11.** 762,301 ● 726,310 **12.** 473,641 ● 473,614

**13.** 2,517,906 ● 3,517,609 **14.** 317,925,436 ● 317,925,436

**15.** 14,205,894 ● 14,205,949 **16.** 206,319,428 ● 206,319

**17.** 4,925,327 ● 4,925,318 **18.** 6,438,712,503 ● 6,438,629,503

**19.** 51,563,421,798,443 ● 51,563,421,798,443

*Write in order from least to greatest. Then write in order from greatest to least.*

**20.** 107,495; 126,312; 107,398 **21.** 9,642; 740; 7,400; 59,435

## Adding Whole Numbers

**A.** Numbers in addition have special names.

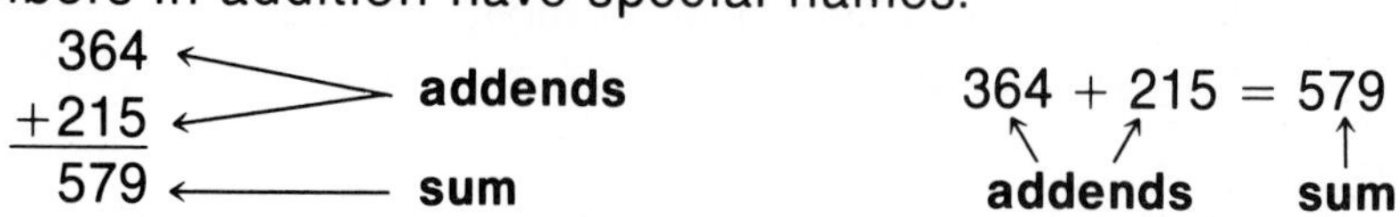


**B.** To add whole numbers add one column at a time, starting with the ones. Sometimes you must regroup.

| Add ones. Regroup. | Add tens. | Add hundreds. Regroup. | Add thousands. |
|---|---|---|---|
| 1 | 1 | 1 1 | 1 1 |
| 4,716 | 4,716 | 4,716 | 4,716 |
| +2,538 | +2,538 | +2,538 | +2,538 |
| 4 | 54 | 254 | 7,254 |

**C.** The **Commutative Property of Addition** allows you to change the order of the addends and get the same sum. You can use this property to check an addition.

```
    111                            111
   86,927           Check:     945,830
+ 945,830                   +   86,927
1,032,757                    1,032,757 ✓
```

The **Addition Property of Zero** is the statement that you can add zero to a number or add a number to zero and the sum is the number itself.

$376 + 0 = 376$ $\qquad$ $0 + 376 = 376$

The **Associative Property of Addition** is the statement that changing the grouping of the addends does not change the sum.

$(4 + 3) + 6 = 13$ $\qquad$ $4 + (3 + 6) = 13$

**D.** When you add three or more numbers, you may get sums of 20 or more in a column.

```
 31  2                             2 12 2
 69,415   21 ones is            3,614,918
 48,309   2 tens 1 one.         4,907,547
 97,631                        +6,715,806
+89,426                        15,238,271
304,781
```

## EXERCISES

*Add. Check your answers.*

| | | | | |
|---|---|---|---|---|
| **1.** 725<br>+264 | **2.** 327<br>+4,651 | **3.** 49,386<br>+20,513 | **4.** 208,534<br>+781,323 | **5.** 11,524<br>+76,421 |
| **6.** 7,263<br>+1,576 | **7.** 3,467<br>+ 425 | **8.** 78,363<br>+10,824 | **9.** 492,536<br>+ 87,313 | **10.** 925,346<br>+ 68,531 |
| **11.** 34,715<br>+ 4,759 | **12.** 59,332<br>+24,429 | **13.** 894,510<br>+ 7,397 | **14.** 563,184<br>+ 94,660 | **15.** 5,784,251<br>+ 170,574 |
| **16.** 5,823<br>+1,579 | **17.** 25,768<br>+ 5,068 | **18.** 52,479<br>+74,457 | **19.** 36,257<br>+53,864 | **20.** 728,753<br>+729,386 |
| **21.** 56,379<br>+46,955 | **22.** 4,893,605<br>+ 392,896 | **23.** 456,564<br>+583,993 | **24.** 93,786<br>+69,425 | **25.** 8,740,829<br>+6,468,281 |
| **26.** 65<br>1,789<br>+ 231 | **27.** 26,547<br>7,008<br>+ 27 | **28.** 4,952<br>260<br>+82,319 | **29.** 78,614<br>345,876<br>+ 993 | **30.** 34,827<br>7,935<br>+ 743 |
| **31.** 40,762<br>980<br>6,446<br>+68,313 | **32.** 500<br>10,014<br>9,268<br>+ 89 | **33.** 713<br>569,524<br>84,497<br>+ 260 | **34.** 1,405<br>40,673<br>6,858<br>+97,739 | **35.** 13,995<br>146,599<br>79,900<br>+ 7,850 |

**36.** 599 + 8,758 = ■

**37.** 28,056 + 30,922 = ■

**38.** 6,407 + 2,891 = ■

**39.** 9,885 + 635 = ■

**40.** 7,356 + 2,401 = ■

**41.** 54,397 + 865,360 = ■

**42.** 27,615 + 7,586 = ■

**43.** 659,937 + 6,283 = ■

**44.** 66,528 + 34,693 = ■

**45.** 72,485 + 541,556 = ■

**46.** 1,457,667 + 586,578 = ■

**47.** 523,761 + 6,237,035 = ■

**48.** 5,692 + 38 + 139 = ■

**49.** 71,361 + 2,854,786 + 52 = ■

**50.** 709 + 96 + 1,643 + 98,005 = ■

**51.** 975 + 896 + 225 = ■

**52.** 71,361 + 854,786 + 2,052 = ■

**53.** 856 + 34 + 122 = ■

**54.** 28,986 + 58,800 + 199,095 = ■

**55.** 447 + 648 + 769 = ■

**56.** 35,648 + 186,400 + 208,006 = ■

**57.** 742,086 + 500 + 645,987 = ■

## Subtracting Whole Numbers

**A.** The answer in subtraction has a special name.

```
 587
-136
 451  <------ difference
```

587 − 136 = 451 ← **difference**

**B.** To subtract whole numbers subtract one column at a time, starting with the ones. Sometimes you must regroup before you can subtract in a place.

Regroup. Subtract ones.

```
   4 13
 8,2 5 3
-4,6 2 9
       4
```

Subtract tens.

```
   4 13
 8,2 5 3
-4,6 2 9
     2 4
```

Regroup. Subtract hundreds.

```
 7 12 4 13
 8, 2 5 3
-4, 6 2 9
     6 2 4
```

Subtract thousands.

```
 7 12 4 13
 8, 2 5 3
-4, 6 2 9
 3, 6 2 4
```

**C.** You may have to regroup twice in a place.

**Example 1**

```
        11
      5  1 10
 8 6 6,2 0 9
-1 3 5,7 8 4
 7 3 0,4 2 5
```

Regroup twice to subtract hundreds

**Example 2**

```
     13     15
 8  3 15 1  5 11
 9,4 5 2,6 1 8
-2,4 6 1,8 3 4
 6,9 9 0,7 8 4
```

**D.** You may have to regroup more than once before you can subtract in a place.

```
   15 9  9
 6  5 10 10 13
 7 6,0 0 3
-2 8,1 6 5
 4 7,8 3 8
```

Regroup 3 times to subtract ones

**E.** When you subtract a number from itself, the difference is always zero.

463 − 463 = 0

When you subtract zero from a number, the difference is always the number itself.

463 − 0 = 463

**F.** To check subtraction, add.

```
   10 12
  4  0  2 16
  5, 1  3  6
 -2, 8  4  7
  2, 2  8  9
```

*Check:*

```
  1 1 1
  2,2 8 9
 +2,8 4 7
  5,1 3 6
```

## EXERCISES

*Subtract.*

| | | | | |
|---|---|---|---|---|
| **1.** 359 − 138 | **2.** 4,867 − 2,840 | **3.** 923,517 − 512,204 | **4.** 35,029 − 31,006 | **5.** 18,756 − 16,506 |
| **6.** 927 − 618 | **7.** 400 − 283 | **8.** 5,468 − 3,075 | **9.** 1,600 − 498 | **10.** 67,584 − 1,801 |
| **11.** 2,005 − 186 | **12.** 6,384 − 2,569 | **13.** 79,362 − 21,804 | **14.** 27,000 − 1,732 | **15.** 728,652 − 135,849 |
| **16.** 30,023 − 26,511 | **17.** 20,003 − 17,639 | **18.** 700,500 − 306,912 | **19.** 50,006 − 5,079 | **20.** 8,409 − 982 |
| **21.** 9,156 − 8,791 | **22.** 4,700,000 − 698,435 | **23.** 160,000 − 39,005 | **24.** 58,006 − 39,905 | **25.** 286,938 − 32,971 |
| **26.** 2,800,000 − 1,329,461 | **27.** 1,308 − 709 | **28.** 93,000 − 89,961 | **29.** 94,898 − 76,089 | **30.** 5,607 − 4,183 |
| **31.** 86,633 − 19,778 | **32.** 24,307 − 7,847 | **33.** 6,509 − 5,817 | **34.** 6,980,372 − 762,154 | **35.** 305,906 − 201,609 |

**36.** 76,853 − 9,186 = ■

**37.** 64,332 − 54,654 = ■

**38.** 1,872,919 − 97,097 = ■

**39.** 603,709 − 27,489 = ■

**40.** 407,311 − 29,357 = ■

**41.** 600,909 − 38,461 = ■

**42.** 56,136 − 18,652 = ■

**43.** 9,800,500 − 506,135 = ■

**44.** 412,363 − 285,897 = ■

**45.** 530,008 − 49,650 = ■

**46.** 87,423 − 47,245 = ■

**47.** 7,903,600 − 3,895,495 = ■

**48.** 210,320 − 96,403 = ■

**49.** 432,706 − 180,423 = ■

**50.** 40,000 − 31,868 = ■

**51.** 403,624 − 398,016 = ■

**52.** 604,030 − 73,196 = ■

**53.** 42,150 − 27,080 = ■

**54.** 94,564 − 38,426 = ■

**55.** 12,536 − 9,781 = ■

**56.** 169,500 − 57,850 = ■

**57.** 68,418 − 36,297 = ■

**58.** 1,846,209 − 1,472,316 = ■

**59.** 4,253,626 − 174,596 = ■

**60.** 5,387,408 − 2,468,563 = ■

**61.** 3,248,173 − 864,800 = ■

## Multiplying by Ones, Tens, Hundreds, and Thousands

**A.** Numbers in multiplication have special names.

$$\begin{array}{r} 9 \\ \times 6 \\ \hline 54 \end{array}$$

9 and 6 → **factors**; 54 → **product**

$6 \times 9 = 54$

6, 9 → **factors**; 54 → **product**

When both factors are whole numbers, the product is a **multiple** of each factor. 54 is a multiple of 9 and of 6.

**B.** When you multiply larger numbers, you may have to save in one or more places.

Multiply ones.

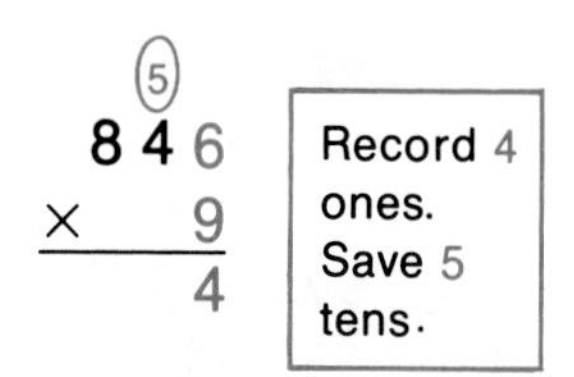


Multiply tens. Then add the tens saved.

(4)(5)

$$\begin{array}{r} 846 \\ \times \quad 9 \\ \hline 14 \end{array}$$

Record 1 ten. Save 4 hundreds.

Multiply hundreds. Then add the hundreds saved.

(4)(5)

$$\begin{array}{r} 846 \\ \times \quad 9 \\ \hline 7{,}614 \end{array}$$

Record 7 thousands and 6 hundreds.

**C.** Multiplying with dollars and cents is like multiplying whole numbers. Remember to record the . and the $ in the product.

(3) (2)

$$\begin{array}{r} \$25.03 \\ \times \quad 7 \\ \hline \$175.21 \end{array}$$

**D.** The **Commutative Property of Multiplication** allows you to change the order of the factors and get the same product.

*To find:*

$$\begin{array}{r} 4 \\ \times 69{,}417 \\ \hline \end{array}$$

*Do:*

(3)(1) (2)

$$\begin{array}{r} 69{,}417 \\ \times \quad 4 \\ \hline 277{,}668 \end{array}$$

The **Associative Property of Multiplication** is the statement that changing the grouping of the factors does not change the product.

$(4 \times 2) \times 3 = ■$

$8 \times 3 = 24$

$4 \times (2 \times 3) = ■$

$4 \times 6 = 24$

**Multiplication Property of Zero**
The product of 0 and any number is always 0.

$7 \times 0 = 0 \qquad 0 \times 7 = 0$

**Multiplication Property of One**
The product of 1 and any number is always the number itself.

$6 \times 1 = 6 \qquad 1 \times 6 = 6$

**E.** It is easy to multiply by 10, by 100, or by 1,000.

$$\begin{array}{r} 2{,}653 \\ \times \quad 10 \\ \hline 26{,}530 \end{array} \qquad \begin{array}{r} 2{,}653 \\ \times \quad 100 \\ \hline 265{,}300 \end{array} \qquad \begin{array}{r} 2{,}653 \\ \times 1{,}000 \\ \hline 2{,}653{,}000 \end{array}$$

You can use the pattern above to multiply by any multiple of 10, 100, or 1,000.

$$\begin{array}{r} \scriptstyle 1 \\ 1{,}325 \\ \times \quad 3 \\ \hline 3{,}975 \end{array} \qquad \begin{array}{r} \scriptstyle 1 \\ 1{,}325 \\ \times \quad 30 \\ \hline 39{,}750 \end{array} \qquad \begin{array}{r} \scriptstyle 1 \\ 1{,}325 \\ \times \quad 300 \\ \hline 397{,}500 \end{array} \qquad \begin{array}{r} \scriptstyle 1 \\ 1{,}325 \\ \times 3{,}000 \\ \hline 3{,}975{,}000 \end{array}$$

## EXERCISES

*Multiply.*

| | | | | |
|---|---|---|---|---|
| **1.** 23 × 3 | **2.** 15 × 6 | **3.** 72 × 4 | **4.** 59 × 8 | **5.** 9 × 48 |
| **6.** 801 × 2 | **7.** 172 × 6 | **8.** 705 × 7 | **9.** 8 × 361 | **10.** $7.19 × 3 |
| **11.** 85,108 × 4 | **12.** 97,234 × 4 | **13.** 800,246 × 9 | **14.** 5 × 67,189 | **15.** $321.23 × 3 |
| **16.** 46 × 10 | **17.** 3,670 × 10 | **18.** 52 × 30 | **19.** 231 × 90 | **20.** $73.69 × 60 |
| **21.** 83 × 70 | **22.** 897 × 30 | **23.** 400 × 10 | **24.** 5,968 × 70 | **25.** $37.23 × 20 |
| **26.** 193 × 100 | **27.** 2,603 × 100 | **28.** 532 × 800 | **29.** 108 × 700 | **30.** 80,175 × 600 |
| **31.** 4,617 × 1,000 | **32.** 84,950 × 1,000 | **33.** 12,507 × 4,000 | **34.** 68,392 × 8,000 | **35.** 92,000 × 6,000 |

**36.** 8 × 7,082 = ▒ **37.** 4 × $9.05 = ▒ **38.** 901,506 × 3 = ▒

**39.** 2 × 54,637 = ▒ **40.** 50 × 25 = ▒ **41.** 300 × 726 = ▒

**42.** 200 × 697 = ▒ **43.** 8,000 × 19,000 = ▒ **44.** 100 × 2,050 = ▒

**45.** 400 × $197.65 = ▒ **46.** 9,000 × $200.79 = ▒ **47.** 302 × 1,000 = ▒

## More Multiplying

**A.** To multiply by 2-digit numbers, multiply the ones and the tens separately. Then add those products.

```
   423
 ×  32
   846  ←  2 × 423
12,690  ←  30 × 423
13,536  ←  32 × 423
```

**B.** You may have to save in one or both steps.

**Example 1**
Saving in the first step

```
  1,2 0 3
×     2 6
  7 2 1 8
2 4 0 6 0
3 1,2 7 8
```

Cross out before multiplying by 20.

**Example 2**
Saving in the second step

```
  2 1,3 1 4
×       4 2
  4 2 6 2 8
8 5 2 5 6 0
8 9 5,1 8 8
```

**Example 3**
Saving in both steps

```
    4,0 8 9
×       5 8
  3 2 7 1 2
2 0 4 4 5 0
2 3 7,1 6 2
```

**C.** Multiplying by larger numbers may take more steps.

**Example 1**

```
      3,1 4 2
×       6 7 3
      9 4 2 6  ←  3 × 3,142
    2 1 9 9 4 0  ←  70 × 3,142
  1 8 8 5 2 0 0  ←  600 × 3,142
  2,1 1 4,5 6 6  ←  673 × 3,142
```

**Example 2**

```
        1 2,0 4 2
×         2,3 1 4
        4 8 1 6 8  ←  4 × 12,042
      1 2 0 4 2 0  ←  10 × 12,042
    3 6 1 2 6 0 0  ←  300 × 12,042
  2 4 0 8 4 0 0 0  ←  2,000 × 12,042
  2 7,8 6 5,1 8 8  ←  2,314 × 12,042
```

**D.** When there are one or more zeros in the first factor, you can use fewer steps.

**Example 1**

```
      9 2 6
    × 8 0 3
    2 7 7 8  ←  3 × 926
7 4 0 8 0 0  ←  800 × 926
7 4 3,5 7 8  ←  803 × 926
```

**Example 2**

```
        9,2 6 7
      × 8,0 0 3
      2 7 8 0 1  ←  3 × 9,267
7 4 1 3 6 0 0 0  ←  8000 × 9,267
7 4,1 6 3,8 0 1  ←  8003 × 9,267
```

**E.** You can use the Commutative Property of Multiplication to check a multiplication.

| | |
|---|---|
| ② | ① ② |
| 23 | 38 |
| ×38 | ×23 |
| 184 | 114 |
| 690 | 760 |
| 874 | 874 ✓ |

EXERCISES

*Multiply.*

| | | | | |
|---|---|---|---|---|
| **1.** 5,040 × 27 | **2.** 898 × 16 | **3.** 1,765 × 59 | **4.** 39 ×940 | **5.** $960.50 × 71 |
| **6.** 2,046 × 450 | **7.** 70,080 × 508 | **8.** 4,296 × 138 | **9.** $8.32 × 715 | **10.** 717 ×93,417 |
| **11.** 3,788 ×2,007 | **12.** 423 ×312 | **13.** 746 ×352 | **14.** 3,042 × 516 | **15.** $23.60 × 74 |
| **16.** 6,217 × 58 | **17.** $90.50 × 803 | **18.** 90,430 × 7,900 | **19.** 593 ×175 | **20.** $6.30 × 630 |
| **21.** 8,917 × 43 | **22.** 6,582 × 36 | **23.** 730 ×932 | **24.** 856 ×491 | **25.** 2,485 × 27 |

**26.** 94 × 695 = ■

**27.** 502 × 1,010 = ■

**28.** 92 × 86.90 = ■

**29.** 785 × 59,643 = ■

**30.** 230 × 2,964 = ■

**31.** 1,588 × 44 = ■

**32.** 73 × $197.50 = ■

**33.** 154 × 7,369 = ■

**34.** 4,009 × 7,368 = ■

**35.** 74 × 2,174 = ■

**36.** 378 × $4.17 = ■

**37.** 35 × 4,761 = ■

**38.** 632 × 5,730 = ■

**39.** 541 × 749 = ■

**40.** 856 × 386 = ■

**41.** 360 × 6,582 = ■

**42.** 704 × 6,825 = ■

**43.** 263 × 1,368 = ■

**44.** 263 × 437 = ■

**45.** 78 × 4,756 = ■

**46.** 526 × 174 = ■

**47.** 4,700 × 1,481 = ■

**48.** 397 × 308 = ■

**49.** 416 × 2,524 = ■

**50.** 67 × 4,926 = ■

**51.** 608 × 744 = ■

**52.** 534 × 930 = ■

**53.** 493 × 7,841 = ■

**54.** 24 × 46,037 = ■

**55.** 567 × 385 = ■

**56.** 77 × 5,899 = ■

**57.** 572 × 7,317 = ■

**58.** 935 × 798 = ■

## Dividing by Ones, Tens, Hundreds, and Thousands

**A.** The numbers in division have special names.

**quotient** → 8 R3 ← **remainder**
**divisor** → 6)51 ← **dividend**
48 ← $8 \times 6$
3

When the remainder is 0, the divisor is a **factor** of the quotient.

9
5)45
45
0

*You can write:*
$45 \div 5 = 9$
5 is a factor of 45.

**B.** When you divide any number by itself, the quotient is always one.

$4 \div 4 = 1$ $\quad 17 \div 17 = 1$ $\quad 326 \div 326 = 1$

When you divide zero by any number, the quotient is always zero.

$0 \div 6 = 0$ $\quad 0 \div 14 = 0$ $\quad 0 \div 831 = 0$

It is important to remember that you can never divide by zero.

**C.** To divide with larger dividends, work one place at a time, starting at the left. Use the greatest multiple of the divisor for each step.

**Example 1**

246 R2
3)740
6 ← $2 \times 3$
14
12 ← $4 \times 3$
20
18 ← $6 \times 3$
2

**Example 2**

1,070 R3
8)8,563
8 ← $1 \times 8$
0 5
0 ← $0 \times 8$
56
56 ← $7 \times 8$
03
0 ← $0 \times 8$
3

**D.** You can use multiplication or multiplication and addition to check division.

$7 > 2$
$7 < 23$
Divide the 23 tens.
Continue to divide.

34 R1
7)239
21 ← $3 \times 7$
29
28 ← $4 \times 7$
1

*Check*
34 ← **quotient**
$\times$ 7 ← **divisor**
238
$+$ 1 ← **remainder**
239 ← **dividend**

**E.** You can write a mixed numeral for the quotient when the remainder is not 0.

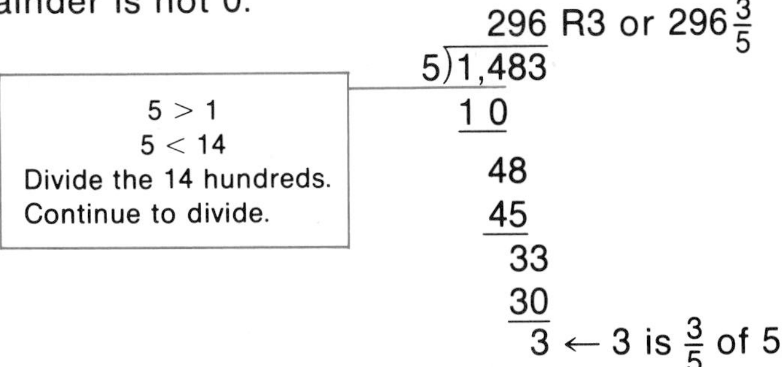


**F.** Dividing with dollars and cents is like dividing whole numbers.

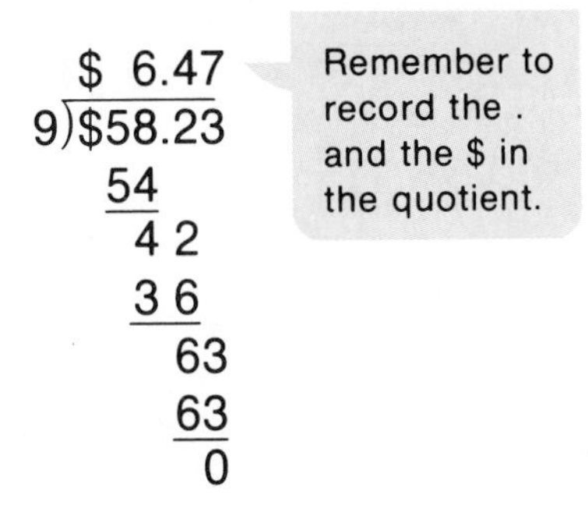


**G.** When dividing by a multiple of 10, you must always regroup at least once at the start.

**Example 1**

```
    29 R4
30)874
   60   ← 2 × 30
   274
   270  ← 9 × 30
     4
```

30 < 87. Divide the 87 tens.

**Example 2**

```
     4 R23
70)303
   280 ← 4 × 70
    23
```

70 > 30
70 < 303
Divide the 303 ones.

When dividing by a multiple of 100, you must always regroup two or more times at the start.

```
       35 R145
200)7,145
    6 00   ← 3 × 200
    1 145
    1 000  ← 5 × 200
      145
```

200 < 714
Divide the 714 tens.

When dividing by a multiple of 1,000, you must always regroup three or more times at the start.

```
             17 R500
6,000)102,500
       60 00   ← 1 × 6,000
       42 500
       42 000  ← 7 × 6,000
          500
```

6,000 > 1,025
6,000 < 10,250
Divide the 10,250 tens.

## EXERCISES

*Divide. Check your answers.*

**1.** 9)64 **2.** 8)56 **3.** 3)29 **4.** 6)42 **5.** 9)56 **6.** 7)91

**7.** 3)39 **8.** 5)63 **9.** 2)28 **10.** 4)57 **11.** 8)65 **12.** 5)49

**13.** 9)58 **14.** 8)24 **15.** 7)58 **16.** 2)59 **17.** 3)85 **18.** 6)96

**19.** 9)99 **20.** 7)83 **21.** 7)62 **22.** 4)80 **23.** 5)62 **24.** 4)32

**25.** 5)642 **26.** 3)159 **27.** 6)108 **28.** 4)413 **29.** 2)$3.24

**30.** 4)5,432 **31.** 5)4,120 **32.** 7)2,812 **33.** 3)7,529 **34.** 9)$63.72

**35.** 8)219 **36.** 9)7,834 **37.** 7)417 **38.** 6)5,238 **39.** 5)$33.75

**40.** 4)507 **41.** 7)266 **42.** 6)659 **43.** 9)785 **44.** 3)924

**45.** 7)8,707 **46.** 5)3,460 **47.** 6)6,012 **48.** 7)3,003 **49.** 8)6,167

**50.** 9)576 **51.** 8)5,032 **52.** 6)$5.22 **53.** 5)1,735 **54.** 9)8,687

**55.** 6)4,042 **56.** 3)7,415 **57.** 7)$49.07 **58.** 4)3,648 **59.** 8)7,673

**60.** 50)561 **61.** 80)929 **62.** 70)5,173 **63.** 20)3,660 **64.** 60)5,281

**65.** 30)15,762 **66.** 40)78,079 **67.** 90)81,540 **68.** 50)20,387 **69.** 60)28,312

**70.** 900)7,259 **71.** 800)3,299 **72.** 200)12,618 **73.** 500)35,000

**74.** 700)1,400 **75.** 800)2,021 **76.** 400)$196.00 **77.** 900)37,800

**78.** 3,000)490,090 **79.** 6,000)124,496 **80.** 4,000)269,057 **81.** 7,000)378,405

**82.** 5,000)190,387 **83.** 2,000)233,064 **84.** 8,000)788,789 **85.** 9,000)909,000

**86.** 10)459 **87.** 100)6,489 **88.** 1,000)$2,730.00 **89.** 300)2,664

**90.** 2,000)475,214 **91.** 20)197 **92.** 600)51,599 **93.** 70)49,211

**94.** 800)166,006 **95.** 4,000)190,087 **96.** 40)49,867 **97.** 7,000)973,031

## More Dividing

**A.** Rounding the divisor to the nearest ten can help you divide by a 2-digit number. Use the rounded divisor to find trial quotients.

Find $62\overline{)1,859}$.

Round 62 down to 60.

**Step 1**
Divide the 185 tens.
▪ × 60 = 185
Try 3.

$$\begin{array}{r} 62 \\ \times\ 3 \\ \hline 186 \end{array} \qquad \begin{array}{r} 62 \\ \times\ 2 \\ \hline 124 \end{array}$$

124 < 185
**Use 2.**

$$\begin{array}{r} 2 \\ 62\overline{)1,859} \\ \underline{1\ 24} \\ 61 \end{array}$$

**Step 2**
Divide the 619 ones.
▪ × 60 = 619
The largest number to try is 9.
Try 9.

$$\begin{array}{r} 62 \\ \times\ 9 \\ \hline 558 \end{array}$$

558 < 619
**Use 9.**

$$\begin{array}{r} 29\ \text{R61} \\ 62\overline{)1,859} \\ \underline{1\ 24} \\ 619 \\ \underline{558} \\ 61 \end{array}$$

**B.** Rounding the divisor can help you divide by larger numbers.

Find $756\overline{)681,957}$.

Round 756 up to 800.

**Step 1**
Divide the 6,819 hundreds.
▪ × 800 = 6,819
Try 8.

$$\begin{array}{r} 756 \\ \times\ \ 8 \\ \hline 6,048 \end{array} \qquad \begin{array}{r} 756 \\ \times\ \ 9 \\ \hline 6,804 \end{array}$$

9 is the largest number to try. **Use 9.**

$$\begin{array}{r} 9 \\ 756\overline{)681,957} \\ \underline{680\ 4} \\ 1\ 5 \end{array}$$

**Step 2**
Divide the 155 tens.
▪ × 800 = 155
**Use 0.**

$$\begin{array}{r} 90 \\ 756\overline{)681,957} \\ \underline{680\ 4} \\ 1\ 55 \\ \underline{0} \\ 1\ 55 \end{array}$$

**Step 3**
Divide the 1,557 ones.
▩ × 800 = 1,557
Try 1.

```
  756      756      756
×   1    ×   2    ×   3
  756    1,512    2,268
```

2,268 > 1,557
**Use 2.**

```
       902 R45
756)681,957
    680 4
      1 55
         0
      1 557
      1 512
         45
```

**C.** Find 5,280)89,760

Round 5,280 down to 5,000.

```
             17
5,280)89,760
      52 80
      36 960
      36 960
           0
```

Start by dividing 8,976 tens.

*Check:*

```
   5,280
 ×    17
  36 960
  52 800
  89,760
```

## EXERCISES

*Divide.*

| | | | |
|---|---|---|---|
| **1.** 24)9,653 | **2.** 91)7,938 | **3.** 34)714 | **4.** 83)6,277 |
| **5.** 78)39,396 | **6.** 22)15,599 | **7.** 35)36,078 | **8.** 96)44,510 |
| **9.** 53)1,809 | **10.** 89)1,935 | **11.** 67)6,988 | **12.** 29)5,604 |
| **13.** 46)14,757 | **14.** 67)19,000 | **15.** 31)2,976 | **16.** 25)22,104 |
| **17.** 96)3,767 | **18.** 43)3,549 | **19.** 79)14,015 | **20.** 59)11,664 |
| **21.** 450)9,360 | **22.** 739)15,826 | **23.** 219)67,350 | **24.** 585)17,680 |
| **25.** 252)19,240 | **26.** 153)24,806 | **27.** 678)22,702 | **28.** 901)66,745 |
| **29.** 385)473,500 | **30.** 309)260,952 | **31.** 575)551,250 | **32.** 426)$1,295.04 |
| **33.** 986)207,000 | **34.** 1,760)26,700 | **35.** 417)35,995 | **36.** 312)440,896 |
| **37.** 217)13,752 | **38.** 5,280)200,845 | **39.** 683)53,386 | **40.** 934)794,362 |
| **41.** 719)410,263 | **42.** 621)$546.48 | **43.** 825)99,048 | **44.** 187)157,435 |
| **45.** 209)686,630 | **46.** 318)336,625 | **47.** 6,304)794,384 | **48.** 3,206)$1,635.06 |

## BASIC—A Computer Language

A **computer language** has its own dictionary of words and its own rules of grammar, or **syntax. BASIC** (**B**eginner's **A**ll-purpose **S**ymbolic **I**nstruction **C**ode) is one of many computer languages.

**A.** Algorithms used by a computer are called **programs.** Instruction lines in a BASIC program are numbered. Programmers usually begin writing a program by numbering lines by tens so that more lines can be added in sequence if needed. A computer reads the lines in numerical order, from the least number to the greatest.

This is a BASIC program for finding some powers of 10:

```
10 PRINT "THE FIRST POWERS OF 10 ARE:"
20 PRINT 10∧1, 10∧2, 10∧3
30 END
```

In BASIC 10∧1 means $10^1$

When the program is run the output is:

```
THE FIRST 3 POWERS OF 10 ARE:

10             100              1000
```

Computers don't use commas in numerals.

The instruction, or **command,** PRINT is used in two different ways:
In line 10 PRINT is used with words inside quotation marks, to tell the computer to print *exactly* what is given there.
In line 20, PRINT is used with arithmetic expressions. The computer is to print only the *result* of the calculations. (The commas space out the items to be printed.)
The command END tells the computer that the program is over.

*Write the output for each BASIC program.*

**1.**
```
10 PRINT "THERE ARE ABOUT"
20 PRINT 365 * (24 * 60)
30 PRINT "MINUTES IN A YEAR."
40 END
```

In BASIC, * means ×

/ means ÷

**2.**
```
10 PRINT "I EARN $ "; 18200/52
20 PRINT "EACH WEEK, BEFORE";
30 PRINT "TAXES."
40 END
```

Semicolons put the result of the computation or the next words in quotes on the same line.

**B.** Whenever a number will be used several times in the same program, it can be named by a **variable.** The number is the **value** of the variable. In this program, the command `LET C = 7.49` (line 10) tells the computer that the variable C has the value 7.49.

```
10 LET C = 7.49
20 PRINT "WHEN 1 ITEM COSTS $";C
30 PRINT "THEN 4 ITEMS COST $";4 * C
40 END
```

When the computer reads the program, it stores the value of C (7.49) in its memory. After that, whenever C appears in the program, the computer uses the value of C that is in its memory.

```
WHEN 1 ITEM COSTS $7.49 ← 1st use of C ── MEMORY
THEN 4 ITEMS COST $29.96 ← 2nd use of C ── C is 7.49.
```

**C.** Special variables, called **string variables,** are used for words. String variables are followed by $. The "value" of a string variable is given by a `LET` command, and is shown with quotation marks: `LET N$ = "NAME"`.

*Write the output for each program.*

**3.**
```
10 LET P = 3.45
20 LET B$ = "NOVEL"
30 PRINT "I BOUGHT A"; B$
40 PRINT "THAT COST $" ;P
50 PRINT "I HAVE $ " ; 10 - P;" LEFT."
60 END
```

**4.**
```
10 LET N$ = "MR. BLAKE"
20 LET W = 25000
30 PRINT N$;" EARNS $"; W
40 PRINT "BEFORE TAXES, AND"
50 PRINT "$";.75 * W;" AFTER TAXES."
60 END
```

**5.** **a.** How could you change the program in Exercise 3 for other purchases?
**b.** How could you change the program in Exercise 4 for other workers?

## Programming with BASIC

**A.** Programs are more flexible when the values of variables are determined as the program is run. The command `INPUT` tells the computer to get the value of one or more variables from the person using the program. The computer prints `?` to tell the user that it is waiting for the values.

This program was used by Lorraine, who is 5 feet 3 inches tall:

```
10 PRINT "WHAT IS YOUR NAME?"
20 INPUT N$ ←—— Value of N$ needed
30 PRINT "HOW TALL ARE YOU?"
40 PRINT "(TYPE FEET, INCHES.)"
50 INPUT F, I ←—— 2 values needed
60 PRINT N$;", YOU ARE"
70 PRINT F * 12 + I;"INCHES TALL."
80 END
```

Output:

```
WHAT IS YOUR NAME?
? LORRAINE ←—— Supplied by user
HOW TALL ARE YOU?
(TYPE FEET, INCHES.)
? 5, 3 ←—— Supplied by user
LORRAINE, YOU ARE
63 INCHES TALL.
```

Notice that when a *user* gives the value of a string variable, quotation marks are *not* used.

*Write the output for each program. Make up the user-supplied values.*

**1.**
```
10 PRINT "GIVE ME 2 NUMBERS LESS THAN 100."
20 INPUT M, N
30 PRINT "YOUR NUMBERS ARE:" ,M, N
40 PRINT "THE SUM OF YOUR NUMBERS IS:" ,M + N
50 END
```

**2.**
```
10 PRINT "WHAT IS YOUR FIRST NAME?"
20 INPUT F$
30 PRINT "I'M PLEASED TO MEET YOU, ";F$
40 END
```

**B.** You can write your own programs, using BASIC.Use this three-part plan.

**a. Plan your work.** For BASIC, the best plan is a *description.* Include any formulas you want to use.

**b. Write an algorithm.** For BASIC, give your algorithm as a *flowchart.*

**c. Translate your algorithm into BASIC.** You may have to choose variables or string variables.

Suppose that you want to write a program to find part of a number.

**Plan:** Get the *base* and the *rate* from the user. Use the formula $r \cdot b = p$ to find the *part.* Then print the part.

**Algorithm:**

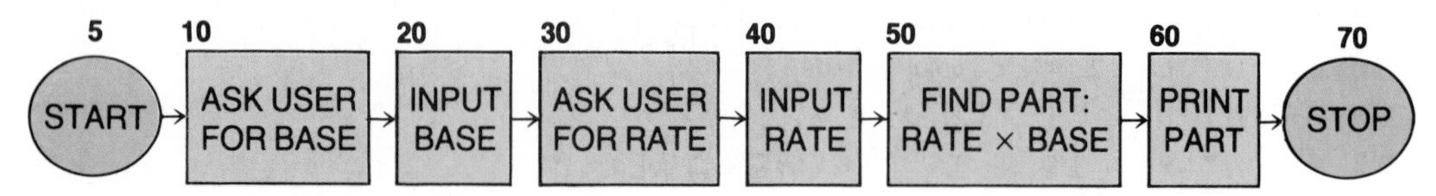


**3. Translate into BASIC:**

```
10 PRINT "WHAT IS THE BASE?"
20 INPUT B
30 PRINT "WHAT IS THE RATE (DECIMAL)?"
40 INPUT R
50 LET P = R * B
60 PRINT R;" OF ";B;" IS ";P
70 END
```

**3.** Use the program above to find .3 of 420. Write the output.

**4.** Sometimes you know only the *percent* form of a rate. Before you multiply to find part of a number, you have to find a decimal for the percent. Use the three-part plan to write a BASIC program for finding part of a number when the rate is given as a percent.

**5.** Use your program from Exercise **4** to find 5% of 1,200. Write the output.

**C.** BASIC programs are easier for other people to read if they contain **remarks** that explain the purpose of each section of the program. These are some remarks that could be included in the program at the top of this page:

```
 2 REM*** THIS PROGRAM FINDS PART OF A NUMBER ***
 5 REM***VARIABLES: B= BASE, R= RATE, P= PART***
45 REM ***        COMPUTE THE PART, P          ***
```

The word `REM` tells the computer that the line does not contain computer instructions. The asterisks (*) are used to make the remarks easy to find.

## Decision Steps in BASIC Programs

Sometimes the user of a program must tell a computer which **branch** of a program to follow. The user answers a Yes/No question.

**A.** This program could be used to find sale prices. Compare this program with the algorithm and flowchart on page 140. The computer program separates *asking for* input and *reading* the input into 2 steps.

```
 10 PRINT "WHAT IS THE REGULAR PRICE?"
 20 INPUT P
 30 PRINT "WHAT IS THE DISCOUNT RATE (DECIMAL)?"
 40 INPUT R
 50 LET K = R * P
 60 LET D = INT (100 * K + .5)/100
 70 LET S = P−D
 80 PRINT "THE SALE PRICE IS $";S
 90 PRINT "DO WE HAVE TO FIND MORE SALE PRICES?"
100 PRINT "(USE 1 FOR YES, 0 FOR NO.)"
110 INPUT A
120 IF A = 1 THEN 10
130 END
```

INT means "Use the whole-number part of the result"

This expression rounds K to the nearest cent

Numerical input expected

The computer's decision is made at line 120. If A (the input) has the value 1, the computer returns to line 10. If A has *any other value,* the computer goes on to line 130.

1. Complete, to find the value of D (line 60) when K = 3.4225:

INT (100 * 3.4225 + .5)/100

INT (■ + .5)/100

INT(■)/100

342/100

■

2. What step would be done after 120, if a user input 5 at line 110?

3. Write the output for using the program above to find the sale prices:
regular price: $7.49 discount: .20; and
regular price: $20.50 discount: .05.

**B.** Input for a decision can be a number, as in the program on page 437, or it can be a word. The program should tell the user which is expected. This program, for finding a team's winning average, asks for a word (line 60).

```
10 PRINT "HOW MANY GAMES HAS THE TEAM WON?"
20 INPUT W
30 PRINT "HOW MANY GAMES HAS THE TEAM LOST?"
40 INPUT L
50 PRINT "WERE THERE ANY TIED GAMES?"
60 PRINT "(USE 'YES' OR 'NO.')"
70 INPUT R$  <----------  Word input expected.
80 IF R$ = "YES" THEN 110
90 LET N = W/(W + L)
100 GOTO 140
110 PRINT "HOW MANY GAMES HAS THE TEAM TIED?"
120 INPUT T  <----------  Computers don't use brackets.
130 LET N = (2 * W + T)/(2 * (W + L + T))
140 LET A = INT(1000 * N + .5)/1000  <----------  This expression rounds N
150 PRINT "THE TEAM'S WINNING";                   to the nearest thousandth.
160 PRINT "AVERAGE IS ";A
170 END
```

**4.** Find the value of A (line 140) when N = .514852.

**5.** Write the output for using the program to find the teams' averages:

**a.** Atlanta Braves: 84 wins, 78 losses

**b.** San Francisco 49ers: 5 wins, 7 losses, 4 ties

## FOR—NEXT Statements

**A.** In BASIC, the `IF-THEN` statement tells a computer what to do if certain conditions are met. By directing the computer to return to a specific line, a portion of the program can be repeated. This repetition is called a **loop.** Loops save time and work.

Another way to write a loop in BASIC is to use `FOR` and `NEXT` statements. The `FOR` statement defines the loop. The `NEXT` statement keeps track of the counter variable, increasing it by one each time the loop is completed. When the counter reaches the maximum value, the computer leaves the loop and moves to the next statement.

The `FOR` and `NEXT` statements appear on different lines; these statements are always used in pairs. The variable used in each statement of a pair must be the same. Any number of other statements may appear between the `FOR` statement and the `NEXT` statement.

The program below prints the integers from 1 to 12.

```
10 PRINT "INTEGERS FROM 1 TO 12"
20 FOR N = 1 TO 12 ◄──────────┐
30 PRINT N                    ├──────── loop
40 NEXT N ◄───────────────────┘
50 END
```

The loop continues until N = 12 in line 20. When this happens, lines 30 and 40 are executed one more time. Then the computer moves on to line 50 and the program ends.

1. Write a BASIC program that will print the numbers of the days in the month of April.

**B.** By using a STEP statement with the FOR statement, you can increase the counter by a number other than 1. The program below prints the even integers from 2 to 24.

```
10 PRINT "EVEN INTEGERS FROM 2 TO 24"
20 FOR N = 2 TO 24 STEP 2
30 PRINT N
40 NEXT N
50 END
```

STEP 2 tells the computer to add 2 to N each time through the loop.

In line 20, if STEP 2 is replaced with STEP 4, the value of N would be increased by 4 each time the line is executed. STEP 1 is the same as not writing STEP at the end of a FOR statement. To count backwards, you would use a negative value in the STEP statement.

Write the FOR–NEXT from the programs that would generate the numbers in each list. Use Y for your variable.

**Line numbers may vary.**

**2.** 1, 3, 5, 9, 11

**3.** 0, 4, 8, 12,...44

**4.** 5, 6.5, 8, 9.5, 11, 12.5, 14

**5.** 7, 7.2, 7.4, 7.6,...9

Each program contains one error. Find the error and write the correct statement.

**6.**
```
10 FOR M = 1 to 50
20 PRINT M
30 END
```

**7.**
```
10 FOR X = 1 to X = 25
20 PRINT 2 * X
30 NEXT X
40 END
```

Write the output of each basic program.

**8.**
```
10 FOR W = 1 to 50
20 PRINT W
30 NEXT W
40 END
```

**9.**
```
10 FOR W = 1 TO 8
20 NEXT W
30 PRINT W
40 END
```

**10.**
```
10 LET J = 0
20 FOR N = 1 TO 5
30 LET J = J + N
40 PRINT J
50 NEXT N
60 END
```

**11.**
```
10 LET L = 0
20 FOR N =  0 TO 6 STEP 2
30 LET L = L + N
40 PRINT L
50 END
```

## Redefining a Variable in BASIC Programs

**A.** Sometimes the values of variables are **redefined** within programs. The value of K is redefined in this program.

Line 30 defines the new value of K as 10 more than the old value of K. It is *not* an algebraic equation.

```
10 LET K = 75          ← Starting value of K
20 PRINT K
30 LET K = K + 10      ← New value of K
40 IF K < 100
   THEN 20
50 END
```

You can record how the value of K changes as the computer reads the program. Value of K:

```
75
75               85               95
85               95               105
85 (<100)        95 (<100)        105 (≥100)
```

*For each program show how the values of the variables change.* **See Answers beginning p. 533.**

**1.**

```
10 LET N = 0
20 LET N = N + 2
30 PRINT N,N∧2
40 IF N < 12 THEN 20
50 END
```

**2.**

```
10 LET C = 1
20 LET A = 5
30 PRINT C,A
40 LET C = C + 1
50 LET A = 3 * A
60 IF C < = 10 THEN 30
70 END
```

In BASIC, $<=$ means $\le$

**B.** The values of variables may be changed for either of 2 reasons: to *count* the number of times a program has been used (as C is used in Exercise 2), or to keep a *running total.* This program shows how a running total can be used for **inventory** records.

```
10 PRINT "HOW MANY ITEMS IN STOCK?"
20 INPUT I             ← Starting value of the running total
30 PRINT "HOW MANY ITEMS WERE SOLD?"
40 INPUT S
50 LET I = I - S       ← The new total is the old total minus S
60 PRINT "WERE THERE MORE SALES? (YES OR NO)"
70 INPUT A$
80 IF A$ = "YES" THEN 30
90 PRINT "CHANGE THE RECORD TO SHOW ";I;" ";
100 PRINT "ITEMS IN STOCK."
110 END
```

3. For each of these situations, decide whether the program would use a *counter,* a *running total,* or *both.*
   a. The program gives a student 15 test items.
   b. The program finds the amount of a company's sales.
   c. The program waits 30 seconds before giving a student an answer.
   d. The program finds the product of 20 numbers.
4. Show how the values of the variables in the program at the bottom of page 441 change when: the record shows 7,500 items in stock; sales were 200, 750, 400, and 350 items.
5. Use the program at the bottom of page 441 to update the inventory record shown at the right.

   October sales were:
   2,000 Woodruff keys to Allen Corp.
   500 Woodruff keys to Basic Repairs
   1,250 Woodruff keys to Cogwell Inc.

**ITEM NAME** ¾ in. Woodruff keys
**ITEM NUMBER** WK-¾

| DATE | ACTIVITY | IN STOCK |
|---|---|---|
| 10/15 | New manufacture | 20,000 |
| 10/22 | Sales of 1,500 | 18,500 |
| | | |

6. The program at the bottom of page 441 works only when items have been *sold.* However, inventories are often *increased* when more items are manufactured. Write a new program that finds new inventory records whether items are added to or taken from stock, or both. First *plan* your work. Be sure to *ask* the user for any values the computer will need. Then, draw a *flowchart.* Finally, *translate* the program in your algorithm into BASIC.

## Structured BASIC Programs

**A.** The simple BASIC programs you have been using have been "in one piece." Each has dealt with a single task, much as a paragraph deals with a single idea. Just as you have to read all of a paragraph to understand what a writer says about the idea, so a computer has to use all of a single-task program to complete the task.

Complex BASIC programs contain 2 or more single-task pieces, much as an essay contains 2 or more paragraphs. Each piece is complete and could be used by itself. Programs that contain 2 or more complete pieces are often called **structured programs.**

A single computer task is called a **routine.** Structured programs are organized to have a **main routine,** which contains the major decisions and calculations, and 1 or more **subroutines,** each of which does a single task that may be used when the program is run.

To use a subroutine, you include a decision step in the main routine. For example,

```
IF A$="YES" THEN
GOSUB 1000
```

IF A$="YES"THEN GOSUB 1000

will send the computer to the subroutine that begins at line 1000, whenever A$ is YES.

At the right is a flowchart of an algorithm for finding a checkbook balance. Only the main routine is shown in detail. Each of the subroutines would be shown in a separate flowchart.

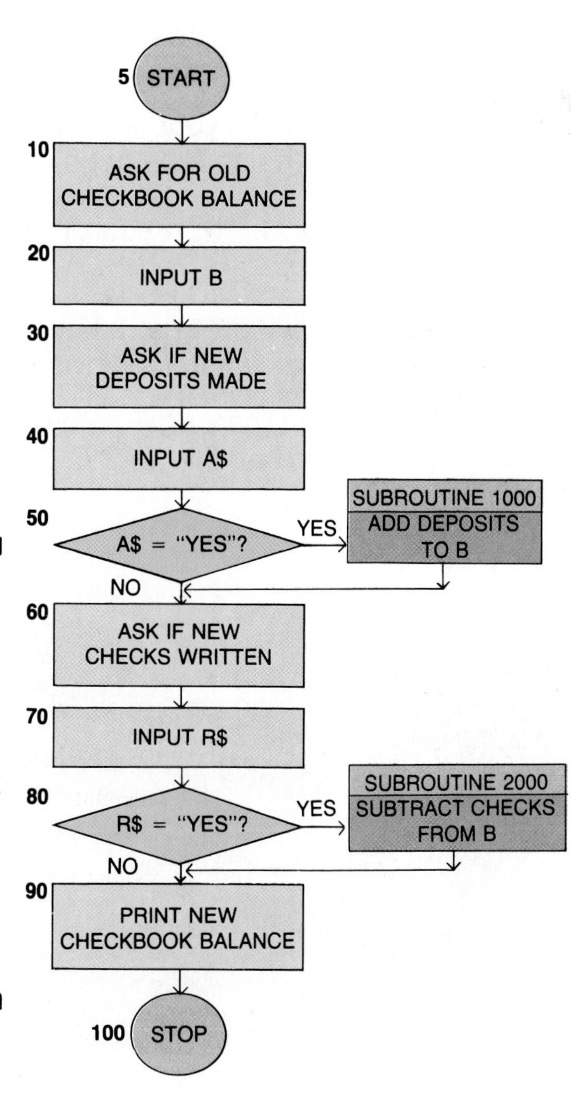


**1.** Translate the main routine shown in the flowchart into BASIC.

**B.** Subroutines usually follow the main routine of a BASIC program. You write subroutines the same way you write any program, *except* that the last command is RETURN, not END. RETURN tells the computer to go back to the main routine, to the line *after* the GOSUB command.

As for main routines, the first step in writing a subroutine is to *plan* your work. This is a plan for the first subroutine shown in the flowchart on page 443:

> Get the amount of the deposit from the user. Add to the checkbook balance (old value of B, from the main routine). Ask if there were any other deposits. If so, repeat the subroutine process. Otherwise, return to the main routine.

2. Draw a flowchart for the plan of the first subroutine.

3. Translate the program in your flowchart from exercise 2 into BASIC. Use this REM line (see page 436) as the first line of the subroutine:

```
1000 REM***SUBROUTINE: ADD DEPOSITS***
```

4. Use the three-part plan to write a BASIC program for the second subroutine shown in the flowchart on page 443.

First, *plan* your work. Then, draw a *flowchart* of your plan. Finally, *translate* the program in your flowchart into BASIC. Be sure to start the subroutine with a REM line.

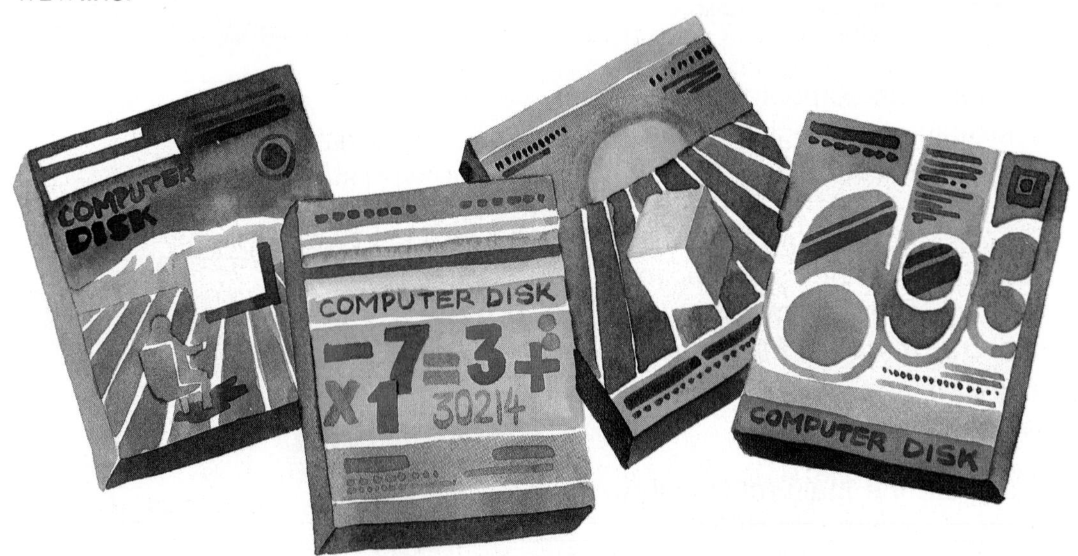

## Using Arrays in BASIC

**A.** Computer programs are often created to keep track of large numbers of related data items. For example, an airline might want to keep track of the number of passengers on all of its flights during the year to determine the most popular month for traveling. A bank might want a record of how many transactions each of its customers makes during a given time period to see how bank service might be improved.

Suppose you are the head of a committee on sports events at your school. In order to estimate the attendance at next year's basketball games, you would want a record of how many students attended this season's games. One way of doing this is to write a program assigning a different variable to each game. If your school played 4 games, your program might look like this:

```
10 PRINT "HOW MANY ATTENDED GAME 1?"
20 INPUT A
30 PRINT "HOW MANY ATTENDED GAME 2?"
40 INPUT B
50 PRINT "HOW MANY ATTENDED GAME 3?"
60 INPUT C
70 PRINT "HOW MANY ATTENDED GAME 4?"
80 INPUT D
90 END
```

You can easily see that it would be very time-consuming to write a program designed to handle more than a few games.

One way to write a more efficient program is by using an **array.** An array is a structure that allows a computer programmer to store and manipulate large collections of related numbers, such as population figures, salaries, or weather statistics. Arrays can also be used to store string data, such as names of people or places.

You must name the array and assign a number, called a **subscript,** to each item, or cell, within the array. You could name the array of attendance figures at basketball games A%. The % sign is necessary to tell the computer that the cells of the array will store integer data. A%(4) represents the value of the integer stored in the fourth cell of the array. A%(2) would represent the value stored in the second cell of the array.

Any BASIC Program using an array must declare the array in a DIM (for DIMension) statement: `10 DIM A%(4)`

4 basketball games

To represent an array that stores string data, the name of the array must be followed by $ instead of %. An array to keep track of 20 vocabulary words could be named W$(20).

20 words

1. Name an array that could be used to store a student's scores on 5 history tests.

2. Write an instruction in BASIC declaring an array that will store the names of the 50 states.

3. Write an instruction in BASIC to print the number of rainy days in the fifth month of a 12-month period.

**B.** A program using an array that will enable a user to enter attendance figures for 4 basketball games follows.

```
10 DIM A%(4)
20 LET C = 1
30 IF C > 4 THEN 80
40 PRINT "HOW MANY ATTENDED GAME ";A%(C);" ?"
50 INPUT A%(C)
60 C = C + 1
70 GOTO 30
80 END
```

In this program, C is used as a counter to keep track of the games for which attendance figures are entered. It is also used as a variable subscript for the array A%. When the program is run, a different value will be printed at line 40 each time the counter increases by 1.

4. Modify the first program in B to accept attendance figures for 10 games.

5. Write a program using an array that asks a user to enter the number of home runs scored by a baseball team for 10 games played. Your program should report the total number of home runs as well as the average number per game.

## Types of Errors and Debugging a Program

Even with careful planning and attention to coding, it is still very easy to make a mistake when writing a BASIC program. Programmers spend a great deal of time trying to find the errors, or "bugs," in their programs. There are three main types of bugs: (1) BASIC syntax errors, (2) run-time errors, and (3) program logic errors.

**A.** BASIC **syntax errors** occur when statements do not follow the rules of spelling and punctuation for BASIC. They are similar to grammatical errors you may make in writing. Syntax errors are the easiest to find and correct. Some versions of BASIC check syntax as soon as a program line is typed. If the line contains a syntax error, you immediately get an error message and you can correct the line. Other versions of BASIC find syntax errors only when you try to run the program. A program with a syntax error will not run; the computer will usually print the line number that contains the error so you can fix it.

**1.** Find the syntax errors in the program below.

```
10 PRINT "CAN YOU FIND
20 PRINT 6 "ERRORS IN THIS PROGRAM"
30 LET M = 4
40 LET N = 3XM
50 PRINT N ÷ M .
```

**B.** **Run-time** errors are harder to find than syntax errors. The syntax of every line may be perfect, but your program still may not run. Although each instruction makes sense by itself, the instructions may not be put together properly. Here are some common run-time errors to look for:

- not enough input in an `INPUT` statement
- omitting the `NEXT` statement at the end of a loop
- branching to a line number that does not exist
- mixing string and numeric variables

Find the run-time errors in the programs below.
**See Answers beginning p. 533.**

**2.**
```
10 INPUT X
20 IF 2 * X > 10 THEN 60
30 GOTO 20
40 PRINT X
50 END
```

**3.**
```
10 PRINT "INTEGER
   SQUARE"
20 FOR N = 1 TO 6
30 PRINT N; "    "; N^2
40 END
```

**c.** Bugs caused by **program logic errors** are usually the hardest to find. These are mistakes in the organization of your program, such as having the computer execute the wrong loop or subroutine, or using variables before you have given values to them. Rather than expecting to fix these errors, you should try to keep them out of your program altogether. You should always do a "dry run" of a program before you actually take it to the computer. Read through the program, trying to imagine that you are the computer. Use simple values that you can check mentally or on paper. However, in a complicated program with many loops and branches, you may only be able to detect program logic errors after the program is actually run. If you have planned your program carefully, you may only have to redesign part of it to fix the error. Sometimes it is better to redesign a whole program than to keep patching bugs, which may result in a mess that is no use at all.

**4.** What are program logic errors? Can you describe others than those mentioned above?

**5.** Write a short BASIC program. Do not use the computer. Exchange programs with another student. Correct each other's programs, indicating the type of error that was made and the proper statements or organization.

**6.** If a computer is available, enter the programs from exercise 5. First try without the corrections, then with corrections if the program did not work the first time.

UNIT 1 **Whole Numbers: Problem Solving**

## Problem Solving: A 5-Step Plan *(pages 12–13)*

In a 3-game series the attendance was 30,256; 23,946; and 37,785. What was the total attendance for the series?

1. **Read** *Must find:* Total attendance *Know:* Attendance for each game
2. **Plan** Total attendance = Game 1 + Game 2 + Game 3
3. **Do** 30,256 + 23,946 + 37,785 = 91,987
4. **Answer** The total attendance was 91,987
5. **Check**

$$\begin{array}{r} 30{,}000 \\ 20{,}000 \\ +40{,}000 \\ \hline 90{,}000 \end{array} ✓$$

1. Mrs. Kane paid $157.50 down on a trip. Later she paid $250.75. Finally she paid $78.49. What was the total cost of the trip?
2. An airline sold 5,964 tickets in January and 9,851 tickets in April. How many tickets did they sell during the two months in all?

*The table shows the population of six cities.*

3. What was the total population of the three largest cities?
4. What was the total population of the three smallest cities?

| City | Population |
|---|---|
| Amarillo | 137,969 |
| Hartford | 162,178 |
| Peoria | 103,162 |
| Raleigh | 93,931 |
| Tacoma | 147,979 |
| Topeka | 119,484 |

Explain the steps you would use to find the total cost of taking your friends to lunch.

## Problem Solving: Using Subtraction *(pages 14–15)*

A truck driver's odometer read 23,911 km when she started a trip, and 26,700 km when she finished it. How long was the trip?

Length = km reading at end − km reading at start of trip
= 26,700 − 23,911
= 2,789 km

1. There are 3,792 students at Flosswood High School. Of these, 896 are seniors. How many are not seniors?
2. Which of the four Bowl games had the largest crowd? The smallest? What was the difference between them?
3. On New Year's day, 77,486 people attended the Sugar Bowl game and 66,714 attended the Orange Bowl. How many fewer attended the Orange Bowl?
4. There were 105,526 people at the Rose Bowl and 72,032 at the Cotton Bowl. How many more were at the Rose Bowl?

Explain how you would find the difference in age between the oldest and youngest members of your family.

## Problem Solving: Using Multiplication *(pages 16–17)*

| | |
|---|---|
| During one month a computer store sold 38 computers for \$739.50 each. How much did the store receive in all for these computers? | Amount received = Number sold × Price per computer<br>= 38 × \$739.50<br>= \$28,101.00 |

1. Ms. Meyer bought 12 computers for her store. Each computer cost \$889.90. What was the total cost?
2. A television manufacturing plant produces 463 TV sets every work shift. How many TV sets would be produced in 45 shifts?
3. Mr. Ward bought 36 color TV sets to sell in his store. He paid \$360.90 for each set. How much did he spend for the color TV sets?
4. Mr. Ward also bought 20 black and white TV sets. He paid \$59.16 for each set. How much did he spend for the black and white sets?

How much would you spend to take several of your friends to a movie at a nearby theater?

## Problem Solving: Using Division *(pages 18–19)*

| | |
|---|---|
| A worker received \$195.60 in wages for working 24 hours. What was the worker's average rate of pay per hour? | Average rate = Total pay ÷ Number of hours<br>= \$195.60 ÷ 24<br>= \$8.15 |

1. Ms. Meyer sold 35 books on computers in one day. She took in \$454.65. What was the average price for a book?
2. A book manufacturer packed 960 books in cartons that hold 15 books each. How many cartons were needed?
3. Ms. Best spent \$68.28 for 12 records. What was the average cost per record?
4. A store buys shirts for \$14 each. How many shirts can the store buy if it spends \$700?
5. A garden center sold all 45 snow blowers at a pre-season sale for \$259.90 each. How much was taken in from the sale of the snow blowers?

Count all the books in your house. How many books would fit on each of six shelves if you wanted an equal number on each shelf?

### **Problem Solving: Answering the Question** *(pages 20–21)*

| | |
|---|---|
| A group of 500 people plan to travel to a convention. How many buses must be hired if each bus holds 42 passengers? | Buses needed = Number of people ÷ Passengers per bus<br>= 500 ÷ 42<br>= 11 R38<br>*Answer:* An extra bus is needed for the people left over. 12 buses are needed. |

1. A warehouse shipped 590 books. If each carton held 16 books, how many cartons were used?
2. A book store spent $13.44 for each of 12 books. How much did it spend all together for these books?
3. Ms. Howard spent 8 hours previewing 3 films. What was the average time spent previewing a film?
4. A store sells grapefruit in packages of four each. How many packages can be filled by 250 grapefruits?
5. A supplier has an order for 5,032 TV's. How many trucks are needed to deliver the order if each truck can hold 296 TV's?

If you were paid $2.75 an hour for helping around your house, how much would you have earned so far this week?

### **Problem Solving: Working with Rates** *(pages 22–23)*

| | |
|---|---|
| Ms. Hanson drove a distance of 770 km in her auto and she used 70 liters of gasoline. What was the rate of distance driven per liter of gasoline? | Rate (km/L) = Distance in km ÷ Liters of gasoline<br>= 770 ÷ 70<br>= 11<br>The rate was 11 km/L. |

1. Mrs. Levy received $32.20 in car expenses, for traveling 230 km. At what rate was she paid?
2. A secretary can type at a rate of 56 words per minute. How many words can he type in 28 minutes?
3. A pilot was given an assignment to fly a jet airplane 4,200 km. It took the pilot 5 hours to complete this assignment. What was the pilot's average speed in km/h?
4. On a full tank Ms. Harris can travel 395 km in city driving or 560 km in highway driving. How much farther can she travel on a full tank with highway driving?

How many times can you say your name and address in one minute? At that rate, how many times could you say it in $2\frac{1}{2}$ minutes, 5 minutes, and an hour?

## Problem Solving: Two-Step Problems *(pages 24–25)*

A theater has 680 seats. Tickets for 125 seats remain unsold. If tickets for each seat cost $6.50, how much did the theater make in ticket sales?

(1) Ticket sales = Tickets sold × Price per ticket
= ? × $6.50
(2) Tickets sold = Total seats − Unsold tickets
= 680 − 125 = 555
Ticket sales = 555 × $6.50 = $3,607.50

1. Mamie gave the cashier $10.00 for a $3.95 item. She still had $2.50 in her wallet. How much money should Mamie have after she gets the change?

2. After buying a shirt that cost $17.85 and a matching tie that cost $6.98, Johanne had $14.08 left. How much money did he have to start with?

3. Last year Ms. Klein's sales were $23,960 over her sales quota. This year her quota was $1,480,000 and her total sales were $1,508,463. By how much more than last year did she go over her sales quota this year?

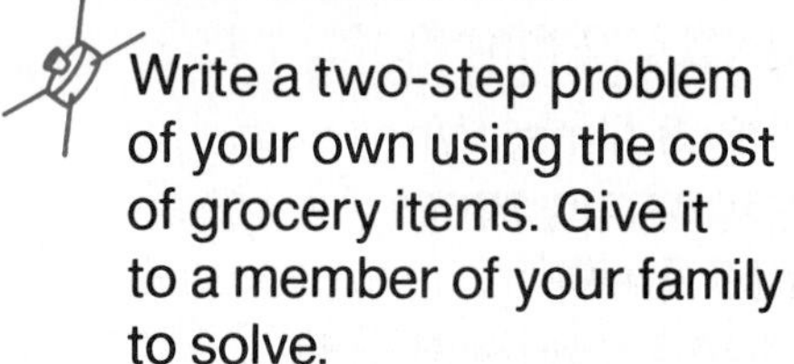

Write a two-step problem of your own using the cost of grocery items. Give it to a member of your family to solve.

## Problem Solving: Three-Step Problems *(pages 26–27)*

Mr. Lynch bought a car on an installment plan. He must pay $260 a month for 36 months. If $40 of each payment is interest, what was the cost of the car without interest?

(1) Cost without interest = Total payments − Total interest
(2) Total payments = Number of payments × Amount per payment
= 36 × $260 = $9,360
(3) Total interest = Number of payments × Interest per payment
= 36 × $40 = $1,440
Cost without interest = $9,360 − $1,440 = $7,920

1. The shop ordered 1,800 tapes. It received 312 tapes on Monday and 36 boxes with 24 tapes in each on Tuesday. How many of the tapes it had ordered had it not received?

2. Ms. Kistner must drive a total of 2,645 km. She drove 602 km the first day. On the second day she drove for 7 h at an average speed of 81 km/h. How far did she still have to go?

3. A store bought 12 tables for $1,235.76 and 8 chairs for $472.64. What was the total cost of 1 table and 1 chair?

If you were to sell all your record albums for $2.98 each and your tapes for $3.25 each, how much would you make?

## Problem Solving: More Three-Step Problems *(pages 28–29)*

To be on schedule a bus must travel at an average speed of 90 km/h. If it completes all but 255 km of its 720-km run in 5h, how much faster than the required average speed has it been traveling?

(1) Rate above required speed = Traveling average − Required speed
= ? − 90

(2) Traveling average = Distance traveled ÷ Hours traveled
= ? ÷ 5

(3) Distance traveled = Total − Part left
= 720 − 255 = 465

Traveling average = 465 ÷ 5 = 93 → Rate above required speed = 93 − 90 = 3 km/h

1. A driver wants to travel 300 km in 4 hours. During the first hour she travels 78 km. What should be her average speed for the remainder of the trip?

2. A store paid $254.40 for 48 place mats and $206.40 for 96 cloth napkins. What was the total price for 1 placemat and 1 napkin?

3. A family of four members had $40.00 to spend for dinner. Three meals cost $6.95 each and one meal cost $7.45. How much money did they have left over?

If you buy two gifts, costing $6.95 and $10.98, for each member of your family, how much money will you have left if you start with $250?

## Problem Solving: More than Three Steps *(pages 30–31)*

On a trip Mr. Howe paid $35 on each of 3 nights for hotel rooms and $45 on each of 2 nights for motel rooms. What was his average cost of lodging per night?

(1) Average cost = Total cost ÷ Number of nights
= ? ÷ ?

(2) Total cost = Hotel cost + Motel cost
= ? + ?

(3) Hotel cost = Number of nights × Hotel rate
= 3 × 35 = 105

(4) Motel cost = Number of nights × Motel rate
= 2 × 45 = 90

Total cost = 105 + 90 = 195 → Average cost = 195 ÷ 5 = $39/night

1. A store bought 5 chairs for $39.75 each, 12 tables for $62.50 each, 20 lamps for $19.95 each, and 9 rugs for $79.85 each. How much did the store spend in all?

2. The basketball coach has a total of $400.00 to spend for shoes and basketballs. If he buys 12 pairs of shoes at $16.50 each, how many basketballs costing $21 each can he buy?

3. A store bought 500 kg of oranges in 25 kg sacks. It paid $18.75 per sack for these oranges. It sold the oranges in 2 kg bags for $1.80 per bag. For how much more than it paid did it sell these oranges?

Make up a money problem with more than three steps. Give it to someone in your class to solve.

## Problem Solving: Finding Needed Data *(pages 32–33)*

*Find or estimate the missing data and solve.*

The distance from St. Louis to Chicago is 460 km. How long would it take to drive from St. Louis to Chicago?

Time for trip = Total distance ÷ Distance per hour

*Know:* Total distance is 460 km.
*Must find:* Distance traveled per hour.
An estimate of the distance traveled per hour is 80 km/h.

Time for trip $= 460 \div 80$
$= 5\frac{3}{4}$ h

1. A race car traveled at a speed of 4 km/min. What is its speed in kilometers per hour?

2. The Bears made 3 touchdowns, 2 extra points and 2 field goals. What was their score?

3. A street lamp was lighted 14 hours each night during March, April, and May. For how long was the lamp lighted?

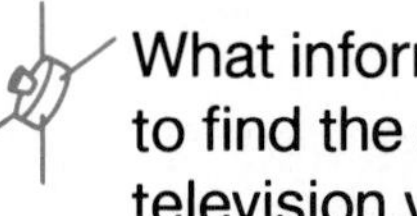

What information would you need to find the average amount of television you watch in 3 months? Work through the problem.

## Problem Solving: Selecting Needed Data *(pages 34–35)*

*Tell what information is not needed to solve the problem. Solve the problem.*

Each 10-kg box of apples contains about 70 apples and costs $10.50. How much does it cost to buy 12 of these boxes?

*Not needed:* mass is 10 kg; each box contains about 70 apples

Total cost = Number of boxes × Cost per box
= 12 × 10.50
= $126.00

1. The air distance between New York and Chicago is 1,185 km. The flight time is about $1\frac{1}{2}$ h. How many kilometers are flown in 17 such flights?

2. Ms. Stevenson bought 24 boxes of pens for her stationery store. Each box contained 8 pens and cost $10.80. What did Mrs. Stevenson pay in all?

3. A store sells shirts for $12.95 each. On Saturday it sold 93 shirts. This was 26 more than it had sold on Friday. How many were sold in all in these two days?

4. A bus can carry 54 people. 8 buses were used to take people to the game. The buses completed the 204 km trip in 3 h. What was their average speed?

Write a problem in which you give more information than necessary. Have a member of your family solve it.

## Problem Solving: Completing Forms *(pages 36–37)*

*Find each new balance in this checkbook record.*

| | Check Number | Date | Item | Amount of Check | | Amount of Deposit | | Balance | |
|---|---|---|---|---|---|---|---|---|---|
| | | | | | | | | 490 | 13 |
| | 439 | 7/12 | Gas and Light Co. | 93 | 68 | | | 396 | 45 |
| 1. | | 7/14 | Deposit | | | 480 | 75 | | |
| 2. | 440 | 7/15 | River Tire Co. | 125 | 46 | | | | |

*Continue the checkbook record for these checks and deposits.*

3. On July 16, check 441 to City Treasurer for $85.25.

4. On July 18, check 442 to Valley Furniture for $207.78.

*Complete an order form for each order. The handling charge is $5.00. The order form below has been completed for 3 pairs of designer jeans and 6 T-shirts.*

| Catalog Number | Name of Item | Quantity | Price Each | | Total Price | |
|---|---|---|---|---|---|---|
| EZ 409 | Designer jeans | 3 | $ 35 | 50 | $ 106 | 50 |
| EX 219C | T-shirt | 6 | 8 | 79 | 52 | 74 |
| | | **Total Order** | | | 159 | 53 |
| | | **Handling Charge** | | | 5 | 00 |
| | | **Total Payment** | | | $164 | 53 |

5. 1 pair of jeans, 3 pairs of socks, 4 T-shirts, 2 plaid shirts.

6. 2 pairs of jeans, 6 pairs of socks, 2 T-shirts, 1 plaid shirt.

7. 1 pair of jeans, 1 pair of socks, 1 T-shirt, 3 plaid shirts.

| | |
|---|---|
| Designer jeans<br>EZ409<br>$35.50 | Socks<br>JO367E<br>3 pairs<br>for $4.99 |
| T-shirt<br>EX219C<br>2 for $8.79 | Plaid Shirt<br>KY502<br>$18.75 |

Think of two items under $100 that you would like to buy. What will your balance be after writing two checks and making a deposit of $45.50? Your initial balance is $248.55.

# UNIT 2 Whole Numbers: Algebra

## Arithmetic Expressions and Sentences *(pages 48–49)*

*Simplify.*

| | |
|---|---|
| $14 \times 3 - 25 + 9 \times 5$ | $[43 - (16 + 11)] \times (26 + 9)$ |
| $42 - 25 + 45$ | $[43 - 27] \times (26 + 9)$ |
| $17 + 45$ | $16 \times 35$ |
| $62$ | $560$ |

**1.** $5 + 8 \times 12 - 6 \div 2$ **2.** $(5 + 8) \times 12 - 4$ **3.** $9 + 15 \div 5 - 10 \div 2$

**4.** $16 \times 5 - 26 + 48 \div 3$ **5.** $45 \div 9 + 2 \times 3$ **6.** $45 \div (9 + 2 \times 3)$

*Tell whether the statement is true or false.*

| | | | |
|---|---|---|---|
| $6 \times 3 = 2 \times 9$ | true | $10 \div 2 \leq 4$ | false |

**7.** $6 \times 9 \neq 56$ **8.** $2 + 3 \times 4 < 18$ **9.** $12 - 4 \div 2 \geq 5$ **10.** $16 - 8 \times 2 = 0$

**11.** $7 \times 8 < 6 \times 9$ **12.** $144 \div 36 > 5$ **13.** $6 \times 8 \leq 30 + 3 \times 6$

Write 3 true arithmetic sentences using $=$, $<$, and $>$.

## Algebraic Expressions *(pages 50–51)*

*Find the value of each algebraic expression when the value of x is 6.*

| |
|---|
| $7x - 11$ |
| $7 \times 6 - 11 = 42 - 11 = 31$ |
| Value of $7x - 11$ is 31. |

**1.** $18 + x$ **2.** $8x$ **3.** $\frac{7x}{2}$

**4.** $20 - 3x$ **5.** $\frac{13x}{3} + 10$ **6.** $79 + 15x$ **7.** $\frac{11x}{3} - 7$ **8.** $20 - (x - 5)$

*Find the value of each algebraic expression when the value of y is 5 and the value of z is 3.*

| |
|---|
| $12y - 3z$ |
| $12 \times 5 - 3 \times 3 = 60 - 9 = 51$ |
| Value of $12y - 3z$ is 51. |

**9.** $y - z$ **10.** $z \cdot y$ **11.** $\frac{z}{3} + \frac{y}{5}$

**12.** $4y + 7z$ **13.** $20 - 2y - z$

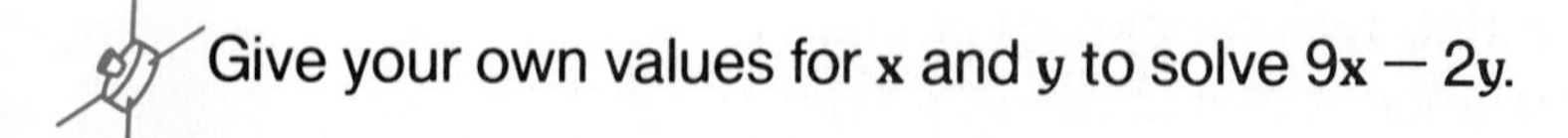

Give your own values for $x$ and $y$ to solve $9x - 2y$.

## Algebraic Sentences *(pages 52–53)*

*Tell whether the sentence is true or false for the given values of the variables.*

| $52 - x = 72$ when x is 20 | $5y + 8 < 25$ when y is 3 |
|---|---|
| $52 - x = 72$ | $5y + 8 < 25$ |
| ↓ ↓ ↓ | ↓ ↓ ↓ |
| $52 - 20 = 72$ | $5 \times 3 + 8 < 25$ |
| $32 = 72$ false | $15 + 8 < 25$ |
| | $23 < 25$ true |

**1.** $14 + x = 8$ when x is 6

**2.** $2y + 5 \geqslant 7$ when y is 3

**3.** $12 - z = 4$ when z is 8

**4.** $\frac{5u}{2} - 3 = 12$ when u is 15

**5.** $x + 8 = 8 + x$ when x is 50

**6.** $2x + 3y < 12$ when x is 3 and y is 2

**7.** $4y - 7z > 20$ when y is 10 and z is 4

**8.** $\frac{4w}{3} + 5v \leqslant 37$ when v is 5 and w is 9

Assign your own values to the variables **a** and **b** in $\frac{3a}{4} + 6b > 15$. Is the sentence true or false?

## Relationships between Operations *(pages 54–55)*

*Use the relationships between operations to complete.*

| $z + 18 - ■ = z$ |
|---|
| ↓ |
| $z + 18 - 18 = z$ |

**1.** $x \cdot 8 \div ■ = x$

**2.** $y - 8 + 8 = ■$

**3.** $3 \cdot (u + 4) = 3u + ■$

**4.** $■ - 12 = 2(t - 6)$

**5.** $\frac{s}{16} \cdot ■ = s$

**6.** $m = 7 \cdot m \div ■$

**7.** $■ = 85 + x - 85$

**8.** $■ \cdot 16 \div 16 = y$

**9.** $■ + 36 = 4 \cdot (r + 9)$

**10.** $■ = 25 \cdot z \div 25$

**11.** $t - ■ + 15 = t$

**12.** $■ + 35 - 35 = y$

**13.** $\frac{x}{■} \cdot 12 = x$

**14.** $6y + 24 = 6 \cdot (y + ■)$

**15.** $(s - 8) \cdot 12 = 12s - ■$

Choose one of the exercises above. Write the steps you used to solve it.

## Solving Equations with Addition and Subtraction *(pages 56–57)*

*Solve the equations. Check.*

$$x + 14 = 40$$
$$x + 14 - 14 = 40 - 14$$
$$x = 26$$

*Solution:* 26

*Check:*

$x + 14 = 40$

↓

$26 + 14 = 40$ true ✔

1. $x - 13 = 19$
2. $63 = 19 + t$
3. $y + 5 = 28$
4. $r - 53 = 61$
5. $0 = z - 37$
6. $75 = 42 + x$
7. $43 = u + 27$
8. $w + 14 = 42$
9. $75 = w - 52$
10. $u - 47 = 100$
11. $41 = 17 + s$
12. $90 = 24 + y$
13. $93 = t + 93$
14. $z + 95 = 95$

Using the sum of digits in your telephone number and the sum of the ages of everyone in your family, write 4 equations requiring addition and subtraction.

## Solving Equations with Multiplication and Division *(pages 58–59)*

*Solve the equations. Check.*

$$\frac{3x}{8} = 45$$
$$\frac{3x}{8} \cdot 8 = 45 \cdot 8$$
$$3x = 360$$
$$3x \div 3 = 360 \div 3$$
$$x = 120$$

*Solution:* 120

*Check:*

$$\frac{3x}{8} = 45$$
$$3 \cdot 120 \div 8 = 45$$
$$360 \div 8 = 45$$
$$45 = 45$$

true

1. $3x = 42$
2. $\frac{x}{7} = 91$
3. $64 = 16y$
4. $20 = \frac{y}{5}$
5. $z \div 16 = 0$
6. $60 = 15 + u$

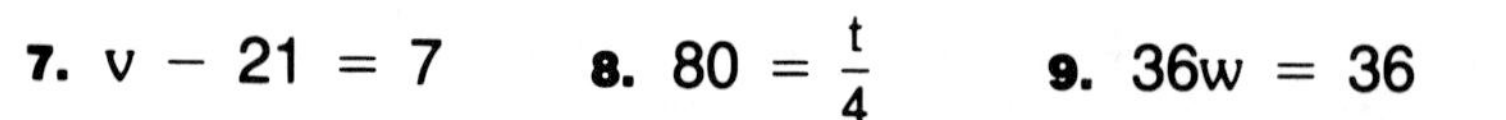

7. $v - 21 = 7$
8. $80 = \frac{t}{4}$
9. $36w = 36$
10. $56 = \frac{u}{7}$
11. $0 = 24t$
12. $\frac{x}{25} = 1$
13. $\frac{4x}{5} = 40$
14. $20 = 8x \div 2$

Solve this equation: your age $= \dfrac{t}{\text{your height in inches}}$

## **Solving Other Equations** *(pages 60–61)*

*Solve the equation. Check.*

| | |
|---|---|
| $\frac{y}{5} + 10 = 25$ | *Check:* |
| $y \div 5 + 10 = 25$ | $75 \div 5 + 10 = 25$ |
| $y \div 5 = 15$ | $15 + 10 = 25$ |
| $y = 75$ | $25 = 25$ true |
| *Solution:* 75 | |

1. $8x + 2 = 90$
2. $\frac{y}{6} - 5 = 7$
3. $9z - 11 = 43$
4. $25 = \frac{2x}{5} + 13$
5. $40 = \frac{u}{4} + 19$
6. $20v - 37 = 63$
7. $15 = \frac{7x}{12} - 13$
8. $\frac{x}{2} - 19 = 81$
9. $14y + 23 = 65$
10. $\frac{x}{9} - 4 = 8$
11. $12w - 17 = 55$
12. $\frac{3x}{8} + 21 = 30$
13. $16t - 29 = 83$

Solve. $\frac{z}{\text{number of pages in your favorite book}} - \text{number of pages in one chapter} = 75$

## **Problem Solving: Using Equations** *(pages 62–63)*

If John tripled the money he has now, he would have \$7 more than \$50. How much money does he have now?

*Must find:* Amount he has now.

*Know:* 3 times the amount is \$7 more than \$50.

$3n - 50 = 7$

$3n = 57$

$n = 29$

*Solution:* 29

John has \$29 now.

*Check:* $3 \times 29 - 50 = 7$

$57 - 50 = 7$

$7 = 7$ true

1. The difference when 17 is subtracted from the result of dividing the product of 7 and a number by 12 is 18. Find the number.
2. If Mary doubled the money she has now, she would still need \$14 more to have a total of \$50. How much money does she have now?
3. Tickets for the school play were sold at \$3.00 each for adults and at \$2.00 each for students. 205 student tickets were sold. How many adult tickets were sold if the total sales were \$785?

Write your own word problem and write an equation to solve it. Give it to someone in your family or class to solve.

## Problem Solving: Using Formulas *(pages 64–65)*

*The total score (S) in a professional basketball game is given by the formula:* $S = 3l + 2s + f$

$l$ = number of long field goals made
$s$ = number of short field goals made
$f$ = number of free throws made

| | |
|---|---|
| The Chicago professional team made 2 long field goals, 39 short field goals, and 17 free throws. What was the team's total score? | $S = 3l + 2s + f$<br>$= 3 \times 2 + 2 \times 39 + 17$<br>$= 6 + 78 + 17$<br>$= 101$<br>The team's total score was 101. |

*Complete the table.*

| | l | s | f | S |
|---|---|---|---|---|
| **1.** | 3 | 39 | 28 | ■ |
| **2.** | 2 | 47 | 21 | ■ |
| **3.** | 2 | 43 | ■ | 117 |
| **4.** | 1 | ■ | 27 | 112 |
| **5.** | ■ | 38 | 24 | 112 |

Find your average for the last 3 test scores in each subject area.

## Problem Solving: Using Flowcharts *(pages 66–67)*

*Use this flowchart to complete the table.*

| a | b | x | y |
|---|---|---|---|
| 3 | 8 | 11 | 6 |
| 2 | 5 | **1.** ■ | **2.** ■ |
| 4 | 8 | **3.** ■ | **4.** ■ |
| 16 | 47 | **5.** ■ | **6.** ■ |
| 53 | 95 | **7.** ■ | **8.** ■ |
| 101 | 124 | **9.** ■ | **10.** ■ |

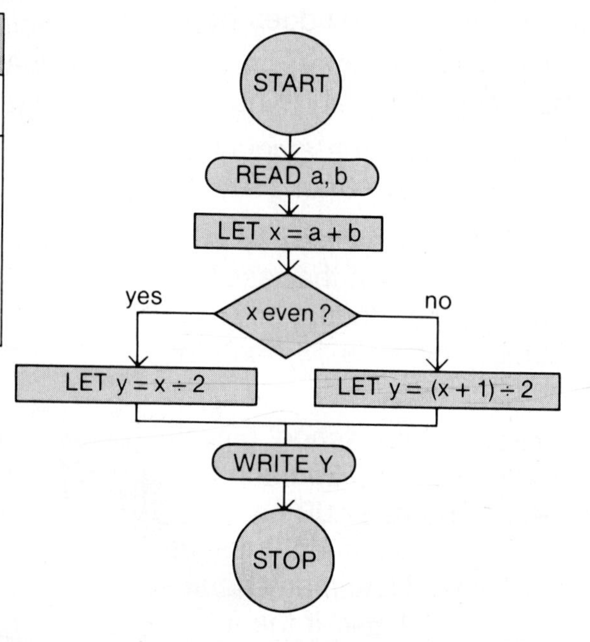


$a = 3 \quad b = 8$
$x = a + b$
$= 3 + 8 = 11$ x even? No
$y = (x + 1) \div 2$
$y = (11 + 1) \div 2$
$= 12 \div 2 = 6$ Write: 6

Write a word problem. Use a flowchart to solve it.

## UNIT 3 Decimals

### Decimals to Millionths (pages 78–79)

*In each decimal name the places of the digits 3 and 7. Then tell what the digits 3 and 7 mean.*

| | |
|---|---|
| 0.043175 | 3 is in the thousandths place.<br>7 is in the hundred-thousandths place.<br>3 means 3 thousandths.<br>7 means 7 hundred-thousandths. |

1. 2.1437
2. 12.43607
3. 0.741623
4. 23.1700
5. 0.04173
6. 0.006237
7. 2.7135
8. 0.027130

*Write the decimals.*

9. four tenths
10. three and seventeen hundredths
11. eight hundredths
12. fifty-three thousandths
13. six hundred seventy-five ten-thousandths
14. four thousand six hundred eleven millionths
15. ninety-two hundred-thousandths
16. Tell what each digit means in the decimal .214596.

Find a decimal on a label or package. Tell what each digit means.

### Comparing with Decimals (pages 80–81)

*Compare. Use $>$, $<$, or $=$ for ●.*

| |
|---|
| .00304 ● .0031<br>.00304<br>.00310<br>$0 < 1$ so<br>$.00304 < .0031$ |

1. .735 ● 1.925
2. 4.386 ● .9482
3. .52 ● 0.520
4. .013821 ● .013812
5. 1.7326 ● 1.73260
6. .012 ● .011985
7. .00685 ● .0204
8. .49257 ● .49256
9. 0.0040 ● .00400

*Order from least to greatest.*

10. .5794; 6.99; .536493
11. .06511; .7034; .67234
12. .06; .058943; .0595; .009
13. 2.493; 1.34; 4.423; 2.06396

Find decimals on 4 labels or packages. Then list them from the greatest to the least.

## **Rounding with Decimals** *(pages 82–83)*

*Round to the nearest thousandth. To the nearest tenth.*

| 0.952498 | 0.952 \| 498<br>0.952 | 4 < 5<br>Round down | 0.9 \| 52498<br>+ 1<br>1.0 | 5 ≥ 5<br>Round up |
|---|---|---|---|---|

**1.** 2.64384 **2.** 1.029486 **3.** 9.9995 **4.** .059618

**5.** .545454 **6.** .454545 **7.** 0.234567 **8.** 0.123456

*Round to the nearest cent.*

**9.** \$3.875 **10.** \$29.0265 **11.** \$.00625 **12.** \$12.666666

Write your own decimal to the millionth's place using 6 different digits. Round to the nearest thousandth. To the nearest tenth.

## **Adding and Subtracting with Decimals** *(pages 84–85) Add or subtract.*

.0143 − .00962 = ■

$$\begin{array}{r} .01430 \\ -.00962 \\ \hline .00468 \end{array}$$

**1.** $\begin{array}{r} .4926 \\ +.5248 \\ \hline \end{array}$ **2.** $\begin{array}{r} \$200 \\ -\ 19.47 \\ \hline \end{array}$ **3.** $\begin{array}{r} .632 \\ +1.98 \\ \hline \end{array}$

**4.** $\begin{array}{r} .002 \\ -.00176 \\ \hline \end{array}$ **5.** $\begin{array}{r} 4.8213 \\ +1.526875 \\ \hline \end{array}$ **6.** $\begin{array}{r} .423 \\ -.4216 \\ \hline \end{array}$

**7.** .362 + .9148 + 1.68 = ■ **8.** \$20 − \$1.07 = ■

**9.** .0183 + 6.18 + .24875 = ■ **10.** .04 − .0098 = ■

*Solve. Check the solution.*

$$x - .146 = 2.05$$
$$(x - .146) + .146 = 2.05 + .146$$
$$x = 2.196$$

*Solution:* 2.196

*Check:*
$$x - .146 = 2.05$$
$$2.196 - .146 = 2.05$$
$$2.050 = 2.05 \checkmark$$

**11.** $y + 2.8 = 5.2$

**12.** $z - 3.7 = 6.2$

**13.** $x + 2.35 = 11.2$

**14.** $m - .264 = 1.3$

**15.** $w - .042 = .1793$

**16.** $v + .05 = .2$

**17.** $.0015 = t - .00075$

Look up the batting averages of any two baseball players. What is the difference between the two?

## **Multiplying with Decimals** *(pages 86–87) Multiply.*

.026 × .34 = ■

```
  .34     2 places
× .026   +3 places
  204
  680
.00884    5 places
```

1. $5.3 \times .08$
2. $27.3 \times .4$
3. $\$48.68 \times 3.5$
4. $.026 \times .15$
5. $.045 \times 2.148$
6. $240 \times .006$
7. $8.325 \times 4.9$
8. $.009 \times 8.56$
9. $3.68 \times .0042$
10. $6.83 \times 40.5$
11. $.072 \times 3.461$
12. .09 × .006 = ■
13. 3.125 × 640 = ■
14. .0014 × 2.05 = ■

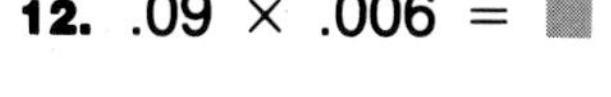

Multiply .125 by the weight in grams of a box of your favorite cereal.

## **Problem Solving: Comparison Shopping** *(pages 88–89)*

*Use the list of prices on page 89. Complete the table.*

| Purchase | | | | Least Cost | |
|---|---|---|---|---|---|
| Oranges | Peppers | Cheese | Pork Chops | Bought at one store | Bought where each cost least |
| 1 kg | .3 kg | | 1.5 kg | $9.39 | $9.38 |
| 1 kg | 1 kg | 1 kg | | 1. | 2. |
| 1.25 kg | | 0.75 kg | | 3. | 4. |
| | 0.25 kg | | 2.3 kg | 5. | 6. |
| 1.3 kg | 0.75 kg | 1.4 kg | | 7. | 8. |
| 4.5 kg | 3.6 kg | 5.2 kg | 8.75 kg | 9. | 10. |

| | | Store A | | Store B | | Store C | |
|---|---|---|---|---|---|---|---|
| Oranges | 1 kg | 1 × .90 | $.90 | 1 × .94 | $.94 | 1 × .88 | $.88 |
| Peppers | .3 kg | .3 × .87 | .26 | .3 × .85 | .26 | .3 × .90 | .27 |
| Pork Chops | 1.5 kg | 1.5 × 5.69 | 8.54 | 1.5 × 5.63 | 8.45 | 1.5 × 5.49 | 8.24 |
| | | | $9.70 | | $9.65 | | $9.39 |

Oranges—Store C .88 + Peppers—Store A or B .26 + Pork Chops—Store C 8.24 = $9.38

Compare the prices of several similar items advertised in two different store ads. Are any prices the same? In which store do the items you compared cost less?

## **Dividing with Decimals** *(pages 90–91)* *Find the quotients.*

```
   .03
65)1.95
    0
   195
   195
     0
```

1. $5\overline{)\$24.30}$
2. $12\overline{).84}$
3. $43\overline{)1.548}$
4. $275\overline{)2.475}$
5. $14\overline{)219.8}$
6. $700\overline{)134.400}$
7. $67\overline{)5.561}$
8. $1{,}436\overline{)\$560.04}$

```
   .255 → .26
73)18.625
   14 6
    4 02
    3 65
     375
     365
      10
```

*Divide.*

9. $7\overline{)2.365}$
10. $9\overline{).383}$
11. $46\overline{)8.437}$
12. $340\overline{)6.129}$
13. $225\overline{)84.695}$
14. $83\overline{)5.848}$

Divide the cost of a box of cereal by the number of servings in it.

## **Rounding Decimals for Quotients** *(pages 92–93)*

*Divide.*

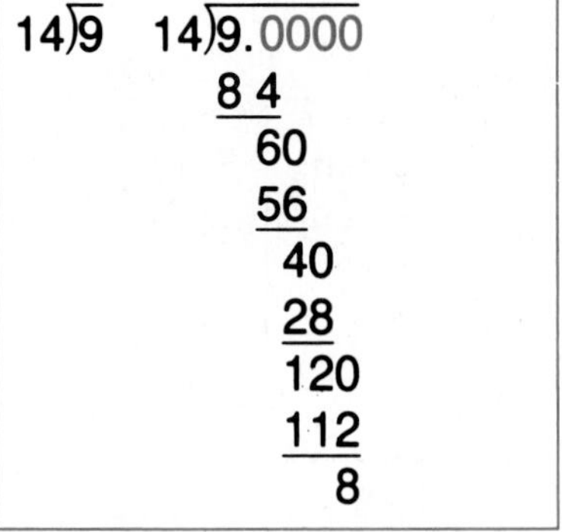


1. $8\overline{)13}$
2. $65\overline{)11.7}$
3. $7\overline{).04}$
4. $51\overline{)19}$
5. $63\overline{)296.1}$
6. $33\overline{)20}$
7. $37\overline{)5.8}$
8. $15\overline{).6}$
9. $400\overline{)117}$

Divide the number of people in your family by the number of rooms in your house. Round your quotient.

## **Powers of Ten and Decimals** *(pages 94–95)* *Multiply or divide.*

$1{,}000 \times 7.25 = 7{,}250.$ (3) $\qquad 5.3 \div 10{,}000 = .00053$ (4)

1. $1{,}000 \times 2.79 =$ ■
2. $382.76 \div 100 =$ ■
3. $12.7 \times 100 =$ ■
4. $3.9 \div 1{,}000 =$ ■
5. $10 \times .00489 =$ ■
6. $.048 \div 10 =$ ■
7. $100 \times 6.523 =$ ■
8. $71.56 \div 1{,}000 =$ ■
9. $1.0006 \times 10 =$ ■

Write your own decimal to the thousandth place. Multiply and divide by 10, 100, and 1,000.

## **Decimals for Divisors** *(pages 96–97)*

*Divide.*

```
       8.5
.45.)3.82.5
     3 60
       225
       225
         0
```

1. $.6\overline{)19.68}$ 2. $.08\overline{)3.488}$ 3. $.003\overline{)1.821}$

4. $7.2\overline{)33.12}$ 5. $.47\overline{).2726}$ 6. $.015\overline{).1275}$

7. $9.38\overline{)2.5326}$ 8. $.364\overline{).019292}$ 9. $.08\overline{)5.9384}$

10. $.27\overline{).9477}$ 11. $.6\overline{).3318}$ 12. $.09\overline{)4.50}$

Add a decimal point before the last four digits of your telephone number. Divide by .985.

## **More Decimals for Divisors** *(pages 98–99)*

*Divide.*

```
                       .2857
.035).01     .035.).010.0000
                     7 0
                     300
                     280
                      200
Quotient              175
rounds to              250
.286.                  245
                         5
```

1. $.8\overline{)3}$ 2. $.05\overline{)2.7}$

3. $.63\overline{)3.94}$ 4. $.46\overline{).904}$

5. $.036\overline{)90}$ 6. $5.26\overline{).216}$

7. $.075\overline{).0015}$ 8. $.382\overline{)5.1}$

9. $12\overline{)77}$ 10. $.004\overline{).23169}$

11. $69.4\overline{)10.6876}$ 12. $.31\overline{).2568}$

Divide the sum of the digits in your house address by .012.

## **Estimation** *(pages 100–101)* *Estimate.*

```
 18.375  →    20                                40.
× .0068  →  ×.007        .043).1.8    .043.)1.800.
             .140                              1 72
                                                  8
```

1. $\begin{array}{r} .08492 \\ +.127563 \\ \hline \end{array}$ 2. $\begin{array}{r} 2.1048 \\ -\ .78435 \\ \hline \end{array}$ 3. $5.8\overline{)1.7982}$ 4. $\begin{array}{r} 23.46 \\ \times\ .079 \\ \hline \end{array}$

5. 3.1416 × .04837 = ■ 6. .7318 + .156 + .2739 = ■

7. $.0125\overline{)13}$ 8. .00418 + .007863 = ■

Write 4 pairs of decimals to the thousandth place. Estimate the sum, difference, product, and quotient for each pair.

## Problem Solving: Unit Pricing *(pages 102–103)*

*How much would one cost?*

3 boxes of frozen corn for \$1.39.

```
   .46
3)1.39   One box costs $.47.
  1 2
   19
   18
    1 ← Stores round up.
```

1. 3 washclothes for \$2.50.
2. 6 towels for \$10.00
3. 4 bunches of radishes for \$.89
4. 5 boxes of frozen peas for \$1.76

*Which is the best buy?*

Potatoes:
3 kg for \$1.58
5 kg for \$2.44
10 kg for \$4.95

```
 .5266 → $.527      $.488
3)1.5800           5)2.4400   4.95 ÷ 10 = $.495
```

5 kg for \$2.44 is the best buy.

5. Sport socks:
   3 pairs for \$1.99
   4 pairs for \$2.60
   5 pairs for \$3.20
6. Paint:
   0.5 L for \$1.29
   1.75 L for \$4.55
   2.5 L for \$6.48

Find examples of items sold in groups of 2, 3, or 4 for a certain price. Find the unit prices.

## Problem Solving: Installment Plans *(pages 104–105)*

A washing machine can be purchased for \$50 cash and 12 monthly payments of \$42.35 each. What is the total cost of the washing machine?

Total = Installment payments + Cash payment
= ? + \$50

Installment payments = Number of payments × Amount for each
= 12 × 42.35 = 508.20

Total = 508.20 + 50 = \$558.20

1. A small car can be purchased for \$950 cash and 24 monthly payments of \$226.75. What is the total cost of the car?
2. The 30 monthly payments for a tractor are \$775 each. The total cost is \$30,000. What is the initial cash payment?
3. The total cost of a refrigerator, including a cash payment of \$75, is \$627. Installments are paid monthly for 12 months. What is the amount of each installment?

Find the cost of something expensive that you would like to have. What would your payments be over a six-month period?

## UNIT 4 Number Theory and Fractions

### **Exponents** *(pages 116–117)*

*Write the standard numeral.*

| $7^4 = 7 \cdot 7 \cdot 7 \cdot 7 = 7 \cdot 7 \cdot 49 = 7 \cdot 343 = 2{,}401$ |
|---|

**1.** $9^2$ **2.** $2^8$ **3.** $15^0$ **4.** $5^4$ **5.** $27^1$ **6.** $3^6$ **7.** $4^5$

| $(3 + 5)^2 = 8^2 = 64$ | $3 + 5^2 = 3 + 25 = 28$ |
|---|---|

**8.** $(7 \cdot 3)^2$ **9.** $7 \cdot 3^2$ **10.** $(5 + 2)^3$ **11.** $5 + 2^3$ **12.** $13^2 - 5^2$

**13.** $7 \cdot 4^2$ **14.** $7 + 4^2$ **15.** $7^2 \cdot 4$ **16.** $(7 \cdot 4)^2$ **17.** $(7 + 4)^2$

Write the standard numeral for the age of a family member times $10^5$.

### **Greatest Common Factor (GCF)** *(pages 118–119)*

*List all factors.*

42

$42 = 1 \times 42$ $\quad 2\overline{)42}$ = 21 $\quad 3\overline{)42}$ = 14 $\quad 4\overline{)42}$ = 10 R2 $\quad 5\overline{)42}$ = 8 R2 $\quad 6\overline{)42}$ = 7 $\quad 7\overline{)42}$ = 6

Factors: 1, 2, 3, 6, 7, 14, 21, 42 STOP!

63

$63 = 1 \times 63$ $\quad 2\overline{)63}$ = 31 R1 $\quad 3\overline{)63}$ = 21 $\quad 4\overline{)63}$ = 15 R3 $\quad 5\overline{)63}$ = 12 R3 $\quad 6\overline{)63}$ = 10 R3 $\quad 7\overline{)63}$ = 9 $\quad 8\overline{)63}$ = 7 R7

Factors: 1, 3, 7, 9, 21, 63 STOP!

**1.** 32 **2.** 51 **3.** 60 **4.** 72 **5.** 85 **6.** 96

**7.** 25 **8.** 56 **9.** 66 **10.** 64 **11.** 80 **12.** 100

*List all common factors and name the GCF.*

| 42 and 63 | Common factors: 1, 3, 7, 21 | GCF: 21 |
|---|---|---|

**13.** 60 and 72 **14.** 32 and 51 **15.** 96 and 32 **16.** 51 and 85

**17.** 56 and 64 **18.** 25 and 66 **19.** 25 and 100 **20.** 80 and 100

List all the factors for the ages of each family member.

## **Divisibility Tests** *(pages 120–121)*

*Tell whether the number is divisible by 2, 3, 5, or 10.*

| | |
|---|---|
| 1,715 | ones digit is *not* 0, 2, 4, 6, or 8 ⟶ *not* divisible by 2 |
| | sum of digits 1 + 7 + 1 + 5 = 14 → $3\overline{)14}$ = 4 R2   *not* divisible by 3 |
| | ones digit is 0 or 5 ⟶ divisible by 5 |
| | 1,715 ÷ 5 = 343 |
| | ones digit is *not* 0 ⟶ *not* divisible by 10 |

**1.** 640   **2.** 663   **3.** 703   **4.** 745   **5.** 771   **6.** 794

**7.** 1,041   **8.** 1,405   **9.** 1,452   **10.** 1,687   **11.** 1,950   **12.** 2,730

**13.** 3,868   **14.** 4,376   **15.** 4,398   **16.** 5,361   **17.** 5,553   **18.** 5,597

Tell whether your house address, your zip code, the last four digits of your telephone number, and the sum of everyone's age in your family is divisible by 2, 3, 5, or 10.

## **Least Common Multiple (LCM)** *(pages 122–123)*

*List the five smallest non-zero multiples.*

| | |
|---|---|
| 45: | 45, 90, 135, 180, 225 |
| 99: | 99, 198, 297, 396, 495 |

**1.** 21   **2.** 30   **3.** 38

**4.** 40   **5.** 42   **6.** 48

**7.** 57   **8.** 63   **9.** 64   **10.** 70   **11.** 105   **12.** 175

*Find the least common multiple (LCM).*

45 and 99   $45\overline{)99}$ = 2 R9   $45\overline{)198}$ = 4 R18   $45\overline{)297}$ = 6 R27   $45\overline{)396}$ = 8 R36   $45\overline{)495}$ = 11   LCM: 495

**13.** 38 and 57   **14.** 63 and 21   **15.** 40 and 48   **16.** 21 and 57

**17.** 30 and 48   **18.** 45 and 105   **19.** 70 and 175   **20.** 42 and 64

Write several pairs of odd and even numbers. Find the least common multiple of each pair.

## Prime and Composite Numbers *(pages 124–125)*

*Determine which are prime and which are composite numbers.*

133 not divisible by 2 → ones digit is not 0, 2, 4, 6, or 8

not divisible by 3 → 1 + 3 + 3 = 7 → $3\overline{)7}$ = 2 R1

not divisible by 4 → $4\overline{)33}$ = 8 R1

not divisible by 5 → ones digit is not 5 or 0

not divisible by 6 → not divisible by 2 and 3

$7\overline{)133}$ = 19

1, 7, 19, 133 are factors. 133 is composite.

197 not divisible by 2, 3, 4, 5, 6, 8, 9, or 10

$7\overline{)197}$ = 28 R1 $11\overline{)197}$ = 17 R10 $12\overline{)197}$ = 16 R5 $13\overline{)197}$ = 15 R2 $14\overline{)197}$ = 14 R1 $15\overline{)197}$ = 13 R2

197 is prime. $13 < \text{divisor}$ STOP!

**1.** 83 **2.** 93 **3.** 107 **4.** 123 **5.** 137 **6.** 151

**7.** 157 **8.** 171 **9.** 179 **10.** 181 **11.** 193 **12.** 199

Write your age, the number of people in your family, and the day you were born. Which are prime and which are composite numbers?

## Prime Factorization *(pages 126–127)*

*Write P for each prime number. Find the prime factorization of each composite number. Use exponents.*

107

107 is *not* divisible by 2, 3, 5 $7\overline{)107}$ = 15 R2 $11\overline{)107}$ = 9 R8 P

819

*not* divisible by 2

$819 \div 3 = 273$ $273 \div 3 = 91$ { 91 *not* divisible by 3, 5 $7\overline{)91}$ = 13

$819 = 3 \times 273$ $819 = 3 \times 3 \times 91$ $819 = 3^2 \times 7 \times 13$

**1.** 48 **2.** 84 **3.** 148 **4.** 187 **5.** 191 **6.** 198

**7.** 223 **8.** 247 **9.** 299 **10.** 593 **11.** 729 **12.** 936

List ten numbers at random. Write P for each prime number. Find the prime factorization of each composite number.

## Using Prime Factorization to Find GCF and LCM *(pages 128–129)*

*Use prime factorization to find the GCF of the numbers.*

108; 120

$108 \div 2 = 54$ $\quad 54 \div 2 = 27$ $\quad 27 \div 3 = 9$ $\quad 9 \div 3 = 3$

$108 = 2 \times 54$ $\quad 108 = 2 \times 2 \times 27$ $\quad 108 = 2 \times 2 \times 3 \times 9$ $\quad 108 = 2 \times 2 \times 3 \times 3 \times 3$

$120 \div 2 = 60$ $\quad 60 \div 2 = 30$ $\quad 30 \div 2 = 15$ $\quad 15 \div 3 = 5$

$120 = 2 \times 60$ $\quad 120 = 2 \times 2 \times 30$ $\quad 120 = 2 \times 2 \times 2 \times 15$ $\quad 120 = 2 \times 2 \times 2 \times 3 \times 5$

GCF: $2 \times 2 \times 3 = 12$

**1.** 85; 30 **2.** 26; 78 **3.** 87; 91 **4.** 54; 72; 84

*Use prime factorization to find the LCM of the numbers.*

108; 120

$108 = 2 \times 2 \times 3 \times 3 \times 3$

$120 = 2 \times 2 \times 2 \times 3 \times 5$

LCM: $2 \times 2 \times 2 \times 3 \times 3 \times 3 \times 5 = 1{,}080$

**5.** 32; 56 **6.** 55; 91 **7.** 147; 49 **8.** 36; 45; 56

Explain how to find the GCF and LCM of the numbers in one of the above exercises.

## Fractions and Equivalent Fractions *(pages 130–131)*

*Find the missing numbers.*

$\frac{5}{8} = \frac{■}{40}$ $\quad \frac{5}{8} = \frac{5 \times 5}{8 \times 5} = \frac{25}{40}$ $\qquad \frac{44}{64} = \frac{■}{16}$ $\quad \frac{44}{64} = \frac{44 \div 4}{64 \div 4} = \frac{11}{16}$

**1.** $\frac{7}{8} = \frac{■}{40}$ **2.** $\frac{45}{54} = \frac{■}{6}$ **3.** $\frac{3}{5} = \frac{36}{■}$ **4.** $\frac{60}{100} = \frac{■}{10}$

**5.** $\frac{3}{10} = \frac{■}{30}$ **6.** $\frac{2}{5} = \frac{■}{100}$ **7.** $\frac{65}{100} = \frac{■}{20}$ **8.** $\frac{375}{1{,}000} = \frac{■}{8}$

*Write the lowest terms fractions.*

**9.** $\frac{35}{42}$ **10.** $\frac{32}{48}$ **11.** $\frac{36}{72}$ **12.** $\frac{72}{96}$ **13.** $\frac{45}{120}$

**14.** $\frac{26}{65}$ **15.** $\frac{36}{84}$ **16.** $\frac{42}{112}$ **17.** $\frac{510}{600}$ **18.** $\frac{875}{1{,}000}$

Write 5 fractions of your own. Write the lowest terms fraction for each.

## Fractions, Mixed Numerals, and Standard Numerals

*(pages 132–133)*

*Find the lowest terms mixed numeral or standard numeral for each.*

$\frac{70}{16} \rightarrow 16\overline{)70}$ quotient $4\frac{6}{16}$; $70 - 64 = 6$; $\frac{6}{16} = \frac{3}{8}$ so $\frac{70}{16} = 4\frac{3}{8}$

$\frac{126}{9} \rightarrow 9\overline{)126}$ quotient $14$; $12 - 9 = 3$, $36 - 36 = 0$ $\rightarrow \frac{126}{9} = 14$

1. $\frac{47}{5}$ 2. $\frac{60}{15}$ 3. $\frac{83}{20}$ 4. $\frac{95}{10}$ 5. $\frac{69}{12}$ 6. $\frac{80}{7}$

7. $\frac{22}{7}$ 8. $\frac{130}{8}$ 9. $\frac{120}{25}$ 10. $\frac{61}{16}$ 11. $\frac{141}{141}$ 12. $\frac{525}{100}$

*Simplify.*

$\frac{18}{27} = \frac{2}{3}$ $\frac{30}{5} = 6$ $\frac{40}{15} = 2\frac{2}{3}$

13. $\frac{175}{50}$ 14. $\frac{102}{34}$ 15. $\frac{54}{78}$

16. $\frac{50}{16}$ 17. $\frac{200}{3}$ 18. $\frac{72}{96}$ 19. $\frac{265}{100}$ 20. $\frac{48}{48}$ 21. $\frac{4,625}{1,000}$

Simplify: $\frac{\text{number of people in your neighborhood}}{\text{number of houses in your neighborhood}}$

## Least Common Denominator *(pages 134–135)*

*Find equivalent fractions with the LCD.*

$\frac{15}{24}, \frac{13}{20}$ Find the LCM of 20 and 24 $\longrightarrow$

$20 = 2 \times 2 \times 5$
$24 = 2 \times 2 \times 2 \times 3$
LCM: $2 \times 2 \times 2 \times 3 \times 5 = 120$

$\frac{15}{24} = \frac{15 \times 5}{24 \times 5} = \frac{75}{120}$ $\frac{13}{20} = \frac{13 \times 6}{20 \times 6} = \frac{78}{120}$

1. $\frac{7}{16}, \frac{11}{20}$ 2. $\frac{17}{15}, \frac{37}{35}$ 3. $\frac{4}{15}, \frac{5}{16}$ 4. $\frac{43}{80}, \frac{9}{16}$

5. $\frac{23}{45}, \frac{8}{21}$ 6. $\frac{40}{33}, \frac{25}{21}$ 7. $\frac{13}{21}, \frac{59}{84}$ 8. $\frac{12}{25}, \frac{10}{21}$

Write three fractions whose denominators are different. Find equivalent fractions with the LCD.

Homework Homework Homework Homework Ho

## **Comparing with Fractions** *(pages 136–137)*

*Write >, <, or = for ●.*

$\frac{17}{30}$ ● $\frac{7}{12}$

12 = 2 × 2 × 3
30 = 2 × 3 × 5
LCM: 2 × 2 × 3 × 5 = 60

60 is the LCD.

$\frac{17}{30} = \frac{34}{60}$

$\frac{7}{12} = \frac{35}{60}$

34 < 35 so

$\frac{34}{60} < \frac{35}{60}$

↓ ↓

$\frac{17}{30} < \frac{7}{12}$

1. $\frac{5}{14}$ ● $\frac{17}{42}$
2. $\frac{7}{12}$ ● $\frac{9}{16}$
3. $\frac{11}{15}$ ● $\frac{13}{20}$
4. $\frac{7}{8}$ ● $\frac{7}{10}$
5. $\frac{7}{20}$ ● $\frac{11}{30}$
6. $\frac{13}{20}$ ● $\frac{63}{100}$
7. $\frac{3}{7}$ ● $\frac{5}{12}$
8. $\frac{13}{25}$ ● $\frac{11}{20}$
9. $\frac{17}{12}$ ● $\frac{51}{36}$
10. $\frac{11}{6}$ ● $\frac{17}{10}$

*List in order from least to greatest.*

11. $\frac{5}{6}; \frac{7}{8}; \frac{7}{10}$
12. $\frac{9}{10}; \frac{11}{12}; \frac{13}{15}$
13. $\frac{17}{20}; \frac{23}{30}; \frac{41}{50}$

Write 3 fractions with different denominators. Then list them in order from the least to the greatest.

## **Problem Solving: Using Equivalent Fractions** *(pages 138–139)*

The Jones family spent $\frac{5}{16}$ of their monthly income on housing. If they spent \$350 on housing, what was their monthly income?

$\text{Part for housing} = \frac{\text{Amount for housing}}{\text{Monthly income}}$

$\frac{5}{16} = \frac{350}{■}$

**Monthly income is \$1,120.**

$\frac{5}{16} = \frac{5 \times 70}{16 \times 70} = \frac{350}{1{,}120}$

1. The Johnson family spent $\frac{2}{5}$ of their weekly income on car repairs. If they spent \$120 on car repairs, what was their weekly income?

2. In Room 201, 15 of the 27 students are female. In Room 202, 17 of the 31 students are female. In which of these rooms is the greater part of the students female?

3. The Horn family spent \$35 of their \$400 weekly income on gasoline. The Clark family spent \$40 of their \$500 weekly income on gasoline. Which family spent the greater part of their income on gasoline?

Compare the number of children to total family members for your family and for one other family. Which family has the greater fraction of children?

## UNIT 5 Fractions and Mixed Numerals

### Addition and Subtraction: Common Denominators *(pages 150–151)*

*Give the simplest form for each sum or difference.*

$$\begin{array}{r} \frac{11}{16} \\ +\frac{13}{16} \\ \hline \frac{24}{16} \end{array} = 1\frac{8}{16} = 1\frac{1}{2} \qquad \frac{21}{25} - \frac{11}{25} = \frac{10}{25} = \frac{2}{5}$$

**1.** $\frac{11}{6} - \frac{5}{6} =$ ■ **2.** $\frac{2}{7} + \frac{5}{7} =$ ■ **3.** $\frac{7}{8} + \frac{3}{8} =$ ■ **4.** $1 - \frac{2}{5} =$ ■

**5.** $\frac{5}{12} + \frac{11}{12} =$ ■ **6.** $\frac{23}{20} - \frac{7}{20} =$ ■ **7.** $\frac{19}{25} - \frac{4}{25} =$ ■ **8.** $\frac{43}{100} + \frac{17}{100} =$ ■

**9.** $\frac{7}{10} - \frac{3}{10}$ **10.** $\frac{3}{4} + \frac{3}{4}$ **11.** $\frac{15}{16} - \frac{3}{16}$ **12.** $\frac{5}{2} - \frac{1}{2}$ **13.** $\frac{7}{15} + \frac{14}{15}$ **14.** $\frac{5}{6} - \frac{5}{6}$ **15.** $\frac{43}{60} + \frac{37}{60}$

Find the sum: $\dfrac{\text{number of males in your family}}{\text{total family members}} + \dfrac{\text{number of females in your family}}{\text{total family members}}$

### Addition: Unlike Denominators *(pages 152–153)*

*Give the simplest form for each sum.*

$\frac{7}{15} + \frac{17}{60} =$ ■

$\downarrow \quad \downarrow$

$\frac{28}{60} + \frac{17}{60} = \frac{45}{60} = \frac{3}{4}$

60 is the LCM of 15 and 60.

$$\begin{array}{r} \frac{7}{8} \longrightarrow \frac{35}{40} \\ +\frac{9}{10} \longrightarrow \frac{36}{40} \\ \hline \frac{71}{40} \end{array} = 1\frac{31}{40}$$

40 is the LCM of 8 and 10.

**1.** $\frac{11}{16} + \frac{1}{2} =$ ■ **2.** $\frac{2}{3} + \frac{3}{4} =$ ■ **3.** $1 + \frac{7}{10} =$ ■ **4.** $\frac{9}{10} + \frac{5}{6} =$ ■

**5.** $\frac{3}{8} + \frac{1}{6} =$ ■ **6.** $\frac{3}{4} + \frac{7}{10} =$ ■ **7.** $\frac{3}{5} + \frac{5}{8} =$ ■ **8.** $\frac{1}{2} + \frac{5}{12} =$ ■

**9.** $\frac{3}{4} + \frac{13}{20}$ **10.** $\frac{5}{12} + \frac{3}{8}$ **11.** $\frac{1}{2} + \frac{1}{3}$ **12.** $\frac{3}{10} + \frac{3}{4}$ **13.** $\frac{21}{100} + \frac{7}{20}$ **14.** $\frac{4}{9} + \frac{3}{4}$ **15.** $\frac{7}{10} + \frac{7}{15}$

Write two fractions with unlike denominators. Find their sum.

## Subtraction: Unlike Denominators *(pages 154–155)*

*Find the difference. Simplify.*

$\frac{3}{4} - \frac{7}{20} = \blacksquare$

$\downarrow \quad \downarrow$

$\frac{15}{20} - \frac{7}{20} = \frac{8}{20} = \frac{2}{5}$

20 is the LCM of 4 and 20.

$$\begin{array}{rcl} \frac{13}{15} & \rightarrow & \frac{52}{60} \\ -\frac{5}{12} & \rightarrow & \frac{25}{60} \\ \hline & & \frac{27}{60} = \frac{9}{20} \end{array}$$

60 is the LCM of 15 and 60.

**1.** $\frac{3}{4} - \frac{1}{2} = \blacksquare$ **2.** $\frac{9}{10} - \frac{3}{5} = \blacksquare$ **3.** $\frac{7}{4} - \frac{5}{6} = \blacksquare$ **4.** $\frac{11}{12} - \frac{2}{3} = \blacksquare$

**5.** $\frac{7}{10} - \frac{1}{4} = \blacksquare$ **6.** $\frac{2}{3} - \frac{3}{10} = \blacksquare$ **7.** $\frac{83}{100} - \frac{3}{4} = \blacksquare$ **8.** $\frac{17}{20} - \frac{3}{25} = \blacksquare$

**9.** $\frac{5}{8} - \frac{1}{6}$ **10.** $\frac{3}{2} - \frac{2}{3}$ **11.** $\frac{3}{4} - \frac{5}{16}$ **12.** $\frac{17}{10} - \frac{5}{6}$ **13.** $\frac{3}{4} - \frac{1}{5}$ **14.** $\frac{2}{3} - \frac{5}{8}$ **15.** $\frac{7}{8} - \frac{3}{10}$

Write two fractions with unlike denominators. Find their difference.

## Comparing with Mixed Numerals *(pages 156–157)*

*Find an equivalent fraction for each.*

$4\frac{7}{8} = \frac{(4 \times 8) + 7}{8}$

$= \frac{39}{8}$

$4\frac{7}{8} = \frac{39}{8}$

**1.** $5\frac{1}{2}$ **2.** $3\frac{2}{5}$ **3.** $6\frac{2}{3}$ **4.** $1\frac{3}{10}$

**5.** $2\frac{3}{4}$ **6.** $3\frac{5}{6}$ **7.** $7\frac{3}{8}$ **8.** $4\frac{11}{12}$

**9.** $2\frac{13}{16}$ **10.** $3\frac{7}{20}$ **11.** $4\frac{13}{25}$ **12.** $2\frac{3}{50}$

*Write >, <, or = for* ●

$3\frac{3}{16}$ ● $3\frac{1}{4}$ 3 = 3

$\frac{3}{16} < \frac{1}{4}$

so

$3\frac{3}{16} < 3\frac{1}{4}$

**13.** $5\frac{5}{8}$ ● $4\frac{7}{8}$ **14.** $2\frac{3}{5}$ ● $2\frac{2}{3}$ **15.** $7\frac{7}{8}$ ● $7\frac{5}{6}$

**16.** $3\frac{1}{5}$ ● $2\frac{5}{4}$ **17.** $5\frac{3}{4}$ ● $5\frac{7}{10}$ **18.** $4\frac{7}{12}$ ● $4\frac{5}{8}$

**19.** $7\frac{1}{2}$ ● $7\frac{7}{15}$ **20.** $3\frac{1}{2}$ ● $2\frac{3}{2}$ **21.** $3\frac{1}{7}$ ● $3\frac{7}{50}$

Find the length of a pencil and pen to the nearest $\frac{1}{8}$ inch. Compare the two mixed numerals.

## Addition with Mixed Numerals *(pages 158–159)*

*Add.*

$$\begin{array}{r} 3\frac{5}{6} \rightarrow 3\frac{25}{30} \\ +2\frac{7}{10} \rightarrow 2\frac{21}{30} \\ \hline 5\frac{46}{30} = 5\frac{23}{15} = 6\frac{8}{15} \end{array}$$

1. $3\frac{7}{12} + 4\frac{1}{12}$
2. $5\frac{3}{8} + 3\frac{1}{2}$
3. $2\frac{1}{6} + 1\frac{3}{5}$
4. $5\frac{7}{16} + 2\frac{11}{16}$
5. $3\frac{5}{8} + 4\frac{3}{10}$
6. $7\frac{5}{12} + 1\frac{3}{4}$
7. $4\frac{7}{10} + 2\frac{1}{10}$
8. $3\frac{3}{16} + 4\frac{5}{8}$
9. $5\frac{5}{8} + 1\frac{1}{6}$
10. $9\frac{3}{5} + 4\frac{9}{10} = \blacksquare$
11. $7\frac{13}{20} + 4\frac{7}{20} = \blacksquare$
12. $12\frac{3}{4} + 16\frac{2}{5} = \blacksquare$
13. $2\frac{5}{6} + 8\frac{9}{10} = \blacksquare$
14. $1\frac{17}{50} + 2\frac{33}{50} = \blacksquare$
15. $3\frac{11}{15} + 7 = \blacksquare$
16. $4\frac{9}{10} + 2\frac{2}{3} = \blacksquare$
17. $3\frac{7}{12} + 5\frac{3}{8} = \blacksquare$

Measure the thickness of two books. Find their sum.

## Subtraction with Mixed Numerals *(pages 160–161)*

*Subtract.*

$$\begin{array}{r} 4\frac{1}{2} \rightarrow 4\frac{5}{10} \rightarrow 3\frac{15}{10} \\ -2\frac{3}{5} \rightarrow 2\frac{6}{10} \rightarrow 2\frac{6}{10} \\ \hline 1\frac{9}{10} \end{array}$$

1. $5\frac{9}{10} - 2\frac{1}{10}$
2. $7\frac{3}{8} - 4\frac{7}{8}$
3. $3 - 1\frac{7}{10}$
4. $7\frac{4}{5} - 2\frac{1}{3}$
5. $5\frac{1}{3} - 4\frac{5}{12}$
6. $2\frac{1}{4} - \frac{3}{5}$
7. $4\frac{3}{8} - 1\frac{5}{6}$
8. $5\frac{1}{4} - 1\frac{17}{20}$
9. $1\frac{3}{10} - \frac{7}{8}$
10. $8\frac{1}{2} - 2\frac{5}{16} = \blacksquare$
11. $5\frac{3}{4} - 2\frac{9}{10} = \blacksquare$
12. $4\frac{5}{8} - 4\frac{3}{10} = \blacksquare$
13. $6\frac{7}{12} - 3\frac{5}{8} = \blacksquare$
14. $7\frac{4}{5} - 7\frac{2}{3} = \blacksquare$
15. $4\frac{1}{6} - 2\frac{3}{5} = \blacksquare$
16. $2\frac{3}{10} - 1\frac{4}{5} = \blacksquare$
17. $12\frac{7}{20} - 8\frac{19}{25} = \blacksquare$

Measure the length and the width of a shoe in inches. Find the difference.

## **Problem Solving: Related Problems** *(pages 162–163)*

A store had 324 ft of wire for hanging pictures. How much wire was left if it:

bought 126 ft, sold 285 ft?

(1) Amount left = Amount in all − Amount sold
= ? − 285

(2) Amount in all = Amount at start + Amount bought
= 324 + 126
= 450

(Plan also works for problems **1.** and **2.**)

Amount left = 450 − 285 = 165 feet

**1.** bought 82.6 ft, sold 116.8 ft?

**2.** bought $112\frac{1}{2}$ ft, sold $78\frac{5}{6}$ ft?

*How many shingles did a worker put on a roof if:*

**3.** 18 of 61 bundles were left?

**4.** 108.8 of 1,426.4 kg were left?

**5.** $4\frac{2}{3}$ of $50\frac{1}{3}$ bundles were left?

Fill in the blanks with
**a.** whole numbers **b.** decimals
**c.** mixed numerals.
Give to someone else to solve.

You run ________ km. Then you run another ________ km. How far can you run in all?

## **Multiplication with Fractions** *(pages 164–165)*

*Multiply.*

$\frac{4}{5} \times \frac{7}{12} = \frac{\overset{1}{\cancel{4}} \times 7}{5 \times \underset{3}{\cancel{12}}} = \frac{7}{15}$

**1.** $\frac{3}{4} \times \frac{1}{2} = ■$ **2.** $\frac{2}{3} \times \frac{9}{10} = ■$ **3.** $\frac{4}{5} \times 60 = ■$

**4.** $\frac{3}{10} \times \frac{10}{3} = ■$ **5.** $\frac{5}{6} \times \frac{1}{4} = ■$ **6.** $\frac{7}{8} \times \frac{1}{3} = ■$ **7.** $26 \times \frac{1}{13} = ■$

**8.** $\frac{4}{11} \times \frac{13}{15} = ■$ **9.** $\frac{5}{12} \times \frac{9}{20} = ■$ **10.** $\frac{7}{16} \times \frac{4}{5} = ■$ **11.** $\frac{3}{4} \times \frac{3}{4} = ■$

*Find the reciprocal of each number. Multiply to check.*

9 $\quad 9 = \frac{9}{1}$ reciprocal is $\frac{1}{9}$

$9 \times \frac{1}{9} = \frac{9}{1} \times \frac{1}{9} = \frac{9 \times 1}{1 \times 9} = \frac{9}{9} = 1$ ✓

**12.** $\frac{7}{11}$ **13.** $\frac{1}{5}$ **14.** 8 **15.** $\frac{20}{9}$

**16.** $\frac{3}{4}$ **17.** $\frac{1}{14}$ **18.** 1 **19.** $\frac{10}{3}$

Multiply your house number by $\frac{3}{5}$.

## **Division with Fractions** *(pages 166–167)*

*Divide.*

$$\frac{4}{5} \div \frac{8}{15} = \frac{4}{5} \times \frac{15}{8} = \frac{\overset{1}{\cancel{4}} \times \overset{3}{\cancel{15}}}{\underset{1}{\cancel{5}} \times \underset{2}{\cancel{8}}} = \frac{3}{2} = 1\frac{1}{2}$$

$$\frac{7}{10} \div 3 = \frac{7}{10} \div \frac{3}{1} = \frac{7}{10} \times \frac{1}{3} = \frac{7 \times 1}{10 \times 3} = \frac{7}{30}$$

**1.** $\frac{3}{8} \div \frac{1}{2} = \blacksquare$ **2.** $4 \div \frac{2}{5} = \blacksquare$ **3.** $\frac{3}{4} \div 5 = \blacksquare$ **4.** $8 \div 12 = \blacksquare$

**5.** $\frac{5}{8} \div \frac{3}{5} = \blacksquare$ **6.** $\frac{2}{3} \div \frac{2}{3} = \blacksquare$ **7.** $\frac{3}{8} \div \frac{8}{3} = \blacksquare$ **8.** $\frac{5}{6} \div \frac{5}{24} = \blacksquare$

**9.** $\frac{1}{7} \div \frac{1}{2} = \blacksquare$ **10.** $5 \div \frac{1}{5} = \blacksquare$ **11.** $\frac{2}{11} \div \frac{11}{12} = \blacksquare$ **12.** $\frac{1}{6} \div \frac{5}{6} = \blacksquare$

**13.** How many $\frac{2}{3}$-foot pieces of wood can be cut from a board that is 12 ft long?

**14.** Each lap is $\frac{2}{21}$ of a mile. An athlete ran $\frac{1}{2}$ mile. How many laps did she run?

Divide the length of your room by $\frac{4}{5}$.

## **Multiplication and Division with Mixed Numerals**

*(pages 168–169)*

*Multiply or divide.*

$$2\frac{7}{10} \times 2\frac{7}{9} = \frac{27}{10} \times \frac{25}{9} = \frac{\overset{3}{\cancel{27}} \times \overset{5}{\cancel{25}}}{\underset{2}{\cancel{10}} \times \underset{1}{\cancel{9}}} = \frac{15}{2} = 7\frac{1}{2}$$

$$1\frac{3}{5} \div 4\frac{4}{15} = \frac{8}{5} \div \frac{64}{15} = \frac{8}{5} \times \frac{15}{64} = \frac{\overset{1}{\cancel{8}} \times \overset{3}{\cancel{15}}}{\underset{1}{\cancel{5}} \times \underset{8}{\cancel{64}}} = \frac{3}{8}$$

**1.** $5\frac{1}{2} \times 4\frac{2}{3} = \blacksquare$ **2.** $2\frac{3}{5} \div 2\frac{1}{10} = \blacksquare$ **3.** $1\frac{3}{4} \times 10 = \blacksquare$ **4.** $10 \div 1\frac{3}{4} = \blacksquare$

**5.** $6\frac{3}{4} \div 4\frac{1}{2} = \blacksquare$ **6.** $3\frac{9}{10} \times 4\frac{1}{6} = \blacksquare$ **7.** $3\frac{1}{5} \div 12 = \blacksquare$ **8.** $4\frac{3}{8} \div 1\frac{7}{20} = \blacksquare$

**9.** $2\frac{11}{12} \times 2\frac{7}{10} = \blacksquare$ **10.** $1\frac{1}{2} \times 1\frac{1}{2} = \blacksquare$ **11.** $1\frac{1}{2} \div 1\frac{1}{2} = \blacksquare$ **12.** $9\frac{1}{6} \div 4\frac{1}{8} = \blacksquare$

Write a mixed numeral. Then multiply it and divide it by $4\frac{5}{8}$.

## Decimals and Fractions *(pages 170–171)*

*Replace each fraction or mixed numeral by a decimal.*

$\frac{9}{25} \rightarrow 25\overline{)9.00}$ = .36

$$\begin{array}{r} .36 \\ 25\overline{)9.00} \\ 7\,5 \\ \hline 1\,50 \\ 1\,50 \\ \hline 0 \end{array}$$

$\frac{9}{25} = .36$

$4\frac{5}{6} \rightarrow 6\overline{)5.00}$ = .83

$$\begin{array}{r} .83 \\ 6\overline{)5.00} \\ 4\,8 \\ \hline 20 \\ 18 \\ \hline 2 \end{array}$$

$4\frac{5}{6} = 4.8\overline{3}$

repeats →

1. $\frac{3}{4}$
2. $\frac{7}{11}$
3. $\frac{5}{8}$
4. $1\frac{5}{6}$
5. $2\frac{6}{7}$
6. $\frac{7}{8}$
7. $2\frac{1}{2}$
8. $7\frac{3}{11}$
9. $\frac{11}{12}$
10. $\frac{13}{15}$
11. $6\frac{2}{3}$
12. $3\frac{7}{9}$
13. $\frac{7}{30}$
14. $\frac{27}{44}$
15. $\frac{8}{37}$

*Replace each decimal by a fraction or mixed numeral. Simplify.*

$.15 = \frac{15}{100} = \frac{3}{20}$ $\quad 3.4 = 3\frac{4}{10} = 3\frac{2}{5}$

16. 8.3
17. .13
18. 4.25
19. 1.625
20. .0189
21. .5625
22. 5.325

What fraction of your family is male? Replace the fraction with a decimal.

## Problem Solving: Using Easier Numbers *(pages 172-173)*

*Solve. Make up whole number problems to help you plan.*

A typist was paid \$37.80 for typing $24\frac{3}{16}$ pages in 4.5 hours. What was the average number of:

Dollars per hour?

Easy made-up whole number problem: \$40 in 5 hours.

Average dollars per hour = Total pay ÷ Hours
= 40 ÷ 5 = \$8/h

Use the same plan in original problem.

Average dollars per hour = 37.80 ÷ 4.5
= \$8.40/h

$$\begin{array}{r} 8.40 \\ 4.5\overline{)37.800} \end{array}$$

1. dollars per page?
2. pages per hour?
3. hours per page?
4. pages per dollar?
5. hours per dollar?

Make up a word problem using a fraction and a decimal.
Then make up a whole number problem to help you plan.

## **Problem Solving: Choosing the Easier Method** *(pages 174–175)*

*Use the rates in the chart on page 175 to solve. Which company charges more fare for each trip? How much more?*

Ms. Cruz travels $3\frac{1}{2}$ miles

(1) Total fare = Fare for first part + Fare for remaining part
(2) Fare for remaining part = Number of remaining parts of miles × Rate for each part-mile.
(3) Number of remaining part-miles = Remaining distance ÷ Length of part-mile
(4) Remaining distance = Total distance − first part

| | Company A | Company B |
|---|---|---|
| Remaining distance: | $3.5 - .1 = 3.4$ | $3\frac{1}{2} - \frac{1}{8} = 3\frac{3}{8}$ |
| No. of remaining part-miles: | $3.4 \div .1 = 34$ | $3\frac{3}{8} \div \frac{1}{8} = 27$ |
| Fare for remaining part: | $34 \times .15 = \$5.10$ | $27 \times .15 = \$4.05$ |
| Total fare: | $.60 + $5.10 = $5.70 | $1.30 + 4.05 = $5.35 |

**Company A** charges $.35 more.

*Which company charges more fare for each trip? How much more?*

**1.** Mr. Cook travels $1\frac{1}{2}$ miles.

**2.** Ms. Murphy travels 5.5 miles.

*If each person traveled at the lower fare and if each gave the cab driver a tip of .2 of the fare, what was the total amount*

**3.** Mr. Cook gave the driver?

**4.** Ms. Murphy gave the driver?

Change the rates of both companies. Rework the problems.

## **Algebra: Solving Equations** *(pages 176–177)* *Solve.*

$$\frac{3}{4}x - \frac{1}{10} = \frac{1}{2}$$

$$\frac{3}{4}x = \frac{1}{2} + \frac{1}{10}$$

$$\frac{3}{4}x = \frac{3}{5}$$

$$x = \frac{3}{5} \div \frac{3}{4} = \frac{4}{5}$$

*Solution:* $\frac{4}{5}$

*Check:* $\frac{3}{4} \cdot \frac{4}{5} - \frac{1}{10} = \frac{1}{2}$ ✓

**1.** $\frac{3}{10}x - 5 = 7$

**2.** $\frac{3}{4} + \frac{y}{12} = \frac{4}{3}$

**3.** $\frac{7}{10}w - \frac{2}{5} = 8$

**4.** $\frac{4}{15}s + \frac{1}{3} = 1$

**5.** $\frac{1}{4} + \frac{5}{6}x = \frac{9}{10}$

**6.** $\frac{1}{5} = \frac{3}{4}z - \frac{3}{10}$

Write your own equation. Work it through, then give it to someone in your class to solve.

## UNIT 6 Integers and Rational Numbers

### Integers (pages 194–195)

*Give the integer for each point.*

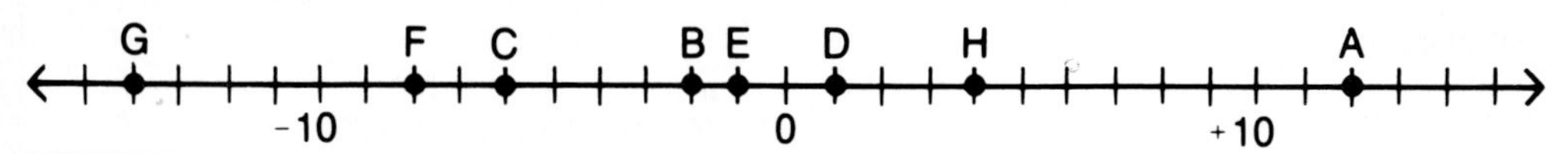


| A → +12 |
|---|

1. B 2. C 3. D 4. E 5. F 6. G 7. H

| $\lvert{}^-9\rvert = 9$ |
|---|

*Find each absolute value.*

8. $\lvert{}^-11\rvert$ 9. $\lvert{}^-27\rvert$ 10. $\lvert 61\rvert$ 11. $\lvert 11\rvert$ 12. $\lvert{}^-61\rvert$

| $\lvert{}^-6\rvert$ ● $\lvert 4\rvert$<br>↓ ↓<br>6 > 4 so<br>$\lvert{}^-6\rvert > \lvert 4\rvert$ |
|---|

*Write >, <, or = for ●*

13. $\lvert{}^-35\rvert$ ● $\lvert 25\rvert$ 14. $\lvert{}^-43\rvert$ ● $\lvert{}^-50\rvert$ 15. $\lvert 125\rvert$ ● $\lvert{}^-125\rvert$

16. $\lvert{}^-17\rvert$ ● $\lvert 30\rvert$ 17. $\lvert 24\rvert$ ● $\lvert{}^-30\rvert$ 18. $\lvert{}^-16\rvert$ ● $\lvert 0\rvert$

Write 4 pairs of integers. Compare each pair.

### Rational Numbers (pages 196–197)

| ${}^-1\frac{1}{2}$ ● ${}^-1.4$<br>${}^-1\frac{1}{2} < {}^-1.4$ |
|---|

*Write >, <, or = for ●*

1. ${}^-1\frac{3}{8}$ ● ${}^-1.4$ 2. ${}^-1\frac{3}{8}$ ● $1.4$ 3. $1\frac{3}{8}$ ● $1.4$

4. ${}^-3.25$ ● $\frac{{}^-13}{4}$ 5. ${}^-3.25$ ● $\frac{13}{4}$ 6. $\frac{1}{12}$ ● $\frac{{}^-1}{6}$

*Complete.*

| $\lvert\frac{{}^-3}{4}\rvert \times \lvert\frac{3}{5}\rvert = ■$<br>↓ ↓<br>$\frac{3}{4} \times \frac{3}{5} = \frac{3 \times 3}{4 \times 5} = \frac{9}{20}$ |
|---|

7. $\lvert{}^-2\frac{5}{12}\rvert - \lvert\frac{7}{12}\rvert = ■$ 8. $\lvert 12.7\rvert + \lvert{}^-3.86\rvert = ■$

9. $\lvert{}^-5.6\rvert \times \lvert .35\rvert = ■$ 10. $\lvert{}^-4\frac{1}{6}\rvert \div \lvert{}^-9\frac{3}{8}\rvert = ■$

11. $\lvert 6\frac{5}{6}\rvert - \lvert{}^-4\frac{1}{2}\rvert = ■$ 12. $\lvert 4.8\rvert \div \lvert{}^-1.2\rvert = ■$

Write your age as a mixed numeral. Then compare it to $\lvert{}^-13.5\rvert$, 13.5, and ${}^-13.5$.

### Addition (pages 198–199)

*Complete.*

| ${}^-3 + 2 = ■$<br>${}^-3 + 2 = {}^-1$<br>$-{}^-7 = ■$<br>$7 + {}^-7 = 0$<br>$-{}^-7 = 7$ |
|---|

1. ${}^-12 + 9 = ■$ 2. $6 + {}^-6 = ■$ 3. ${}^-9 + {}^-12 = ■$

4. ${}^-9 + 12 = ■$ 5. $7 + {}^-11 = ■$ 6. ${}^-7 + 11 = ■$

7. ${}^-7 + {}^-11 = ■$ 8. ${}^-7 + 7 = ■$ 9. ${}^-8 + 3 = ■$

10. $8 + {}^-3 = ■$ 11. $8 + {}^-8 = ■$ 12. ${}^-8 + {}^-3 = ■$

13. $-{}^-5 = ■$ 14. $-{}^+15 = ■$ 15. $-{}^-30 = ■$ 16. $-{}^-15 = ■$ 17. $-{}^+30 = ■$

Write 4 integers between ${}^-10$ and 10. Use them in pairs to write as many addition exercises as you can.

## More Addition *(pages 200–201)* *Add.*

${}^{-}40 + 25 =$ ■

|negative| > |positive|

$|{}^{-}40| - |25| = 15$

${}^{-}40 + 25 = {}^{-}15$

1. $14 + {}^{-}19 =$ ■
2. ${}^{-}14 + {}^{-}19 =$ ■
3. $19 + {}^{-}14 =$ ■
4. $73 + {}^{-}73 =$ ■
5. $216 + {}^{-}139 =$ ■
6. ${}^{-}485 + 361 =$ ■
7. ${}^{-}305 + 305 =$ ■
8. ${}^{-}174 + {}^{-}96 =$ ■
9. ${}^{-}108 + 186 =$ ■
10. ${}^{-}206 + {}^{-}104 =$ ■
11. $493 + 725 =$ ■
12. ${}^{-}493 + 725 =$ ■
13. $493 + {}^{-}725 =$ ■
14. ${}^{-}493 + {}^{-}725 =$ ■

Add your zip code and house address in as many ways as you can by making each number positive or negative.

## Subtraction *(pages 202–203)* *Subtract.*

${}^{-}34 - {}^{-}20 =$ ■

↓ ↓

${}^{-}34 + {}^{+}20 = {}^{-}14$

1. $26 - {}^{-}43 =$ ■
2. $37 - 62 =$ ■
3. ${}^{-}52 - {}^{-}24 =$ ■
4. ${}^{-}48 - {}^{-}33 =$ ■
5. ${}^{-}21 - 73 =$ ■
6. $83 - 47 =$ ■
7. ${}^{-}17 - {}^{-}42 =$ ■
8. ${}^{-}76 - {}^{-}76 =$ ■
9. ${}^{-}8 - {}^{-}4 =$ ■
10. $36 - 40 =$ ■
11. ${}^{-}11 - {}^{-}9 =$ ■
12. $72 - {}^{-}72 =$ ■
13. $89 - 27 =$ ■
14. $89 - {}^{-}27 =$ ■
15. ${}^{-}89 - 27 =$ ■
16. ${}^{-}89 - {}^{-}27 =$ ■
17. $147 - 526 =$ ■
18. ${}^{-}147 - 526 =$ ■

Subtract your age and your height in inches in as many ways as you can by making each number positive or negative.

## Multiplication *(pages 204–205)* *Multiply.*

${}^{-}8 \times 40 =$ ■

$|{}^{-}8| \times |40| = 320$

One negative, one positive.
Product is negative.

${}^{-}8 \times 40 = {}^{-}320$

1. ${}^{-}7 \times 69 =$ ■
2. ${}^{-}8 \times {}^{-}216 =$ ■
3. ${}^{-}42 \times 0 =$ ■
4. ${}^{-}1 \times 156 =$ ■
5. ${}^{-}24 \times {}^{-}35 =$ ■
6. ${}^{-}18 \times 47 =$ ■
7. $58 \times 75 =$ ■
8. $31 \times {}^{-}85 =$ ■
9. $32 \times {}^{-}6 =$ ■
10. ${}^{-}6 \times 0 =$ ■
11. ${}^{-}5 \times {}^{-}5 =$ ■
12. $23 \times 6 =$ ■
13. ${}^{-}40 \times {}^{-}300 =$ ■
14. $65 \times 95 =$ ■
15. ${}^{-}65 \times 95 =$ ■
16. $65 \times {}^{-}95 =$ ■
17. ${}^{-}65 \times {}^{-}95 =$ ■

Multiply the length and width of a book in as many ways as you can by making each number positive or negative.

## Division *(pages 206–207)*

*Divide.*

$80 \div {}^-5 = \blacksquare$

$|80| \div |{}^-5| = 16$

One positive, one negative. Quotient is negative

$80 \div {}^-5 = {}^-16$

1. $84 \div {}^-6 = \blacksquare$
2. ${}^-196 \div 7 = \blacksquare$
3. ${}^-51 \div {}^-9 = \blacksquare$
4. $83 \div {}^-5 = \blacksquare$
5. ${}^-800 \div 25 = \blacksquare$
6. $0 \div {}^-43 = \blacksquare$
7. ${}^-463 \div {}^-463 = \blacksquare$
8. $642 \div {}^-1 = \blacksquare$
9. $48 \div {}^-6 = \blacksquare$
10. $72 \div {}^-4 = \blacksquare$

*Solve.*

${}^-7x = 140$

${}^-7x \div {}^-7 = 140 \div {}^-7$

$x = {}^-20$

*Solution:* ${}^-20$

*Check:* ${}^-7 \cdot {}^-20 = 140$ ✔

11. ${}^-8x = {}^-120$
12. $\frac{y}{10} = {}^-5$
13. $\frac{z}{{}^-12} = 4$
14. $16m = {}^-400$
15. $\frac{n}{{}^-6} = {}^-24$
16. ${}^-25w = 900$

Solve: $\frac{y}{\text{your age}}$ = the sum of everyone's age in your family.

## Problem Solving: Using Number Scales *(pages 208–209)*

From a temperature of ${}^-12$°C there was a temperature change of ${}^-14$°C. What was the temperature after the change?

| Temperature after | = | Temperature before | + | Change in temperature |
|---|---|---|---|---|
| | = | ${}^-12$ | + | ${}^-14$ |
| | = | ${}^-26$ | | |

The temperature was ${}^-26$°C after the change.

1. After a change of ${}^-12$°C in temperature the temperature was ${}^-20$°C. What was the temperature before this change?
2. From a temperature of ${}^-8$°C there was a temperature change of 15°C. What was the temperature after the change?
3. After a change of ${}^-\$2\frac{5}{8}$ the value of one share of stock was $\$37\frac{7}{8}$. What was the value before the change?
4. The change in value of one share of a company's stock was ${}^-\$1\frac{3}{8}$. What was the change in value of 250 shares of stock?
5. Find the difference in altitudes between Atlanta and the Puerto Rico Trench. (See page 208, Example 3.)

Look in the newspaper to find the change in value of three stocks. Then calculate the change in value for 300 shares of each.

## Integers as Exponents *(pages 210–211)*

*Complete. Use exponents.*

| | | |
|---|---|---|
| $5^7 \times 5^{-3} = \blacksquare$ | $2^{-3} \times 2^{-4} = \blacksquare$ | $4^{-2} \div 4^{-5} = \blacksquare$ |
| $7 + {}^-3 = 4$ | ${}^-3 + {}^-4 = {}^-7$ | $2 - {}^-5 = {}^-2 + 5 = 3$ |
| $5^7 \times 5^{-3} = 5^4$ | $2^{-3} \times 2^{-4} = 2^{-7}$ | $4^{-2} \div 4^{-5} = 4^3$ |

**1.** $5^2 \times 5^4 = \blacksquare$ **2.** $2^8 \div 2^2 = \blacksquare$ **3.** $7^3 \div 7^{-3} = \blacksquare$ **4.** $3^{-8} \times 3^4 = \blacksquare$

**5.** $7^5 \times 7^{-8} = \blacksquare$ **6.** $\frac{3^6}{3^2} = \blacksquare$ **7.** $\frac{4^3}{4^5} = \blacksquare$ **8.** $\frac{2^{-2}}{2^3} = \blacksquare$

**9.** $(2 \cdot 2 \cdot 2 \cdot 2) \cdot (2 \cdot 2 \cdot 2 \cdot 2 \cdot 2) = \blacksquare$

**10.** $(3 \cdot 3 \cdot 3) \cdot (3 \cdot 3 \cdot 3 \cdot 3) \cdot (11) = \blacksquare$

**11.** $(5 \cdot 5) \cdot (5 \cdot 5 \cdot 5) \cdot (7 \cdot 7) = \blacksquare$

**12.** $(5 \cdot 5) \cdot (5 \cdot 5) \cdot (11 \cdot 11 \cdot 11) = \blacksquare$

**13.** $\frac{7^4 \cdot 7^3}{7^2} = \blacksquare$ **14.** $5^3 \cdot 7^{-2} \cdot 5^{-1} \cdot 7^4 = \blacksquare$ **15.** $\frac{2^7 \cdot 3^{-3}}{3^{-1}} = \blacksquare$

Make up a set of division and multiplication exercises using integers as exponents. Exchange problems with a classmate and solve.

## Scientific Notation *(pages 212–213)*

*Write scientific notation for each number.*

| | |
|---|---|
| (1) $27{,}400 = 2.74 \times 10^{\blacksquare}$ | (1) $.000516 = 5.16 \times 10^{\blacksquare}$ |
| (2) $27{,}400 = 2.7400.$ (4 places) | (2) $.000516 = .0005.16$ (4 places) |
| $= 2.74 \times 10^4$ | $= 5.16 \times 10^{-4}$ |

**1.** 16,300 **2.** .000078 **3.** 5,327,000,000 **4.** .00563

**5.** 3.14159 **6.** 560,000 **7.** .00019 **8.** $.0048 \times 10^2$

*Write a standard numeral or decimal for each number.*

| |
|---|
| $4.8 \times 10^{-3} = .004.8 = .0048$ (3 places) |

**9.** $3.2 \times 10^5$ **10.** $1.83 \times 10^{-3}$

**11.** $4.93 \times 10^8$ **12.** $5.6 \times 10^{-5}$

**13.** $3.14 \times 10^0$ **14.** $6.9 \times 10^{-4}$ **15.** $5.8 \times 10^2$ **16.** $7. \times 10^{-6}$

Write a standard numeral for the number of pages in a magazine times $10^{-6}$.

## **Problem Solving: Using Scientific Notation** *(pages 214–215)*

*Give scientific notation for answers. Round to keep 3 digits in first factors. Use the information on pages 214 and 215.*

| | |
|---|---|
| The maximum distance of the moon from Earth is about $4.07 \times 10^5$ km. About how many seconds does it take light to travel from the moon to Earth? | Total time in seconds = Total distance ÷ Distance per second<br>$\doteq (4.07 \times 10^5) \div (3.0 \times 10^5)$<br>$\doteq \frac{4.07}{3.0} = \frac{10^5}{10^5}$<br>$\doteq 1.36 \times 10^0$ seconds |

1. About how many seconds does it take light to travel from Earth to Mars? to Jupiter?
2. About how many hours does it take light to travel from Earth to Mars? to Jupiter?
3. The maximum distance of Pluto from the earth is $7.47 \times 10^9$ km. Is Pluto or Saturn farther from the Earth?
4. The speed of sound is $3.31 \times 10^2$ meters per second. How long does it take the sound of a thunderclap to travel 5 km?
5. About how many times farther is the sun from Earth than is the moon from Earth?

Find the maximum distances of other planets from Earth. Write a problem with this data and give it to a classmate to solve.

## **Real Numbers** *(pages 216–217)* *Complete. Watch the signs.*

| |
|---|
| $.5 \times {}^-.07 = ■$<br>$\lvert .5 \rvert \times \lvert {}^-.07 \rvert$<br>↓ ↓<br>$.5 \times .07 = .035$<br>One positive, one negative. Product is negative.<br>$.5 \times {}^-.07 = {}^-.035$ |

1. ${}^-4.28 + {}^-1.937 = ■$
2. ${}^-17.6 - 4.93 = ■$
3. $2.6 \times {}^-.054 = ■$
4. ${}^-105 \div 2.5 = ■$
5. ${}^-.18 + .097 = ■$
6. ${}^-4\frac{5}{8} - {}^-7\frac{3}{4} = ■$
7. ${}^-3.6 \times 0 = ■$
8. ${}^-8.01 \div 8.01 = ■$
9. $\frac{^-2}{5} \times \frac{3}{10} = ■$
10. $\frac{3}{10} + \frac{^-2}{3} = ■$
11. $\frac{^-3}{5} - \frac{3}{4} = ■$
12. $\frac{^-9}{10} \div \frac{^-4}{15} = ■$
13. $3.14 \div {}^-5 = ■$
14. $\frac{^-2}{5} \times \frac{^-5}{6} = ■$

Write a pair of fractions and a pair of decimals. Add, subtract, multiply, and divide each pair as many ways as you can by making each number positive or negative.

## Using a Square-Root Table (pages 218–219)

*Use the table on page 218. Round to the nearest hundredth.*

> $\sqrt{3} \times \sqrt{27}$ (Compare with $\sqrt{81}$)
> $\sqrt{3} \times \sqrt{27} \doteq 1.73 \times 5.20$
> $\doteq 8.996 \doteq 9.00$
> $\sqrt{81} = 9$ is the same number.

1. $\sqrt{5} \times \sqrt{20}$ (Compare with $\sqrt{100}$)
2. $\sqrt{20} - \sqrt{5}$ (Compare with $\sqrt{15}$)
3. $\sqrt{20} + \sqrt{5}$ (Compare with $\sqrt{25}$)
4. $\frac{\sqrt{20}}{\sqrt{5}}$ (Compare with $\sqrt{4}$).
5. $\sqrt{12} - \sqrt{9}$ (Compare with $\sqrt{3}$)
6. $\sqrt{16} \times \sqrt{4}$ (Compare with $\sqrt{64}$)
7. $\frac{\sqrt{81}}{\sqrt{27}}$ (Compare with $\sqrt{3}$)
8. $\sqrt{6} + \sqrt{30}$ (Compare with $\sqrt{36}$)

Make up a set of 4 comparisons. Exchange papers with a classmate. Round to the nearest hundredth.

## Estimating Square Roots (pages 220–221)

*Use the method on page 220 to estimate these square roots to the nearest hundredth.*

> $\sqrt{22}$ $E_1 = 4$ $4^2 < 22 < 5^2$
> $E_2 = (22 + 4^2) \div (2 \cdot 4)$
> $= 38 \div 8 \doteq 4.75$
> $E_3 = (22 + 4.75^2) \div (2 \cdot 4.75)$
> $= 44.5625 \div 9.50 \doteq 4.69$
> $E_4 = (22 + 4.69^2) \div (2 \cdot 4.69)$
> $= 43.9961 \div 9.38 \doteq 4.69$
> $E_3 \doteq E_4 = 4.69$ $\sqrt{22} \doteq 4.69$

1. $\sqrt{19}$ 2. $\sqrt{28}$ 3. $\sqrt{33}$
4. $\sqrt{35}$ 5. $\sqrt{43}$ 6. $\sqrt{54}$
7. $\sqrt{60}$ 8. $\sqrt{69}$ 9. $\sqrt{72}$
10. $\sqrt{75}$ 11. $\sqrt{95}$ 12. $\sqrt{200}$

Estimate the square root of the age of each member of your family.

## Algebra: Graphs of Sentences in One Variable (pages 222–223)

*Draw the graph of each sentence.*

$x \geq {}^-3.5$

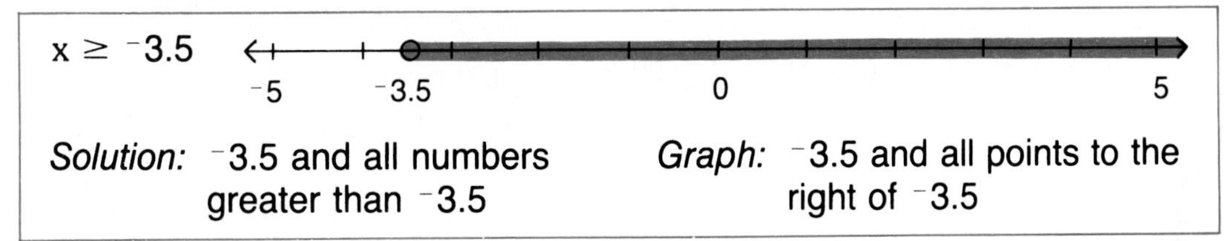


*Solution:* ⁻3.5 and all numbers greater than ⁻3.5

*Graph:* ⁻3.5 and all points to the right of ⁻3.5

1. $x > 4$
2. $y \leq {}^-4$
3. $|z| = 4$
4. $u = 4$
5. $m > \frac{^-5}{2}$
6. $p < 1.5$
7. $|t| = \sqrt{3}$
8. $s \geq {}^-.\overline{3}$

Draw a graph of $x \geq$ your age, $x \leq$ your age, $|x| =$ your age, and $x \geq |\text{your age} - 20|$

# UNIT 7 Measurement Systems

**Metric Units** *(pages 234–235)*

*What unit would you use to measure:*

| the mass of a truck? | metric ton (t) |
|---|---|

1. the height of a table lamp?
2. the mass of a truck tire?
3. the capacity of a water pail?
4. the thickness of a tin strip?
5. the width of a highway?
6. the capacity of a cooking pot?
7. the mass of a soda cracker?
8. the width of a pencil lead?

List ten household items and tell what metric unit you would use to measure them.

**The Metric System** *(pages 236–237)*

*Complete.*

| 7 mm = ■ m | .08 L = ■ mL | 5,000 mg = ■ dg |
|---|---|---|
| 7 mm = 7 · (0.001 m) | .08 L = .08 · (1,000 mL) | 5,000 mg = 5,000 · (0.01 dg) |
| = 0.007 m | = 80 mL | = 50 dg |

1. 4 kg = ■ g
2. 60 mm = ■ m
3. 0.03 km = ■ m
4. 0.2 L = ■ mL
5. 0.8 m = ■ cm
6. 9 cm = ■ mm
7. 70 mg = ■ g
8. 10,000 m = ■ km
9. 40 mL = ■ dL
10. 5 dam = ■ km
11. 30 hg = ■ g
12. 0.9 km = ■ dam

Find a product label that lists the mass of the product in grams. Then find its mass in milligrams and in kilograms.

**Changing Units** *(pages 238–239)*

*Complete.*

450 mL = ■ L

| | L | dL | cL | mL | | | L | dL | cL | mL | | |
|---|---|---|---|---|---|---|---|---|---|---|---|---|
| 450 mL = | 0 | 4 | 5 | 0. | mL = | | 0. | 4 | 5 | 0 | L = | 0.450 L |

1. 685 mm = ■ m
2. 16.8 cm = ■ mm
3. 8.7 cm = ■ m
4. 0.05 g = ■ mg
5. 0.35 L = ■ mL
6. 45 cm = ■ dm
7. 7.3 dL = ■ mL
8. 73 mg = ■ dg
9. 5.97 m = ■ mm

Measure the width of a car in meters. What is its width in centimeters and millimeters?

## Changing Units: Multiples *(pages 240–241)*

*Complete.*

| | |
|---|---|
| 5.1 km = ■ m | 5.1 km = \| 5. \| 1 \| 0 \| 0 \| km = \| 5 \| 1 \| 0 \| 0. \| m = 5,100 m (columns: km, hm, dam, m) |
| 93 dag = ■ kg | 93 dag = \| 0 \| 9 \| 3. \| dag = \| 0. \| 9 \| 3 \| kg = 0.93 kg (columns: kg, hg, dag) |

1. 5.75 km = ■ m
2. 600 g = ■ kg
3. 243 m = ■ km
4. 0.08 kg = ■ g
5. 25 L = ■ daL
6. 0.425 kg = ■ hg
7. 0.32 km = ■ dam
8. 1,500 g = ■ hg
9. 125 m = ■ dam
10. 640 dag = ■ kg
11. 7.3 hm = ■ m
12. 3.25 hL = ■ L

Find something in your house that is measured in liters.
Then write the measure in dekaliters, hectoliters, and kiloliters.

## Problem Solving: Using Metric Measures *(pages 242–243)*

A supermarket received the following order of soft drinks:
250 mL: 5 boxes of 36 bottles
600 mL: 4 boxes of 20 bottles
750 mL: 8 boxes of 12 bottles
How many bottles did the store receive? How many liters of soft drinks were received?

Total bottles = 250-mL bottles + 600-mL bottles + 750-mL bottles
= 5 × 36 + 4 × 20 + 8 × 12
= 180 + 80 + 96 = 356 bottles

Total mL = 180 × 250 + 80 × 600 + 96 × 750
= 45,000 + 48,000 + 72,000
= 165,000 mL = 165 L

1. A distance runner ran 2,000 meters in 6 minutes. What was the runner's rate in kilometers per hour?

2. A container held 10.5 liters of milk. If forty-five 200-ml glasses were filled from this container, how much milk was left?

3. The speed of sound in air is 331 meters per second. About how far away, in kilometers, was a bolt of lightning if the thunder was heard 4.5 seconds after the flash was seen?

Make up a word problem using meters, centimeters, and millimeters or liters and milliliters. Give it to a classmate to solve.

## Problem Solving: Special Metric Relations *(pages 244–245)*

*Find the volume and mass of the water that fills each box.*

$$\text{Volume} = \text{length} \times \text{width} \times \text{height} = 50 \times 40 \times 60 = 120{,}000 \text{ cm}^3 = 120 \text{ dm}^3 = 120 \text{ L}$$

$$\text{Mass of water} = \text{Number liters} \times 1 \text{ kg} = 120 \times 1 \text{ kg} = 120 \text{ kg}$$

| length | width | height | volume | | mass |
|---|---|---|---|---|---|
| 50 cm | 40 cm | 60 cm | 120 dm³ | 120 L | 120 kg |
| 8 cm | 6 cm | 5 cm | **1.** ▒ cm³ | **2.** ▒ mL | **3.** ▒ g |
| 7 m | 5 m | 4 m | **4.** ▒ m³ | **5.** ▒ kL | **6.** ▒ t |
| 95 cm | 60 cm | 75 cm | **7.** ▒ dm³ | **8.** ▒ L | **9.** ▒ kg |
| 125 mm | 80 mm | 45 mm | **10.** ▒ cm³ | **11.** ▒ mL | **12.** ▒ g |

Find the approximate volume and mass of the water that would fill your bathroom sink.

## Units of Time *(pages 246–247)*

*Add, subtract, multiply, or divide. Give the simplest form.*

5 h 17 min → 4 h 77 min
−2 h 35 min → 2 h 35 min
2 h 42 min

4 min 35 s
× 4
16 min 140 s = 16 min + 2 min 20 s
= 18 min 20 s

**1.** 11 h 39 min + 9 h 54 min

**2.** 8 min − 3 min 41 s

**3.** 2 h 48 min × 5

**4.** 6 d 13 h − 5 d 20 h

**5.** 5)3 wk 4 d

**6.** 2 yr 11 mo + 4 yr 9 mo

**7.** 4 min 25 s × 14

**8.** 24)53 min 30 s

**9.** 3 wk 2 d − 1 wk 6 d

**10.** 4 min 57 s + 2 min 48 s

**11.** 2 yr 3 mo × 6

**12.** 7)2h 41 min

Subtract the number of hours and minutes you slept last night from the number of hours in a day.

## **Clock Time** *(pages 248–249)*

*Give the 24-hour clock times.*

10:25 A.M. → 10 h 25 min → 1025

7:38 P.M. → 7 h 38 min + 12 h = 19 h 38 min → 1938

1. 5:40 A.M.
2. 5:50 P.M.
3. 12:17 P.M.
4. 1:43 P.M.
5. 10:05 A.M.
6. 10:05 P.M.
7. 1:56 P.M.
8. 12:00 noon

*Give the 12-hour clock times.*

0945 → 9 h 45 min → 9:45 A.M.

1420 → 14 h 20 min − 12 h = 2 h 20 min → 2:20 P.M.

9. 1415
10. 0440
11. 2112
12. 2359
13. 1046
14. 2246
15. 1224
16. 1339

Give your daily schedule in 24-hour and 12-hour clock times.

## **Elapsed Time** *(pages 250–251)*

*Find the time or the elapsed time.*

between 10:45 A.M. and 3:23 P.M.

10:45 A.M. → 10 h 45 min
3:23 P.M. → 3 h 23 min

Elapsed time = Ending time − Beginning time
= 15 h 23 min − 10 h 45 min
= 14 h 83 min − 10 h 45 min
= 4 h 38 min

1. 4 h 40 min after 10:35 A.M.
2. between 8:15 A.M. and 3:40 P.M.
3. 13 h 25 min before 10:00 P.M.
4. between 5:49 A.M. and 7:08 A.M.
5. 8 h 30 min after 7:45 A.M.
6. 8 h 45 min before 11:00 P.M.
7. between 12:18 P.M. and 5:12 P.M.
8. 6 h 50 min before 1:25 P.M.

Find the time that has elapsed between the time you woke this morning and the time right now.

## **Customary Units** *(pages 252–253)*

*What unit would you use to measure:*

| the weight of a truck? | ton (tn) |
|---|---|

1. the height of a table lamp?
2. the weight of a truck tire?
3. the capacity of a water pail?
4. the thickness of a board?
5. the length of a knife?
6. the weight of a person?
7. the capacity of a pool?
8. capacity of a milk bottle?
9. the width of a highway?
10. the capacity of a cooking pot?
11. the weight of a soda cracker?
12. the width of a pencil lead?

List 10 household items. Which customary unit would you use to measure each?

## **Changing Customary Units** *(pages 254–255)*

*Complete.*

5 ft 10 in. = ■ in.

1 ft = 12 in.
5 ft = 5 × 12 in.

$$\begin{array}{r} 12 \text{ in.} \\ \times\ 5 \\ \hline 60 \text{ in.} \end{array} \qquad \begin{array}{r} 60 \text{ in.} \\ +10 \text{ in.} \\ \hline 70 \text{ in.} \end{array}$$

5 ft 10 in. = 70 in.

$4\frac{7}{8}$ lb = ■ oz

1 lb = 16 oz

$$4\frac{7}{8} \text{ lb} = 4\frac{7}{8} \times 16 \text{ oz}$$

$$= \frac{39}{8} \times 16$$

$$= \frac{39 \times \overset{2}{\cancel{16}}}{\underset{1}{\cancel{8}} \times 1}$$

$$= 78 \text{ oz}$$

1. $6\frac{1}{2}$ ft = ■ in.
2. 15 qt = ■ gal ■ qt
3. 50 fl oz = ■ cups
4. 9,500 lb = ■ tn
5. 29 in = ■ ft ■ in
6. 10,000 yd = ■ mi ■ yd
7. 35 oz = ■ lb ■ oz
8. 7 pt = ■ cups
9. 25 gal = ■ qt
10. $1\frac{3}{4}$ tn = ■ lb
11. $3\frac{1}{4}$ lb = ■ oz
12. 14,494 ft = ■ mi ■ ft
13. A football player runs $\frac{3}{4}$ mi a day. How many yards is that?
14. A recipe lists 30 fl oz of milk. How many cups is that?

How many people of your weight would it take to equal the weight of a $1\frac{1}{4}$ ton elephant?

## Problem Solving: Using Customary Units *(pages 256–257)*

A $1\frac{1}{2}$-lb loaf of bread costs \$1.29. A 20-oz loaf of bread costs \$1.09. Which is the better buy?

| **$1\frac{1}{2}$-lb loaf:** | **20-oz or 1.25-lb loaf:** |
| --- | --- |
| ↓ \$.86 per lb | ↓ \$.872 per lb |
| 1.5)\$1.29 | 1.25)\$1.090 |

\$.86 < \$.872 so the $1\frac{1}{2}$-lb loaf is the better buy.

1. When a gasoline tank is $\frac{1}{12}$ full, it contains 1 gal 3 qt of fuel. What is its capacity in gallons?

2. A family drinks $4\frac{1}{2}$ pt of milk each day. How many cups of milk do they drink each week?

3. A 60-story building has a height of 230 yards. What is the average height of a story, in feet?

4. A $1\frac{1}{2}$-lb package of cheese costs \$2.89. A 10-oz package costs \$1.19. Which is the better buy?

Estimate the amount of milk your family consumes in one day. In one week. Use cups, quarts, and gallons.

## Problem Solving: Special Customary Relations *(pages 258–259)*

*Find the volume and weight of the water that fills each box.*

$$\begin{aligned}\text{Volume} &= \text{length} \times \text{width} \times \text{height}\\ &= 15 \times 10 \times 14\\ &= 2{,}100 \text{ in.}^3\end{aligned}$$

$$\begin{aligned}\text{Volume (gal)} &= \text{Number in.}^3 \div 231 \text{ in.}^3\\ &= 2{,}100 \div 231\\ &\doteq 9.091 \text{ gal}\end{aligned}$$

$$\begin{aligned}\text{Weight} &= \frac{\text{Number}}{\text{gal}} \times \text{Weight/gal}\\ &\doteq 9.091 \times 8.3\\ &\doteq 75.5 \text{ lb}\end{aligned}$$

| length | width | height | volume | | weight |
| --- | --- | --- | --- | --- | --- |
| 15 in. | 10 in. | 14 in. | 2,100 in.$^3$ | 9.091 gal | 75.5 lb |
| 9 ft | 6 ft | 5 ft | **1.** ■ ft$^3$ | **2.** ■ gal | **3.** ■ lb |
| 10 in. | 7 in. | 8 in. | **4.** ■ in.$^3$ | **5.** ■ gal | **6.** ■ lb |
| 40 ft | 25 ft | 8 ft | **7.** ■ ft$^3$ | **8.** ■ gal | **9.** ■ lb |

Find the volume and weight of the water that would fill your bathroom sink. Use customary measures.

## UNIT 8 Ratio, Proportion, and Percent

### Ratio and Proportion *(pages 270–271)*

$$\frac{x}{\frac{3}{4}} = \frac{2}{5} \qquad \frac{x}{\frac{3}{4}} \cdot \frac{3}{4} = \frac{2}{5} \cdot \frac{3}{4}$$

$$x = \frac{\overset{1}{\cancel{2}} \cdot 3}{5 \cdot \underset{2}{\cancel{4}}} = \frac{3}{10}$$

value of $x$ is $\frac{3}{10}$

$$\frac{7}{y} = \frac{24.5}{42} \qquad 24.5 \cdot y = 7 \cdot 42$$
$$y = (7 \cdot 42) \div 24.5$$
$$y = 294 \div 24.5$$
$$y = 12$$

value of $y$ is 12

1. $\frac{77}{35} = \frac{11}{t}$
2. $\frac{3}{4} = \frac{v}{72}$
3. $\frac{x}{8} = \frac{7}{20}$
4. $\frac{3}{5} = \frac{y}{24}$
5. $\frac{1}{z} = \frac{3}{5}$
6. $\frac{20}{9} = \frac{5}{u}$
7. $\frac{m}{1.4} = \frac{5}{8}$
8. $\frac{.09}{v} = \frac{2.4}{3.6}$
9. $\frac{x}{\frac{1}{2}} = \frac{7}{3}$
10. $\frac{5}{9} = \frac{1\frac{3}{4}}{y}$
11. $\frac{x}{13} = \frac{7.5}{65}$
12. $\frac{\frac{5}{8}}{y} = \frac{15}{16}$
13. $\frac{z}{.4} = \frac{33}{12}$
14. $\frac{5}{16} = \frac{1}{w}$
15. $\frac{1\frac{5}{9}}{5\frac{5}{6}} = \frac{v}{1\frac{2}{3}}$

Use the proportion $\frac{\text{number}}{\text{number}} = \frac{x}{\text{number}}$. You choose the numbers. Find the value of $x$.

### Problem Solving: Using Proportions *(pages 272–273)*

A pickup truck used 28 L of gasoline to travel 112 km. At this rate, how much gasoline will be used to travel 850 km?

$$\frac{\text{liters of gasoline}}{\text{distance in km}} = \frac{28}{112} = \frac{x}{850}$$
$$112 \cdot x = 28 \cdot 850$$
$$x = 23{,}800 \div 112$$
$$x = 212.5$$

The truck will use 212.5 L of gasoline.

1. A machine wraps 4 packages every 10 seconds. How many packages will it wrap in 1 h?
2. Mr. Mills earned \$12.50 for working $2\frac{1}{2}$ h. At this rate what would he earn for working 40 h?
3. A race driver drove 7.5 km in 2 min. At this rate how long will it take the driver to complete a 600 km race?
4. In a poll of 250 voters, 145 said they would vote for Ms. Holmes. If these voters are a representative sample of all the voters, about how many of the 36,000 voters will vote for Ms. Holmes?

What would you charge per hour to babysit? Using that rate, how much would you make in $2\frac{1}{2}$ hours? 3 hours?

## Problem Solving: Scale Drawings *(pages 274–275)*

*Use the diagram at the right. Find the actual distance (d) from:*

A to B

$$\frac{\text{actual distance (km)}}{\text{map distance (cm)}} = \frac{5}{1} = \frac{d}{4.3}$$

$$1 \cdot d = 5 \cdot 4.3$$
$$d = 21.5$$

The actual distance is 21.5 km.

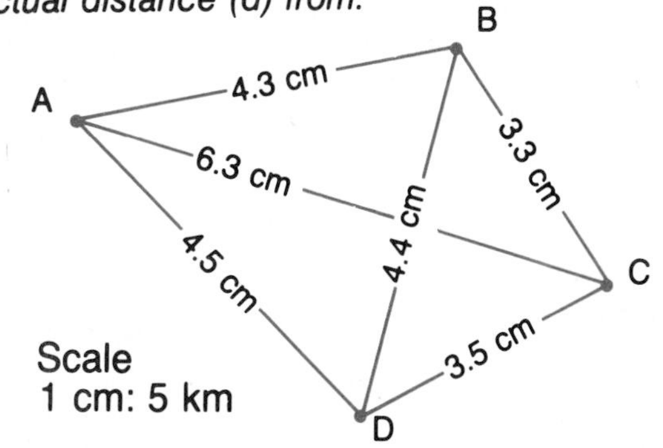


**1.** A to C **2.** A to D **3.** B to C **4.** B to D **5.** C to D

*Complete the table.*

| Scale | 1 cm: 1.6 km | 1 cm: 12.5 km | 1 cm: 80 km | 1 cm: 6.5 m |
|---|---|---|---|---|
| map distance | 22.5 cm | **7.** ■ cm | 43.4 cm | **9.** ■ cm |
| actual distance | **6.** ■ km | 600 km | **8.** ■ km | 130 m |

Make a scale drawing of a room in your house. Decide the unit (for example, feet or meters) you will use on the drawing to represent the actual lengths.

## Percent *(pages 276–277)*

*Write a decimal and fraction for each percent.*

49% $\quad 49.\% = .49 = \frac{49}{100}$ $\qquad$ 361% $\quad 361.\% = 3.61 = \frac{361}{100}$

**1.** 41% **2.** 15% **3.** 4% **4.** 75% **5.** 307% **6.** 63%

**7.** 73% **8.** 98% **9.** 2% **10.** 45% **11.** 400% **12.** 12%

*Write a percent for each.*

.06 $\quad .06 = .06.\% = 6\%$ $\qquad$ $1\frac{7}{100}$ $\quad 1\frac{7}{100} = 1.07 = 1.07.\%$

**13.** $\frac{17}{100}$ **14.** .93 **15.** $\frac{80}{100}$ **16.** .09 **17.** 2.50 **18.** $\frac{113}{100}$

**19.** $\frac{3}{100}$ **20.** .02 **21.** $\frac{29}{100}$ **22.** 1.20 **23.** .60 **24.** $1\frac{18}{100}$

Find the different rates of interest at a local bank. Change each to a decimal and a fraction.

## More About Percent *(pages 278–279)*

*Write a decimal and fraction for each percent.*

4.8%

$4.8\% = .04.8 = \frac{48}{1{,}000} = \frac{6}{125}$

$62\frac{1}{2}\%$

$62\frac{1}{2}\% = 62.5\% = .62.5 = \frac{625}{1{,}000} = \frac{5}{8}$

**1.** 8.7% **2.** $14\frac{1}{2}\%$ **3.** 73.25% **4.** $\frac{1}{2}\%$ **5.** $29\frac{3}{4}\%$ **6.** 108.5%

**7.** $4\frac{3}{8}\%$ **8.** 36.5% **9.** $\frac{3}{4}\%$ **10.** .625% **11.** 143.2% **12.** 4.65%

*Write a percent for each.*

.095

$.095 = .09.5\%$

$\frac{7}{20}$

$\frac{7}{20} \rightarrow 20\overline{)7.00}$ (quotient .35) $\rightarrow .35 = .35.\%$

**13.** .516 **14.** $\frac{17}{25}$ **15.** 3.875 **16.** $\frac{3}{8}$ **17.** .028 **18.** $4\frac{1}{2}$

**19.** .0825 **20.** 1.6 **21.** $\frac{3}{16}$ **22.** $1\frac{2}{5}$ **23.** $\frac{13}{20}$ **24.** .005

Find what the percentages are of the recommended daily allowances of the vitamins and minerals in one serving with milk of your favorite cereal. Change each to a fraction.

## The Basic Percent Formula: Finding the Part *(pages 280–281)*

$12\frac{3}{4}\%$ of \$680 = ■

$12\frac{3}{4}\% = 12.75\% = .1275$

$r \cdot b = p$

$.1275 \cdot 680 = p$

$86.7000 = p$

$12\frac{3}{4}\%$ of \$680 = \$86.70

**1.** 65% of 180 is ■. **2.** What is 175% of 72? **3.** ■ is $18\frac{3}{4}\%$ of \$640.

**4.** ■ is 4.5% of 16. **5.** 12.4% of \$750 is ■. **6.** What is 325% of \$54?

**7.** 80% of 90 is ■. **8.** ■ is $7\frac{3}{4}\%$ of 800. **9.** $62\frac{1}{2}\%$ of 180 is ■.

**10.** Vale has an adult population of 8,250. In the last election, 84% of the adults voted. How many people voted?

**11.** In Smithton $7\frac{1}{2}\%$ of the adults did not vote during an election. If the adult population is 4,640, how many people voted?

Find a newspaper ad in which the price of an item is reduced by a certain percent. Find the original price and the sale price.

## The Basic Percent Formula: Finding the Rate *(pages 282–283)*

$20.40 is ■% of $240.

$$r \cdot b = p$$
$$r \cdot 240 = 20.40$$
$$r \cdot 240 \div 240 = 20.40 \div 240$$
$$r = .085$$
$$.085 = .08.5\%$$

$20.40 is 8.5% of $240.

1. What % of 76 is 57?
2. $26 is what % of $400?
3. ■ is $37\frac{1}{2}$% of 104.
4. What is 112% of 850?
5. 288 is ■% of 240.
6. $0.34 is ■% of $13.60.
7. ■% of 400 is 29.
8. 490 is what % of 700?
9. 120% of 300 is ■.

What percent of your family, including aunts, uncles, cousins, and grandparents, is below the age of 18?

## The Basic Percent Formula: Finding the Base *(pages 284–285)*

$50 is $12\frac{1}{2}$% of ■.

$12\frac{1}{2}\% = 12.5\% = .125$

$$r \cdot b = p$$
$$.125 \cdot b = 50$$
$$.125 \cdot b \div .125 = 50 \div .125$$
$$b = 400$$

$50 is $12\frac{1}{2}$% of $400

1. $29.75 is $8\frac{1}{2}$% of ■.
2. 45% of what is 198?
3. What is 89.5% of $780?
4. $84.16 is 160% of what?
5. 42 is ■% of 120.
6. 12.36 is 82.4% of ■?
7. 35% of ■ is 1.61.
8. 1,875 is 250% of ■.
9. $18 is $\frac{1}{2}$% of what?
10. Bill paid $30.80 for a coat that was on sale. He paid 80% of the regular price. What was the regular price?
11. One day $2\frac{1}{2}$% of the 480 students at Taft School were absent because of illness. How many students were absent?

Make up your own word problem in which the base has to be found by using the basic percent formula. Exchange your problem with someone in your class. Solve the problem.

## More About Fractions and Percents *(pages 286–287)*

*Find a percent for each.*

$\frac{17}{45}$

$45\overline{)17.0000}$ = $.3777 \rightarrow 37.8$

$\frac{17}{45} \doteq .378 \doteq 37.8\%$

**or** $\frac{17}{45} = \frac{n}{100}$, $1{,}700 = 45n$, $37\frac{7}{9} = n$

**so** $\frac{17}{45} = \frac{37\frac{7}{9}}{100}$, $\frac{17}{45} = 37\frac{7}{9}\%$, $\frac{17}{45} \doteq 37.8\%$

**1.** $\frac{4}{9}$ **2.** $2\frac{2}{3}$ **3.** $\frac{19}{24}$ **4.** $\frac{1}{30}$ **5.** $\frac{7}{15}$ **6.** $\frac{15}{16}$

*Find a decimal and find a lowest terms fraction or mixed numeral for each percent.*

$9\frac{7}{12}\%$

$12\overline{)7.0000}$ = $.5833 \rightarrow .583$

so $9\frac{7}{12}\% \doteq 9.583\% \doteq .09583$

$9\frac{7}{12}\% = \frac{9\frac{7}{12}}{100} = 9\frac{7}{12} \div 100$

$= 9\frac{7}{12} \times \frac{1}{100}$

$= \frac{23}{240}$

**7.** $8\frac{1}{3}\%$ **8.** $183\frac{1}{3}\%$ **9.** $27\frac{7}{9}\%$ **10.** $6\frac{1}{4}\%$ **11.** $4\frac{2}{3}\%$ **12.** $108\frac{3}{4}\%$

Find a percent for $\frac{\text{doors in your house}}{\text{windows in your house}}$.

## Problem Solving: Percent Increase or Decrease *(pages 288–289)*

An employee's new salary was \$27,000. The old salary was \$24,000. What was the percent increase?

$r \cdot b = p$

$r \cdot 24{,}000 = 3{,}000$

p = new salary − old salary

$r = 3{,}000 \div 24{,}000 = .125 = 12.5\%$

The percent increase was $12\frac{1}{2}\%$.

**1.** An employee received an $8\frac{1}{3}\%$ salary increase. The increase was \$150 per month. What was his monthly salary before the increase? After the increase?

**2.** A farmer sold some wheat for \$4.20 per bushel. A month later the price was \$3.78 per bushel. What was the percent decrease in price for the month? **10%**

**3.** Bank A invested \$200,000. Its value increased by 4% during the first month, then decreased by 2% during the second month. What was the value of the investment at the end of the second month?

Choose a weekly salary. Then give yourself a $4\frac{1}{4}\%$ pay increase. How much is the increase? How much would you now be earning?

## Problem Solving: Buying and Selling *(pages 290–291)*

A clothing store is having a "25% off" sale. What is the sale price of a suit whose regular price is \$180? What is the total cost if the sales tax rate is 5%?

Sale price = Regular price − Discount
= 180 − Discount

Discount = Rate × Regular price
= .25 × 180 = 45

Sale price = 180 − 45 = \$135

Sales tax: $r \cdot b = p$
$.05 \cdot 135 =$ \$6.75

Total cost = Sale price + Sales tax
= 135 + 6.75 = \$141.75

1. Ken earned \$5.50 per hour. His boss offered him an additional 25% of his hourly wage if he would work at night unpacking stock. How much per hour would Ken earn at night?
2. A clothing store held a sale on shirts. The regular price of one shirt was \$20.00. Two shirts were sold at a sale price of \$35.00. What was the percent discount per shirt?
3. A furniture store held a "30% off" sale. The Browns bought a dining room set for \$595. What had been the regular price?
4. Ms. Carr received a 16% commission on the value of her sales. She received \$3,500 in commissions. What was the amount of her sales?

Write your own store ad. Give the percent discounts. Have a classmate find the sale prices.

## Problem Solving: Income Tax *(pages 292–293)*

*Use the tax table on page 292. Find the income tax due on each taxable income. (Round to the nearest dollar.)*

\$26,500 Income tax due = \$5,367 + 39% of Amount over \$23,500
= \$5,367 + 39% of (\$26,500 − \$23,500)
= \$5,367 + 39% of \$3,000
= \$5,367 + (.39 × \$3,000)
= \$5,367 + \$1,170
= \$6,537

1. \$17,380
2. \$23,225
3. \$38,470
4. \$53,600
5. \$103,400
6. Ms. Jason's taxable income is \$19,500. During the year, \$4,854 in taxes was deducted from her pay. How much should she get back?

Make up your own problem using the tax table. Give the problem to a classmate to solve.

**Problem Solving: The Simple Interest Formula** *(pages 294–295)*

*Find the simple interest on:*

| | |
|---|---|
| \$720 at $1\frac{1}{2}\%$ per month for 9 months. $r = 1\frac{1}{2}\% = 1.5\% = .015$ <br> $P = 720;\ n = 9;\ I = ?$ | $I = n \cdot (r \cdot P)$ <br> $= 9 \cdot (.015 \times 720)$ <br> $= 9 \cdot 10.80$ <br> $= \$97.20$ |

1. \$800 at $1\frac{1}{2}\%$ per month for 8 months.
2. \$5,000 at 12% per year, for 3 years.
3. \$1,800 at 2% per month, for 1 year.
4. \$40,000 at $16\frac{3}{4}\%$ per year, for 30 months.
5. \$8,000 at $7\frac{1}{2}\%$ per year, for 20 years.
6. \$75,000 at $12\frac{1}{2}\%$ per year, for 3 months.

Suppose you deposit some amount of money into a savings account. How much interest would your money earn at $5\frac{3}{4}$ % per month for one month?

**Problem Solving: Compound Interest** *(pages 296–297)*

*Use the table on page 296. Find the compound interest on:*

\$500 at 1.5% per month, for $2\frac{1}{2}$ years.

$$\text{Number of periods} = \text{Number of years} \times \text{Number of months per year}$$
$$= 2\frac{1}{2} \times 12 = 30$$

For \$1 at 1.5% of 30 periods the compound interest is \$.56.

For \$500 the compound interest is $500 \times \$.56 = \$280.00$.

1. \$12,000 at 15% per annum, for 5 years.
2. \$250 at 1.5% per month, for 8 months.
3. \$17,000 at 8% per 6-month period, for 10 years.
4. \$3,000 at 1.5% per month, for $2\frac{1}{2}$ years.
5. Ms. Lee has \$400 in a savings account that pays 8% per annum. How much compound interest will it earn in 20 years? How much money will be in the account?
6. Mr. Marcus borrowed \$50,000 for 2 years at 8% per 6-month period. What was the interest? How much money did he owe after two years?

Find the cost of something that you would need a loan to purchase. If you borrowed the money at 1.5% interest per month for $1\frac{1}{2}$ years, what would the compound interest be?

## UNIT 9 Geometry

### Figures, Terms, and Symbols *(pages 308–309)*

*For each exercise, copy points A, B, C, and D on grid paper. Draw the figures.*

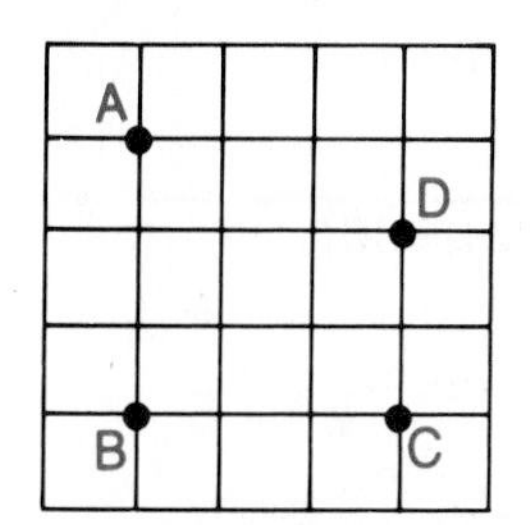


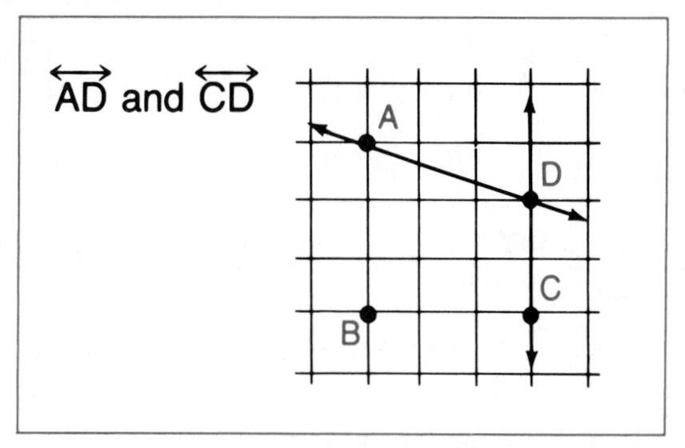


1. A pair of intersecting lines.
2. A pair of parallel lines.
3. $\overrightarrow{AC}$
4. $\overrightarrow{CA}$
5. $\overleftrightarrow{DB}$
6. $\overline{BC}$
7. ∠ABC
8. ∠BAC
9. ∠BCA
10. ∠ABD
11. Draw $\overleftrightarrow{AC}$ and $\overleftrightarrow{BD}$. (Use this figure for **12.** and **13.**) Label the intersection E.
12. Name six line segments.
13. Name the 4 rays with endpoint E.
14. A pair of congruent line segments.

Place 4 points at random on grid paper and label each one. Connect the points in as many ways as you can. Identify intersecting and parallel lines, and angles.

### Angles and Angle Measures *(pages 310–311)*

*Find the measure of each angle. Label each as right, acute, obtuse, or straight.*

| ∠APE | m∠APE = 90° |
|---|---|
| | ∠APE is a right angle. |

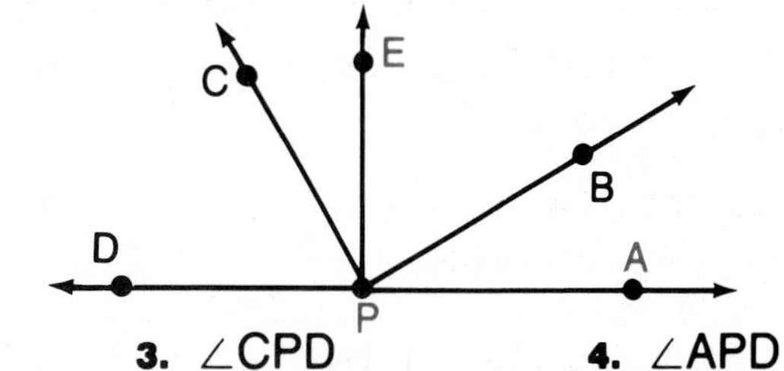

1. ∠APB
2. ∠BPC
3. ∠CPD
4. ∠APD
5. ∠BPD
6. ∠CPA
7. ∠BPE
8. ∠EPC
9. Name three pairs of supplementary angles.
10. Name three pairs of complementary angles.

Print your entire name in capital letters. Label and measure all the angles that are formed.

## Lines and Angles *(pages 312–313)*

*Use Figure 1 to find the measures.*

| $\angle 7$ |
|---|
| $m\angle 7 = 90°$ |

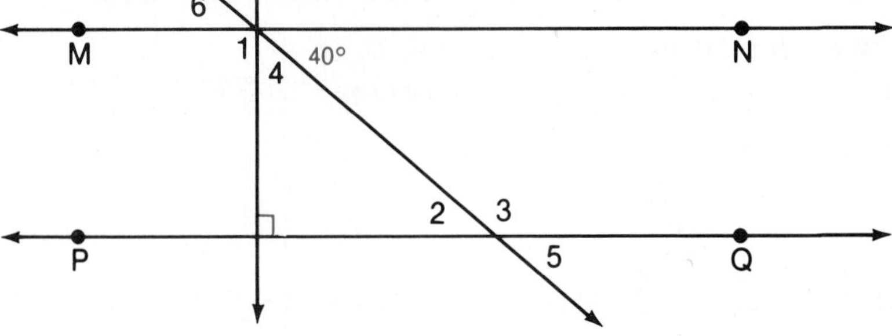


1. $\angle 1$
2. $\angle 2$
3. $\angle 3$
4. $\angle 4$
5. $\angle 5$
6. $\angle 6$

*Use Figure 2 to find the measures.*

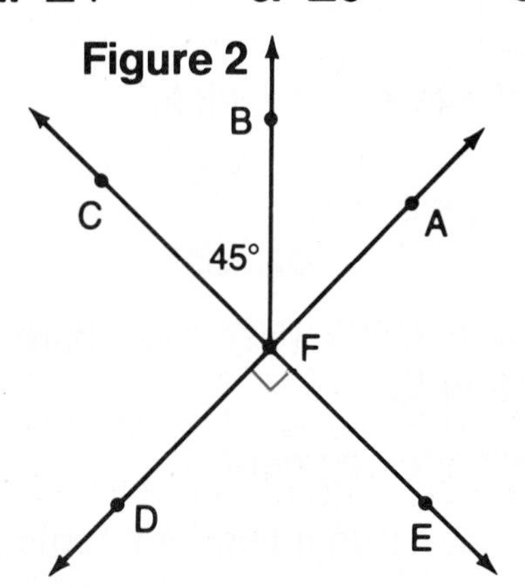


7. $\angle AFC$
8. $\angle AFB$
9. $\angle AFE$
10. $\angle CFD$
11. Name the bisector of $\angle AFC$
12. Name two perpendicular lines.

Draw a pair of parallel lines. Add three lines that intersect each other and the parallel lines. Measure each angle that is formed.

## Constructions *(pages 314–315)*

*Draw an acute angle. Copy it.* **Copy.**

M ③ ① ④ ② N

1. Draw a line segment $\overline{AB}$. Construct its perpendicular bisector $\overleftrightarrow{XY}$, X not on $\overline{AB}$.
2. Label the midpoint of $\overline{AB}$, P. Construct the bisector of $\angle APX$, and label it $\overrightarrow{PC}$.
3. Copy $\angle BPC$, label it $\angle FGH$, and construct the bisector of $\angle FGH$. Label the bisector $\overrightarrow{GU}$.
4. What are the measures of $\angle APX$, $\angle APC$, and $\angle FGU$?

Use a compass and a straightedge to design your own figures. Explain the steps you used.

## **Triangles** *(pages 316–317)*

*Name each triangle and classify it two ways.*

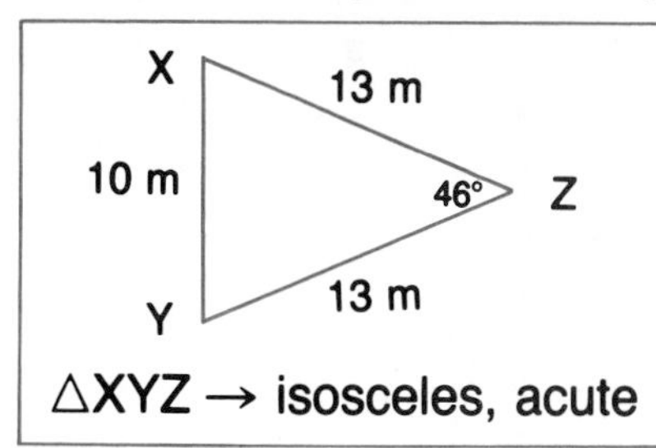


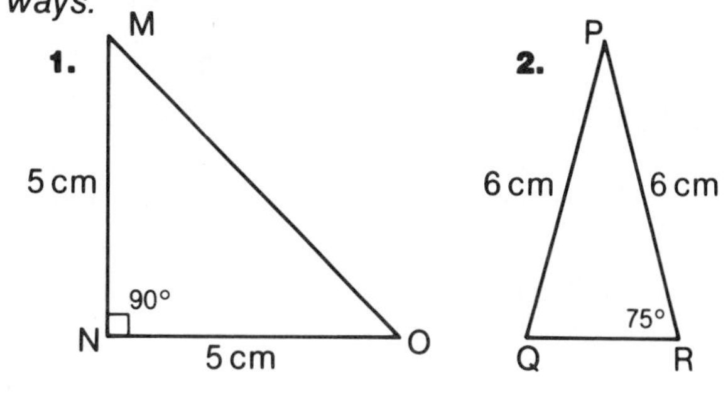


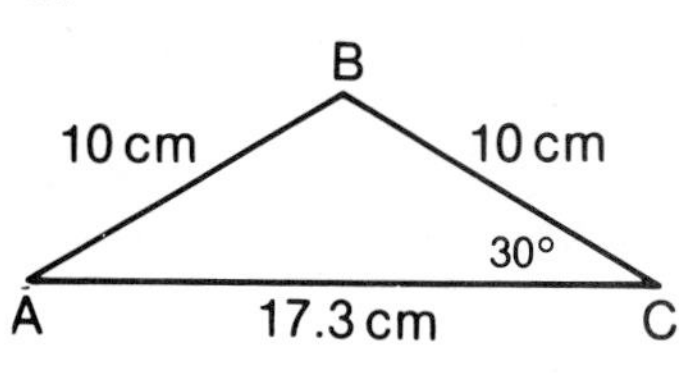


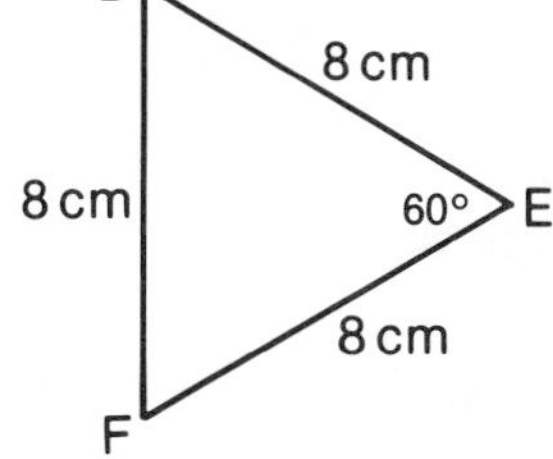


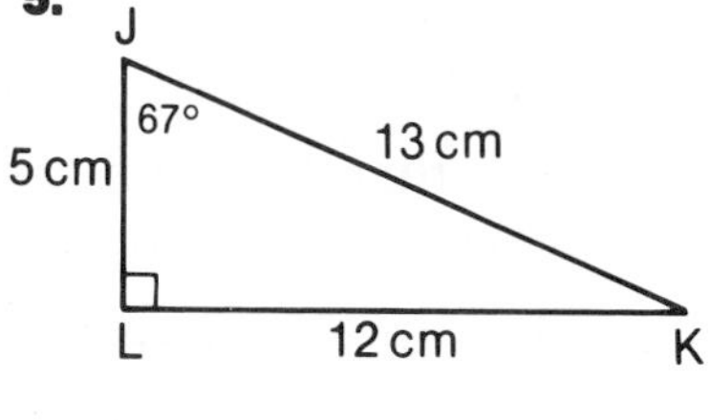


Find the measures of the other angles in △XYZ above.

$$m\angle X + m\angle Y = 180^\circ - 46^\circ = 134^\circ \rightarrow m\angle X = m\angle Y \text{ so } m\angle X = \frac{1}{2} \cdot 134^\circ = 67^\circ$$

**6.-10.** *Find the measures of the other angles in Exercises* **1.-5.**

Draw 3 different triangles. Measure the sides and angles. Classify each triangle two ways.

## **Polygons and Circles** *(pages 318–319)*

*O is the center of this circle. Name the following:*

**1.** 3 radii

**2.** a diameter

**3.** 5 chords

**4.** a diagonal of ABCD

**5.** a regular polygon

**6.** all central angles and their measures

**7.** an isosceles obtuse triangle

**8.** m ∠BAO

**9.** m ∠ABC

Find the diameter and radius of 5 circular objects in or around your home.

## Special Quadrilaterals *(pages 320–321)*

*Identify each quadrilateral as a trapezoid, parallelogram, rhombus, rectangle, or square.*

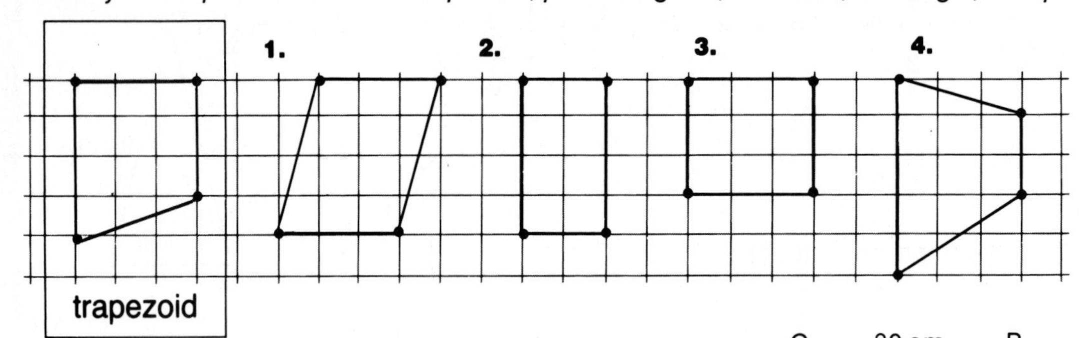


*Use the figure to the right. FBCE is a parallelogram.*

5. Name a rhombus and give the measure of all its sides and angles.
6. Name a trapezoid and give the measures of all its sides and angles.

Explain how you might use a triangle to construct a parallelogram, a rectangle, and a square.

## Similar Triangles *(pages 322–323)*

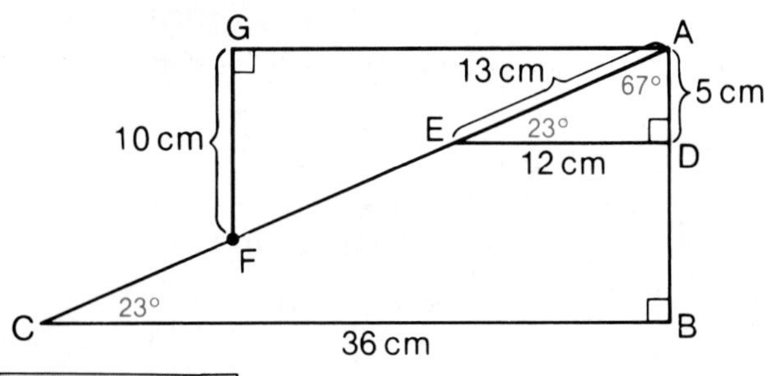


Any two of the triangles △ABC, △ADE, and △FGA are similar to each other.

*Copy and complete the table.*

| Similar triangles | Pairs of corresponding angles | sides |
|---|---|---|
| △ABC and △ADE | ∠BAC ↔ ∠DAE<br>∠ABC ↔ ∠ADE<br>∠ACB ↔ ∠AED | **1.** |
| △ABC and △FGA | **2.** | **3.** |
| △ADE and △FGA | **4.** | **5.** |

Find the length of:

**6.** $\overline{AB}$ **7.** $\overline{AC}$

**8.** $\overline{EC}$ **9.** $\overline{BD}$

**10.** $\overline{AG}$ **11.** $\overline{AF}$

**12.** $\overline{CF}$ **13.** $\overline{EF}$

Draw a pair of similar triangles. Explain how you did it.

## Congruent Triangles *(pages 324–325)*

*Which triangles are congruent to △PQR? Write SAS, ASA, or SSS to show how you decided that the triangles are congruent. Write a congruence statement for the triangles.*

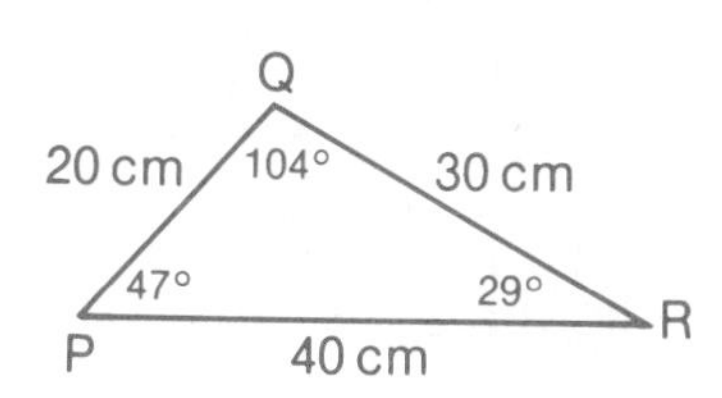


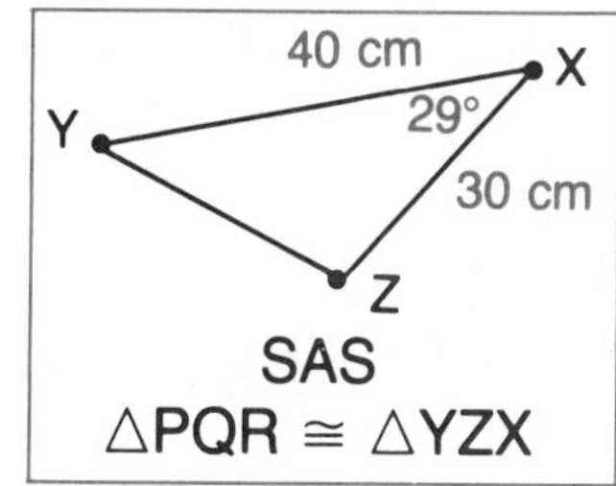


**1.**

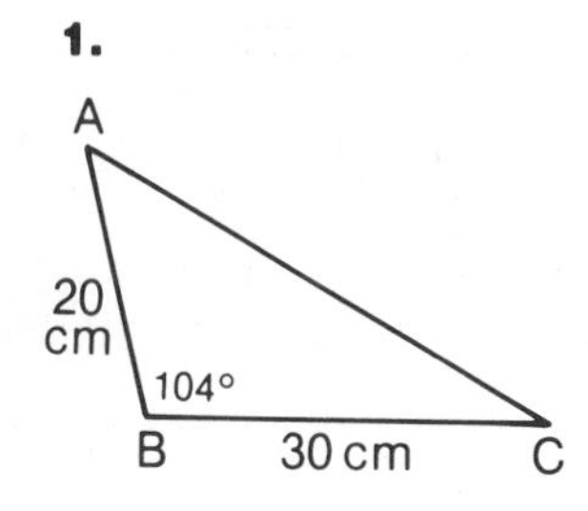


**2.**

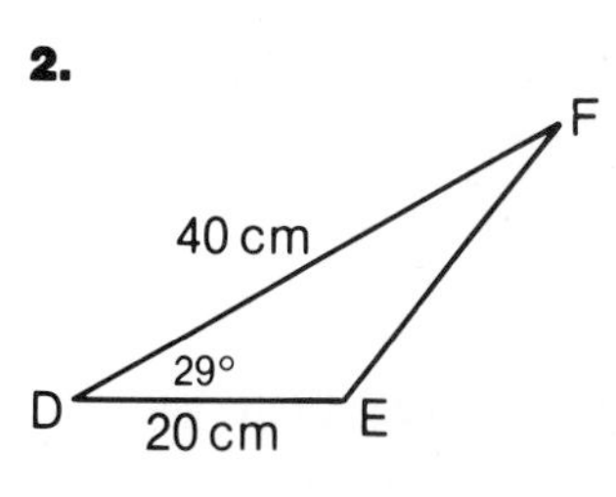


**3.**

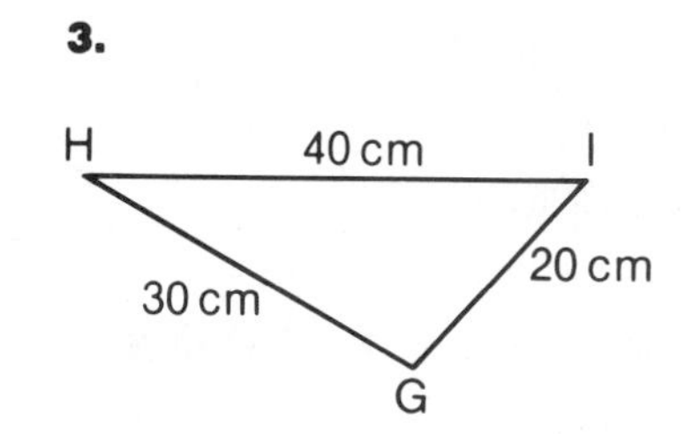


**4.**

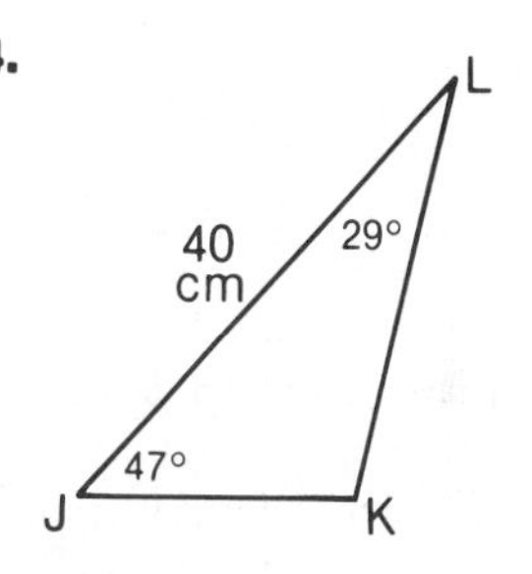

Draw two congruent triangles. Explain the steps you used to draw them.

## Problem Solving: Using Perimeter Formulas *(pages 326–327)*

A garden has the shape of a regular hexagon. The perimeter is 51 m. What is the length of each side of the garden?

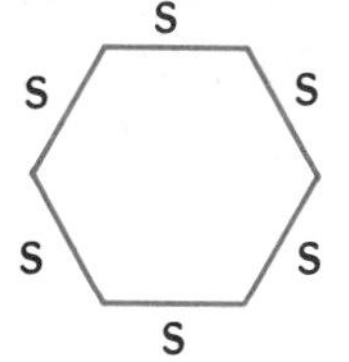


$$P = 6 \cdot s$$
$$51 = 6 \cdot s$$
$$51 \div 6 = s$$
$$8.5 = s$$

Each side has length 8.5 m

1. The perimeter of a regular pentagonal pool is 42.6 m. What is the length of each side of the pool?
2. The length of a rectangular pool is 30.5 m. The width is 10.7 m shorter than the length. What is the perimeter of the pool?
3. A garden has the shape of a parallelogram. Its perimeter is 60 m. If one side has length 18 m, what are the lengths of the other sides?
4. A garden has the shape of a regular octagon. The length of a side is 4.5 m. If fencing costs \$2.50/m, how much does it cost to put a fence around the garden?

If you were going to frame your favorite poster or drawing, how much molding would you need?

## **Problem Solving: Using Area Formulas** *(pages 328–329)*

*Find the area of each figure.*

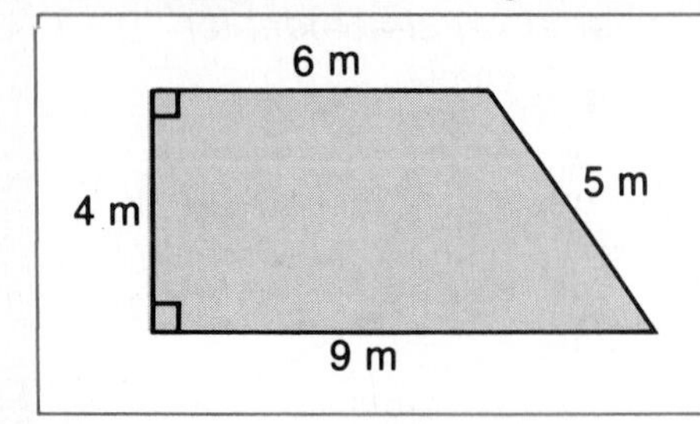


$$A = \frac{1}{2} \cdot (B + b) \cdot h$$
$$= \frac{1}{2} \times (9 + 6) \times 4$$
$$= 30$$

The area of the figure is 30 m².

**1.**

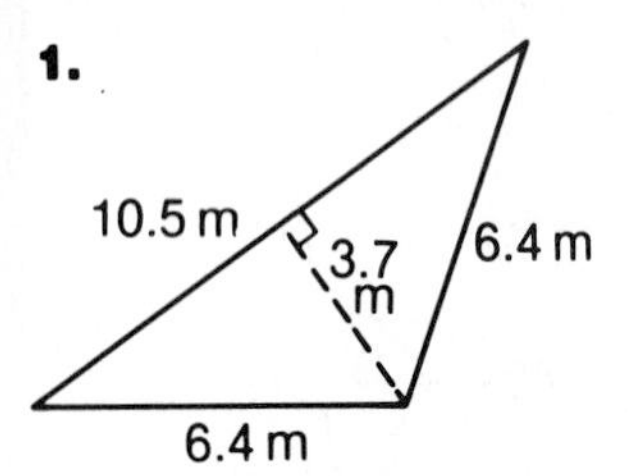


**2.**

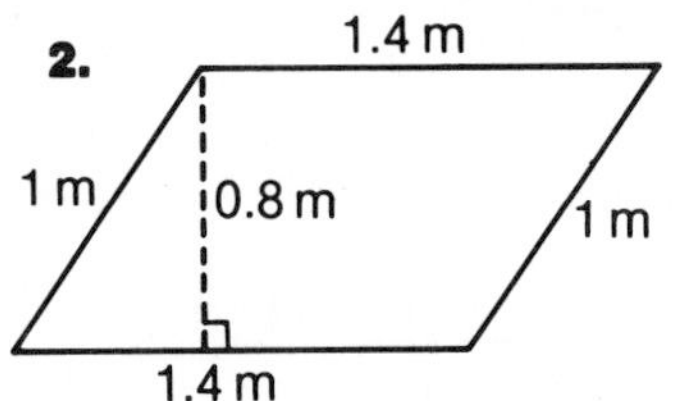


**3.**

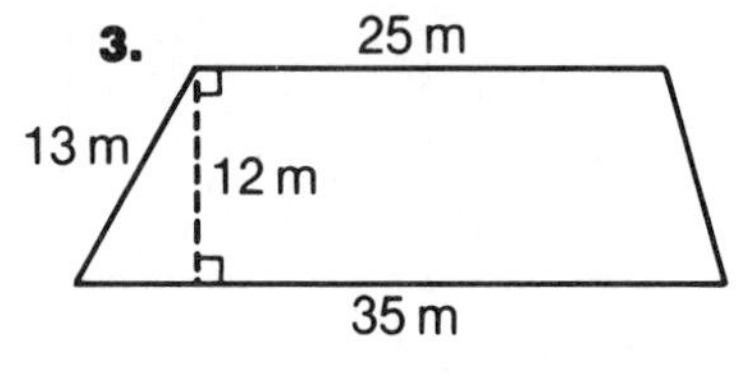


**4.** Find the cost of a rectangular carpet that is 5.4 m long and 4.5 m wide. The carpet sells for $14.50/m².

**5.** A pasture has the shape of a trapezoid with parallel sides of lengths 6.5 km and 4.2 km. The distance between the sides is 5.0 km. Find its area.

Draw a triangle, a parallelogram, and a trapezoid. Mark the dimensions of each. Which figure has the greatest area?

## **The Rule of Pythagoras** *(pages 330–331)*

*Find the length of the third side of each right triangle.*

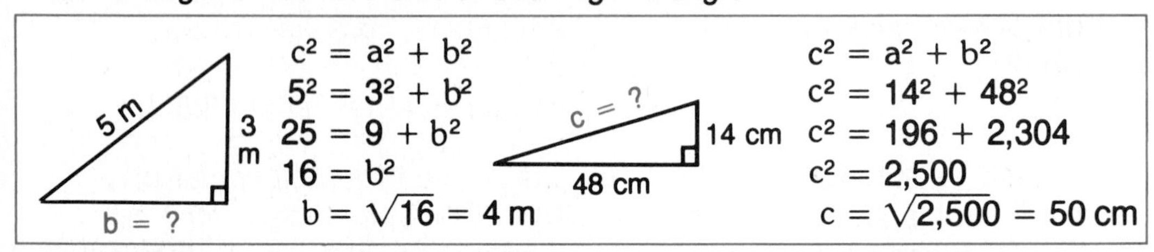


| | | | | | | | |
|---|---|---|---|---|---|---|---|
| **Leg** | 15 cm | 7 m | 30 cm | **4.** | 60 cm | 35 cm | 9 cm |
| **Leg** | 20 cm | 24 m | **3.** | 21 m | 11 cm | **6.** | 40 cm |
| **Hypotenuse** | **1.** | **2.** | 34 cm | 29 m | **5.** | 37 cm | **7.** |

**8.**

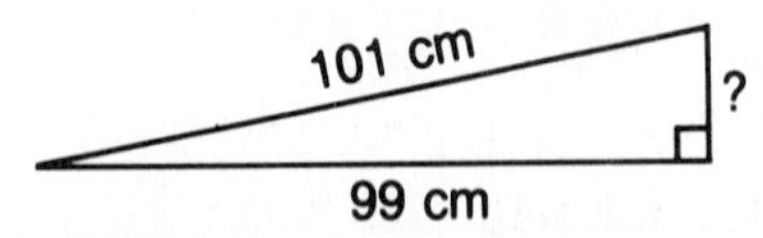


**9.**

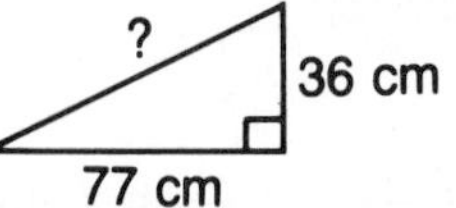

Test the Rule of Pythagoras on a triangle you have drawn.

## Circles *(pages 332–333)*

*Find the circumference and area of each circle. Use 3.14 for $\pi$.*

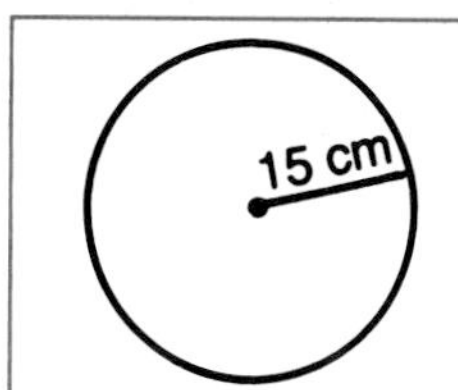


$$C = 2\pi r$$
$$\doteq 2 \times 3.14 \times 15$$
$$\doteq 94.2$$

The circumference is 94.2 cm.

$$A = \pi r^2$$
$$\doteq 3.14 \times 15^2$$
$$\doteq 706.5$$

The area is 706.5 cm$^2$.

**1.** 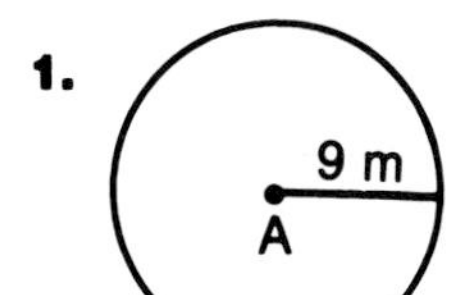


**2.** 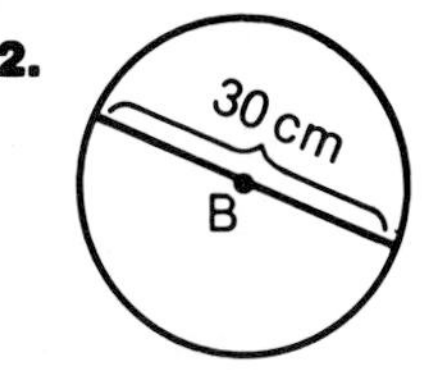


**3.** 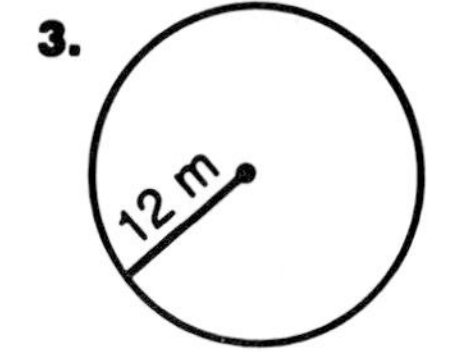


**4.** 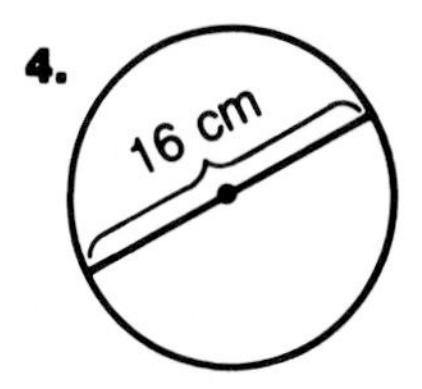


*Find the arc length and the area of the shaded portion determined by each central angle. Use 3.14 for $\pi$.*

**5.** 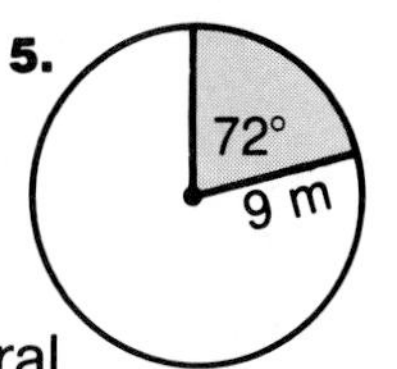


**6.** 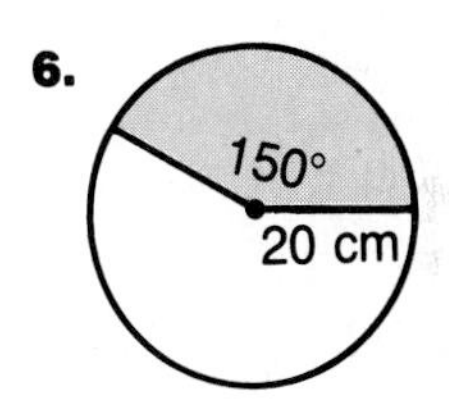

Find the circumference and area of several circular objects in or around your house.

## Problem Solving: Circle Graphs *(pages 334–335)*

1. The Turner family's monthly income is budgeted as shown in the table. Draw a circle graph for this budget. The part for housing is shown in the circle graph.

| | |
|---|---|
| **Housing** | 30% |
| **Food** | $22\frac{1}{2}$% |
| **Savings** | 5% |
| **Clothing** | 10% |
| **Transportation** | 15% |
| **Entertainment** | 5% |
| **Other** | $12\frac{1}{2}$% |

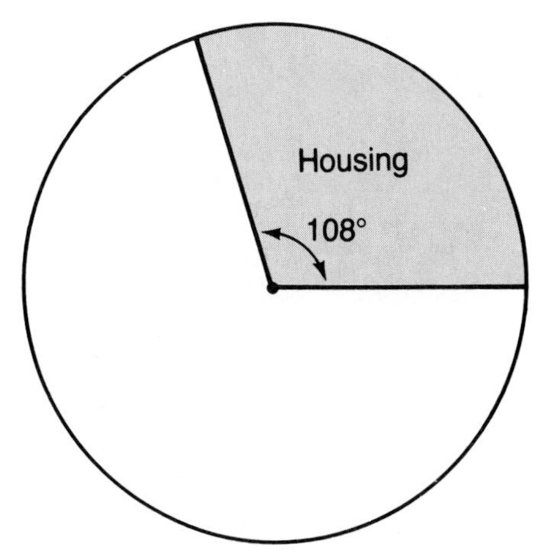


For housing: $r = 30\%$, $b = 360°$
$$r \cdot b = p$$
$$.30 \cdot 360° = p$$
$$108° = p$$

2. If their monthly income is \$1,850, how much money is budgeted for each category?

Make a circle graph to show how you spend a typical 24-hour day.

## Prisms and Pyramids *(pages 336–337)*

*Find the surface area and volume.*

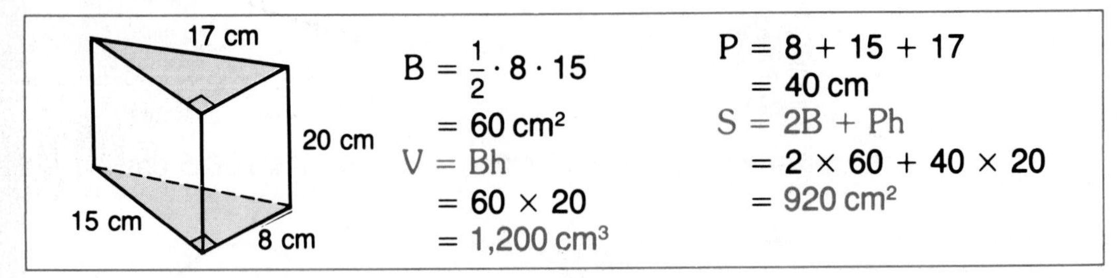


$B = \frac{1}{2} \cdot 8 \cdot 15$
$= 60 \text{ cm}^2$
$V = Bh$
$= 60 \times 20$
$= 1{,}200 \text{ cm}^3$

$P = 8 + 15 + 17$
$= 40 \text{ cm}$
$S = 2B + Ph$
$= 2 \times 60 + 40 \times 20$
$= 920 \text{ cm}^2$

**1.**

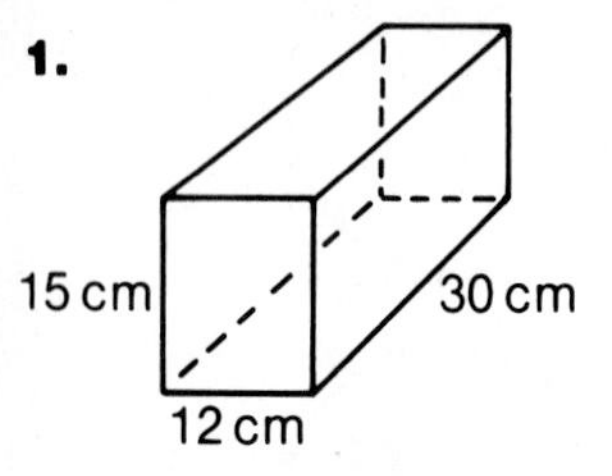


**2.**

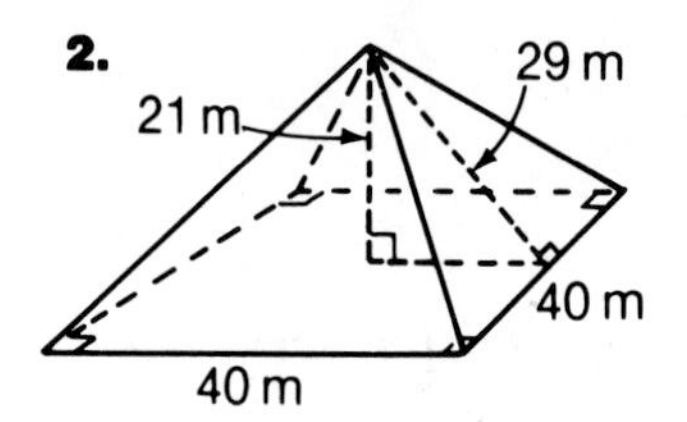


**3.**

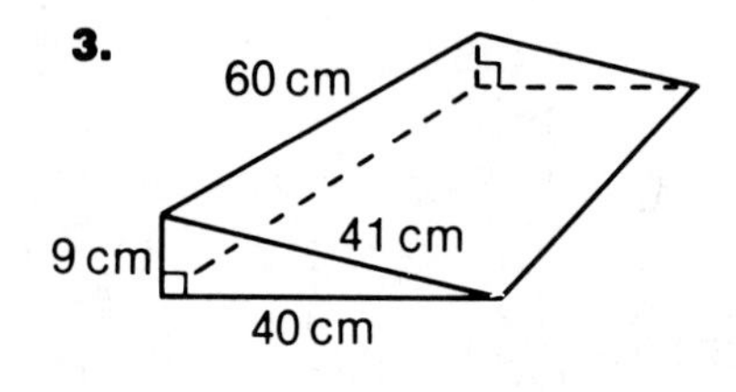

Find the surface area and volume of several food boxes found in your home.

## Cylinders, Cones, and Spheres *(pages 338–339)*

*Find the surface area and volume. Use 3.14 for π. Round your answers to the nearest hundredth.*

36 cm
85 cm
77 cm

$C = 2\pi r$
$\doteq 2 \times 3.14 \times 36$
$\doteq 226.08 \text{ cm}$
$B = \pi r^2$
$\doteq 3.14 \times 36^2$
$\doteq 4{,}069.44 \text{ cm}^2$

$S = B + \frac{1}{2}Cl$
$\doteq 4{,}069.44 + \frac{1}{2} \times 226.08 \times 85$
$\doteq 4{,}069.44 + 9{,}608.4$
$\doteq 13{,}677.84 \text{ cm}^2$
$V = \frac{1}{3}Bh$
$\doteq \frac{1}{3} \times 4{,}069.44 \times 77$
$\doteq 104{,}448.96 \text{ cm}^3$

**1.**

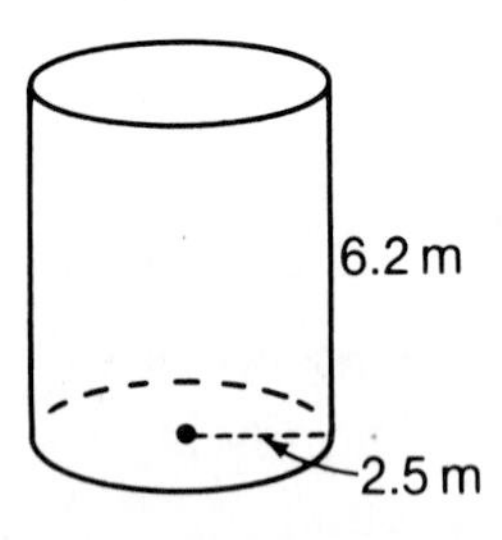


**2.**

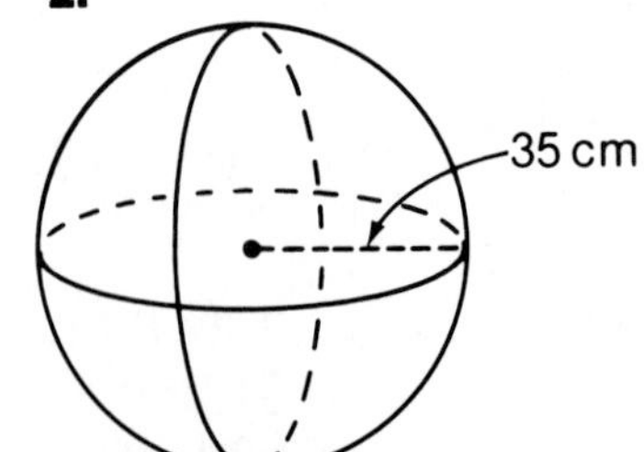


**3.**

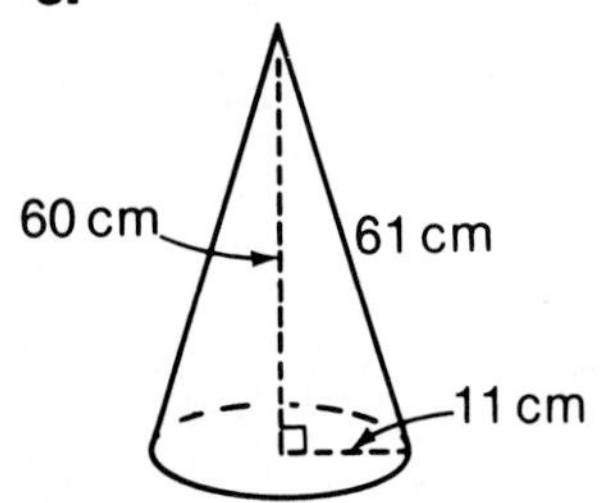

Find the surface area and volume of 3 food cans in your home.

## **Problem Solving: Using Formulas (Metric)** *(pages 340–341)*

A rectangular yard is 30.4 m long and 10.5 m wide. If fencing costs \$4.50/m, find the cost of building a fence around the yard.

Cost = Perimeter × Cost/m
$= P \times \$4.50$

$P = 2l + 2w$
$= 2 \times 30.4 + 2 \times 10.5$
$= 81.8$ m
Cost $= 81.8 \times 4.50$
$= \$368.10$

1. Find the area of the garden in the example.
2. A storage bin has the shape of a circular right cylinder. The length of the diameter and height are both 3.2 meters. If the bin is 75% full, how many cubic meters of grain are stored in the bin?
3. A sports arena has the shape of a hemisphere. The radius has length 50 m. What is the surface area of the curved roof? What is the volume enclosed by the building?
4. The base of a cylindrical water tank is a hemisphere and the top is a right cone. Find the total surface area and the cubic meters of water it holds, when it is filled to the top of the cylindrical part.

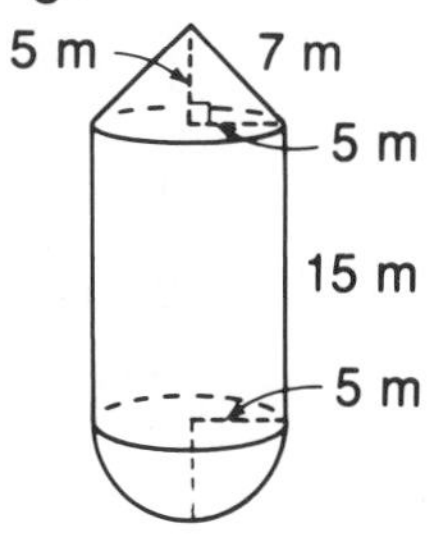


Find the surface area of a drinking glass in square centimeters. Find its volume in cubic centimeters.

## **Problem Solving: Using Formulas (Customary)** *(pages 342–343)*

A square garden has sides of length $23\frac{1}{2}$ ft. What is the area?

Area $= s^2$
$= 23\frac{1}{2}^2 = 552\frac{1}{4}$ ft$^2$

1. A building with a square base has a roof in the shape of a square-based pyramid.

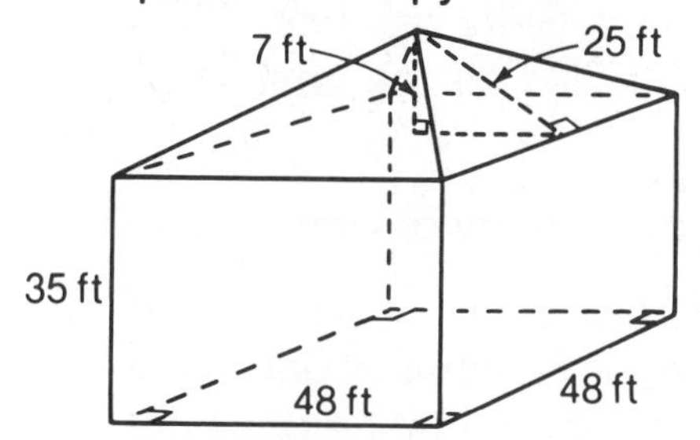


Find the total surface area of the four sides and roof of the building.

2. A cylindrical tank has ends in the shape of hemispheres.

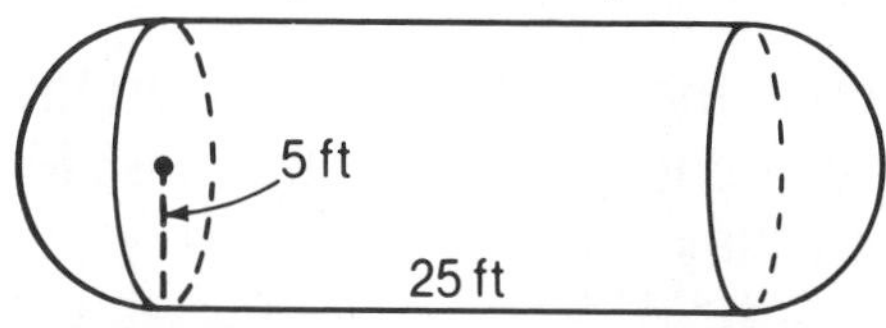


Find the volume of the tank.

3. The length of a radius of a sphere is 6 in.. Find the surface area and the volume of the sphere. Find the area of the great circle of the sphere.

Find the surface area of the ceiling in your room in square feet.

## UNIT 10 Probability and Statistics

### **Probability** *(pages 354–355)*

*Find the probabilities.*

A jar contains 5 orange cards numbered 1 through 5, 4 yellow cards numbered 1 through 4, and a white card numbered 1. One card is selected at random.

P (yellow) Cards are shown by: 01, 02, 03, 04, 05, y1, y2, y3, y4, w1.

4 of the 10 cards are yellow $P(\text{yellow}) = \frac{4}{10} = \frac{2}{5} = .4$

P(yellow or even)

Must be one of the six cards y1, y2, y3, y4, 02, 04.

$P(\text{yellow or even}) = \frac{6}{10} = \frac{3}{5} = .6$

1. P (orange)
2. P (orange and 1)
3. P (white or yellow)
4. P (4 or 5)
5. P (orange or 4)
6. P (not white)
7. P (odd number)
8. P (yellow and 5)
9. P (orange or yellow or 1)

Change the number of orange, yellow, and white cards.
Find the new probabilities for exercises 1–9.

### **Problem Solving: Empirical Probability** *(pages 356–357)*

Wendy has gotten a hit in 32 of her last 84 times at bat in a softball league. What is the probability she will get a hit her next time at bat?

$P(\text{hit}) = \frac{32}{84}$

$\doteq .38$

(rounded to the nearest hundredth)

In 90 games they have played, Ken has won 30 times, Betty has won 32 times, and Henry has won 28 times. Find the probabilities for the next game they play.

1. P (Ken or Betty wins)
2. P (Betty loses)
3. P (Betty or Henry wins)
4. What is the probability of rain today if the present conditions have produced rain on 160 of 400 previous observations?
5. Charles has gotten a hit in 16 of his previous 56 times at bat. What is the probability that he does *not* get a hit his next time at bat?

What is the probability that you will bring lunch to school tomorrow? Use your record for the past month to decide.

### Using "Or" in Compound Statements *(pages 358–359)*

*Find the probabilities.*

For the four runners in a race, P (Tim wins) = .3, P (John wins) = .25, P (Phil wins) = .18, and P (Mace wins) = .27.

> P (John loses) "John loses" is the negative of "John wins".
>
> P (John loses) = 1 − P (John wins)
> = 1 − .25 = .75
>
> P (Tim and Mace lose)
> The only way for "Tim and Mace lose" to be true is for "John or Phil wins" to be true.
>
> P (Tim and Mace lose) = P (John or Phil wins)
> = P (John wins) + P (Phil wins)
> = .25 + .18 = .43

1. P (Tim loses)
2. P (John or Mace wins)
3. P (Tim or Phil wins)
4. P (Marty wins)
5. P (Mace loses)
6. P (Tim and John lose)
7. P (Phil loses)
8. P (Tim or Phil or Mace wins)
9. P (Tim and John and Phil lose)

List the birthdays of your family members and two friends. What is the probability that two were born in the same month?

### Multiple Selections: Independent Statements *(pages 360–361)*

*Find the probabilities.*

Teams A, B, and C are playing in three different tournaments. P (A wins) = .6, P (B wins) = .4, P (C wins) = .7.

> P (A loses) "A loses" is the negation of "A wins".
> P (A loses) = 1 − P (A wins) = 1 − .6 = .4
>
> P (A loses and B wins)
> P (A loses and B wins) = P (A loses) × P (B wins)
> = .4 × .4 = .16

1. P (A and B win)
2. P (A wins and B loses)
3. P (B and C lose)
4. P (A and C lose)
5. P (A loses and C wins)
6. P (A and C win)
7. P (A and B lose)
8. P (A wins and C loses)
9. P (B wins and C loses)

Put 4 pairs of different colored socks into a paper bag. Then calculate the probability of picking different color combinations.

## Multiple Selections: Dependent Statements *(pages 362–363)*

A jar contains 5 cards numbered 1, 4 cards numbered 2, and 1 card numbered 3. One card is selected at random, then a second is selected.

*Find each probability if the first card is replaced before the second card is selected.*

P (2 then 1)

$$P(2 \text{ then } 1) = P(2) \times P(1)$$
$$= \frac{2}{5} \times \frac{1}{2} = \frac{1}{5}$$

| 1 | 1 | 1 | 1 | 1 |
|---|---|---|---|---|
| 2 | 2 | 2 | 2 | 3 |

1. P (1 then 2)
2. P (both 1)
3. P (2 then 3)
4. P (both 3)
5. P (3 then 2)
6. P (both 2)
7. P (1 then 3)
8. P (3 then 1)

*Find each probability if the first card is* not *replaced.*

$$P(2 \text{ then } 1) = P(2) \times P(1 \text{ given } 2)$$
$$= \frac{2}{5} \times \frac{5}{9} = \frac{2}{9}$$

**9.–16.** Use exercises **1.–8.**

Change the number of cards numbered 1, 2, and 3 in the jar. Then complete exercises 1–8.

## Listing Outcomes *(pages 364–365)*

*Use tree diagrams.*

Amy, Bess, and Chris race. How many possible outcomes for 1st and 2nd place are there?

There are 6 possible outcomes.

| 1st | 2nd | |
|---|---|---|
| Amy | Bess | (Amy, Bess) |
| | Chris | (Amy, Chris) |
| Bess | Amy | (Bess, Amy) |
| | Chris | (Bess, Chris) |
| Chris | Amy | (Chris, Amy) |
| | Bess | (Chris, Bess) |

1. There are 5 runners in a race. Give the possible outcomes for first and second in the race.
2. In how many different ways can the 4 winners of a contest line up to be introduced?
3. In a contest, there are 4 winners. In how many ways can the winners be selected from the 5 finalists?
4. Mr. Thomas selects 2 of the 5 best math papers to put on the bulletin board. How many different sets of 2 papers can he select?

Use a tree diagram to show the possible outcomes for first and second places if all the members of your family were in the race.

**Permutations** *(pages 366–367)*

*Find the number of permutations. Give factorial notation and the standard numeral.*

$_9P_6$

$_9P_9$

$$_9P_6 = \frac{9!}{(9-6)!} = \frac{9 \times 8 \times 7 \times 6 \times 5 \times 4 \times \overset{1}{\not 3} \times \overset{1}{\not 2} \times 1}{\underset{1}{\not 3} \times \underset{1}{\not 2} \times 1} = 60{,}480$$

$$_9P_9 = \frac{9!}{(9-9)!} = \frac{9!}{0!} = \frac{9!}{1} = 9! = 9 \times 8 \times 7 \times 6 \times 5 \times 4 \times 3 \times 2 \times 1$$
$$= 362{,}880$$

1. $_8P_2$
2. $_4P_3$
3. $_{64}P_1$
4. $_7P_4$
5. $_6P_5$
6. $_{10}P_3$
7. Three people enter a room with 12 chairs. In how many ways can they seat themselves?
8. In how many different ways can the manager make a batting order using 9 players of the baseball team if the pitcher must bat last?

If all the members of your family decide to sit at the kitchen table at the same time, in how many ways can they seat themselves?

**Combinations** *(pages 368–369)*

*Find the number of combinations or permutations. Give factorial notation and the standard numeral.*

$_7C_4$

$$_7C_4 = \frac{7!}{(7-4)!\,4!} = \frac{7 \times \overset{1}{\not 6} \times 5 \times \overset{1}{\not 4} \times \overset{1}{\not 3} \times \overset{1}{\not 2} \times 1}{\underset{1}{\not 3} \times \underset{1}{\not 2} \times 1 \times \underset{1}{\not 4} \times \underset{1}{\not 3} \times \underset{1}{\not 2} \times 1} = 35$$

1. $_9C_3$
2. $_9P_3$
3. $_{10}C_3$
4. $_8C_8$
5. $_8P_8$
6. $_{12}C_1$
7. $_4C_2$
8. $_9P_5$
9. $_9C_5$
10. $_4P_1$
11. $_4C_1$
12. $_{10}C_7$

Find the number of combinations of foods you can use to make a sandwich for lunch today.

**Some Important Statistics** *(pages 370–371)*

*Find the statistics. Use this set of data: 14, 16, 16, 20, 21, 27*

Range = greatest − least = 27 − 14 = 13

1. mean
2. median
3. mode

*Use this set of data:* 180, 150, 212, 194, 140, 150, 169, 200, 162

4. mean
5. median
6. mode
7. range

Poll 13 friends or neighbors to find their height to the nearest foot. Then find the mean, median, and range of your data.

## **Grouped Data and Histograms** *(pages 372–373)*

*Use this histogram for grouped test scores.*

*Find:*

| Total Number of Scores |
|---|
| Sum of class frequencies: |
| 2 + 7 + 6 + 5 = 20 |

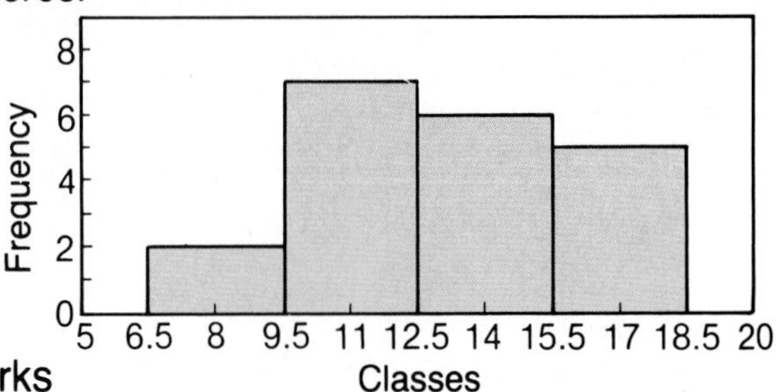


**1.** class limits **2.** class marks **3.** mean **4.** median **5.** mode **6.** range

**7.** Draw a frequency polygon for the grouped test scores.

*Complete the table.*

| Class Limits | Class Mark | Class Frequency |
|---|---|---|
| 17.5–24.5 | 21 | 6 |
| 24.5–31.5 | **8.** ■ | 9 |
| 31.5–38.5 | 35 | 19 |
| **9.** ■–■ | **10.** ■ | 11 |
| 45.5–52.5 | 49 | 5 |

**11.** How many numbers are in this set of grouped data?

*Find:*

**12.** mean **13.** median

**14.** mode **15.** range

**16.** Draw a histogram for this set of grouped data.

Draw a histogram and a frequency polygon using the ages of all your family members, including grandparents, aunts, uncles, and cousins.

## **Problem Solving: Using Probability and Statistics** *(pages 374–375)*

*Use the pictograph on page 374.*

| Find the mean length of the 5 longest bridges. | Mean = (Number of ● × 4,000) ÷ 5 |
|---|---|
| | $= (32\frac{1}{2} \times 4{,}000) \div 5$ |
| | = 26,000 m |

**1.** Find the mean length of the 3 shortest bridges.

*For the card selections described on page 374, find the probabilities.*

**2.** P (1st member gets one of the 3 longest and 2nd gets the shortest)

**3.** P (1st gets one of the 3 longest or a San Mateo-Hayward bridge)

**4.** P (1st and 2nd and 3rd get the shortest)

**5.** P (1st gets one of the 2 longest and 2nd gets a San Mateo- Hayward bridge)

Make a pictograph to show the populations of five neighboring towns of your choice.

## **Problem Solving: Using Sampling** *(pages 376–377)*

When polled, 162 members of a sample of 300 said they would vote for Ms. Landis for representative. If 165,000 people are expected to vote, how many will vote for Ms. Landis?

$\frac{\text{Sample for Landis}}{\text{Total sample}} = \frac{162}{300} = .54$

Expected vote for Landis = Sample part for Landis × Number of voters

= .54 × 165,000 = 89,100

1. If 52 people in a sample of 200 agree with a statement, how many in the entire group of 100,000 that the sample represents would be predicted to agree with the statement?

2. Would 5 straight rainy days cause you to question the truth of the statement "For each day this month, P (rain) = .30"? (Consider probabilities <.001 as questionable.)

3. If you decide to question the fairness of a number cube when a statement with probability less than .001 is true, how many 4's in a row $\left(P(4) = \frac{1}{6}\right)$ would you *accept* without questioning?

Think of one yes or no question you'd like your town's opinion on. Ask a sample of the total town and then find how many of the total town would have that opinion.

## **Problem Solving: Interpreting Information** *(pages 378–379)*

A shirt at Store A was on sale at "15% off" the regular price of $18.40. At Store B the same shirt was on sale at "35% off" the regular price of $24.60. Where was the better buy?

A: Sale Price = 18.40 − (.15 × 18.40)
= $15.64

B: Sale price = 24.60 − (.35 × 24.60)
= $15.99

Better buy at Store A.

1. How does a store hope you will interpret the advertisement "Our prices are 20% less"? What less strong statement about prices could this mean?

2. Who had the higher bowling score? Player I who bowled 35% over an average of 160. Player II who bowled 30% over an average of 170.

3. The cost of Product A is 200% of its cost 15 years ago. The cost of Product B has increased 150% in that time. Which product had the greater rate of increase?

4. One stock purchased for $20 per share increased to $25 per share. One bought at $30 per share increased to $36. Which had the greater rate of increase?

Find two stores each selling the same product at a discount. Calculate which of the stores is offering the better buy.

# UNIT 11 Coordinate Graphing

## The Real Number Plane *(pages 390–391)*

*Give the point named by each ordered pair.*

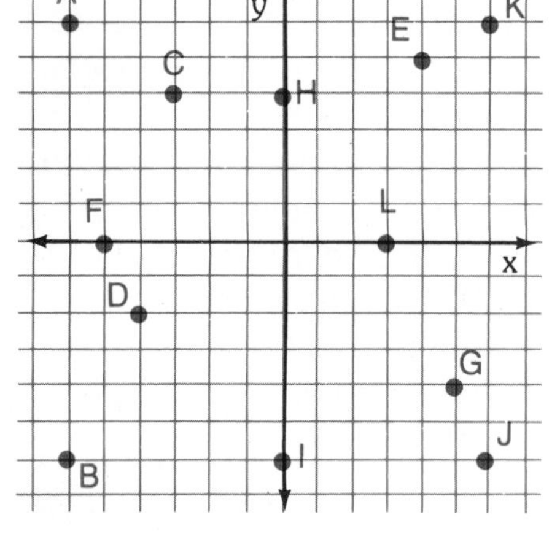


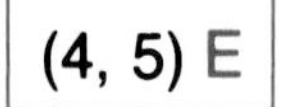


**1.** $(^-4, ^-2)$ **2.** $(6, ^-6)$

**3.** $(0, 4)$ **4.** $(^-6, 6)$ **5.** $(^-5, 0)$

*Give the coordinates of each point.*

L (3, 0) **6.** G **7.** C

**8.** I **9.** B **10.** K

*Use grid paper to draw a coordinate system. Graph and label each point.*

**11.** A $(4, 0)$ **12.** B $(^-4, 6)$ **13.** C $(4, 6)$ **14.** D $(^-4, 0)$

**15.** E $(^-6, 4)$ **16.** F $(0, ^-4)$ **17.** G $(^-4, ^-6)$ **18.** H $(4, ^-6)$

Draw a coordinate grid. Place four points in each quadrant. Then give the coordinates of each point.

## Algebra: Graphing Equations in Two Variables *(pages 392–393)*

*Graph each equation.*
*Use these values of x: $^-4$, $^-2$, 0, 2, 4*

$y = 2 - x$

| x | $y = 2 - x$ |
|---|---|
| $^-4$ | 6 |
| $^-2$ | 4 |
| 0 | 2 |
| 2 | 0 |
| 4 | $^-2$ |

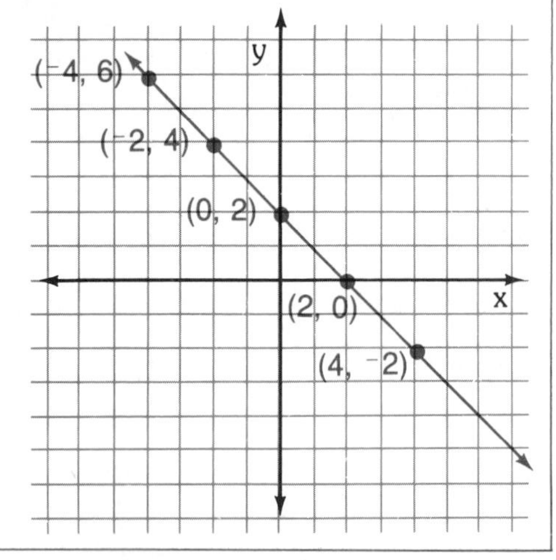


**1.** $y = x + 3$ **2.** $y = 4x$ **3.** $y = {}^-2x - 3$ **4.** $y = 2x - 4$

**5.** $y = 4 + 2x$ **6.** $y = x - 4$ **7.** $y = {}^-4x$ **8.** $y = 1 - 2x$

**9.** $y = 3x$ **10.** $y = {}^-x + 1$ **11.** $y = 2x + 1$ **12.** $y = 3x + 2$

Write your own equation with two variables. Graph the equation using your own values for the variables.

## Algebra: More Graphing Equations in Two Variables *(pages 394–395)*

*Find three solutions for each equation. Graph the equations.*

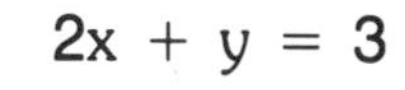

$2x + y = 3$

$2 \cdot 1 + y = 3$
$y = 3 - 2$
$y = 1$
*Solution:* (1, 1)

$2 \cdot 4 + y = 3$
$y = 3 - 8$
$y = {}^-5$
*Solution:* (4, $^-5$)

| x | y |
|---|---|
| 1 | 1 |
| 4 | $^-5$ |
| $^-2$ | 7 |

$2 \cdot {}^-2 + y = 3$
$^-4 + y = 3$
$y = 3 - {}^-4$
$y = 7$
*Solution:* ($^-4$, 7)

1. $x + y = 6$
2. $2x - y = 6$
3. $3x + 2y = 6$
4. $^-5x + y = 0$
5. $^-3x + y = 6$
6. $5x - y = {}^-10$
7. $x - 2y = 4$
8. $y = {}^-2x + 2$
9. $y = 3x + 4$

Write your own equation. Find four solutions. Graph the results.

## Problem Solving: Using Graphs *(pages 396–397)*

*Use the graph on page 397. Find the length of the bar when the temperature:*

is $^-20$°C. ($^-20$, 9998) is on the graph.
Length is 9,998 mm.

1. is 40°C
2. is $^-40$°C
3. is $^-35$°C

*Find the temperature if the bar has length:*

4. 9,999 mm
5. 10,002.5 mm
6. 1,000.5 mm

*Write an equation. Find three solutions. Graph the equation. Find five more solutions.*

7. Four times a number (x) is 5 less than another number (y).
8. The difference of twice a number (x) and another number (y) is zero.

Write a problem similar to exercise 7. Have another person in your class write and graph the equation.

## **Algebra: Solving Systems of Equations by Graphing** *(pages 398–399)*

*Solve each system of equations.*

$2x + y = 6$
$3x - y = {}^-1$

$2x + y = 6$

| x | y |
|---|---|
| 0 | 6 |
| 2 | 2 |
| 4 | $^-2$ |

$3x - y = {}^-1$

| x | y |
|---|---|
| 2 | 7 |
| 0 | 1 |
| $^-2$ | $^-5$ |

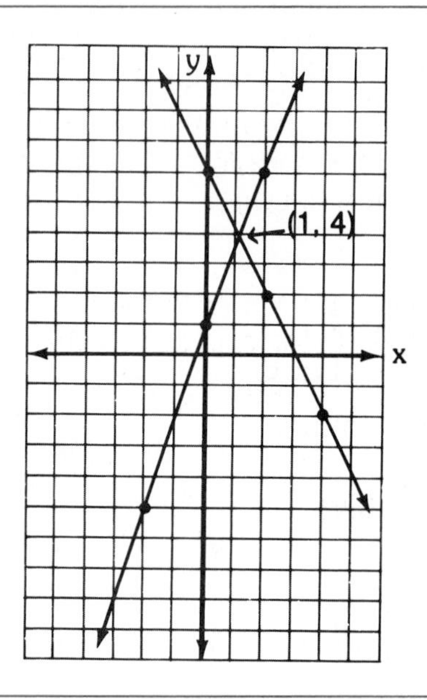


The point of intersection of the graphs is (1, 4).

*Solution of the system:* (1, 4)

**1.** $x + y = 7$
$x - y = 1$

**2.** $y = x + 7$
$y = {}^-2x - 2$

**3.** $2x - y = 4$
$^-x + 2y = 4$

**4.** $4x + y = 0$
$x + y = 3$

**5.** $x + 3y = {}^-18$
$^-2x + y = 1$

**6.** $x + y = 0$
$2x + y = 5$

Make up your own system of equations in which the ordered pair is a solution of each equation. Graph the equations on one coordinate grid and find the point of intersection.

## **Problem Solving: Using Systems of Equations** *(pages 400–401)*

*Twice a first number (x) is 7 greater than a second number (y). The sum of the two numbers is 8.*

Write two equations. $2x - y = 7$
$x + y = 8$

**1.** Solve this system of equations. Use graphs.

*The perimeter of a rectangle is 60 meters. It is four times as long as it is wide.*

**2.** Write an equation for the perimeter. (Use y for length and x for width.)

**3.** Write an equation that gives the relation of the length and width.

**4.** Draw the graphs of these equations. Find the solution of this system of two equations.

**5.** Use the solution of the system to give the length and width of the rectangle.

Using the perimeter of something in your home, complete exercises 2–5.

## Unit 1 Use Logical Reasoning *(page 39)*

A man with a valuable gold chain, but no money, arrived at a hotel. He agreed to pay 1 link of the chain each morning for the previous night's lodging. The manager agreed to use links he had been given as change. Since the man intends to return to redeem his chain and restore it to one piece, he wants to cut as few links as possible. The first night he cut the 3rd link for the next morning's payment.

*Solve.*

1. The 2nd link the man should cut is the 9th link. Copy and complete the table for the payments with the 6 new links.

2. What is the 3rd link the man should cut? How many nights in all can he stay with the links from the 3 cuts?

| Day (d) | Give | Get | Have Left |
|---|---|---|---|
| 0 | | | |
| 1 | a 1-link | 0 | a 2-link |
| 2 | a 2-link | a 1-link | a 1-link |
| 3 | a 1-link | 0 | 0 |
| 4 | a 1-link | 0 | a 5-link |

**Cut**

3rd link

9th link

3. What is the 4th link the man should cut? How many nights in all can he stay with the links from the 4 cuts?

4. Look for a pattern. Find the 5th link the man should cut. How many nights in all can he stay?

## Unit 2 Draw a Diagram *(page 69)* *Draw diagrams to solve these problems.*

1. Vinnie and Amy leave the stable at the same time on horseback. Vinnie rides 8 km west, 5 km south, 3 km west, 2 km north, 6 km east, and 1 km north. Then he stops to rest. Amy rides 9 km south, 3 km east, 1 km south, 5 km west, and 8 km north. How far and in what direction must Amy ride to meet Vinnie?

2. Larry finished a race 1 second ahead of Maureen. Maureen was not last. Beth finished 7 seconds ahead of Henry. Henry's time was 3 seconds longer than Larry's. Dave finished 5 seconds ahead of Larry. List the finish order and tell how many seconds separated each runner from the person just behind.

3. Mrs. Melendes has a rectangular-shaped garden. There are 8 equally-spaced fence posts along each end and 16 equally-spaced fence posts along each side. How many fence posts are there in all?

4. A shark was caught off the coast of Florida. The report described the shark as follows: "The shark is 420 cm long. Its tail is twice as long as its head. Its body is as long as its head plus its tail." How long was each part of the shark?

## Unit 3 Make a Table *(page 107)* *Make tables to solve these problems.*

1. Tony is filling two empty tanks with water. He begins to fill Tank A 4 min before he begins to fill Tank B. Tank A fills at the rate of 700 L per min and Tank B fills at the rate of 1,100 L per min. How long after Tony begins filling Tank B will the two tanks contain the same amount of water?

2. In the first month of publication, *Career* magazine's circulation was 18,500 copies and *Data World* magazine's circulation was 11,000 copies. Each month after that, *Career's* circulation dropped by 400 copies and *Data World*'s increased by 350. How many months did it take before both magazines had the same circulation?

3. A car and a bus start from the same point and ride along the same road. The bus starts first and goes 90 km before the car starts. Including rest stops, the bus averages 66 km per hour and the car averages 81 km per hour. How many hours will it take the car to be 30 km ahead of the bus?

4. In January 1975, Kay began working at an annual salary of $9,000 and Terry began working at an annual salary of $11,000. Kay received a $750 raise every 6 months and Terry received a yearly raise of $1,200. Who was earning more money in January 1986? How much more?

## Unit 4 Mixed Strategies *(page 141)* *Solve.*

1. Alan, Brenda, and Chris weighed themselves two at a time. Alan and Brenda weighed 238 pounds together. Alan and Chris weighed 244 pounds, and Brenda and Chris weighed 222 pounds. How much does each person weigh?

2. It is the year 2110. The population of Alphaville is 129,500 and the population of Beta City is 115,000. Each year, Beta City has a net increase in population of 800 and Alphaville has a net decrease of 650. In what year will the population of both places be equal?

3. Perry is 4 years older than Jan. Lucy is 6 years younger than Perry. Sylvia is 26, 8 years older than Jan. Eric's age is the average of Lucy's age and Perry's age. Ann is as old as Lucy and Jan combined. Ruth's age is midway between Sylvia's and Ann's. List everyone's ages in order from youngest to oldest.

4. The music school is open Monday through Saturday. Classes in piano and guitar are given each day. Instruction on drums is offered every other day starting Monday, and there are violin classes every other day beginning Tuesday. Voice lessons are offered daily from Tuesday on. On which day are the fewest classes offered?

## Unit 5 Work a Simpler Problem *(page 179)*

*Solve.*

1. The local train made 16 stops before arriving at Union Station. It picked up two passengers at the first stop, four at the second stop, six at the third stop, and so on. If none of the passengers got off the train, how many of them arrived at Union Station?

2. There are 256 chess players in a tournament. If each two-person game results in one winner, how many games must be played to determine the tournament champion? In another tournament, it took 63 games to determine the champion. How many players took part?

3. Find the sum of the even integers from 2 to 250. Can you give a general rule? Find the sum of the odd integers from 1 to 249. Can you give a general rule?

4. How many squares are there on an 8 x 8 checkerboard? (Squares can be of different sizes, and one square may overlap another.)

## Unit 6 Logical Reasoning with Clues *(page 56)*

*Solve.*

1. Phil, Quentin, Randy, and Sheila play in a band. One plays piano, one plays guitar, one plays drums, and one plays trumpet. They each have a different hair color: red, blond, gray, and brown. Use the clues to find each person's instrument and hair color.

   1. Phil does not play guitar or trumpet.
   2. Randy has blond hair.
   3. Sheila plays the heaviest instrument.
   4. The guitarist has brown hair.
   5. Phil has red hair.

2. Alice, Barry, Cindy, Dan, and Ella are in the same mathematics class. Their last names are Ames, Boyd, Cruz, Davis, and Estes, although not necessarily in that order. Each student received a grade of A, B, C, D, or E on a quiz. No two students received the same grade. Use the clues below to find each student's last name and grade.

   1. Nobody's first and last initial are the same.
   2. Nobody's grade and first initial are the same.
   3. Barry and Ella got the highest grades.
   4. Cindy studies with Boyd and Estes.
   5. Dan got two grades higher than Alice.
   6. Alice's last name is Davis.
   7. Cruz and Ella wished they had gotten an A.

## Unit 7 Guess and Check *(page 261) Solve.*

1. The Lions beat the Bears by 22 points. If the Bears had scored twice as many points, they would have beaten the Lions by 3 points. How many points did each team score?

2. On Sunday, there were 145 more people at the game than on Saturday. If Saturday's attendance were doubled and 110 were subtracted from the number, the result would be Sunday's attendance. How many people were at the game each day?

3. Tracy's math book has half as many pages as her history book. Her literature book has one and a half times as many pages as her history book. All together, the three books have 1,290 pages. How many pages does each book have?

4. A portable television costs twice as much as a tape player. A video recorder costs as much as the television and tape player together. All three items together cost $630. How much does each item cost?

## Unit 8 Mixed Strategies *(page 299) Solve.*

1. The sum of the digits of a two-digit number is 14. If 18 is subtracted from the number, the result is the number with the digits reversed. Find the original number.

2. A group of campers in a van traveled 2,100 miles in one week. Each day they rode 45 miles more than the previous day. How many miles did they travel each day?

3. Harry, Gary, and Larry entertain at birthday parties. One dances, another sings, and another is a comedian. The comedian, who has his own car and carries no passengers, is the tallest. Gary, who rides in Larry's car, is taller than the singer. Who does what?

4. In a basketball league, each team plays every other team exactly once. If there are 10 teams in the league, how many games are played? Suppose the following year, each of the 10 teams plays every other team twice. How many games are played?

5. A hotel manager is setting up tables for a large dinner party. The tables are square and seat two people on each side. The tables are placed end-to-end to form one long table. How many tables are needed to seat 104 guests? If 30 tables are used and there are no empty seats, how many guests were at the party?

6. Jena needs to take her cat, her dog, and a large sack of dog food across a river. She can swim across, but she can only carry one item at a time. She cannot leave the dog alone with the cat, or the dog alone with the food. How can Jena get them all across the river in the fewest number of trips?

## Unit 9 Make a Model *(page 345)*

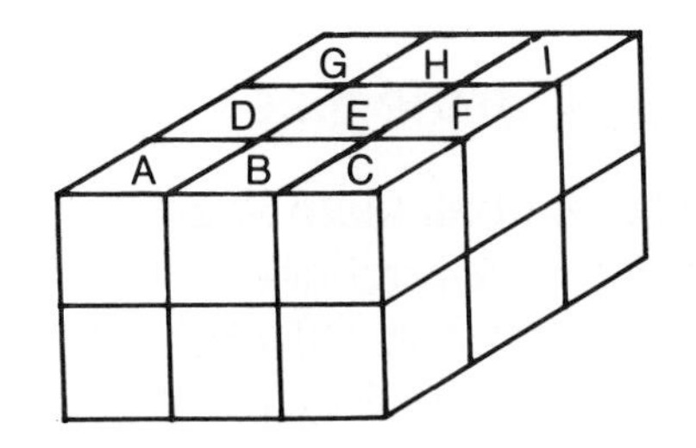


*Solve.*

The solid shown at the right is made up of 1-cm cubes.

1. What is the surface area of the solid?
2. What is the surface area of the remaining solid if just cube A is removed?
3. What is the surface area of the remaining solid if just cube E is removed?
4. What is the surface area of the remaining solid if just cube B is removed?
5. What is the surface area of the remaining solid if cubes B and E are removed?
6. Suppose you remove cubes A and B. Then you remove one more cube. The surface area of the remaining solid is 40 $cm^2$. Which was the third cube you removed?

## Unit 10 Make an Organized List *(page 381)*

*Solve.*

| CARL'S CLOTHES | | | |
|---|---|---|---|
| gloves | \$3.95 | mufflers | \$3.75 |
| hats | \$4.00 | socks | \$2.25 |
| belts | \$4.50 | (prices include tax) | |

1. Luke wants to buy 3 different items at Carl's Clothes. He has \$12. How many different groups of 3 items can he choose?
2. What is the most expensive group of 4 items Jake can buy if he has \$15?
3. A record shop, dress shop, laundromat, and pharmacy want to rent stores side by side along Main Street. All the stores are the same size. However, the record shop does not want to be located next to the laundromat. How many different arrangements are possible?
4. Fred, Glenda, Hal, and Irene are standing in line. How many different arrangements are possible? How many different ways can they line up if boys and girls must alternate? How many arrangements are possible if there are 3 boys and 3 girls and they must alternate?

## Unit 11 Mixed Strategies *(page 403)* *Solve.*

1. A school basketball team needs new bats and new catcher's gloves. Each bat costs $15 and each glove costs $28. The team has $200 to spend on new equipment. How many of each item can the team buy if they spend all their money?

2. Adams, Brandt, and Colson work for a publishing company. One is sales manager, one is publicity manager, and one is editorial manager. If Colson is publicity, then Brandt is editorial. If Colson is editorial, then Brandt is sales. If Brandt is not publicity, then Adams is editorial. If Adams is sales, then Colson is editorial. What is each person's job?

3. Fred has some pennies, nickels, and dimes that total 47¢ in all. If he has 17 coins, how many of each coin does he have?

4. A large cube, 10 cm by 10 cm by 10 cm, is made up entirely of 1-cm cubes. The large cube is divided into two new solids, each 5 cm by 10 cm by 10 cm. What is the percentage increase in total surface area of the new solids from that of the original large cube?

5. Lynn had cardboard squares in each of the following colors: orange, red, white, blue, green, yellow, purple. She cut the squares in half, then rearranged the pieces to make new, two-color squares. How many different squares could she create? (Note that a red-blue square is different from a blue-red square.)

6. Use the dart board shown below. Suppose that a player throws three darts, all of which hit the board. How many different scores are possible?

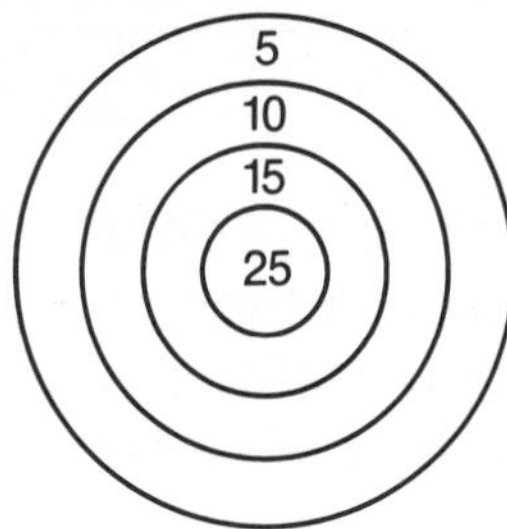


7. Three points are non-colinear if they do not lie on the same line. How many lines are determined by 3 non-colinear points? by 4 points, no three of which are colinear? by 20 points, no three of which are colinear? Can you find a general rule for *n* points?

8. Use the rule from problem 7. How many points, no three of which are colinear, are needed to determine 666 lines?

# Tables of Measure

## METRIC UNITS

**Prefixes**

*milli* means 0.001
*centi* means 0.01
*deci* means 0.1
*deka* means 10
*hecto* means 100
*kilo* means 1,000

**Length**

1 millimeter (mm) = 0.001 meter (m)
1 centimeter (cm) = 0.01 meter
1 decimeter (dm) = 0.1 meter
1 kilometer (km) = 1,000 meters

**Liquid Volume**

1 liter (L) = 1,000 milliliters (mL)
1 kiloliter (kL) = 1,000 liters

**Mass**

1 milligram (mg) = 0.001 gram (g)
1 kilogram (kg) = 1,000 grams
1 metric ton (t) = 1,000 kilograms

## CUSTOMARY UNITS

**Length**

1 foot (ft) = 12 inches (in.)
1 yard (yd) = 3 feet
1 mile (mi) = 1,760 yards = 5,280 feet

**Liquid Volume**

1 cup (c) = 8 fluid ounces (fl oz)
1 pint (pt) = 2 cups
1 quart (qt) = 2 pints
1 gallon (gal) = 4 quarts

**Weight**

1 pound (lb) = 16 ounces (oz)
1 ton (tn) = 2,000 pounds

## METRIC AND CUSTOMARY UNITS

**Time**

1 minute (min) = 60 seconds (s)
1 hour (h) = 60 minutes
1 day (d) = 24 hours
1 week (wk) = 7 days
1 year (yr) = 12 months (mo) = 52 weeks
1 century (cen) = 100 years

# Formulas

## PERIMETER AND CIRCUMFERENCE

**Rectangle** $P = 2\ell + 2w$
**Parallelogram** $P = 2a + 2b$
**Regular polygon** (n-sided) $P = ns$
**Circle** $C = \pi d = 2\pi r$ ($\pi \doteq 3.14 \doteq 3\frac{1}{7}$)

## AREA

**Rectangle** $A = \ell w$
**Square** $A = s^2$
**Parallelogram** $A = bh$
**Triangle** $A = \frac{1}{2}bh$
**Circle** $C = \pi r^2$ ($\pi \doteq 3.14 \doteq 3\frac{1}{7}$)

## VOLUME

**Prism** $V = Bh$
**Cylinder** $V = Bh$
**Pyramid** $V = \frac{1}{3}Bh$
**Cone** $V = \frac{1}{3}Bh$
**Sphere** $V = \frac{4}{3}\pi r^3$ ($\pi \doteq 3.14 \doteq 3\frac{1}{7}$)

## SURFACE AREA

**Prism** $S = 2B + Ph$
**Cylinder** $S = 2B + Ch$
**Pyramid** $S = B + \frac{1}{2}P\ell$
**Cone** $S = B + \frac{1}{2}C\ell$
**Sphere** $S = 4\pi r^2$ ($\pi \doteq 3.14 \doteq 3\frac{1}{7}$)

# Estimation Strategies

| Strategy | Examples |
|---|---|
| **1. Rounding** | $74.92 + 8.3$: 74.92 → about 75; 8.3 → about 8. The sum is about 83. |
| | $439.83 - 24.1$: 439.83 → about 440; 24.1 → about 24. The difference is about 416. |
| **2. Comparison** | $589.83 - 203.007$: less than 600; more than 200. The difference is a little less than 400. |
| **3. Clustering** | $15\frac{5}{7} + 18\frac{2}{3} + 4\frac{1}{8} + 21\frac{1}{2}$: about 20; about 40. The sum is about 60. |
| **4. Compatible Numbers** | $809.32 \div .917 = \blacksquare$<br>$809,320. \div .917.$<br>close to 810,000; close to 900<br>810,0~~00~~ ÷ 9~~00~~ = 900<br>The quotient is about 900. |
| **5. Reasonable in Context** | A record album is about .3 cm thick. If 150 albums are stacked on a shelf, how thick is the stack?<br>**a.** 147 cm **b.** 45 cm<br>**c.** 500 cm **d.** 4.5 cm<br>.3 cm for 1 album<br>almost 1 cm for 3 albums<br>almost 50 cm for 150 albums<br>Answer **b.** is reasonable. |

# Mental Math Strategies

| Method | Examples |
|---|---|
| 1. Work from left to right. | 437.34<br>+ 572.59<br>900 + 100 + 9 + .8 + .13<br>1000 + 9 + .93 = 1,009.93<br>The sum is 1,009.93. |
| 2. Start with the first number and add or subtract from left to right. | 43.19 + 8.6 = ■<br>43.19 + 8 = 51.19<br>51.19 + .6 = 51.79<br>The sum is 51.79. |
| | 339.57 − 37.39 = ■<br>339.57 − 30 = 309.57<br>309.57 − 7 = 302.57<br>302.57 − .3 = 302.27<br>302.27 − .09 = 302.18<br>The difference is 302.18. |
| 3. Compensate: Add to or subtract from the given numbers to work with easier numbers. (In subtraction make the bottom number the easy number.) | 139.11 − .08 = 139.03<br>+ 29.92 + .08 = 30.00<br>169.03<br>The sum is 169.03. |
| | 39.3 + .7 = 40.0<br>− 24.9 + .7 = 25.6<br>14.4<br>The difference is 14.4. |
| 4. Use the distributive property. | 5 × 3.95 = ■<br>3.95 is 4 − .05.<br>5 × 4 = 20<br>5 × .05 = .25<br>20 − .25 = 19.75<br>The product is 19.75. |
| | 25)8.75<br>8.75 is 8.00 + .75.<br>8.00 ÷ 25 = .32<br>.75 ÷ 25 = .03<br>.32 + .03 = .35<br>The quotient is .35. |

# Glossary

**Addition** An operation on two numbers that tells how many or how much in all.

$$\begin{array}{r} 26 \\ +17 \\ \hline 43 \end{array} \begin{array}{l} \leftarrow \text{addends} \\ \leftarrow \text{sum} \end{array} \qquad 1.2 + 3.64 = 4.84$$

(1.2 and 3.64: addends; 4.84: sum)

*Properties* of addition are:

$x + y = y + x$ *(Commutative Property)*
$(x + y) + z = x + (y + z)$ *(Associative Property)*
$x + 0 = 0 + x = x$ *(Property of Zero)*

Addition is related to subtraction by:

$$(x + y) - y = x$$

The addends are rounded to *estimate* sums.

$$\begin{array}{rcr} 3{,}496 & \rightarrow & 3{,}500 \\ +\ \ 817 & \rightarrow & +\ \ 800 \\ \hline & & 4{,}300 \end{array} \leftarrow \text{Estimate of the sum}$$

**Algebraic Expressions and Sentences** An algebraic expression is formed using numerals, symbols for operations, and *variables*. For the *value* 3 of x and the value of .5 of y the *value of the expression:*

$6 \cdot (.4x + 2) + 8y$ is $6 \times (.4 \times 3 + 2) + 8 \times .5 = 23.2$

An algebraic sentence is formed by joining two algebraic expressions by a symbol for a relation ($>, <, =, \geq, \leq$). A *solution* of an algebraic sentence is a value of its variable or a set of values for its variables that gives a true statement. To *solve* a sentence means to find all of its solutions.

Sentence: $2y + 3 = 15$ Solution: 6

Sentence: $t \leq 7$ Solution: 7 and all numbers less than 7.

A *simultaneous solution* of a *system of equations* is a solution of each equation in the system.

Equations: $2x + y = 9$, $3x - y = 11$ Simultaneous solution $(x, y) : (4, 1)$

**Angle** A figure formed by two rays (*sides*) with the same endpoint (*vertex*): $\overrightarrow{AB}$ and $\overrightarrow{AC}$ form $\angle$ BAC. A common unit used to measure angles is the *degree* (°). Angles are classified as *acute* (measure $<90°$), *right* (measure $= 90°$), *obtuse* (measure $>90°$ but $<180°$), and *straight* (measure $= 180°$). *Supplementary* angles (2 angles) have 180° as the sum of their measures. *Complementary* angles (2 angles) have 90° as the sum of their measures. $\overrightarrow{AD}$ is the *bisector* of $\angle$ BAC if $\angle BAD \cong \angle DAC$.

**Area** The number of unit squares that will fit inside a figure.

**Arithmetic Expressions and Sentences** An arithmetic expression is a name for a number formed using numerals and symbols for operations. To *simplify* an expression means to find the standard numeral for the number it names by working inside parentheses first, then working left-to-right, doing all multiplications and divisions, and then all additions and subtractions.

$(\mathbf{3} + \mathbf{9}) \times 5 \div 6 - 2 = \mathbf{12} \times \mathbf{5} \div 6 - 2$
$= \mathbf{60} \div \mathbf{6} - 2 = \mathbf{10} - \mathbf{2} = 8$

An arithmetic sentence is formed by joining two expressions by a symbol for a relation ($>, <, =, \geq, \leq, \neq$). Sentences can make true statements or false statements.

$8 + 7 \neq 15$ (false) $\qquad 5 \cdot 4 \geq 40 \div 2$ (true)

**Circle** All points in a plane that are the same distance from a point form a circle with the given point as *center.*

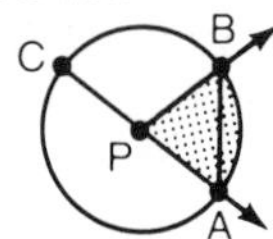


*Center*: P *Radii*: $\overline{PA}$, $\overline{PB}$, $\overline{PC}$
Chords: $\overline{AB}$, $\overline{AC}$ *Diameter*: $\overline{AC}$
$\angle$ APB is a *central angle*

The shaded region is a *sector.* The edge of the shaded region is an *arc*. The *circumference* of a circle is its length.

**Clock Time** Reports of time using a 12-hour or a 24-hour clock:

| | | |
|---|---|---|
| 12-h clock: | 9:30 A.M. | 9:30 P.M. |
| 24-h clock: | 0930 | 2130 |

**Common Denominator** Two fractions with the same denominator have a *common denominator.* The *least common denominator (LCD)* for two fractions is the *least common multiple (LCM)* of their denominators.

**Computer Literacy** Knowledge of what computers can and cannot do, how computers operate, how to communicate with computers, and how to use computers to solve problems. Ability to use, write, and edit computer programs in one or more higher-order computer languages (such as BASIC).

**Cone** A closed solid figure with one *curved face* and one *flat face*. Its *base* is bounded by a circle and its *vertex* is directly above the center of its base.

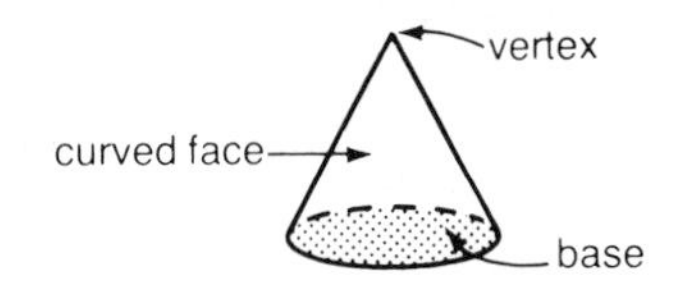

**Congruent** Figures that would fit exactly on each other are congruent. Two line segments or angles that have equal measures are congruent. Two triangles are congruent if they have these three pairs of congruent *corresponding parts:*

2 sides and the angle between them.
2 angles and the side between them.
3 sides.

**Coordinate System** Two perpendicular *real number lines* that determine an *ordered pair* of real numbers to name each point of a *real number plane.*

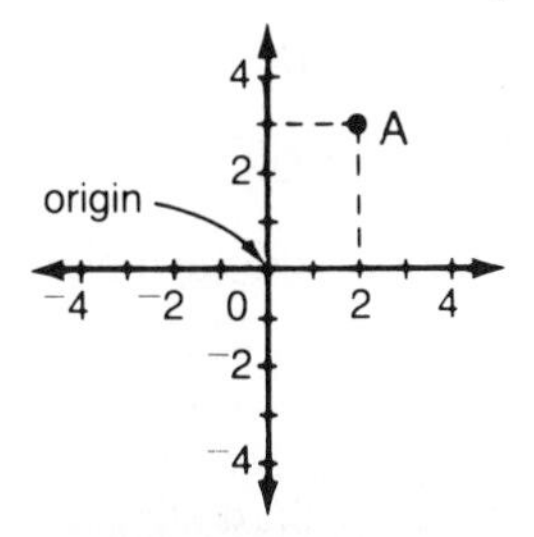


(2, 3) is the *set of coordinates* of A. A is the *graph* of (2, 3). The *graph of a sentence* with two variables contains all graphs of its solutions.

**Customary Measurement System** The traditional system of measurement used in the United States. Customary units of length, liquid volume or capacity, weight, and time are given in *Tables of Measures* page *447*. Customary units of area are the *square inch* ($in.^2$), the *square foot* ($ft^2$), the *square yard* ($yd^2$), and the *square mile* ($mi^2$). Customary units of volume are the *cubic inch* ($in.^3$), the *cubic foot* ($ft^3$), and the *cubic yard* ($yd^3$). The customary unit of temperature is the *degree Fahrenheit* (°F).

**Cylinder** A closed solid figure with one curved face and two flat faces. Its bases are bounded by circles having radii of equal lengths. The center of one base is directly above the center of the other.

**Decimal** A name for a number formed using *digits* selected from 0, 1, 2, ..., 9, a *place value system,* and a *decimal point.* A *place value table* for decimals is shown below.

| Ones | Tenths | Hundredths | Thousandths | Ten-thousandths | Hundred-thousandths | Millionths |
|---|---|---|---|---|---|---|
| 1. | 2 | 3 | 4 | 5 | 6 | 7 |

decimal point

Every fraction is equivalent to a *terminating decimal* ($\frac{1}{4}$ = .25) or to a *repeating decimal* ($\frac{1}{3}$ = .333 ... = $.\overline{3}$).

**Distance** The distance between two points is the length of the straight path joining the points.

**Distributive Properties** Multiplication has distributive properties with respect to addition and subtraction:

$$x \cdot (y + z) = (x \cdot y) + (x \cdot z)$$
$$(y + z) \cdot x = (y \cdot x) + (z \cdot x)$$
$$x \cdot (y - z) = (x \cdot y) - (x \cdot z)$$
$$(y - z) \cdot x = (y \cdot x) - (z \cdot x)$$

**Division** An operation on two numbers that tells how many sets of the same size can be formed from a given set and how many objects will be left over. It also tells the greatest number per set and the number left over when a given number of sets of the same size are formed from a set that is given.

*quotient* → 7R1 ← *remainder* **or** *quotient* → $7\frac{1}{5}$
*divisor* → 5 )36 ← *dividend* 5 )36

0 cannot be used as a divisor. For non-zero divisors:

$$0 \div x = 0 \qquad x \div x = 1$$

Division is related to multiplication by:

$$(x \div y) \cdot y = x$$

Quotients of whole numbers can be *estimated* by determining one non-zero digit and writing 0's for the other digits.

210R113 ← exact    **200** ← estimate
236 )49,673    236 )49,673

**Estimation** Numbers are estimated by rounding them to any place. Rounded numbers are used to estimate results of computations.

**Exponent** For any integer n greater than 1:

exponent → n factors
base → $x^n = x \cdot x \cdot \ldots \cdot x$ = $n^{th}$ *power of x*
$x^1 = x$

For $x > 0$

$$x^0 = 1 \qquad x^{-1} = \frac{1}{x} \qquad x^{-n} = \frac{1}{x^n}$$

**Factor** For whole numbers a, b, and c, if $a = b \cdot c$, then b and c are factors of a. A number that is a factor of two or more numbers is a *common factor* of the numbers. The largest common factor of two or more numbers is their *greatest common factor (GCF).*

**Fraction** A symbol such as $\frac{1}{2}$, $\frac{3}{4}$, or $\frac{11}{9}$ that names part of an object or set, or the quotient of two whole numbers (a *fractional number*).

*numerator* → 2 ← 2 pieces in the part named
*denominator* → 3 ← 3 pieces in the set or object

$$\frac{4}{5} = 4 \div 5$$

*Equivalent fractions* name the same quantity. *Lowest terms fractions* have 1 as the greatest common factor of their numerator and denominator.

**Graph** A picture used to show data. This graph is a *bar graph.*

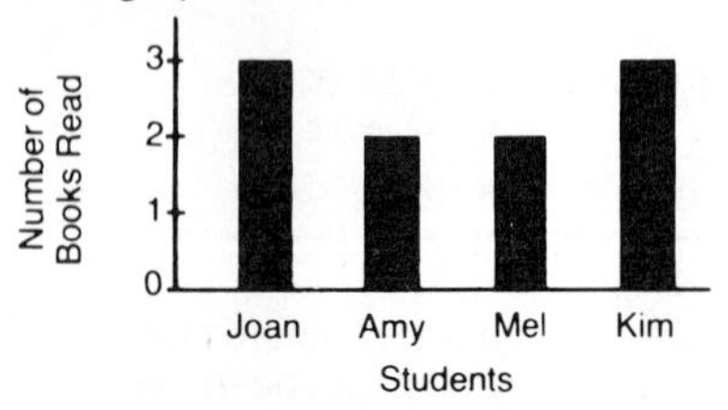


This is a *broken-line graph.*

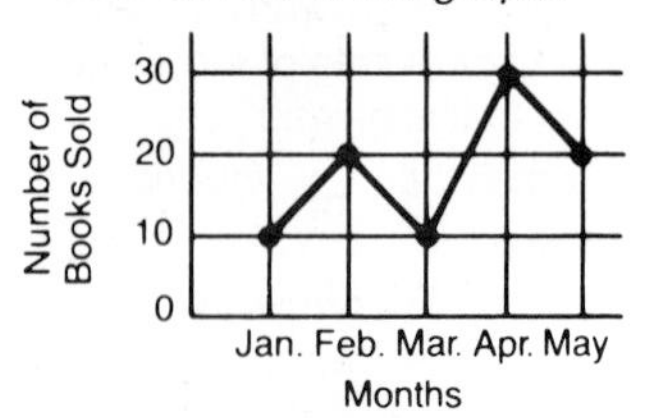


This is a *pictograph.*

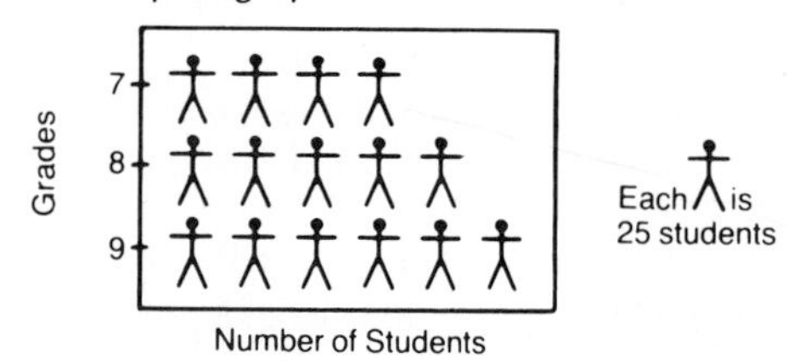


This is a *circle graph.*

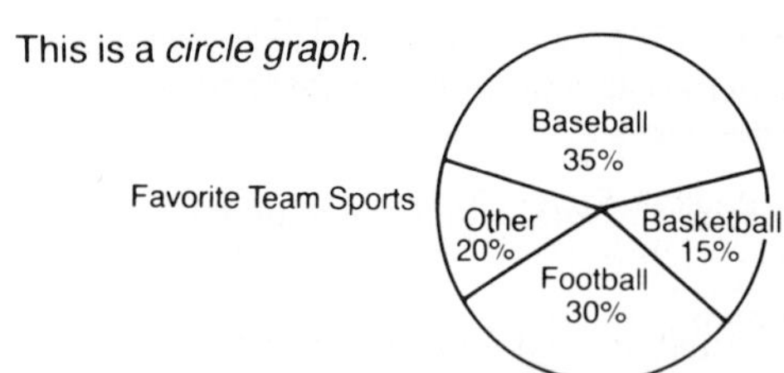


The *graph of an algebraic sentence* is the set of all points that are graphs of its solutions.

**Greater Than (>), Less Than (<)** Relations for comparing numbers. ($4.6 > 3.9$, $3.9 < 4.6$)

**Integer** Any of the numbers ..., $^{-}100$, ..., $^{-}2$, $^{-}1$, 0, $^{+}1$, $^{+}2$, ..., $^{+}100$, ... The numbers ..., $^{-}100$, ..., $^{-}2$, $^{-}1$ are *negative integers.* Non-zero whole numbers are *positive integers.* Zero is an integer that is neither positive nor negative. The *absolute value* of an integer is the distance on a number line from the point it names to the zero point. ($|^{+}4| = |^{-}4| = 4$). Two integers whose sum is 0 are *additive inverses* or *opposites* of each other. ($^{-}8 + {^{+}8} = 0$ so $^{-}8 = -\,{^{+}8}$ and $^{+}8 = -\,{^{-}8}$)

**Interest** Money paid for the use of money (the *principal*). *Compound interest* is automatically added to the principal when due.

Interest/period = rate/period × principal.

**Line (straight)** A straight path that "extends forever" in two directions.

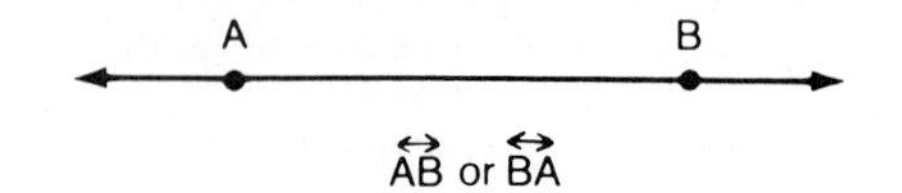


$\overleftrightarrow{AB}$ or $\overleftrightarrow{BA}$

*Intersecting lines* are lines that have a common point.

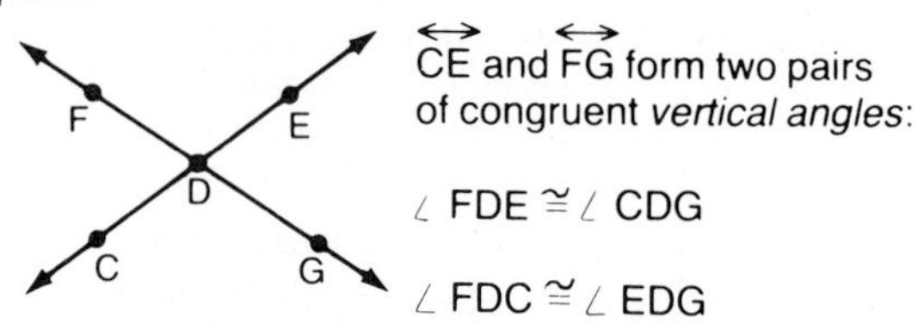


$\overleftrightarrow{CE}$ and $\overleftrightarrow{FG}$ form two pairs of congruent *vertical angles*:

$\angle FDE \cong \angle CDG$

$\angle FDC \cong \angle EDG$

*Perpendicular lines* form four right angles at their point of intersection.

*Parallel lines* are lines in a plane that do not intersect.

A *line of symmetry* of a figure separates the figure into two congruent parts.

**Line Segment** A straight path with two endpoints.

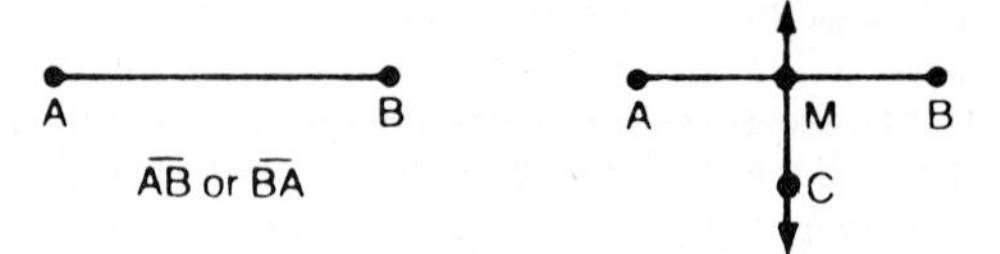


$\overline{AB}$ or $\overline{BA}$

If $\overline{AM} \cong \overline{MB}$, M is the *midpoint* of $\overline{AB}$. If $\overleftrightarrow{MC}$ is perpendicular to $\overline{AB}$, $\overleftrightarrow{MC}$ is the *perpendicular bisector* of $\overline{AB}$.

**Metric System of Measurement** A system of measurement used in almost all countries. Metric units of length, liquid volume or capacity, mass, and time are given in *Table of Measures* (page *447*). Metric units of area are the *square centimeter* ($cm^2$), the *square meter* ($m^2$), and the *square kilometer* ($km^2$). Metric units of volume are the *cubic centimeter* ($cm^3$), the *cubic decimeter* ($dm^3$), and the *cubic meter* ($m^3$). The metric unit of temperature is the *degree Celsius* (°C).

**Mixed Numeral** A numeral formed of a standard numeral for a whole number and a fraction. A *lowest terms mixed numeral* contains a lowest terms fraction less than 1.

*Mixed numerals:* $4\frac{2}{6} = 4 + \frac{2}{6}$ $5\frac{3}{2} = 5 + \frac{3}{2}$

*Lowest terms mixed numerals:* $4\frac{1}{3}$ $6\frac{1}{2}$

**Multiple** For whole numbers a, b, and c if $c = a \cdot b$, c is a multiple of both a and b. A number that is a multiple of each of two or more numbers is a *common multiple* of those numbers; the smallest common multiple is the *least common multiple* (*LCM*) of the numbers.

**Multiplication** An operation on two numbers that tells how many in all in a given number of sets of the same size. With measures, it tells the total measure of a number of objects of the same measure.

```
  28 ⟵ factors          .02 × .3 = .006
× 6  ⟵                    ↑    ↑     ↑
 168 ⟵ product           factors   product
```

*Properties* of multiplication are:

$x \cdot y = y \cdot x$ *(Commutative Property)*

$(x \cdot y) \cdot z = x \cdot (y \cdot z)$ *(Associative Property)*

$x \cdot 1 = 1 \cdot x = x$ *(Property of One)*

$x \cdot 0 = 0 \cdot x = 0$ *(Property of Zero)*

Multiplication is related to division by: $(x \cdot y) \div y = x$

The factors are rounded to *estimate* products.

```
  6,894 →      7,000
×    42 →   ×     40
            280,000 ⟵ estimate of
                       the product
```

**Number Line** A line with each point named by a real number is a *real number line.* Positive real numbers name the points of one ray; negative real numbers name the points of the other ray. 0 names the common endpoint of the rays.

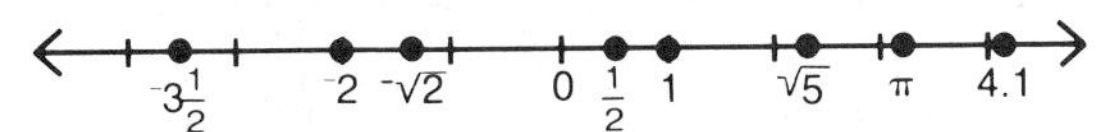


**Numeral** A symbol for a number.

*Standard numerals* 1, 42, $^-3$, $^-75$

*Decimals* .3, 7.96, $^-8.42$

*Fractions* $\frac{1}{2}, \frac{5}{8}, \frac{7}{3}, \frac{^-3}{5}$

*Mixed Numerals* $2\frac{1}{3}, 4\frac{2}{5}, {}^-7\frac{1}{2}$

**Parentheses** Symbols of grouping used to tell which operation is to be performed first. *Brackets* are also used as symbols of grouping.

$(3 + 4) \cdot 5 = 7 \cdot 5 = 35,$

while $3 + 4 \cdot 5 = 3 + 20 = 23$

$2 \cdot [15 - (9 + 3)] = 2 \cdot [15 - 12] = 2 \cdot 3 = 6$

**Percent (%)** A ratio in which the second number in the comparison is 100.

$4{:}100 = \frac{4}{100} = .04 = 4\%$

The *basic percent formula* is:

$r \cdot b = p \Longleftrightarrow$ *rate* of *base* is *part*

**Perimeter** The sum of the lengths of the sides of a polygon.

**Permutation, Combination** A permutation is an ordered set. A combination is an unordered set.

| Different permutations | Same combination. |
|---|---|
| 1. Pres. : John, V.P. : Maria | 1. Committee : Ed, Helen |
| 2. Pres. : Maria, V.P. : John | 2. Committee : Helen, Ed |

**Pi** (π) The ratio of the circumference to the length of a diameter of any circle. $\pi \doteq 3.14 \doteq 3\frac{1}{7}$.

**Plane** A flat figure that "extends forever" in all directions.

**Point** A "position without size or shape." Line segments, rays, lines, and planes are sets of points.

**Polygon** A closed plane figure formed by line segments *(sides).* The endpoints of its sides are *vertices* of the polygons. A polygon has only one inside.

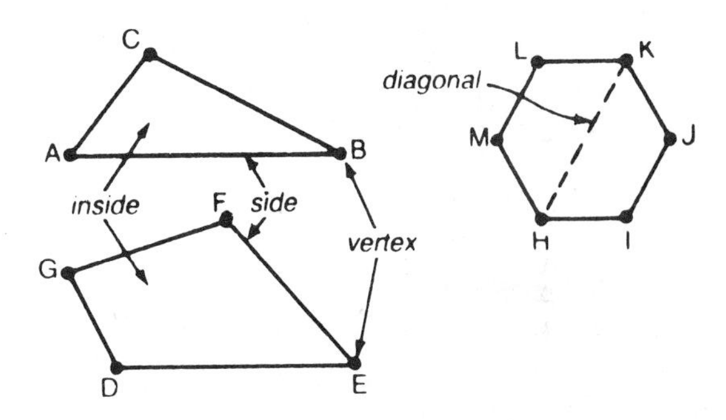


A *diagonal* of a polygon is a line segment that is not a side but has vertices as endpoints.

A *regular polygon* has all of its sides and all of its angles congruent.

*Triangles, quadrilaterals, pentagons, hexagons, octagons,* and *decagons* are types of polygons.

**Prime Number** A whole number that has exactly two different whole number factors.

*Prime numbers:* 2 (= 1 × 2) 3 (= 1 × 3) 41 (= 1 × 41)

Whole numbers other than 0 and 1 that are not prime numbers are *composite numbers.* The *prime factorization* of a composite number expresses the composite number as a product of prime numbers.

**Prism** A closed solid figure with flat faces. Its bases are two opposite faces bounded by congruent polygons. Its other faces are bounded by rectangles.

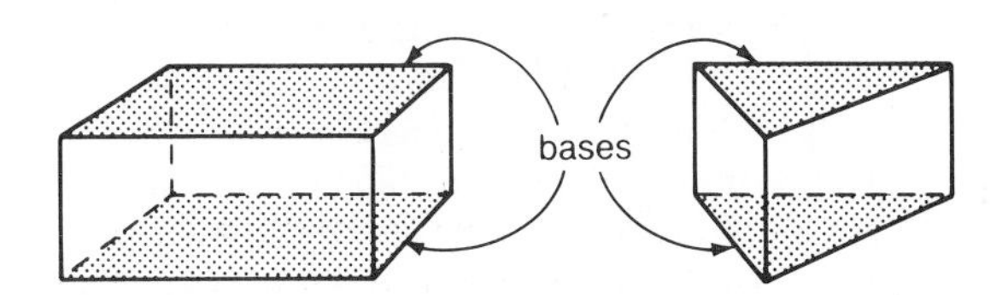

**Probability** A number from 0 through 1 that tells the chance that a statement about the outcome of a random selection will be true. If $\frac{2}{3}$ of the possible outcomes make a statement true, the probability of the statement is $\frac{2}{3}$. This means the statement will be true in *about* $\frac{2}{3}$ of a *large number* of selections.

An *empirical probability* is determined by a number of previous outcomes instead of by all possible outcomes.

**Pyramid** A closed solid figure with flat *faces.* Its *base* is bounded by a regular polygon and its other faces are bounded by congruent isosceles triangles.

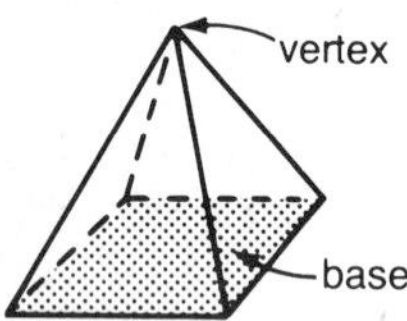


**Pythagoras (Rule of)** For a right triangle with *legs* of lengths a and b and *hypotenuse* of length c:

$$c^2 = a^2 + b^2$$

**Quadrilateral** A polygon with four sides. A *trapezoid* is a quadrilateral with at least one pair of opposite sides parallel. A *parallelogram* is a quadrilateral with both pairs of opposite sides parallel.

In a parallelogram opposite sides and opposite angles are congruent. Adjacent angles are supplementary. A parallelogram with:
four congruent sides is a *rhombus,*
four right angles is a *rectangle.*
A *square* is a rectangle with four congruent sides.

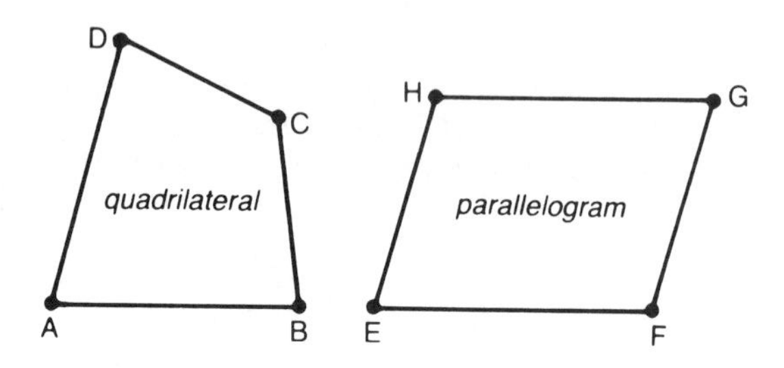


**Ratio** A comparison of two quantities. For 5 teachers and 40 students the ratio of teachers to students is 5 to 40, or 5:40, or $\frac{5}{40}$.

Decimals and percents also name ratios. The ratio of teachers to students is .125, (125 to 1,000) or 12.5% (12.5 to 100).

Equivalent fractions name equal ratios. A statement that two ratios are equal is a *proportion.*

**Rational Number** Any number that is the quotient of two integers.

**Ray** A straight path with one endpoint that "extends forever" in one direction.

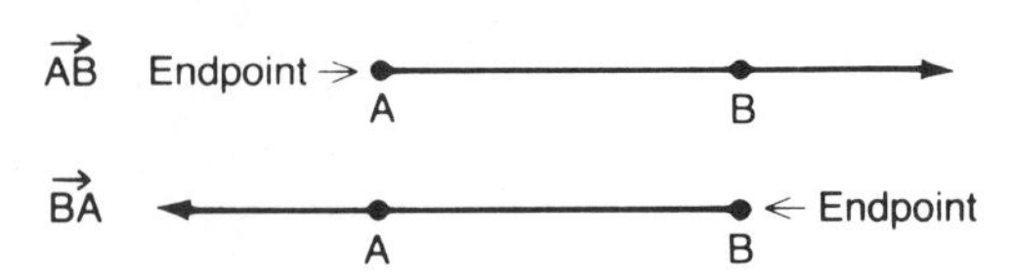


**Real Number** Each rational number (quotient of integers) and each *irrational number* ($\sqrt{2}$, $^-\sqrt{3}$, $\pi$, ...) is a real number. Real numbers can be used to name all points of a line.

**Reciprocal** Two numbers whose product is 1 are reciprocals of each other.

**Rounding (Estimating) a Number** Expressing a number to the nearest thousand, ten, tenth, thousandth, or any place in its numeral. Rounded to the nearest thousand,

6,517.0269 $\doteq$ 7,000
↑ is about equal to

6,517.0265 $\doteq$ 6,520 (nearest ten)
$\doteq$ 6,517.0 (nearest tenth)
$\doteq$ 6,517.027 (nearest thousandth)

**Scientific Notation** An expression for a number as a product of a number 1 or greater but less than 10 and a power of ten.

$568 = 5.68 \times 10^2$ $\quad .00084 = 8.4 \times 10^{-4}$

**Similar Figures** Two figures that have the same shape. Pairs of corresponding angles of similar figures are congruent angles. The ratios of corresponding sides of similar figures are equal ratios. $\triangle ABC$ and $\triangle DEF$ are similar triangles.

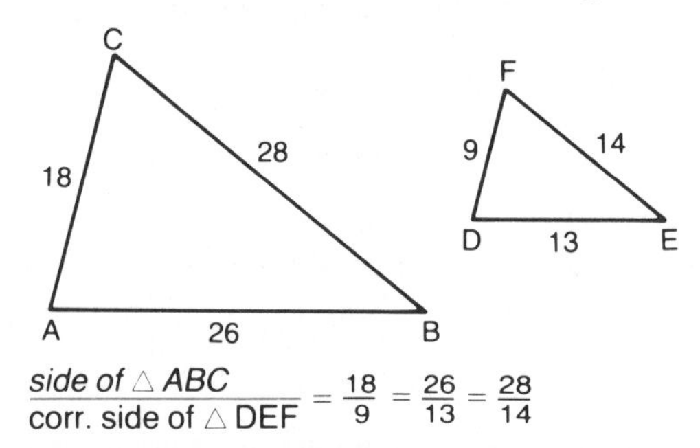


$$\frac{\textit{side of } \triangle ABC}{\text{corr. side of } \triangle DEF} = \frac{18}{9} = \frac{26}{13} = \frac{28}{14}$$

A *scale drawing* is similar to the region or object the drawing represents. The *scale* of the drawing is the ratio of each distance in the drawing to the actual distance it represents.

**Sphere** A closed solid figure formed by all points the same distance from a point that is the *center* of the sphere.

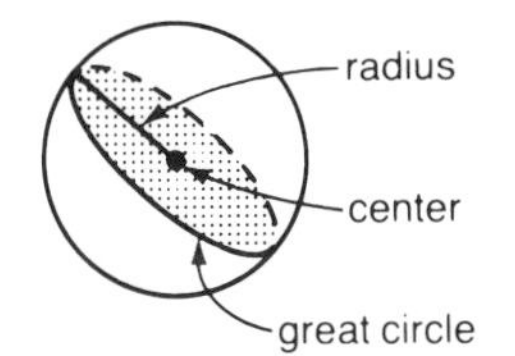


A circle with the same center and length of radius as the sphere is a *great circle*.

A great circle separates a sphere into two *hemispheres*.

**Square Root** If $a^2 = b$ then $a = \sqrt{b}$ is a square root of b. Square roots of all whole numbers through 100 except 0, 1, 4, 9, 16, 25, 36, 49, 64, 81, and 100 are *irrational numbers*.

**Standard Numeral** A numeral for a whole number formed using *digits* 0-9 and a *place value system*.

| Billions | | | Millions | | | Thousands | | | (Ones) | | |
|---|---|---|---|---|---|---|---|---|---|---|---|
| H | T | O | H | T | O | H | T | O | H | T | O |
| 1 | 2 | 3, | 4 | 5 | 6, | 7 | 8 | 9, | 0 | 1 | 2 |
| | | | 7 | 8 | 9, | 0 | 0 | 0, | 0 | 0 | 0 |
| 6 | 0 | 0, | 0 | 0 | 0, | 0 | 0 | 8, | 0 | 0 | 0 |

Commas (or spaces) separate numerals into *periods*. The next period to the left is the *trillions* period.

The numerals in the *place value table* above are read:

123 billion 456 million 789 thousand 12
789 million
600 billion 8 thousand

**Statistics** Numbers that are used to describe a set of numbers. The *mean*, or *average*, of a set of numbers is found by adding the numbers in the set then dividing by the number of numbers in the set. The *median* is the middle number in the set when the numbers are arranged from smallest to largest (or the average of the two middle numbers of the set if the set contains an even number of numbers). The *mode* is the number that occurs the most times in the set. (There can be more than one mode.) The *range* is the difference: largest number – smallest number.

The numbers in large sets of data are often grouped into *classes*. *Class marks* are used to represent all numbers in a class. A *histogram* is a bar graph showing grouped data.

**Subtraction** An operation on two numbers that tells how many are left when some are taken away, how many more are in one set than in another, and how many more are needed to have a given number. With measures it tells the measure of the part left, the part more, or the part needed.

86
47
39 ← *difference*

$\frac{4}{5} - \frac{3}{5} = \frac{1}{5}$ ← difference

Some properties of subtraction are:

$x - 0 = x \qquad x - x = 0$

Subtraction is related to addition by:

$(x - y) + y = x$

Rounded numbers are used to *estimate* differences.

42,598 → 43,000
6,417 → 6,000
37,000 ← estimate

**Surface Area** The sum of the areas of the faces of a solid figure.

**Triangle** A polygon with three sides. The sum of the measures of the angles of any triangle is 180°. Triangles are classified by angles as *acute* (3 acute angles), *right* (1 right angle), or *obtuse* (1 obtuse angle). They are also classified by sides as *scalene* (no 2 sides congruent), *isosceles* (at least 2 sides congruent), or *equilateral* (all 3 sides congruent).

**Trigonometric Ratios** For any number x between 0 and 90 and for any right triangle with an acute angle with measure $x^\circ$:

tangent of $x^\circ$ = $\tan x^\circ = \frac{a}{b}$

sine of $x^\circ$ = $\sin x^\circ = \frac{a}{c}$

cosine of $x^\circ$ = $\cos x^\circ = \frac{b}{c}$

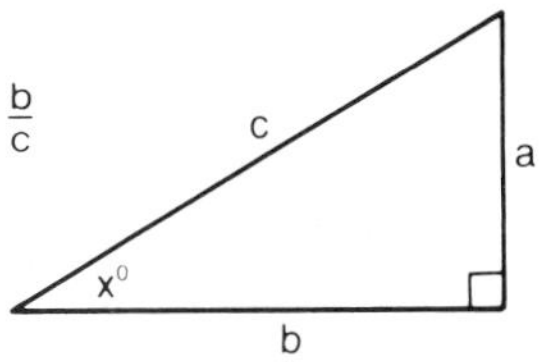

**Unit of Measure** The amount of a measurable property to which 1 is assigned as the measure.

**Volume** The number of unit cubes that would fill the inside of a solid figure if it were hollow.

**Whole Number** Any of the numbers 0, 1, 2, 3, ... Whole numbers with 2 as a factor are *even numbers*. All other whole numbers are *odd numbers*.

# Index


- Absolute value, 194-197, 216, 228
Addition
  addend, 420
  in algebra
  with decimals, 84-85, 133, 135
    estimating sums, 100-101
  in finite number systems, 230-231
  with fractions, 150-153
  of integers, 194-195, 198, 201
  with mixed numerals, 158-159, 232
  problem solving, 13, 76, 84-85, 110, 114, 150-151, 153, 158-159, 180-186, 194-195, 198-203, 228, 230-232
  properties, 54-55, 420
  of rational numbers, 196-201
  of real numbers, 216-217
  relation to subtraction, 54-55, 422
  sum, 420
  of whole numbers, 2-3, 420-421
    estimating sums, 100-101, 524
Additive inverses, 198-199, 230-231
Algebra
  equations
    to check, 84
    equivalent, 56, 72
    as formulas, 64-65, 73, 280-297, 304-305, 326-343
    graphs of, 222-223, 392-393, 408-409
    problem solving, 51, 53, 57, 59, 61, 63, 65, 67, 69, 73, 76, 126-127, 155, 372
    proportions, 138-139, 270-275, 302, 322-323, 334-335, 346-347
    solving, 52, 62, 73, 76, 84-85, 89, 96-97, 111, 138-139, 176-177, 183, 186, 206-207, 216-217, 222-223, 229, 270-275, 302, 322-323, 334-335, 346-347, 392-400
    stating properties, 54-55, 72
    with two variables, 392-393
      solving systems of, 398-399
    writing, 57, 59, 61-63, 73, 177, 397, 400-401
  expressions
    defining functions, 74-75, 346-347, 392-393, 408-409
    forming sentences, 52-53
    in formulas, 64-65, 326-333, 336, 340-343
    variable, 50-51, 75, 116
      value of, 50-51, 75, 89
    value of, 50-51, 75, 151, 153, 155, 165, 167
  inequalities
    graphs of, 222-223
    solving, 52-53, 72, 222-223
Angles
  adjacent, 312-313, 320
  bisector of, 309-310, 311
  classification by measure
    acute, 310-311, 315
    obtuse, 310-311, 315, 348
    right, 310-313, 348
    straight, 310-311
  complementary, 310-311, 313, 348
  congruent, 310, 312, 316-317, 322-323
  construction of, 314-315
  degree measure of, 310, 316-318, 320, 348
  naming, 308-309
  opposite, 320-321
  of polygons, 318-319
  sides of, 308, 323
  supplementary, 310-313, 320
  using a protractor
    to draw, 310-311, 334
    to measure, 310-311, 332-334
  vertex of, 308-309, 348
  vertical, 312-313
Area, 328-329, 332-333, 336-343, 367
Associative property
  of addition, 420
  of multiplication, 424
Averages, finding, 22-23, 65, 90-91, 99, 102-103, 173, 185, 370-375
Axes (of a coordinate system), 390-391

- BASIC programming language, 298, 433-448
Bisector
  of an angle, 310-311, 314-315
  of a line segment, 308-309, 314-315

- Calculator(s), 23, 101, 127, 201, 220
  estimation to check calculations, 100-101
  multiple operations with, 38, 101, 106, 178, 260
  simplifying expressions with 3, 6, 7, 9, 101
  solving problems on, 38, 106, 178, 260, 344
  to solve proportions, 271-272, 291
  working with large numbers, 127
Circle(s)
  arc of, 332-333
  area of, 332-333
  center, chord, diameter, radius of, 318-319, 332
  central angle of, 318-319, 332-334
  circumference of, 332-333
  graph of, 334-335
  pi ($\pi$), 216, 332-333, 338-339, 382
  sector of, 332-333
Circumference, 332-333
Combinations, 368-369
Commutative property
  of addition, 84, 420
  of multiplication, 424
Comparing
  with decimals, 80-81, 110
  with fractions, 136-137, 145
  with mixed numerals, 156-157
  rational numbers, 194-197, 228
  real numbers, 222-223
  using scientific notation, 214-215
  whole numbers, 59, 419
Computer(s)
  algorithms, 140
    computer programs, 298
      See BASIC programs below
    flowcharts, 66-67, 140
    human language, 298
  artificial intelligence,
  BASIC programs
    editing,
    redefining variables in,
    statements in
      END, LET, PRINT, 298
      GOSUB,
      IF-THEN GOTO,
      INPUT, 298
      INT(X),
      REM,
    structured,
    using, 68
    writing, 140, 298
  hardware
    central processing unit (CPU), 68
    input devices, 68
    output devices, 68
    peripheral devices, 68
    RAM (random-access memory), 68
    ROM (read-only memory),
    storage media, 68
  inventors of,
  languages
    assembly, 68, 298
    higher order (BASIC, FORTRAN, PASCAL, APL), 298
    machine, 68
  problem solving related to, 224
  protecting information in,
  robots,
  terms
    algorithm, 140
    artificial intelligence, 68
    bits, 68
    bytes, kilobytes, megabytes, 68
    flowchart, 66-67, 73, 140
    graphics, 402
    hardware, 68
    input devices, 68
    microcomputer, 68
    modem, 402

output devices, 68
peripheral devices, 68
processing units, 68
programming languages, 298
programs, 298, 380
RAM (random-access memory), 68
ROM (read-only memory), 68
robots,
spreadsheet, 224
storage media, 68, 298
structured program, 298
subroutine,
use as a tool
attributes, 380
limitations, 380
tasks performed by, 140, 298, 380
Computer Programming, 433-448
Cone, 338-339
Congruent figures, 308-309, 324-325
Constructions (straightedge-compass),
angle congruent to a given angle, 314-315
bisector of an angle, 314-315
line parallel to a given line through a given point, 315
line segment congruent to a given segment, 314-315
perpendicular bisector of a line segment, 314-315
using compass and straight-edge, 314-315, 328, 348
Consumer math
*See* Problem Solving
Coordinate System(s)
for a line
graphs of sentences, 222-223
for a plane
axes of, 390-391
graphs
of direct and inverse variation, 408-409
of equations, 392-397
of ordered pairs, 390-391
of systems of equations, 398-399
transformations, 350-351
Cube root, 219
Customary System
area
of plane figures, 328-329
of surfaces, 342-343
units of, 342
arithmetic with measures, 252-263, 342-343
changing customary units, 254-255, 265
length
estimating, 252-253, 264
units, 252
liquid volume or capacity
estimating, 252-253, 264
units of, 252
perimeter, 342-343
problem solving, 208-209, 255-259, 261-266, 343
special relations, 258-259
temperature (degree Fahrenheit), 208-209
time, 246-251, 262-263
units of, 246
*See also* Time
volume
of cones, 338-339, 341
of cylinders, 338-341
of prisms, 258-259, 336-337
of pyramids, 336-337
of spheres, 338-339, 341
units of, 336
weight
estimating, 252-253, 264
units of, 252
Cylinder, 338-341, 343

• Data search, 41, 103, 110, 209, 227
Decimals
addition, 84-85, 110, 114
estimating sums, 85, 100-101,
comparing with, 80-81, 110, 114
concept, 78-79
decimal point, 78-80, 86, 90, 100
division, 90-103
with decimal divisors, 98-99, 110, 114
estimating quotients, 100-101, 111
zeros in the quotient, 90-92
rounding quotients, 90-92
with whole number divisors, 96-97, 102-103, 110
equivalent, 78-79
for fractions, 170-171, 217
to a fraction, 170-171
for irrational numbers, 216-217
for mixed numerals, 170-171, 217
to a mixed numeral
multiplication 86-89, 110
estimating products, 100-101
by powers of 10, 94-95, 110
for percents, 276-279, 286-287, 302
to a percent, 276-279
for points on a number line, 82, 196-197, 216-217
problem solving, 81, 85-89, 91, 93, 97, 100, 102-103, 104-105, 111, 217
for rational numbers, 196-197, 201, 203-204, 207, 214-215
for real numbers, 216-217, 229
reading/writing, 78-79, 110, 114
repeating, 170-171
rounding, 82-83, 110, 114
in scientific notation, 212-213, 229
solving equations with, 84-85, 96-97, 280-295, 302
subtraction, 84-85, 110
estimating differences, 84-85
terminating, 170-171
using rough estimates, 100-101
for whole numbers, 78, 84, 86, 96
Digit, 78-79, 110, 134, 418
Distributive properties, 8, 54-55
Divisibility, tests for, 120-121, 144
Division
with decimals, 90-91, 134
estimating quotients, 100-101
dividend, 428
divisor, 428
with fractions, 166-167
of integers, 206-207
mental math with, 9, 185
with mixed numerals, 168-169
problem solving, 19, 76
*See also* Problem Solving
properties, 54-55, 428
quotient, 428
of rational numbers, 206-207
of real numbers, 216-219
relation to multiplication, 54-55, 428
using laws of exponents, 210-211, 214-215
of whole numbers, 18-19, 428-433
divisibility tests for, 120-121, 144
estimating quotients, 100-101
remainder, 428
short division, 10, 185

• Equation(s)
algebraic, 56-63, 84-85, 96-97, 176-177, 202-203, 206-207, 216-219, 222-223, 392-393, 408-409
use word equations to solve, 25, 27, 29
proportions, 138-139, 270-275, 302, 322-323, 334-335, 346-347, 400-401, 407, 409
Estimation
of differences, 2-3, 100-101, 524
of irrational numbers, 216-217
of products, 2, 7, 59, 100-101
of quotients, 2, 9, 59, 100-101
of square roots, 218-221
of sums, 2-3, 59, 100-101, 524
Even and odd numbers, 124-125, 335
Exponent(s)
base of, 116-117, 144
division with, 210-211
mental math with, 184-185
multiplication with, 210-211
negative, 210-213
for powers of the base, 116-117
in scientific notation, 212-213

simplifying expressions with, 116-117, 144, 210-211
0 and 1 as, 116-117
Exponential notation, 116-117, 126-127, 144, 146-147, 210-213

• Factor(s)
common, 118-119
greatest common, 118-119, 128-129
prime, 126-129, 144
using tree diagrams to find, 126-127
Factorial notation, 366-369, 384
Finite number systems, 230-231
Flowcharts, 66-67, 73, 140
Formula(s), 64-65, 280-297, 303-305, 326-329, 336-343, 346-349
customary, 342-343
for finding interest, 294-297, 303-305
in geometry, 326-333, 336, 340-343
metric, 340-341
other, 64-65
for trigonometric ratios, 346-347
using percent, 280-285, 288-293, 303, 334
Fraction(s)
addition
common denominators, 150-151, 182
different denominators, 152-153, 182
common denominator, 134-135
least, 134-135, 145
common factor, 118-119
greatest, 118-119, 128-129, 144, 232
common multiple, 122-123
least, 122-123, 128-129, 144
comparing with, 136-137, 156-157, 182
for decimals, 170-171, 183, 217
to a decimal, 170-171
denominator, 130-131
different denominators, 152-153
division, 166-167, 182
equivalent, 130-131, 138
dividing to find, 130-131
for equal ratios, 270-271, 302
lowest terms fraction, 130-132, 144
multiplying to find, 130-131
for proportions, 270-271, 302
using fractional number lines (rulers) to find, 130-131
for mixed numerals, 156-157, 182
to a mixed numeral, 132-133
multiplication, 164-165, 182
using a short cut, 164-165, 183
numerator, 130-131
for parts of sets or objects, 130-131, 276-277
for percents, 276-277, 286-287, 302
to a percent, 276-277, 286-287
for points on a number line, 130-132, 196-197, 216-217
for probabilities, 354-357
problem solving, 129, 131, 133, 139, 145, 153, 165, 167, 173, 182-183
for rational numbers, 196-197
for ratios, 270-275, 302, 346-347
for real numbers, 216-217
reciprocal, 164-167, 183
solving equations with, 176-177, 270-275, 302
for standard numerals, 150-151, 160-161
to a standard numeral, 130-133, 144
subtraction
common denominators, 150-151
different denominators, 154-155, 182
Fractional number line (ruler), 130-131
Fractional numbers, 130-131
Functions, 74-75, 346-347, 392-393, 408-409

• Geometry
coordinate, 222-223, 350-351, 390-405
plane figures, 308-331, 350-351
circles, 318-319, 332-335
polygons, 296, 316-331, 350-351
solid figures, 244-245, 258-259, 336-342
latitude and longitude, 180-181
surface area, 336-343
volume, 244-245, 258-259, 264, 336-343
symmetry, lines of, 350-351
topology, 266-267
transformational, 350-351
Graphs
bar, 34, 226-227, 229, 372-373
histogram, 372-373
broken line, 227
circle, 334-335
draw a circle graph, 335, 410
curved line, 70-71, 226-227, 409
of inequalities, 222-223
line, 227, 372, 378-379
of a line, 319, 392-397
slope, 319
of ordered pairs, 390-391
picto, 374-375, 385
of sentences
one variable, 222-223
two variables, 392-397
of systems of equations, 398-400
problem solving, 70-71, 223, 334-335, 410
See also Problem Solving
Greatest possible error, 300-301

• Indirect measurement, 274-275, 346-347
Inequalities, solving, 48-49, 222-223
Integer(s)
absolute value of, 194-195, 228
addition, 194-195, 198-201, 228
additive inverse (opposite), 198-199
comparing with, 194-195, 228
division, 206-207, 228
as exponents, 210-211, 229
graphing
of ordered pairs, 390-391
of sentences with one variable, 222-223
of sentences with two variables, 390-391
multiplication, 204-205, 228
for points on a number line, 194-197, 216-217
positive, negative, zero, 194-195
problem solving, 208-209, 214-215
solving inequalities with, 214-215
subtraction, 194-195, 202-203, 228
Inverse relationship
between addition and subtraction, 54-55, 422
between multiplication and division, 54-55, 428
Irrational numbers, 216-217

• Latitude and longitude, 180-181
Length, 234-245, 252-256, 300-301
Line(s)
intersecting, 308-309, 312
naming, 308-309, 312
parallel, 308-309, 312
perpendicular, 312-315
skew, 309
Line segment(s)
bisector of, 308-309
congruent, 308, 310, 315
constructions, 314-315
endpoints of, 308-309, 318, 348
midpoint of, 308-309, 314
naming, 308-309
perpendicular bisector of, 314-315
Liquid volume or capacity, 234-241, 244-247, 252-253, 258-259

• Mass, 95, 234-241, 244-245, 264
Measurement
of angles, 312-313
customary units of, 246-259, 342-343, 349
metric units of, 234-251, 306-321 326-341, 348-349,
time, 246-251, 262-263

using similar figures in, 322-323, 346-347
Mental math, 4, 6, 8, 184-185, 281, 525
Metric System
area
of plane figures, 328-329, 332-333, 340-341
of surfaces, 336-337
units of, 328-329
arithmetic with measures, 242-251, 326-341
changing metric units, 220-225
multiples of principal unit, 240-241
submultiples of principal unit, 238-239
length
estimating, 234-235, 264
precision, 264, 300-301
units of, 234-241, 264, 327
mass
estimating, 215, 229, 234-235, 264
units of, 234-241
perimeter, 326-327
prefixes used in, 236-241
problem solving, 208-209, 229, 237, 239, 241-245, 247, 251, 264, 265, 273, 279, 327, 329, 331, 336-339, 345, 347-349
special relations, 184, 236, 244-245, 258
temperature (degrees Celsius), 70, 208-209, 223, 227, 229, 397
time, 246-247
units of, 230-231
volume
of cones, 338-340
of cylinders, 338-340
of prisms, 244-245, 336-337, 340-341
of pyramids, 336-337, 340-341
of spheres, 338-340
units of, 234
Mixed numeral(s)
addition, 158-159
comparing with, 156-157
for decimals, 170-171
to a decimal, 170-171
division, 168-169
for fractions, 132-133, 168-169
to a fraction, 156-157, 168-169
lowest terms, 132-133
multiplication, 168-169
for percents, 276-279
to a percent, 276-279
for points on a number line, 132-133, 196-197, 216-217
for quotients of whole numbers, 18-19, 429
solving equations with, 176-177, 270-271
for standard numerals, 160
subtraction, 160-161
Money
operations with
addition, 12-13
division, 18-19, 429-430
multiplication, 16-17, 424-428
subtraction, 14-15
problem solving, 88-89, 91, 95, 97, 173, 251, 256-257, 265, 273, 304-305
rounding
to the nearest cent, 83-86, 110
to the nearest dollar, 419
Multiplication
with decimals, 86-87, 134
estimating products, 100-101
factors, 118-119, 422
in finite number systems, 230-231
with fractions, 164-165
of integers, 204-205
mental math with, 184, 186-187
with mixed numerals, 168-169
multiple, 116, 122-123
common, 122-123
least common, 122-123, 128-129
product, 87, 424
properties, 54-55, 424
of rational numbers, 204-205
of real numbers, 216-219
relation to division, 54-55, 428
short cut, 164
using laws of exponents, 210-211, 214-215
of whole numbers, 16-17, 424-427
estimating products, 100-101
Multiplicative inverse (reciprocal), 164-167, 231

• Networks, 266-267
Number(s)
decimals for, 78-105, 170-171, 196-223, 270-297, 302
even and odd, 124-125
finite systems, 230-231
fractions for, 130-139, 150-167, 270-297, 302
integers, 194-223, 390-400
irrational, 216-221
mixed numerals for, 132-133, 156-163, 168-169
prime and composite, 124-125, 163
rational, 196-223, 270-297, 302, 390-400
real numbers, 216-223, 390-400
whole numbers, 12-58, 418-432
Number lines, 82, 130-132, 194-197, 216-217, 222-223, 226-229, 372-373, 378-379, 390-401
Number theory, 116-129
Numeral(s)
base (4, 7, 12), 146-147
decimals, 78-79, 196-197, 216-217
exponential notation, 116-117
factorial notation, 366-369
fractions, 130-135, 196-197, 216-217, 270-271
for integers, 194-197, 216-217
for irrational numbers, 216-219
mixed, 132-133, 156-157, 196-197, 216-217
other numeration systems, 44-45
for rational numbers, 196-197, 216-217
for real numbers, 216-217
Roman,
scientific notation, 212-213
standard (base 10) 146-147, expanded forms, 146-147

• One, properties of, 424, 428
Origin (of a coordinate system), 390-391

• Parallelogram(s)
area of, 328-329
base of, 328-329
diagonal of, 318-319, 325
height of, 328-329
perimeter of, 326-327
properties of angles, 320-321
properties of sides, 320-321, 327
special, 320-321
Percent(s)
basic formula, 280-281
base, part, rate, 280-281
finding the base, 284-285
finding the part, 280-281
finding the rate, 282-283
compound interest formula, 296-297, 304-305
decimals within names for, 278-279, 286-287
to a decimal, 276-279, 286-287
fractions within names for, 278-279, 286-287
for fractions, 276-279, 286-287
to a fraction, 276-279, 286-287
increase or decrease, 288-289
for mixed numerals, 276-277
to a mixed numeral, 276-279, 286-287
for parts of sets or objects, 276-277, 334
problem solving, 277, 279, 281, 285, 287, 289, 303
reading, 276-277
simple interest formula, 294-295
Perimeter, 326-327, 342-343, 388
Permutations, 366-367
pi ($\pi$), 216, 332-333, 338-339, 367
Place value numeral(s)
base (4, 7, 12), 146-147

decimals, 78-79
scientific notation, 212-213
standard, 418
commas in, 418
expanded forms, 146-147
reading, 418
through trillions, 418
Plane, 308-309, 390
Point, 308-309, 390-391
Polygon(s)
angles of, 318-319
area by counting, 328-329
congruent, 324-325
corresponding parts of, 322-325
diagonals of, 318-319
on a grid, 328, 350-351
other, 318-319
perimeter, 326-327
quadrilateral, 318-321, 326-331
regular, 318-319, 326-327
sides of, 318-319
similar, 322-323
symmetry, lines of, 350-351
triangles, 316-317, 319, 323, 328-329
vertex (vertices), 318-319
Precision in measurement, 300-301
Prime and composite numbers, 124-125
Prime factorization, 126-129
using a calculator to find, 127
using to find GCF and LCM, 128-129
Prisms, 244-245, 258-259, 336-337, 340-343, 367
Probability, 354
compound statements, 354-355, 358-363, 382
empirical, 356-357
listing outcomes, 364-369
combinations, 368-369
permutations, 366-367
tree diagrams, 364-365, 384
multiple selections, 360-363, 384
dependent statements, 362-363
independent statements, 360-361
single selections, 354-355, 358-359, 384, 410
exclusive statements, 358-359, 384
0 and 1 as probabilities, 354-355
Venn diagrams, 358-359
Problem Solving
computer-related
following instructions, 38-39, 66-67, 121, 230-231
using flowcharts, 66-67
writing instructions, 66-67, 121, 177
consumer-related
airline schedule, 34, 250-251, 263
averages, 22-23, 90-91, 102-103, 370-375
bank statement, 40-41
best buy (unit pricing), 102-103, 111, 114, 256-256, 265, 303
budgets, 334-335
catalog order forms, 37, 43
checking accounts, 36-37, 43
comparison shopping, 88-89, 102-103
compound interest, 296-297, 304-305
computing the electric bill, 142-143
credit card, 295
discount and sale price, 288-291, 303-306
elapsed time, 250-251
income tax, 101, 111, 292-293, 303
installment buying, 104-105, 111, 186, 295
service charge, 295, 410
map reading, 180-181, 262-263, 274-275, 306
payroll records, 108-109, 290-291
salary/commission, 86-87, 111, 291, 303
sales tax, 100, 290-291
savings account, 297, 303
simple interest, 294-295, 303, 306
stock, 169, 208-209, 229, 388
taxi (rates, tip), 175
time cards, 109
train schedules,
with customary units, 250-251, 256-259, 342-343
estimates
as answers, 33, 100-101, 181, 524-525
to check, 12-19, 24-31, 242-243
finding information from
catalogs, 36-37
experiment, 382-383
graphs, 12-19, 70-71, 208-209, 224-227, 334-335, 372-375, 378-379, 396-397
outside sources, 32-37
pictures, 14, 23, 33-34, 36, 39, 40-41, 43-45, 66, 78, 102-103, 130, 133, 164, 166, 180, 199, 202, 204, 208, 244, 251, 256, 258, 262, 266-267, 274-276, 300, 308-309, 326-327, 330, 354, 358
tables, 50, 112, 117-118, 124, 125-126, 133, 218, 392
complete the table, 51, 65, 72, 83, 108-109, 113, 142, 179, 231, 245, 249, 259, 266, 273, 295, 393, 406
using tables, 81, 88-89, 99, 107-109, 162, 175, 179, 223, 226, 236, 245, 259, 263, 288, 289, 291-293, 296, 301, 331, 335, 371, 373, 385
too much or too little given, 32-35
following instructions, 36-37, 88-89, 112-115, 230-231, 266-267, 272-273, 294-295, 314-315
logical reasoning, 15, 17, 23, 33, 39, 107, 171, 197, 203, 225, 311, 315, 323, 363, 373
with metric units, 205, 215, 225, 229, 232, 242-245, 250-251, 326-327, 340-341, 367
with money
multiple-step problems, 24-31, 139, 175, 273, 304-306
single-step problems, 2-10, 24-26
on your own, 13, 63, 67, 71, 103, 105, 110, 139, 173, 181, 209, 227, 259, 263, 275, 289, 251, 293, 335, 342, 347, 383, 405
organizing information, 39-40, 66-67, 107, 112-113, 162-163, 354-355, 358-359, 372-373, 381
with percent, 175, 288-297, 304-305, 334-335
with probability, 356-357, 374-375
with proportions, 138-139, 272-275, 334-335, 346-347
with rates, 22-23
think, 49, 51, 55, 57, 63, 67, 71, 79, 81, 83, 95, 97, 99, 103, 119, 121, 123, 125, 127, 129, 131, 135, 137, 151, 153, 155, 157, 159, 161, 167, 169, 177, 199, 203, 207, 211, 219, 221, 235, 241, 245, 247, 249, 253, 257, 271, 273, 277, 284, 285, 313, 317, 319, 355, 357, 359, 361, 363, 365, 369, 372, 372, 375, 377, 393, 399
in statistics, 374–383
strategies
answering the question, 20-21
choosing the easier method, 172-175, 179
constructing tables, 39-40, 112-113, 266-267
draw a diagram, 69
drawing and using graphs, 70-71, 223, 226, 335
drawing pictures, 39-40
guess and check, 27, 81, 95, 205, 261, 295
interpreting data, 378-379
using algebra (writing equations), 53, 56, 59, 61-63, 272-275, 348-349, 400-401, 408

using algorithms (human language),
using back-to-front analysis, 24-31, 36-37, 101, 104-105, 162-163, 242-243, 289-292
using computer programs,
using a 5-step plan, 12-20, 24-31, 62-63, 138-139, 172-173, 242-243, 400-401
using flowcharts, 66-67, 73, 401
using formulas, 64-65, 280-297, 304-305, 326-329, 336-343, 346-349
increase, decrease, 289-292, 303
using meanings of operations, 12-23, 102-103
mixed strategies, 141, 299
make a model, 345
using number scales, 208
using easier numbers, 172-173, 179
using tree diagrams, 364-365
using Venn diagrams, 358-359
using word equations,
multiple-step problems, 24-37, 108-109, 162-163, 242-243, 288-291
single-step problems, 12-23
with time
clock time
12-hour, 248-249
24-hour, 248-249
elapsed, 250-251
operations with, 246-247, 273
time zones, 262-263
using deductive reasoning
geometric patterns, 32, 125, 266-267, 309, 313, 350-351, 399
number patterns, 19, 25, 31, 35, 63, 85, 117, 121, 201, 213, 304-305, 391, 395, 401
using sampling, 376
using similar figures, 322-323
work backwards, 101, 159, 166, 175, 223
Problem solving projects
computing the electric bill, 142
drawing and using graphs, 70, 226
finding total earnings, 108
latitude and longitude, 180
precision and relative error, 300
time zones, 262
trigonometry, 346, 404
using probability to approximate, pi ($\pi$), 382
Problem solving strategies
draw a diagram, 69
guess and check, 261
logical reasoning with clues, 107
make a model, 345
make an organized list, 381
make a table, 225
mixed strategies, 141, 299, 403
trigonometry, 346
work a simpler problem, 179
Properties
of addition, 54-55, 420
of division, 54-55, 424-425
of multiplication, 54-55, 424-425
of subtraction, 54-55, 420
Proportions
of sides of similar triangles, 322-323
solving, 270-275, 322-324, 334-335, 346-347
using a calculator, 271
using cross products, 270-273
Protractor, 310-311, 334
Pyramid, 336-337, 340-343
Pythagoras, Rule of, 330-331

• Quadrilateral(s)
angles and sides of, 318-321
special, 320-321
properties of, 320-321

• Ratio(s)
comparing with, 270-271
concept, 270
equal (proportion), 270-275, 322, 346-347
naming, 270-271, 276-277
using fractions, 270-271
using percents, 276-277
using special names, 270-271
percent name for, 276-277
trigonometric, 346-349
Rational number(s)
absolute value of, 196-197
addition, 196-201, 216-217
additive inverse (opposite), 198-201
comparing with, 196-197
division, 196-197, 206-207, 216-217
graphing
of ordered pairs, 390-391
of sentences with one variable, 222-223
of sentences with two variables, 390-400
multiplication, 196-197, 204-205, 216-217
for points on a number line, 196-197, 216-217
positive, negative, zero, 196-197
decimals for, 170-171, 216-217
solving equations with, 207, 217
solving inequalities with, 222-223
subtraction, 196-197, 202-203, 216-217
Ray
endpoint, 308-309
naming, 308-309
Real number(s)
as cube roots, 219
irrational, 216-221
as other roots, 221
real number line, 216-217, 222-223
real number plane, 390-400
as square roots, 218-221, 387
Reciprocal (multiplicative inverse), 164-167, 231
Rectangle(s)
angles and sides, 320-321
area of, 328-329, 345
perimeter of, 326-327
Relative error, 301
Rhombus, 320-321
Right triangle(s), 316-317
Rule of Pythagoras for, 330-331
trigonometric ratios for, 346-347
Roman numerals,
Rounding, 2, 59, 76, 82-83, 134, 163, 333, 339-340
decimals for quotients, 90-93, 110, 388

• Scale drawings, 208, 226, 274-275, 303, 410
Scientific notation, 212-215, 229
comparing with, 214-215, 229
operations with, 214-215, 229
Sentences
algebraic, 52
arithmetic, 48
Set(s)
of data, 74-75, 370-375
domain of a function, 74-75
finite, 230
infinite, 74-75, 230
of possible outcomes, 364-369
range of function, 74-75
as represented by a Venn diagram, 358-359
Similar triangles
properties of, 322-323, 346-347
using in indirect measurement, 274-275, 346-347
Sphere(s)
great circle of, 338-339
hemisphere, 338-339
latitude and longitude, 180-181
Square(s)
angles and sides, 320-321
area of, 328-329
perimeter of, 326-327
Square root(s)
estimation of, 220-221, 229, 232
negative, 221
operations with, 218-219, 229
rounding to nearest hundredth, 218-221, 229
table of, 218, 229

Standard deviation, 368-369, 387
Standard numeral, 117, 146-147, 369, 418
Statistics
  grouped data
    class frequencies, limits, marks, 372-373
    computing statistics from, 372-373
    frequency polygons for, 372-373
    histograms for, 372-373
  important statistics
    average, 65, 90-91, 370-375
    average difference, 386-387
    mean, 370-375, 385, 388
    median, 370-375, 385
    mode, 370-375, 385
    standard deviation, 386-387
  sources of data
    graphs, 374-375
    tables, 371-373
  using in problem solving
    interpreting information, 378-379
    with probability, 374-375
    in sampling, 376-377
Subtraction
  with decimals, 84-85, 134
    estimating differences, 100-101
  difference, 422
  with fractions, 150-155
  of integers, 194-195, 202-203
  with mixed numerals, 160-161
  properties, 54-55, 422
  of rational numbers, 202-203
  of real numbers, 216-219
  relation to addition, 14, 54-55
  of whole numbers, 14-15, 422-423
    estimating differences, 100-101, 524
Surface area, 336-343
Symmetry, lines of, 350-351
Systems of equations, 398-401

• Table(s)
    making, 50-51, 107, 127, 225, 226, 162-163
    of measures, 523
    of square roots, 218
    of trigonometric ratios, 346
    using,
  Technology
    Algorithms and Flowcharts, 140
    Computers and Data Bases, 80
    Computer Spreadsheets, 224
    Division with Remainders on a Calculator, 106
    Graphics and Communications with Computers, 402
    Kinds of Computer Languages, 298
    Prime Factorization with a Calculator, 178
    Solving Problems on a Calculator, 38
    Volume, Mass, Time, and Weight on a Calculator, 260
Temperature, 70, 195, 199, 208-209, 223, 227, 229
Time
  changing units of, 246-247, 264
  clock time
    12-hour, 248-249, 264
    24-hour, 248-249, 264
  elapsed, 250-251
  operations with, 247-248
  problem solving, 247, 249-251, 263-264
  time zones, 262-263
  units of, 246-247, 264, 268
Topology, 266-267
Transformational geometry, 350-351
Trapezoid, 320-321, 328-329, 349
Tree diagrams, 126-127, 364-365
Triangle(s)
  angles of, 316-317
  area of, 328-329
  base of, 328-329
  classification by
    angle measures, 316-317
    lengths of sides, 316-317, 322
  congruent
    conditions for (SSS; SAS; ASA), 322-324
    corresponding parts of, 322-325
  height of, 328-329
  naming, 316-317, 322, 348
  perimeter, 326-327
  right
    Rule of Pythagoras for, 330-331
    trigonometric ratios for, 346-347
    sides of, 316-317
    similar, 322-323, 346-347
      corresponding parts of, 316, 322-323, 346-347
    sum of angle measures of, 316-317
    vertex (vertices) of, 316, 318, 322, 324
Trigonometric ratios, 346-349, 404
Truth tables, 112-113

• Visual perception, 87, 93, 167, 255, 237, 257, 287, 297, 309, 327, 337
Variable, 50-51, 116
Variation
  direct, 408
  inverse, 408
Venn diagram, 358-359
Volume, 244-245, 258-259, 336-342

• Weight, 252-253, 258-259, 264
Whole number(s)
  addition, 3, 420-421
    estimating sums, 100-101, 524
  comparing with, 2
  division, 9, 428-432
    divisibility tests, 120-121
    estimating quotients, 100-101
    short division, 185
    *See also* division
  even and odd, 124-125
  as exponents, 116-119, 126-129, 146-147
  multiplication, 7, 424-428
    estimating products, 100-101, 428
    by powers of 10, 425
    using exponents, 116-119, 126-129, 146-147, 210-211
  numerals for, 146-147, 418
  for points on a number line, 82-83, 194-197, 216-217
  prime and composite, 124-125
  problem solving, 119, 123, 125, 162, 171
  rounding, 171
  sentences containing, 48-49
  simplifying expressions for, 48-49, 72
    using a calculator, 106
    rule of order, 48-49, 72
  solving equations with, 56-65, 72
  subtraction, 5, 422-423
    estimating differences, 100-101
Whole number review, 418-432

• Zero, properties of, 420, 424, 428